Contemporary Biographical Quotations

Compiled by Frank S Pepper

Sphere Reference

Sphere Books Ltd.
30–32 Gray's Inn Road
London WC1X 8JL

First published 1986

Reproduced, printed and bound in Great Britain by
Collins, Glasgow

Preface

Since the publication of my previous anthologies, *Handbook of 20th Century Quotations* and *Dictionary of Biographical Quotations*, I have had many letters from readers, taking me to task for having left out their own favourite quotations. I am most grateful to all those who have been kind enough to take the trouble to write and express an interest. I shall certainly hope to make use of their suggestions at some future time. However, none of my anthologies pretends to be definitive. They have been compiled from the files I have built up during the sixty years I have been earning my living as a writer, and are a selection from items which I have recorded over the years because they interested me, and which I felt might one day interest other people.

My intention has been to attempt to present a resumé of the twentieth century through quotes about people who have influenced it and contributed to it in some sphere — the arts, entertainment, literature, politics, science and sport.

Some of the people included were born well before 1900, and were already making their mark before the turn of the century. They are represented here only by quotations concerned with their twentieth-century activities. For example, there is nothing about Edward VII while he was Prince of Wales; nothing about Shaw before he wrote *Man and Superman*. Others, like Tolstoy, who survived into this century but really belonged to the last one, have been left out altogether. Appropriate quotations about these and many others will be found in the *Dictionary of Biographical Quotations*.

Frank S. Pepper
1986

Foreword

Politicians seem to attract spite. Why don't we mind?

Denis Healey described Keith Joseph as a 'mixture of Rasputin and Tommy Cooper'. We won't be long into the twenty-first century before we have forgotten who Denis Healey, Keith Joseph and Tommy Cooper are. In the meantime this kind of savagery is pleasing. And justifies this collection. Incidentals like this help us to get a hold on our times. It's a difficult task. The political and social picture changes so quickly. Perhaps it has never changed so rapidly as in this century. Baldwin, Bevan, Beveridge, Bevin, and Butler can barely be differentiated now (perhaps it was their hats).

Maybe, at one time, there was general agreement with Alec Douglas-Home's description of Khrushchev as 'always a load of laughs'. History seems to have been a little harder on him. The laughing face we see in the photographs looks sinister. And, though Stalin's laugh 'could be heard above all the other noises at the Kremlin Banquet', one can't imagine it was full of great good humour. History may not change our image of George V, however, who 'liked a vulgar joke, so long as the point was obvious'. Nancy Mitford's highest praise was to think a thing 'terribly amusing'. The sort of sense of humour one could well do without. Though no sense of humour might be worse. John Betjeman loathed C. S. Lewis because he 'could not see *any* humour in religion'.

Seriousness and 'goodness' are, of course, related. But not in a simple way. Of Balfour it was said he might 'in a gust of mirth let slip a British interest'. The secret might be to be malicious and compassionate. We can forgive John Gielgud his foot-in-mouths because we know his gossip derives from self-effacement and not egotism. Even W. C. Fields' wit could be turned in on himself, if he wished. Asked what he was doing when found reading the Bible, he said, 'Looking for loopholes'. When in old age a stranger asked Tallulah Bankhead if she was indeed who she was, she said, 'What's left of her'. Humour maturing to sadness.

Editor
Sphere Reference
1986

Contents

A
Acheson, Dean 1
Adenauer, Konrad 2
Agate, James 2
Alanbrooke, Viscount 4
Aldington, Richard 4
Alexander, Earl 5
Alexander of Tunis, Earl 5
Alexandra, Queen 6
Ali, Muhammad 7
Amin, Idi 7
Amis, Kingsley 8
Amundsen, Roald 8
Anderson, Elizabeth Garrett 9
Anderson, John 9
Anderson, Maxwell 9
Anderson Sherwood 9
Andrews, Julie 10
Andropov, Yuri 10
Anne Princess 10
Anouilh, Jean 11
Appleton, Sir Edward 11
Archer, William 12
Arlen, Michael 12
Armstrong, Louis 13
Arrhenius, Svante 13
Ashton, Sir Frederick 14
Asquith, H. H. 14
Asquith, Margot 16
Astaire, Fred 17
Astor, Nancy 17
Ataturk, Kemal 20
Attlee, Clement 21
Auchinleck, Sir Claude 22
Auden, W. H. 22

B
Bacon, Francis 24
Baden-Powell, Robert 24
Bagnold, Enid 25
Baird, John Logie 25
Baldwin, James 26
Baldwin, Stanley 27
Balfour, A. J. 30
Bankhead, Tallulah 31
Barbirolli, Sir John 32
Bardot, Brigitte 33
Baring, Maurice 34
Barrie, Sir J. M. 34
Barrymore, John 37
Bartók, Béla 37
Baruch, Bernard 37
Bax, Sir Arnold 38
Beaton, Sir Cecil 38
Beaverbrook, Lord 39
Beckett, Samuel 40
Beecham, Sir Thomas 40
Beerbohm, Sir Max 41
Begin, Menachem 42
Behan, Brendan 43
Bell, Gertrude 44
Belloc, Hilaire 44
Bellow, Saul 45
Benn, Anthony Wedgewood 45
Bennett, Arnold 46
Benny, Jack 48
Benson, E. F. 48
Berenson, Bernard 48
Bergson, Henri 49
Berlin, Irving 50
Bernhardt, Sarah 50
Betjeman, John 51
Bevan, Aneurin 52
Beveridge, William 53
Bevin, Ernest 53
Birkenhead, First Earl of 55
Blériot, Louis 56
Bliss, Sir Arthur 56
Blunden, Edmund 57
Blunt, Wilfried Scawen 57
Bogart, Humphrey 58
Bondfield, Margaret 58
Bonhoeffer, Dietrich 58
Boothby, Robert 59
Bottomley, Horatio 59
Boult, Sir Adrian 60
Bracken, Brendan 61
Bradman, Don 62
Brecht, Bertolt 62
Brezhnev, Leonid 63
Britten, Benjamin 63
Brooke, Rupert 64
Brown, George 65
Buchan, John 65
Burton, Richard 66
Busby, Sir Matt 66
Butler, Lord 67

C
Callaghan, James 68
Campbell, Mrs Patrick 68
Campbell, Roy 71
Capone, Al 71
Capote, Truman 72
Carnegie, Andrew 73
Carson, Edward 73
Carter, Jimmy 74
Caruso, Enrico 74
Castle, Barbara 75
Castro, Fidel 76
Cavell, Edith 76
Chaliapin, Feodor 76
Chamberlain, Austen 77
Chamberlain, Neville 78
Chandler, Raymond 80
Chaplin, Charlie 80
Charles, Prince of Wales 81
Chesterton, G. K. 81
Chiang Kai-shek 82
Christie, Agatha 83
Churchill, Winston 84
Ciano, Count Galeazzo 87
Clemenceau, Georges 87
Cockburn, Claud 88
Cocteau, Jean 89
Connelly, Marcus 90
Connolly, Cyril 91
Conrad, Joseph 91
Coolidge, Calvin 92
Cooper, Duff 93
Cooper, Diana 93
Cooper, Gary 94
Coward, Sir Noel 95
Crawford, Joan 96
Crippen, Dr 97
Cripps, Sir Stafford 97
Crosby, Bing 98
Crowley, Aleister 99
Cukor, George 99
Curzon, Lord 99

D
Dali, Salvador 101
Dalyell, Tam 102
D'Annunzio, Gabriele 102
Davies, W. H. 103
Davis, Bette 104
De Gaulle, Charles 104
Delius, Frederick 105
De Mille, Cecil B. 106
De Valera, Eamon 107
Diaghilev, Serge 107
Dietrich, Marlene 108
Disney, Walt 109
Douglas-Home, Sir Alec 109
Dreiser, Theodore 109
Dulles, John Foster 110
Du Maurier, Sir Gerald 111
Duncan, Isadora 111
Durante, Jimmy 113

Duse, Eleanora 113

E
Eden, Anthony 114
Edison, Thomas 115
Edward VII, King 116
Edward VIII, King 116
Einstein, Albert 117
Eisenhower, Dwight D. 118
Elgar, Sir Edward 119
Eliot, T. S. 121
Elizabeth II, Queen 123
Ellington, Duke 124
Ellis, Havelock 124
Epstein, Sir Jacob 124
Evans, Dame Edith 126

F
Fairbanks, Douglas 128
Farouk, King 128
Faulkner, William 129
Ferber, Edna 130
Fields, Gracie 131
Fields, W. C. 132
Fisher, John Arbuthnot 133
Fitzgerald, F. Scott 133
Flecker, James Elroy 134
Fleming, Sir Alexander 135
Fleming, Ian 136
Flynn, Errol 136
Foch, Ferdinand 137
Foot, Michael 138
Ford, Gerald 138
Ford, Henry 139
Forster, E. M. 139
France, Anatole 140
Franco, General Francisco 141
Frazer, Sir J. G. 141
French, John 142
Freud, Sigmund 143
Frost, Robert 143

G
Gable, Clark 145
Gagarin, Yuri 145
Gaitskell, Hugh 145
Galsworthy, John 146
Gandhi, Indira 147
Gandhi, Mahatma 147
Garbo, Greta 147
George V, King 148
George VI, King 149
Gershwin, George 150
Getty, Paul 151
Gide, André 151
Gielgud, Sir John 152
Gish, Lillian 152
Glyn, Elinor 153
Goebbels, Joseph 154
Goering, Hermann 154
Goldwyn, Sam 156
Gorky, Maxim 157
Grainger, Percy 157
Grant, Cary 157
Graves, Robert 158
Greene, Graham 158
Grey of Fallodon, Edward 159

H
Haig, Earl 160
Haile Selassie 160
Hailsham, Lord 161
Haldane, J. B. S 161
Haldane, Richard Burdon 162
Halifax, Earl of 163
Hall, Radclyffe 163
Harding, Warren 164
Harlow, Jean 165
Hearst, William Randolph 165
Heath, Edward 166
Hemingway, Ernest 166
Hepburn, Katherine 167
Herbert, Sir A. P. 167
Hess, Rudolf 168
Hillary, Sir Edmund 168
Himmler, Heinrich 168
Hindenburg, Paul von 169
Hitchcock, Alfred 169
Hitler, Adolf 170
Hoare, Sir Samuel 171
Hoover, Herbert 172
Hoover, J. Edgar 172
Housman, A. E. 173
Howe, Sir Geoffrey 174
Hughes, Howard 174
Huxley, Aldous 175

I
Ibn Saud 176
Inge, Dean W. R. 176
Ionesco, Eugene 177
Isherwood, Christopher 177

J
Jellicoe, Earl 178
Jenkins, Roy 178
Joad, C. E. M. 178
John, Augustus 179
John XXIII, Pope 179
John Paul II, Pope 179
Johnson, Lyndon 180
Jolson, Al 180
Joseph, Sir Keith 180
Joyce, James 181

K
Kafka, Franz 182
Kaunda, Kenneth 182
Kelly, Sir Gerald 182
Kennedy, John F. 182
Kern, Jerome 183
Keynes, John Maynard 183
Khrushchev, Nikita 184
King, Martin Luther 814
Kinnock, Neil 184
Kipling, Rudyard 185
Kissinger, Henry 185
Kitchener, Lord Horatio Herbert 186
Klemperer, Otto 186
Knox, Ronald 187
Korda, Sir Alexander 187
Kreisler, Fritz 187

L
Lansbury, George 188
Laughton, Charles 188
Laval, Pierre 189
Law, Andrew Bonar 189
Lawrence, D. H. 189
Lawrence, T. E. 190
Lee, Laurie 191
Leigh, Vivien 191
Lenin, Vladimir Ilyich 191
Lennon, John 192
Levant, Oscar 192
Lewis, C. S. 193
Lewis, Percy Wyndham 194
Lewis, Sinclair 195
Lindbergh, Charles 195
Linklater, Eric 196
Livingstone, Ken 196
Lloyd George, David 196
Loos, Anita 197
Louis, Joe 197
Lutyens, Sir Edwin 197

M
MacArthur, General Douglas 199
MacCarthy, Sir Desmond 199
MacDonald, James Ramsay 199
Mackenzie, Sir Compton 200
Macmillian, Harold 200
Mallory, George Leigh 201
Mansfield, Katherine 201
Mao Tse-Tung 202
Marconi, Guglielmo 202
Mary, Queen 202
Masefield, John 203
Mason, James 203
Matisse, Henri 204
Matthews, Sir Stanley 204
Maugham, W. Somerset 204
Mayer, Louis B. 205
Meir, Golda 205
Melba, Dame Nellie 295
Menuhin, Yehudi 206

Miller, Henry 206
Milne, A. A. 206
Mitford, Nancy 207
Molotov, Vyacheslav Mikhailovitch 207
Monroe, Marilyn 208
Montague, C. E 208
Montgomery of Alamein, Viscount 208
Moore, George 209
Moore, Henry 210
Morgan, J. P. 210
Morrison, Herbert, 210
Morton, J. B. 211
Mosley, Sir Oswald 211
Mountbatten, Earl 212
Muggeridge, Malcolm 213
Munnings, Alfred 213
Mussolini, Benito 213

N
Naipaul, V. S. 215
Nehru, Jawaharlal 215
Nicholas II, Tsar 215
Nichols, Beverley 215
Nijinsky, Vaslav 216
Nin, Anaïs 217
Nixon, Richard M. 217
Norman, Lord Montagu 217
Northcliffe, Viscount 218
Novello, Ivor 219
Nuffield, Lord 219
Nureyev, Rudolf 220

O
O'Casey, Sean 221
Olivier, Lord 221
O'Neill, Eugene 221
Orpen, Sir William 222
Orwell, George 222

P
Pachmann, Vladimir de 223
Paderewski, Ignacy Jan 223
Pankhurst, Dame Christabel 224
Parker, Dorothy 224
Pasternak, Boris 225
Pavlova, Anna 225
Peron, Eva 226
Philip, Prince 226
Picasso, Pablo 226
Pickford, Mary 227
Pirandello, Luigi 227
Pound, Ezra 228
Powell, Enoch 229
Presley, Elvis 229
Priestley, J. B. 230

R
Rasputin, Grigori 232
Rattigan, Terence 232
Reading, Marquess of 232
Reagan, Ronald 233
Redgrave, Sir Michael 234
Reith, Lord John 234
Ribbentrop, Joachim von 235
Richardson, Sir Ralph 236
Robeson, Paul 236
Robey, Sir George 236
Rockefeller, John D. 237
Rodin, Auguste 238
Rogers, Will 238
Rommel, Erwin 239
Roosevelt, Eleanor 239
Roosevelt, Franklin D. 240
Roosevelt, Theodore 241
Rosebery, Earl of 241
Russell, Bertrand 241
Rutherford, Ernest 242

S
Sackville-West, Victoria 243
Sadat, Anwar El 243
Samuel, Viscount Herbert 244
Sandow, Eugen 244
Sargent, John Singer 244
Sargent, Sir Malcolm 245
Saroyan, William 245
Sartre, Jean-Paul 246
Sassoon, Siegfried 246
Sayers, Dorothy L. 246
Schnabel, Artur 247
Schweitzer, Albert 247
Scott, Robert Falcon 248
Selznick, David O. 249
Service, Robert W. 249
Shaw, George Bernard 249
Sibelius, Jean 252
Sickert, Walter 252
Simon, Viscount 243
Sitwell, Dame Edith 253
Sitwell, Sir Osbert 255
Sitwell, Sir Sacheverell 255
Smuts, Jan 255
Smyth, Dame Ethel 255
Snow, C. P. 256
Snowden, Philip 256
Spark, Muriel 257
Spencer, Sir Stanley 257
Stalin, Joseph 258
Stein, Gertrude 258
Steinbeck, John 260
Stevenson, Adlai 260
Stokowski, Leopold 260
Stopes, Marie 260
Strachey, Lytton 261
Stravinsky, Igor 262
Strindberg, August 262
Sutherland, Graham 263
Synge, J. M. 264

T
Tagore, Sir Rabindranath 265
Taylor, Elizabeth 265
Tebbit, Norman 266
Temple, Shirley 266
Teresa of Calcutta, Mother 266
Terry, Ellen 267
Thatcher, Margaret 268
Thomas, Dylan 268
Thomas, James 269
Thorndike, Dame Sybil 270
Thurber, James 270
Tito, Josip Broz 271
Tolkien, J. R. R. 272
Toscanini, Arturo 272
Toynbee, Arnold 273
Tracy, Spencer 274
Tree, Sir Herbert Beerbohm 274
Trotsky, Leon 275
Truman, Harry S. 275

U
Ustinov, Peter 277
Utrillo, Maurice 277

V
Valentino, Rudolph 278
Vaughan Williams, Ralph 278

W
Wallace, Edgar 279
Walton, Sir William 279
Warhol, Andy 280
Waugh, Evelyn 280
Wavell, Earl 281
Webb, Beatrice 281
Webb, Sidney 281
Wedgwood, Veronica 282
Welles, Orson 282
Wells, H. G. 283
West, Mae 283
West, Rebecca 284
Wharton, Edith 284
Whistler, Rex 284
Wilkinson, Ellen 285
Williams, Charles 285
Williams, Shirley 286
Williams, Tennessee 286
Williamson, Henry 287
Wilson, Harold 287
Wilson, Woodrow 288
Windsor, Duchess of 288

Wingate, Orde 289
Wodehouse, P. G. 289
Wood, Sir Henry 290
Woolf, Virginia 290
Woollcott, Alexander 291

Y

Yeats, W. B 292

Z

Zaharoff, Sir Basil 293
Zanuck, Darryl F. 293
Ziegfeld, Florenz 293

DEAN (GOODERHAM) ACHESON

Born 1893. American politician. Truman's Secretary of State 1945–53. Played an important role in the establishment of NATO and the conduct of the Korean War. Died 1971.

1 Mr Dean Acheson might be broadly described as America's Anthony Eden. Not only in personality and in many aspects of policy, but even in appearance there is a strong similarity between the two men. Dean Acheson is tall, with a neat moustache, an easy, pleasant manner and a reputation for dressing well and, like Mr Eden, his official life has been almost exclusively bound up with foreign affairs.
Geoffrey Cox, News Chronicle 8 *Jan* 1949

2 Acheson found it difficult to conceal his contempt for the contemptible.
D. S. Freeman. Quoted Merle Miller, PLAIN SPEAKING, A BIOGRAPHY OF HARRY S TRUMAN

3 The best description of Dean Acheson that I know is that he is a 'Gentleman of the Old School'. It so happens that for two years I lived opposite him in Washington. We would meet at the post-box, pass in the street, even occasionally compete for taxis. But no word — not the slightest flicker of recognition — ever came from that bristly Cheltenham colonel's countenance. The explanation, though it puzzled me at the time, should have been obvious enough. We had not, after all, been introduced . . . It was all somehow wonderfully Victorian — and in its way strangely endearing.
Anthony Howard, Observer, Very superior person 26 *Apr* 1970

4 There is a danger in making fun of Mr Acheson. The lofty, Ivy League bishop's son was, when all is said and done, one of the principal shapers of the world in which we now live.
Ibid.

5 A ramrod for American intervention — whether in Greece, Turkey, Korea or the NATO defence of Western Europe — the charge he should be answering is one of bearing responsibility for creating the conditions of the Cold War.
Ibid.

6 Like Lord Curzon, he could not help communicating to his fellow human beings his own idea of himself as 'a very superior person'.
Ibid.

7 He believes that diplomacy cannot legislate for future generations and that problems must be taken, and if possible settled, as and when they arise. 'Always remember', is one of his mottoes, 'that the future comes one day at a time.'
Harold Nicolson, Observer 23 *Jul* 1961

8 Being a perfect gentleman himself, he can stimulate gentlemanlike feelings even in Slav cads.
Ibid.

9 Mr Acheson is a tactful man. He knows how to handle the poor whites of Europe.
Ibid.

10 It was in his relations with Congress that Acheson's mastery of his own nature was put to its greatest test. He had often to deal with men who were slow to thought, quick to take offence, ignorant of world affairs, suspicious of 'diplomats'. Never once did he let a quick temper or his eager sense of the ludicrous betray him.
Observer, Profile 22 *May* 1949

11 Acheson, in strong contrast to the President, has something of the air of a country gentleman with his loose-fitting tweeds and 'Guards' moustache. He is thoroughly happy on his Maryland estate, planning a better gladioli bed or pottering in his carpenter's shop, while his wife gets on with her painting and the three children exercise their horses in the paddock. But even in the country his favourite relaxation is conversation and he will sit with his guests till dawn discussing existentialism or the problems of risk capitalism.
Ibid.

12 Not only did he not suffer fools gladly, he did not suffer them at all.
Lester Pearson, Time magazine 25 *Oct* 1971

13 It was not flattery when the Under Secretary said on his departure from the State

Department: 'You, sir, are a true public servant.'
Lord Sherfield, The Times 23 *Apr* 1970

DR KONRAD ADENAUER

Born 1876 in Germany. Founder of the Christian Democrat Party, 1945 and Chairman until 1966. Chancellor of the West German Republic 1949–63. Prime instigator of the post-war reconciliation between Germany and France. Died 1967.

1 Dr Adenauer is neither a genius nor a demagogue, he is not even particularly persuasive in public debate or private argument. But he knows his own mind very well, and in a country like Germany, which tends to feel lost without a leader and father figure this has been enough, over the years, to give him an almost unassailable pre-eminence.
Sebastian Haffner, Observer 1957

2 Whether or not he was injected with monkey glands, as rumour had it, I do not know, but he was possessed of exceptional vitality and a clear, incisive mind. His face looked like a brown nut, and his jaws like nutcrackers. At the age of 85 he was still in full possession of his faculties.
Lord Home, THE WAY THE WIND BLOWS 1976

3 Year after weary year Adenauer argued Western leaders out of their more far-reaching demands, and got them to regard him increasingly as a colleague rather than a defeated enemy. In France he found an ally in Robert Schuman, with whose ideas on European conciliation he was in full sympathy.
Anthony Mann, Daily Telegraph 21 *Apr* 1966

4 The story of Konrad Adenauer in the post war decades is the story of the confrontation of Western democracy and Soviet communism . . . Not least it is the story of unremitting effort towards Franco-German friendship and a United Europe.
Ibid.

5 Had Adenauer remained in municipal work for two more years, the German Social Democrats with their doctrinaire brand of Marxist nationalism, might well have carried the day in 1949. This could have radically changed the course of history.
Ibid.

6 As long ago as May 1926 his guiding vision was that Germany should link up with the West and present a hostile front to the East. He has bravely and stubbornly nursed these ideas, founded on his Roman Catholic faith, when they were not only 'unrealistic' but heretical to the point of being treasonable; he had to change not a jot of them when the international circumstances of 1948 took a shape that fitted them like a glove.
Observer, Profile 13 *Apr* 1958

7 The taming of the Nazis must be regarded as Dr Adenauer's most astonishing, if somewhat ambiguous internal achievement. Quite unembittered by his personal experiences he has continued to regard the bulk of the Nazis as erring children rather than as dangerous criminals, and to reserve his real severity for the Communists.
Ibid.

8 There are many stories of his phenomenal physical vigour and sprightliness, his patriarchal family life, his rose-growing, his social charm, and his innocent addiction to chocolates and fast motoring.
Ibid.

9 He is not an opportunist; he is rather the opposite, a one-idea man.
Ibid.

10 There are darker sides to his public personality; a sense of humour which is not always free from cynicism, a certain cavalier way with unwelcome facts, a habit of talking down to audiences, and sometimes of offending the intelligence of interviewers, and a readiness to impute motives to political opponents.
Ibid.

11 Dr Adenauer is a straightforward individualist and competition is in his blood. He will try to win back for Germany her old trade markets, and will do so whether the planners here like it or not.
Harold Walton, Evening News 15 *Jul* 1949

JAMES (EVERSHED) AGATE

Born 1877. English dramatic critic and novelist. Contributed to *Manchester Guardian, Saturday Review* and *Sunday Times*. Published the first volume of his reminiscences in *Ego* 1935, later extended into a further eight volumes, the final one appearing after his death in 1947.

12 I sent an article to the *Manchester Daily Despatch* suggesting that in *Cinderella* Robert Courtneidge had produced a thing of beauty. I was invited to become the paper's

dramatic critic. Asked what salary I wanted I replied that I would leave it to the proprietors who should pay me at the end of the year whatever I had been worth to them. During the year I contributed forty-nine articles. On Christmas Eve I received a cheque for £7. I gave it to the cabman who drove me regularly between the theatres and the newspaper office, and told the editor what I had done. He sacked me.
James Agate, T.P.'s Weekly 12 *May* 1928

1 My last novel *Gemel in London* was my twentieth book. And the proudest achievement of my career is that I have inveigled eleven publishers into publishing me, all of whom have lost money thereby. For I possess this unique distinction that of all writers with twenty books to their credit I am the worst seller. Nobody has ever read me in book form. Nobody ever will. A few old ladies residing in boarding houses in Tunbridge Wells occasionally borrow me. That is all.
Ibid.

2 Do, for the Lord's sake, have that damned awful portrait of me destroyed. It looks just like me at the age of seventeen contemplating self-destruction. And I never contemplated self-destruction at seventeen. That was at sixteen.
James Agate in a letter to Reginald Pound, features editor of the Daily Express

3 Alan Dent [Agate's secretary] dispels the legend — which Agate created — that he walked all the way from his native Ayrshire in order to be employed by 'the old wizard'. It was not the truth, but Agate, as Alan Dent explains, was not 'exactly a liar'. In *Ego* and throughout his life he indulged in what he called 'the higher truth'. Other people might say he was given to romanticising.
George W. Bishop, Daily Telegraph 4 *Aug* 1961

4 At a party in the early 1920s at Marie O'Neill's house in Chelsea I found him squatting on the floor, with a glass of champagne in his hand, engaged in furious argument with Ashley Dukes and Nigel Playfair. I knew, of course, that he was the most lively and influential dramatic critic of the day, but he certainly didn't look the part. There was something rather horsey about him. Indeed he might have been taken for a bookmaker in a rather well-cut suit.
James Laver, The Times 14 *Sep* 1963

5 It is probable that from the age of 17 to his death he was never out of debt. He had a passion not only for horses but also for motor cars and as he never learned to drive that meant a chauffeur. Even when he passed to the *Sunday Times* and its larger emoluments, demand notes and dunning letters continued to descend upon him. His answer was to take on more work.
Ibid.

6 Lunched at *Le Jardin des Gourmets*, Greek Street, with James Agate in whose company I nearly always feel that I am living beyond my means. He ordered the food and wine like an expert deciding on investment.
Reginald Pound, THEIR MOODS AND MINE 1937

7 Eric Linklater and I haddocked at the Savage Club where Jimmy Agate was making a supper of cold beef, pickles and Pol Roger. He has so much of the ebullience of his favourite drink that I would like to point out to him that if he had his bowler hat painted gold he would personify a magnum of it.
Ibid.

8 Agate carefully told Linklater that the Savage Club lavatory occupied the site of David Garrick's death chamber. I doubted him and he then swore to it.
Ibid.

9 At the Ivy, a restaurant off the Charing Cross Road, Alan Dent sat waiting for his host, James Agate, who was delayed. He decided to while away the time by catching up on some writing. Suddenly he became aware of a figure standing looking over his shoulder. It was Agate; 'What are you doing — writing my obituary?' 'As a matter of fact I am,' admitted Dent. Agate insisted on seeing it and the lunch was spent discussing the details.
Donald Sinden, A TOUCH OF THE MEMOIRS 1982

10 He was fond of giving acting advice to the young, and would begin by asking a question. If we knew the answer he would over-ride us. *He* wanted to tell *us*. 'Now if I asked you for a match for my cigar, what would you do? The aristocracy would throw me a box; the middle class would pass me a box; the lower class would take out a match and light it for me.'
Ibid.

11 He had begun his theatre-going by watching Irving. 'Did you ever *speak* to Irving?' I once asked. 'Certainly not,' glowered J.A. '*Greatness* is not to be spoken to. I don't know how you can sit there speaking to *me* like that.'
Ibid.

1 James Agate, a homosexual, who had the appearance of a prize-fight promoter, he was a short, bulky man with a large bony head, whose protruding upper teeth made his S's difficult to pronounce.
Ibid.

FIELD MARSHAL VISCOUNT ALANBROOKE

Born England 1883. Soldier. Chief of Imperial General Staff 1941–6. Died 1963.

2 He held high command in the field for only a brief period in 1940, but has been universally recognised as one of the greatest – intellectually and in military knowledge the greatest – soldiers of his generation.
The Times, Obituary 18 *Jun* 1963

3 He liked to obtain his information and 'briefing' from the same small group of men, so that though he was the dominant personality at the War Office he was hardly known by sight to the majority of its inmates and there were persons on the same floor who never caught sight of him for months on end.
Ibid.

4 He possessed a gift for lucid explanation and exposition which was an invaluable asset at international conferences and also enabled him to succeed in the task in which so many soldiers have failed, of talking convincingly to politicians.
Ibid.

RICHARD ALDINGTON

Born 1892. Poet, novelist and biographer. Was severely shell-shocked in World War I and this influenced his writing. His most successful novel was *Death of a Hero*, 1929. Caused much controversy with two hostile books on T. E. Lawrence. *Portrait of a Genius But —*, 1950 and *Lawrence of Arabia*, 1955. Died 1962.

5 As a writer he seems to have been as compulsively industrious as Arnold Bennett, ridden by guilt when not writing.
Walter Allen, Daily Telegraph 17 *Oct* 1968

6 Aldington's anger never abated though it became attached to new targets. He ended his days in bitter exile, having incurred Churchill's wrath through debunking T. E. Lawrence in a brilliant biography, and he became one of the great unknowns.
Anthony Burgess, Observer 21 *Oct* 1984

7 In *Lawrence of Arabia* (1955) he gave offence to practically everybody who cherished the memory of his subject or the inspiration of the Lawrence legend: what he said needed saying; though perhaps not with quite such evident relish.
Philip Day, Daily Telegraph 8 *Jul* 1962

8 There is nothing Aldington does not view [in *Death of a Hero*] in hellish images. One has the impression of reading the testimony of a madman.
Kay Dick, The Times, A perverse and all-embracing hatred 8 *Sep* 1984

9 Richard Aldington was a writer who went sour. It has been said that his experiences as an infantryman enduring the horrors of the First World War (he was gassed and shell-shocked) so embittered him that he became psychologically damaged. To a large extent this was clearly true. Yet one has to parallel his case with that of Siegfried Sassoon and Robert Graves, both equally emphatically anti-war yet who remained able to respond to (and to love) the human race, which Aldington could never do. Aldington's near paranoiac hatred of his fellow man was not unrelated to the continuous disasters of all his personal relationships.
Ibid.

10 Richard Aldington is exactly the same inside, murder, suicide, rape — with a desire to be raped very strong — same thing really — just like you — only he doesn't face it, and gilds his perverseness.
D. H. Lawrence, letter to Aldous Huxley

11 Gay but caustic.
Sir Herbert Read, RICHARD ALDINGTON: AN INTIMATE PORTRAIT 1965

12 If ever there was a post-War pessimist it is he. He tries to laugh off his pessimism; but (like that of Jack Point) 'his laughter has an echo that is grim' and he makes a hollow job of it. The world and that frightful British middle-class are too much for him. Being by temperament serious he covers his seriousness with a crust of merriment. In print the crust wears off.
Frank Swinnerton, THE GEORGIAN LITERARY SCENE 1935

13 Aldington cannot see a spinster as anything but one thwarted by a damnable society of prudes.
Ibid.

14 He does not mean to be rude, but is nervously exaggerative and his hand sometimes weighs as much as a brick.
Ibid.

1 Having embraced, for some reason unknown to me, a contrary view of life to that of the ultra-respectable he sees all those who are not happy in their environment as in some way victims of mass cruelty and as individually defensible upon moral grounds. This, I need hardly point out, is the attitude of sentimentality.
Ibid.

2 Aldington's satire, unsweetened and unsalted by strong humour, remains too often as rudimentary as the back answers of an adolescent.
Ibid.

3 Poet, critic, novelist, biographer, translator, Richard Aldington was nevertheless not a real man of letters. He always conveyed the impression of having a driving force greater than writing itself. He was an angry young man of the generation before they became fashionable, he remained something of an angry old man to the end.
The Times, Obituary 30 *Jul* 1962

EARL (A.V.) ALEXANDER OF HILLSBOROUGH

Born 1885. First Lord of the Admiralty 1929–31 (at the time of the Invergordon Mutiny, occasioned by cuts in naval pay), 1940–45, 1945–56. Leader of Labour peers in the House of Lords 1955–65. Died 1965.

4 He was proud of his working-class beginnings, once telling the House of Lords, after a debating battle with Lord Hailsham, that he was thankful that 'he did not have to go to Oxford University to learn to be a bully'.
The Times, Obituary 12 *Nov* 1965

FIELD MARSHAL EARL ALEXANDER OF TUNIS

Born 1891. Commanded 1st Division at Dunkirk. C-in-C Southern Command 1940–2; G.O.C. Burma 1942; C-in-C Middle East 1942–3; C-in-C Allied Armies in Italy 1944; Supreme Allied Commander Mediterranean 1944–5; Governor-General Canada 1946–52. Died 1969.

5 He was the outstanding general's general of the European war. He brought to his command the reasonableness and patience and modesty of a great soldier.
General Omar Bradley, Daily Telegraph, Obituary 17 *Jun* 1969

6 Nothing ever disturbed or rattled him, and duty was a full satisfaction in itself, especially if it had seemed perilous or hard. But all this was combined with so gay and easy a manner that the pleasure of his friendship was prized by all who enjoyed it.
Winston Churchill

7 The ace card in the British Empire's hand.
Dwight D. Eisenhower

8 He might have been a greater commander if he had not been so nice a man.
Liddell Hart

9 He had a genius for making people like him and Britain.
Selwyn Lloyd

10 If Montgomery was the Wellington, Alexander was certainly the Marlborough of this war.
Harold Macmillan, THE BLAST OF WAR

11 He was an enigma of a sort, but of a gentle sort; he succeeded not by inspiration, nor even by thrust, but by grace and loyalty.
Jun Morris, The Times 29 *Mar* 1973

12 He had almost every quality you could wish to have, except that he had the average brain of the average English gentleman. He lacked that extra little cubic centimetre which produces genius.
Lord Mountbatten

13 He won his wars by niceness — what an epitaph for a general!
Ibid.

14 Alexander was no sphinx. Duplicity, moral or intellectual, was alien to him.
Nigel Nicolson, ALEX: THE LIFE OF FIELD-MARSHAL EARL ALEXANDER OF TUNIS 1973

15 He had great panache. He was a *beau sabreur*. He had chic but he never showed off. He had the aristocratic gift. He could be fun. He was always prepared to be kind and amusing and he had excellent manners. His supreme quality was that he was always so transparently honest. All his foibles, frailties and strength of character combined into a man for whom anybody who met him would willingly die.
Field Marshal Templer

QUEEN ALEXANDRA

Born 1844. Daughter of Christian IX of Denmark. Consort of Edward VII. Died 1925.

1 When the king walked into the room which had been prepared for an operating theatre his wife was at his side. There followed an odd and rather macabre little scene, which would be unthinkable today. Queen Alexandra remained in the room while the anaesthetic was administered and as King Edward began to throw his arms about and grow black in the face she struggled to hold him down, crying out in great alarm 'Why don't you begin?' To his horror the surgeon, Frederick Treves, realised that she intended to be present throughout the operation. However, when he told her she must leave, Queen Alexandra went without further ado into her bedroom next door. There, forty minutes later, Treves told her the operation had been a complete success.
Georgina Battiscombe, QUEEN ALEXANDRA 1969

2 The princess learnt from people rather than books. Even if she had possessed perfect hearing she would never have been a clever, well-instructed woman, but she need not have become a stupid one.
Ibid.

3 It is popularly supposed that Rose Day provided her with a pleasant interest in her declining years. In fact it was an occasion she acutely disliked. She referred to 'the tiresome Alexandra Day, *which I dread*'. No one, however, who saw her on what was once described as 'her radiant progress' through London, stopping here and there to speak to the various rose-sellers, could have guessed at her real feelings.
Ibid.

4 She gave unstinted time and energy to hospital visiting and was completely uninhibited in her approach. She noticed a man looking particularly downcast and was told that he had been wounded in the leg and had just realised his knee would be permanently stiff and useless. Immediately the Queen was at his bedside. 'My dear, dear man, I hear you have a stiff leg: so have I. Now watch what I can do with it', and lifting up her skirt she swept her lame leg clear over the top of his bedside table.
Ibid.

5 On January 21, 1915 Queen Alexandra wrote Fisher a letter which must have astonished even that believer in unorthodox methods of warfare. Zeppelin raiders had recently appeared over Sandringham and dropped bombs in the neighbourhood. 'Please let me have a lot of rockets with spikes or hoops on to defend our Norfolk coast,' she demanded. 'I am sure you could invent something of the sort which would bring down a few of those rascals.'
Ibid.

6 Dighton Probyn, her devoted Comptroller, did his very best to keep some sort of control over her charitable giving but she had ways and means of evading his vigilance. On one occasion she sent for Lord Knutsford, chairman of the London Hospital, and, with a great display of secrecy, fished out from beneath her sofa cushions a crumpled envelope which contained a cheque for £1,000 and a further £1,000 in notes, which she pressed into his hand as a gift for the hospital.
Ibid.

7 Before the Coronation Queen Alexandra sent for Archbishop Maclaglan to explain her predicament. Like most women of her age and generation she augmented her own hair with a toupet. If she were to be properly anointed she felt that the holy oil must actually touch her own body; she therefore begged the Archbishop to be sure that some of the oil ran down her forehead. This he did; on returning to Buckingham Palace she refused to wipe the oil off, wishing to bear the mark of her anointing as long as possible.
Ibid.

8 Her deafness was a sad handicap. Often when she came into the room King Edward would pretend to be asleep rather than exhaust himself by trying to make her hear.
Ibid.

9 Although she much enjoyed smoking she usually took the very greatest care that no one outside her immediate circle should see her do so, but when Randall Davidson, then Bishop of Winchester, joined the party on board the royal yacht at Cowes she amused and astonished everyone by persuading him to smoke a cigarette with her.
Ibid.

10 Easily amused, kind, affectionate and simple, had little taste for pomp or ceremony but loved the easy relationships of Edwardian social life.
Roger Fulford, FROM HANOVER TO WINDSOR 1960

11 Mama, as I have always said, is one of the most selfish people I have ever known.
George V

1 Feather-brained she might be, but she knew how to exploit her weaknesses. She would terminate tiresome arguments, as she once did with the Kaiser: 'Willy dear, you know that you always speak rather indistinctly. I am afraid I have not heard a single word you have been saying.'
Elizabeth Longford, The Times 11 *Oct* 1969

2 When a queen has breath-taking beauty and comes from the land of Hans Andersen the fairy-tale element seems bound to predominate. Yet strangely enough, for lack of just one gift at her christening — brains — Alexandra of Denmark could neither interest others during her heyday nor amuse herself during her old age.
Ibid.

3 It was lack of imagination that made this affectionate and always well-meaning lady a bossy mother-in-law. Though her taste, except in clothes, was poor she patronised the cultivated young Princess May, who had to live in a ghastly little mock-Tudor villa with hideous furniture, almost on the doorstep of Sandringham.
Raymond Mortimer, Sunday Times 5 *Oct* 1969

4 Queen Alexandra, perhaps owing to her deafness, didn't wish to address anyone too directly for fear that he should make an answer which she wouldn't be able to hear, but I have seen her make a remark to a roomful of people, with a wonderfully comprehensive gesture of the hand, and everyone in the room went away thinking that the remark had been addressed to him or her personally.
Ernest Thesiger, PRACTICALLY TRUE 1927

MUHAMMAD ALI

Born 1942 in America. Original name Cassius Marcellus Clay. Heavyweight boxer. Won world title 1964. Title withdrawn 1967 because of his refusal to serve in the US Army. Recovered title by defeating George Foreman 1974.

5 At home I am a nice guy: but I don't want the world to know. Humble people, I've found, don't get very far.
Muhammad Ali, Sunday Express 13 *Jan* 1963

6 He's not only a lousy fighter, he's a bad actor. Joe Louis or Rocky Marciano could have whipped him by telephone.
Don Digilio, Las Vegas Review Journal Nov 1965

7 Clay phoned me and listed all the fights he'd won until my ear fell off.
Angelo Dundee, his future trainer

8 A fighter better known for the size of his mouth than his potency in the ring.
Herbert Kretzmer, Daily Express, 28 *May* 1963

9 Amid all the sad confusion of his life — his own erratic and unconvincing espousal of the Black Muslim creed and the sordid exploitation of him by others — the beauty and verve of his performances in the ring provided him with an unassailable sense of validity.
Hugh McIlvenney, Observer 25 *Jan* 1970

10 The Prince of Ego.
Norman Mailer, Sunday Times 14 *Mar* 1971

11 Working apparently on the premise that there was something obscene about being hit, he boxed with his head back and drew it further back when attacked, like a kid who is shy of punches in a street fight, but because he had a waist that was more supple than the average fighter's neck, he was able to box with his arms low, surveying the fighter in front of him, avoiding punches by the speed of his feet and the reflexes of his waist.
Ibid.

12 What we have as current heavyweight champion of the world is a showman and a clever fighter without a punch.
The Times 24 *Nov* 1965

IDI AMIN

Born Uganda 1925. Seized power in a military coup 1971. Head of Organisation of African Unity 1975. Overthrown and driven into exile 1979.

13 I myself consider myself the most important figure in the world.
Idi Amin, BBC Radio 11 *Aug* 1976

14 I remember Amin as being a typical, good warrant officer type. He was a big, bluff, cheerful soldier who always had a great beaming smile on his face. I never thought he had any great intellect. He was just a

good, rough, tough soldier and a bustling rugby forward.
General Sir Richard Goodwin

1 Within seven years of enlisting [in 1953] he was promoted to lance-corporal and was displaying the qualities that so endeared him to his British superiors — instant obedience, fierce regimental pride, reverence towards Britain and the British, a uniform which crackled with razor-sharp starched creases and boots with toe-caps like black mirrors.
Alexander Mitchell and Russell Miller, Sunday Times, Amin — the Untold Story 29 *Oct* 1972

2 His is a clown's face, all the more terrible for its drollery masking in Mr Smith's words 'The solitary conductor of an orchestra of devils'; Satan's buffoon.
Tony Samstag, The Times, review of George Ivan Smith's GHOSTS OF KAMPALA 1 *Oct* 1980

KINGSLEY AMIS

Born 1922. Poet and novelist. Gained recognition with his first novel *Lucky Jim* 1954.

3 *Lucky Jim* was a freshly-formed book dealing with a world where mores, values and social relations had been changed by a recent war. It signalled to the young that ways of thinking and writing about society had to be different, and that the cleansing comic vision had something to do with it.
Malcolm Bradbury, The Times 17 *May* 1984

4 Amis hides a taste for decency behind a kind of literary machismo.
Ibid.

5 Amis values stylish prejudice and has a taste for heroes who are self-confessed shits, assuming it's what you like that does you good, and you may have to be a bit nasty to get it.
Ibid.

6 The author who started off as an undergraduate communist at St John's Oxford in 1941 ('the only party I ever joined'), and declared himself a probable lifetime Labour voter in 1957, now describes himself as a non-wet Tory with a few liberal bits (on abortion, hanging and homosexuality). He has little time for socialism or intellectuals, and is a well-known scourge of such extraordinary things as Modernism.
Ibid.

7 He was greeted as a hero because he had dared to make professors, neurotic girls and culture-lovers as ludicrous as angry schoolmasters, severe aunts and tattling children; because he was, in other words, up to date. His prose made public the tone in which people in authority were frequently described in private.
Simon Gray, The Times 3 *Feb* 1966

8 The publication of *Lucky Jim* was certainly the literary event of the mid-fifties. It provoked Lord Snow (then C.P.) to laughter, and Somerset Maugham to frenzied denunciations — from his villa in France — of the young scum that threatened England . . . But the intellectual weeklies rejoiced that a new spirit was abroad in the land. Honest, anarchic; knifer of hypocrisy and pursuer of pleasure, the anti-hero of our age had burst upon us.
Ibid.

9 When it comes down to it *Lucky Jim* is *Just William*, bigger and bespectacled, literate and funny, but scarcely grown up. What Christine is to the one, a bag of bullseyes is to the other. They both identify their enemies in the same way, from the same types, and use approximately the same weapons.
Ibid.

10 He writes slowly, making notes on the back of cheque books, old envelopes and other scraps of paper. Then when he has time, they go into a 1s 3d exercise book. Finally, when the plot is clear he starts writing, straight on to a typewriter.
Observer, Profile 14 *Jan* 1962

CAPTAIN ROALD AMUNDSEN

Born 1872. Norwegian polar explorer. First to reach the South Pole 14 Dec 1911, a month ahead of Scott. Died attempting to rescue General Nobile, whose airship *Italia* had crashed in the Arctic, 1928.

11 So extended and complete were our magnetic observations that the scientists to whom we delivered them on our return to Europe in 1906 have spent nearly twenty years in digesting their meaning, having only last year finished their calculations based on these data. Nothing anywhere nearly so complete regarding the phenomenon of the

North Magnetic Pole has ever been given to science.
Roald Amundsen, MY LIFE AS AN EXPLORER 1927

1 The thing I most feared, happened. By the time we had ridden out the storm we were more than a hundred miles within the icefield . . . For thirteen months we lay caught in the vice of this icefield. Two of the sailors went insane. Every member of the ship's crew was afflicted with scurvy. The commander and captain took to their beds and made their wills.
Ibid.

2 At twenty-one he was 'hardening his muscles' by a mid-winter adventure on the storm-bound plateau that lies between Oslo and Bergen — a venture that nearly cost him his life. His equally daring — or equally foolhardy? — companion had to dig him out of a coffin of solid ice that had frozen round him in the night. They staggered back to the nearest human habitation, after eight days on the verge of starvation.
T. Foster, T.P.'s Weekly 31 *Dec* 1927

3 On May 25 1928 the Italian airship *Italia*, commanded by Umberto Nobile, crashed on the ice while returning from the North Pole to Spitzbergen. On June 18 Amundsen set off from Tromsoe to rescue him, in a seaplane and accompanied by a crew of four. The regions of snow and ice which he had dared for years claimed him. He was never heard of again. The irony is that the news that he was missing arrived on the day that Nobile, the man he had set out to help, was found and rescued by the Swedish airman, Captain Lundborg.
Ronald Walker, News Chronicle 16 *Jul* 1936

ELIZABETH GARRETT ANDERSON

Born 1836. Pioneer woman doctor. First woman to become a mayor — of Aldeburgh, in 1908. Died 1917.

4 She disarmed a hostile profession and won the trust of a whole generation of women patients.
Naomi Mitchison, REVALUATIONS — STUDIES IN BIOGRAPHY

5 Mrs Anderson was not one to consider unduly the effects of overwork or fatigue on herself or her colleagues. She was a persistent, shameless and highly successful beggar.
Mary Scharlieb, REMINISCENCES

JOHN ANDERSON

Born 1881. Home Secretary 1939–40. The Anderson shelter was named after him. Member of the War Cabinet. Chancellor of the Exchequer 1943–5. Created Viscount Waverley 1952. Died 1958.

6 The case of Sir John Anderson is even more confusing. For failing to solve the shelter problem, for diminishing public liberty, and for foolishly imprisoning the best anti-Nazis who have ever set foot on these shores, he has been promoted to the cabinet of eight.
Hugh Cudlipp, Daily Mirror 6 *Oct* 1940

7 When Chamberlain died Anderson was made lord president. He gradually became the supreme figure in civil administration and ran the war on the civil side so far as one man could be said to do so.
A. J. P. Taylor, ENGLISH HISTORY 1914–1945 1965

MAXWELL ANDERSON

Born 1888. American playwright. Works include *Interest* in blank verse 1935. His *Lost in the Stars,* 1950, was an adaptation of Alan Paton's novel, *Cry, the Beloved Country*. Died 1959.

8 He has brought verse and the form of verse back to the American stage — not as an experiment, not as an oddity, but as an essential of the later plays he has written. And because of it he has opened a shut door.
Stephen Vincent Benet. Quoted Jean Gould, MODERN AMERICAN PLAYWRIGHTS

9 Maxwell Anderson is a dramatist to be respected even if he is one who cannot always be enjoyed or understood. He has courage, a mind of his own — rarest of all he has ears which he likes to bathe in sound.
John Mason Brown, DRAMATIS PERSONAE

10 His best plays have a seriousness of purpose and theme which raises them above the rut, but their very earnestness and self-conscious universalising through verse is no more than service in an honourable cause.
Eric Mottram, AVENEL COMPANION TO AMERICAN LITERATURE 1971

SHERWOOD ANDERSON

Born 1876. American novelist and short story writer. Achieved a major success with *Poor White* 1920. Died 1941.

11 Anderson is a man of practically no ideas – but he is one of the very best and finest

writers in the English language today. God, he can write.
F. Scott Fitzgerald, letter to Maxwell Perkins, 1 Jun 1925

1 His characters are puzzled, grasping, baffled, and possess no vision of order or channel for directing their energies against the frustrations of contemporary existence.
James D. Hart, OXFORD COMPANION TO AMERICAN LITERATURE

2 If a girl was with us I was sure to hear Swatty open up as a searcher for deep truths. You could tell how smitten he was with the girl by how ardently he started praising himself. He called it self-revelation.
Ben Hecht, LETTER FROM BOHEMIA

JULIE ANDREWS

Born 1935. Daughter of English cabaret and radio stars Ted and Barbara Andrews. Made her debut unannounced in *Starlight Roof*, 1947, and stopped the show. Went to Hollywood and gained an international reputation with *Mary Poppins* and *The Sound of Music*.

3 Having got to the top by being sweet and old-fashioned she quickly showed signs of disliking her own image. 'I don't want to be thought of as wholesome' she said in 1966, and promptly proved it by accepting a sexy role. She was also seen wearing a badge which said 'Mary Poppins is a junky'.
Leslie Halliwell, FILMGOER'S BOOK OF QUOTES 1978

4 She is like a nun with a switchblade.
Ibid

5 She has that wonderful British strength that makes you wonder why they lost India.
Moss Hart

6 Working with her is like being hit over the head with a Valentine's card.
Christopher Plummer, after making The Sound of Music

7 She is everybody's tomboy tennis partner and their daughter, their sister, their mum.
Time magazine

8 Julie Andrews, 12-years-old coloratura soprano, stopped the show in her first West End appearance in last night's opening of *Starlight Roof* at the London Hippodrome. After singing the 'Mignon' Polonnaise she left the theatre with cheers and applause ringing in her ears and was driven home to Walton-on-Thames — and bed. Julie's name was not in the programme. She was kept as a surprise item — a self-assured little girl with fair pigtails, who emerged one of the big hits in a company of fifty. Her parents, Ted and Barbara Andrews, radio and cabaret stars, are allowing her 5s a week pocket money out of her first West End salary. The rest is going into a trust for her future.
Cecil Wilson, News Chronicle 24 *Oct* 1947

YURI (VLADIMIROVICH) ANDROPOV

Born Nagutskaya USSR 1914. Chairman of KGB 1967–82. Succeeded Brezhnev as General Secretary of CPSU 1982. Became head of state 1983. Died 1984.

9 Today's dissenters now languishing in camps and lunatic asylums were put where they are now by Andropov himself, who also presided over the expulsion of Solzhenitsyn and the sequestration in Gorky of Sakharov. It will take a lot of enlightened action on his part to reduce scepticism about his intentions.
Edward Crankshaw, Observer, The perfect soviet man 26 *Jun* 1983

10 Brezhnev was a Russian soul; Andropov is a Russian computer.
Helmut Schmidt. Quoted Observer, Sayings of the week 29 *May* 1983

HRH PRINCESS ANNE (ELIZABETH ALICE LOUISE)

Born 15 Aug 1950. Daughter of Queen Elizabeth II and Prince Philip, Duke of Edinburgh.

11 I'd prefer a quiet wedding, but Mummy wants Westminster Abbey.
Princess Anne

12 I learned just by going around. I know all about Kleenex factories, and all sorts of things.
Princess Anne. Quoted by Noël St George, ROYAL QUOTES

13 When I appear in public people expect me to neigh, grind my teeth, paw the ground and swish my tail.
Ibid.

14 You ask me what it is like to be royal. I don't know what it is like *not* to be royal. I couldn't answer that question unless I had a comparison. I don't have one. I've always been me.
Princess Anne to an interviewer

15 They'll have a job marrying me off to someone I don't want. I'll marry the man I

choose no matter who he is or what he does.
Princess Anne in 1969

1 Don't irritate Princess Anne by asking opinions about women's hats. Although she will be receptive to chat about tanks and submachine guns.
Life magazine

2 She'll wear the pants in that marriage.
Harvey Smith

3 To make sure Princess Anne would be able to negotiate the narrow companion-ways, steep ladders and hatchways when she visited HMS *Eastbourne*, Lieutenant-Commander Emberton went through a special rehearsal—in drag.
Western Morning News

JEAN ANOUILH

Born 1910. French playwright. Among his best-known works are *Antigone* 1942 and *The Lark* 1953.

4 I have never been a writer with a message.
Jean Anouilh. Quoted Bryan Appleyard, The Times 23 *Apr* 1984

5 In defiance of those who demand 'relevance' of their drama, the one function he attributes to his plays is that they allow his audiences to forget for a couple of hours that they are going to die. His drama is a powerful, self-contained, self-alluding distraction.
Bryan Appleyard, The Times 23 *Apr* 1984

6 He has remained a central figure in French drama, though never a static one. He has drifted in and out of fashion with regularity. When out the French critics were characteristically vituperative, dismissing him as a populist trickster with no depth when compared to the politician and philosopher playwrights of the avant-garde. When in he was accepted as the master magician whose stagecraft and wit placed him alongside Molière.
Ibid.

7 He was a £3-a-week secretary at a Champs Elysées theatre for Louis Jouvet who lent him odds and ends of theatre props to furnish his flat. One day stage hands called to borrow back the props for a new play.
Frank Tole, Evening News 24 *Aug* 1951

8 To get food for his family he wrote theatre sketches for which other people took the credit.
Ibid.

9 He will not have his number in the phone book, and occasionally sends a theatre ticket as a recompense to another Monsieur Anouilh who does have his number in the book and is constantly being rung up by mistake.
Ibid.

10 When he finally got a play on in Paris it was so coolly received that the leading actress, Paulette Pax, put her head through the curtains and shouted to the critics: 'You fools! You did not understand a word!'
Ibid.

SIR EDWARD (VICTOR) APPLETON

Born 1892. Physicist. Discoverer of the ionised belt in the upper atmosphere which became known as the Appleton Layer, and which played a crucial part in the development of radar. Awarded Nobel Prize for Physics 1947. Died 1965.

11 In the past seven years he has spent 200 nights in the hut on top of King's College, The Strand, charting the upper atmosphere by sending out short waves to a height of hundreds of kilometres and timing their return to a millionth of a second. He discovered the upper layer of electrons which makes short wave and beam transmission possible having first pierced the first layer 60 miles high.
J. L. Hodson, New Chronicle 12 *Jan* 1932

12 In 1901 when Marconi first transmitted wireless messages across the Atlantic the fact that communication could be established between England and America caused much astonishment since there seemed to be no adequate reason why the waves should bend round and follow the curvature of the earth to the extent necessary . . . It was Appleton who initiated and carried through a striking series of experiments which demonstrated the existence of conducting layers of ionised air, and who followed this up by prolonged investigations into the structure and properties of this electrified layer, now known as the ionosphere.
The Times, Obituary 23 *Apr* 1965

13 It was Appleton's work that really led to the use of radar for locating distant aircraft, for the detection of wireless waves reflected from aircraft was first carried out by methods he had devised for the detection of waves reflected from the ionosphere.
Ibid.

WILLIAM ARCHER

Born 1856 in Scotland. Dramatic critic and dramatist. Greatly influenced the career of G. B. Shaw by encouraging him to turn from music criticism and novel writing to writing plays. His translations from the Norwegian introduced Ibsen to the London stage. Wrote one highly successful drama, *The Green Goddess*. Died 1924.

1 His success as a dramatist, in which role he deemed he could never succeed, was a great reward for his last years. After reading Freud on dreams he had taken to writing down his night thoughts and visions. *The Green Goddess* was the result of a dream which came to him on the night of 1 September 1919, and was carefully set down.
Lt-Col C. Archer, WILLIAM ARCHER, LIFE, WORKS AND FRIENDSHIPS 1931

2 Barrie twitted Archer on his nightly critical performance: 'Want of facial expression. This is your greatest want. You get worse and worse. I am thinking particularly of your laugh, which you seem to have cut out in the long ago . . . My grand ambition is to make you laugh — just once.'
Ibid.

3 He won his battle for an intelligent theatre, above all he won his battle for Ibsen, although, in the process of that campaign, he suffered bitter calumny and was cursed as a 'muck-ferreting dog' by Clement Scott, the great thunderer of the conservative stage, but he had the eager comradeship of G.B.S.
Ivor Brown, John o'London's Weekly 11 *Jul* 1931

4 There is an absolute gratuitousness about your perversity that is inexplicable unless one sees you as a sort of child in fairyland who has never learnt to live in the world and who resents the intrusion of moral problems as angrily as it joyfully welcomes the advent of the poetic glamour.
G. B. Shaw, letter to William Archer

5 You really are a curious character. You admit the superiority of your talent and wit. You are quite wrong. Incredible as it sometimes seems you have just as much talent and wit as I have. You have all the tools of the trade but you have no conscience.
Ibid.

MICHAEL ARLEN

Born 1895 in Bulgaria, original name Dikran Kuyumjian. Novelist. Educated in England, naturalised British subject 1922. Most famous novel *The Green Hat* 1924. Died in Hollywood 1956.

6 In the Colony Restaurant, Michael Arlen told Dorothy Kilgallen why he hadn't written a novel for a long time. 'You know those charming people I used to write about? I can't stand them any more.'
Bennett Cerf, SHAKE WELL BEFORE USING 1948

7 I never heard him discuss books. In fact he was isolated by his success and by the limitations of that success. A little man who bounded into fashion on *The Green Hat*, made a lot of money and bought a yellow Rolls-Royce, he stayed in fashion with *These Charming People* and retired gracefully before the East Winds of the Thirties.
Cyril Connolly, The Sunday Times 11 *Aug* 1968

8 At my surprising piece of news about myself — of being the father of seven children — he put down his wine glass, looked searchingly at me from under his astrakhan eyebrows and exclaimed 'Good God' in italics. Some of his more dutiful admirers would have laughed, for he has that impressive trick of making perfectly ordinary remarks sound like epigrams.
Reginald Pound, THEIR MOODS AND MINE 1937

9 No doubt if he had been more severe with himself Arlen would not have made a fortune. It was the silliness that sold his books in such quantities. Yet even the silliness is no worse than, say, *Lady Chatterley's Lover*.
Anthony Powell, Daily Telegraph 1 *Aug* 1968

10 His first novel *The London Venture* appeared in 1920. Noël Coward borrowed £250 on the strength of it, which made possible the staging of *The Vortex* — an extraordinarily appropriate incidence.
Ibid.

11 *The Green Hat* by Michael Arlen was the deliberately unreal fabrication of a hard-headed Rumanian. It was solemnly accepted by social critics as a picture of contemporary manners.
A. J. P. Taylor, ENGLISH HISTORY 1914–1945 1965

12 *The Green Hat* is, generally speaking, so preposterously, obviously and comically bad

that it is one of those rare bad books from which a good book is darkly struggling to release itself. It resembles some Loch Ness of profound absurdity in which a passing motorist imagines for a moment or two that he sees the black undulations of the veritable monster.
Philip Toynbee, Observer 18 *Aug* 1968

1 In life Michael Arlen was a quiet, unambitious but delightfully witty man. A virile American hostess cried out at a party, 'Why, Mr Arlen, you almost look like a woman'. M.A. 'So do you, Madam! So do you!'
Ibid. (Cf. Edna Ferber's remark to Noël Coward)

2 The gigantic faults of *The Green Hat* are the corrigible faults of excess, bad taste, affectation, puppyish exuberance. To us it must seem a pity that Arlen's novel had such a debilitating success; but for this lazy, good-humoured man his wealth was no doubt a great blessing and satisfaction.
Ibid.

3 Adultery is a commonplace in the Shepherd's Market of *The Green Hat* — always undertaken out of a brave defiance of life's boredom or in the mad careless raptures that follow midnight bathing. and sins more strange than adultery are hinted at in the world of Mayfair and Deauville.
Angus Wilson, Observer 6 *Oct* 1957

LOUIS ARMSTRONG

Born America 1900. Jazz trumpeter, band leader and singer.

4 (In his dressing room) he'd be sitting down in his underwear with a towel around his lap, one round his shoulders and that white handkerchief on his head, and he'd put that grease on his lips. Look like a minstrel man, ya know — an laughin', you know, natural the way he is — an' everybody's lookin'. Got their eyes dead on him, just like they were lookin' at a diamond.
Danny Barker. Quoted James Lincoln Collier, LOUIS ARMSTRONG 1984

5 Armstrong was by temperament shy, indecisive and easily put down. He liked to have his mind made up for him.
James Lincoln Collier, LOUIS ARMSTRONG 1984

6 He has always managed to look the part without even trying. The staring banjo eyes, the rivers of honest sweat dabbed away with a whiter-than-white handkerchief, the slack lower jaw that gave him the nickname of Satchmo (satchel-mouth), the illusion of row upon row of sparkling white teeth, the fixed smile and the alarming gravel voice which can somehow make even the most excruciating jive-talk seem witty.
Benny Green, Observer 5 *Jul* 1970

7 His life became an allegory of genius transcending the accidents of poverty and race; simple and modest in his personality, imperially authoritative in his work, he had by the end of his life grown into an internationally-accepted symbol not only of jazz, but of good will and good humour.
Philip Larkin, Observer 25 *Mar* 1984

8 He was at once a jovial yet dignified father figure of entertainment, a considerable comedian in his own right, the man who led the way in transforming jazz from a folk music into an art.
The Times, Obituary 7 *Jul* 1971

SVANTE AUGUST ARRHENIUS

Born 1859 in Sweden. Awarded the Nobel Prize for Chemistry, 1903, for his work on electrolytic dissociation (ionisation) which produced an explanation for the ability of certain substances in solution to conduct electricity. Died 1929.

9 Life, he thought, need not necessarily have first been created on Earth. He believed the germ of it was forever floating through the realms of space, seeking a foothold, such as on the Earth it found, and on the Earth developed.
Children's Newspaper 22 *Oct* 1927

10 The work of Arrhenius forms one of the foundations of the electrochemistry which runs through all chemical enquiry today. Not only did it go far to explain why, for electric reasons, some substances dissolve more readily than others, but it led to a closer understanding of the behaviour of the corpuscles of our blood and the cells of which our nerves and muscles are composed.
Ibid.

11 In person he was stoutly built, blond, blue-eyed, and rubicund, a true son of the Swedish countryside. His nature was frank, generous and expansive. He was full of robust vitality and primitive force. He had hearty likes and dislikes and beneath his inborn geniality and good humour was a

latent combativeness, easily aroused in the cause of truth and freedom.
Royal Society, Obituary 1928

1 It has been said that his particular gift was a union of speculative imagination with an extraordinary power of dealing with figures.
Prof. J. Arthur Thomson, John o' London's Weekly 8 *Dec* 1928

2 He was a genius in the sense that he was a new pattern with a new outlook of his own; not merely a very talented man, but with an original mind; an intellectual mutation of considerable magnitude.
Ibid.

3 He was fascinated by the old problem of the Northern Lights, which he linked to his theory of the repulsion of minute particles from the sun by radiation pressure.
Ibid.

4 He became extraordinarily interested in serum therapy, and along with Madsen tackled the extremely difficult problem of immunity, laying the foundations of which he termed 'Immunochemistry'.
Ibid.

SIR FREDERICK ASHTON

Born in Ecuador in 1904. British choreographer and dancer. Became a pupil of Marie Rambert in 1925. Became director of the Royal Ballet, 1963. Major works include *Facade*, 1931, *Enigma Variations*, 1968, and the film *Tales of Beatrix Potter*, 1971.

5 One day Gertrude Stein had a plan for us to go to a certain monastery to hear these Gregorian chants. Billy Chapman and Bobby Helpmann were with me and very frivolous and we got the most appalling giggles. Afterwards Alice B. Toklas said to us 'Well, I've learned a lesson today. I thought only *girls* giggled.'
Sir F. Ashton. Quoted Julie Kavanagh, The Times profile 27 *Sep* 1984

6 It is Ashton's joyous vision of things that allows him to make even the most trivial subjects poetical. Who else could make a ballet anthropomorphising vegetables (*Pas des Legumes*) or Beatrix Potter animals without lapsing into coyness and sentimentality.
Julie Kavanagh, The Times profile 27 *Sep* 1984

7 He always smokes very theatrically, like the Hostess in *Les Biches*, his hand posed gracefully away from his face.
Ibid.

8 I am puzzled by some of the critical reactions to *Ondine*. Before *Ondine* they said I had not fully exploited Margot Fonteyn's talents; after it they said I had concentrated on her too much.
The Times 27 *May* 1966

9 He does not like reviving his own ballets. 'Making a ballet is like a love affair; reviving one is too cold and calculated; the drive is gone. Anyway, I forget.'
Ibid.

10 He does not use any of the dance notation systems and is not too keen on them. 'I do not want the future cluttered up with old ballets. Each generation should make its own. The really tough ones will survive anyhow.'
Ibid.

HERBERT HENRY ASQUITH, FIRST EARL OF OXFORD AND ASQUITH

Born 1852. Liberal politician. Chancellor of the Exchequer 1904–8. Prime Minister of a Liberal administration 1908–15, and a war-time coalition 1915–16 until displaced by Lloyd George. Created earl 1925. Died 1928.

11 His famed lucidity is a lucidity of phrase only, and not of thought, a lucidity which explains but never enlightens.
L. S. Amery, in 1914

12 The light fell on his hair, now tinged with grey, and on his broad massive forehead, and beneath it on a sheaf of papers and on a collection of curious little objects, minute crystal animals, and midget silver figures, which were arranged in strangely assorted groups in front of his blotting pad.
Hon. Herbert Asquith, MOMENTS OF MEMORY 1937

13 His family knew what the public did not begin to appreciate until his career was nearly closed – that the reserve did not proceed from coldness, but was the mask under which it was the habit of a naturally shy man to conceal an unusually warm and sensitive heart. It did his credit in men's eyes much wrong, as he knew, but it was his humour and he could not depart from it.
Ibid.

14 I had my individuality, my hopes and my ambitions trampled under foot by those marching legions of which, for so many years, Mr Asquith was the head.
Stanley Baldwin. Speech at Mansion House 13 *May* 1925

HERBERT HENRY ASQUITH

1 Last night I dined with the Asquiths. As the fortunes of debate would have it Asquith and I had a rather sharp passage in the House after dinner. Asquith was the challenger; but I felt a mild awkwardness in replying to a man in the strength of his own champagne! I did it all the same, and with considerable vigour.
A. J. Balfour, in a letter 1900. *Quoted Blanche E. C. Dugdale*, JAMES ARTHUR BALFOUR 1937

2 A cross between a Dissenting Minister and a seller of marine stores.
A. C. Benson. Quoted Geoffrey Madan, NOTEBOOKS 1981

3 So far from being hard and cold about the War, it affected him so deeply in all its colossal tragedy that in a sense it stunned him. He was numbed by the death of his eldest son, Raymond. It is not surprising to find that he hated the Two Minutes Silence on Armistice Day. 'This sort of ritual', he writes, 'is not in my taste and I remained in my den contemplating one Great Western van and one taxi.'
Robert Bernays, John o' London's Weekly 9 *Dec* 1933

4 I remember a pink face, blue eyes, white hair and a halo of cigar smoke. When I arrived he would take the ring of his cigar, which he had kept, recite with apparent pleasure and absolute regularity *The Owl and the Pussycat* placing the cigar ring on my finger as he reached 'Said the Piggy, I will'.
Mark Bonham Carter. Introduction to the 1962 edition of Margot Oxford's autobiography

5 Incapable of intrigue, he was equally incapable of dealing with it. He could fight for a cause, for his party, for his country. What he could not fight for was himself.
Lady Violet Bonham Carter, The Times 2 *Nov* 1964

6 After Asquith had ceased to be Prime Minister we were discussing one day whether he had suffered from his fall. He was too grand, built too much 'after the high Roman fashion' to show weakness or betray emotion, and somebody advanced the view that after a premiership of nearly ten years he was perhaps glad of a rest and that his fall had not hurt him. 'Nonsense,' growled Augustine Birrell, 'of course it hurt him. I know how much it hurt me when I fell off my donkey, so I can imagine what he felt like when he fell off his elephant.'
Duff Cooper, OLD MEN FORGET 1953

7 The PM, wearing a very light brown overcoat, the collar turned up, his long white hair sticking out behind, and his very red face, was a striking, cheerful figure.
Duff Cooper, DIARY *Mar* 1916

8 He is oblivious to young men and lecherous of young women.
Duff Cooper in 1916. *Quoted Philip Ziegler*, DIANA COOPER 1981

9 He lacks some element of character; perhaps hardiness. I should say he was a soft man: and his chin recedes when an attack is possible or imminent.
Lord Esher, DIARY 28 *Nov* 1907

10 My colleagues tell military secrets to their wives, except Asquith, who tells them to other men's wives.
Lord Kitchener. Quoted Philip Magnus, KITCHENER

11 When the coalition was forced upon him in 1915 he remained a stern, ambitious, intellectually proud man, fighting his way with all necessary ruthlessness.
Stephen Koss, ASQUITH 1976

12 As Prime Minister you have not devoted yourself absolutely to co-ordinating all the moves of the war because so much of your time and energy has been devoted to controlling the political machine.
Bonar Law, in a letter to Asquith 2 *Nov* 1915

13 He had the guide-book mind in sublimation, and always prepared himself for any sights we were to see, mugging-up his Thucydides, for instance, before our stop at Syracuse, and giving us on the spot a masterly review of the Sicilian Expedition.
Edward Marsh, A NUMBER OF PEOPLE 1939

14 The quality of Asquith was both intellectually and morally so transcendent that, however fiercely he may have been assailed by his contemporaries, he is regarded by posterity as an exceptional figure, meriting pondered appraisal, and not as a subject for partisan prejudice or superficial criticism.
Harold Nicolson, Observer 12 *Oct* 1958

15 He knew and cared little about military or naval affairs, although it should never be forgotten that it was the insistence of this lucid civilian that prevented Sir John French, at the time of the retreat from Mons, from withdrawing the British Army behind the Seine. Asquith was thus one of the architects of the victory of the Marne.
Ibid.

1 Asquith never expected too much of mortal brains or character.
Harold Nicolson, Observer 2 *Nov* 1958

2 The PM is absolutely devoid of all principles except one — that of retaining his position as Prime Minister.
Frances Stevenson, DIARY 30 *Nov* 1916

3 Lloyd George says he is for all the world like a sultan with his harem of 23, using all his skill and wiles to prevent one of them from eloping.
Ibid.

4 A corker . . . a fleshy, sanguine, wine-bibbing, medieval abbot of a personage — a glutinous, lecherous, cynical old fellow — ugh! — you should have seen him making towards Dora Carrington — cutting her off at an angle as she crossed the lawn.
Lytton Strachey, letter to James Strachey

5 One curiosity attracted my attention. His tongue — a little, pointed, cunning tongue — was perpetually darting out and licking his lips.
Lytton Strachey 1 *Mar* 1918

6 If I hadn't known who he was I should have guessed him to be one of those Oxford dons who have a smattering of the world — one of those clever, cautious, mediocre intelligences who make one thank heaven one was at Cambridge.
Lytton Strachey 6 *May* 1918

7 Asquith was the first prime minister since the younger Pitt who is said to have been manifestly the worse for drink when on the Treasury Bench. George Robey was uncomfortably near the truth when he sang, 'Mr Asquith says in a manner sweet and calm; Another little drink won't do us any harm'.
A. J. P. Taylor, ENGLISH HISTORY 1914–1945 1965

8 Asquith, the Prime Minister, was a strong character unshakeable as a rock and, like a rock, incapable of movement. His initiative, if he ever had any, was sapped by years of good living in high society.
Ibid.

MARGOT ASQUITH, COUNTESS OF OXFORD AND ASQUITH

Born 1864, née Tennant. Married H. H. Asquith in 1894. Her uninhibited *Autobiography* caused a sensation when it was published in 1920. Died 1945.

9 When I first remember her she was already over sixty. As a child I saw her through her physical appearance; small, neat and angular. Her gestures were sharp yet free, her hands bony and claw-like with long blood-red nails and big rings. I was fascinated by her nose, which she explained had been broken while hunting, and her short, almost misshapen upper lip. Her voice was as low as a man's, and vehement.
Mark Bonham Carter, Introduction to the 1962 *edition of Margot Asquith's autobiography*

10 Margot had never received a systematic education (she always counted on her fingers).
Ibid.

11 She felt it her duty to tell people the truth, particularly about themselves, and she was constantly surprised by the way they reacted. Her candour knew no bounds. On one occasion she unwisely agreed to present at Court a lady of doubtful reputation. The application was refused and Margot received a furious letter of protest from her acquaintance. Her reply was in her best vein. 'I am sure that what you say is perfectly true and that many people just as, if not even more, immoral than you have been presented at Court . . .'
Ibid.

12 She lived much of her time in a daydream world founded on her experience of the real world so altered by her sense of the dramatic as to bear only an intermittent relation to it. She was like a little boy who, because he would have liked to kill a lion, tells you he has done so; like the little boy, she believed her own stories.
Lord David Cecil, Observer, Staying with Margot 20 *Dec* 1981

13 When Margot Asquith had a fancy for learning to drive a car — luckily for the safety of herself and others the fancy did not last long — she appeared dressed in breeches and a flying helmet. She was close on 70.
Ibid.

14 People dined, including Lady Oxford, self-invited as usual. She wore a flowing black dress like a priest and was charmingly *cassante*, rude, dictatorial and magnificent. She is the cleverest woman I know, and a magnificent character. I suppose she must be 75. Her crisp penetrating phrases are riveting. This evening she played Bridge until 1.30 without a pause, passing judgment on everyone in politics and society the while.
Sir Henry Channon, DIARY 14 *Mar* 1937

1 Lady Oxford rushed up to me in her dominating manner . . . she looks like a scarecrow, or a mad raven, yet there is still fire in that antique skeleton, and she has ever been my friend and ally.
Ibid. 28 *Jul* 1943

2 Ava Anderson told me that old Margot Oxford had lunched with her and complained that all she had to live on now was macaroni and memorial services.
Ibid. 12 *Sep* 1943

3 This featherweight daredevil, mounted upon enormous horses, who with faultless nerve and thrust and inexhaustible energy, spurred by love of chase and desire to excel, came sometimes to grief but always to the fore.
Winston Churchill

4 I had seen Mrs Asquith once before, at a Royal Academy Private View, hopping like a raven in a black-feathered hat from one gallery to another and criticising the exhibits in a raucous voice.
John Gielgud, AN ACTOR AND HIS TIME 1979

5 She had a remarkable ability not merely to shock, but to captivate, and even to inspire.
Roy Jenkins, ASQUITH 1966

6 She was incorrigibly a child of Nature, spontaneous in her wit, her generosity and, alas, her disregard for tact, She endeared herself to her husband's clever colleagues such as Birrell, but not to the ordinary run of his supporters, many of them Nonconformists.
Raymond Mortimer, Sunday Times 1 *Nov* 1964

7 I can't decide whether it is her profile or her fortune-telling voice that makes me think of gipsies when I see this woman. There is something splendidly steadfast in her. I could talk to her for ever.
Reginald Pound, THEIR MOODS AND MINE 1937

8 'Her ladyship says will you come upstairs?' I followed Lady Oxford's footman up into a bedroom at 44 Bedford Square; it reminded me, at my first look, of a theatre dressing-room without the usual powder smell. The impression was heightened when I saw her sitting up in bed playing at being Queen Elizabeth. For me, no one can ever look the part again with such dignity and rightness as she did at that moment . . . She may have been posing as Margot Oxford, the redoubtable woman we all know about. I took it for an unself-conscious portrait of Gloriana in a mood of majestic good humour.
Ibid.

9 Mrs Asquith belongs spiritually to the demi-monde: she should have been the mistress of Foch, or the Kaiser.
G. M. Young. Quoted Geoffrey Madan, NOTEBOOKS 1981

FRED ASTAIRE

Born 1899 in Omaha, Nebraska, of Austrian parentage. Began in vaudeville in partnership with his sister Adele in 1905, as a child dancing act. Gained film fame with Ginger Rogers in *The Gay Divorce* 1934.

10 The nearest we are ever likely to get to a human Mickey Mouse.
Graham Greene

11 He can give the audience pleasure just by walking across the floor.
Gene Kelly

12 Can't act. Can't sing. Can dance a little.
Studio report after his first screen test

NANCY (WITCHER) ASTOR, VISCOUNTESS ASTOR

Born America, 1879. Wife of second Viscount Astor. First woman MP to take her seat in House of Commons, as member for Plymouth. Died 1964.

13 All the members of her household, secretaries and servants as well as those relations who were still in regular attendance, came completely under her spell. She worked on them a strange enchantment, both fortifying their lives and at the same time disqualifying them, in some strange way, from living fully in any other context.
Michael Astor, TRIBAL FEELING

14 The sudden outbursts of mimicry and burlesque could happen at any time. It might be a charade, in which case everyone joined in, but as often as not it started by my mother slipping a pair of celluloid false teeth into her mouth in the middle of dinner.
Ibid.

15 I am a novel principal, and have to be endured.
Nancy Astor. Speech, House of Commons 1921

1 Years of work for and with the wounded have made me rather like a soldier myself. So if my manners are slightly like a sergeant-major's you will know the reason why. Although I am one of the most serious-minded women in England today I have got the sort of mirth of the British Tommy, I can laugh when I am going over the top.
Nancy Astor, election campaign speech, Oct 1919

2 My first weeks in the House of Commons were a sheer nightmare to me. It was just horrible — and I was scared to death. I never dared go anywhere about the House. I can recall as well as yesterday one occasion when I actually sat there for five hours after I had wanted to get up and leave — all because I was afraid to walk out of the House through all those groups of unfriendly men.
Nancy Astor, Sunday Dispatch 26 *Nov* 1944

3 She could exchange compliments or insults on equal terms with dukes or dockers.
Lord Attlee, Observer 3 *May* 1964

4 Her attitude to nursery schools, which she did so much to promote, was typical of her; she wanted them not only because they were good for children, but because they took some of the burdens off working class mothers.
Ibid.

5 On the occasion of an important debate, Ambassadors packed the Distinguished Visitors Gallery. Nancy arrived wearing a huge bunch of scarlet carnations. Will Thorne shouted across the floor of the House to ask for one. Under the chilly eye of the Speaker she strolled across and put one in his buttonhole. Then she handed one to Mr Attlee and put one each in the coats of Mr Baldwin and Sir John Simon. The House rang with laughter but she was quite unperturbed.
John Beevers, Sunday Referee 19 *Feb* 1939

6 Her maiden speech was — naturally — about the temperance question. She attacked Sir John Rees for his tolerance of the brewers. Sir John listened patiently and then rose to his feet and in Biblical language said: 'The Hon. lady has been unto me a rod of chastisement. I must kiss the rod.' The members laughed and Nancy blushed.
Ibid.

7 She got her biggest laugh, unintentionally, when in one of her speeches she announced that 'despite the efforts of Mussolini and the Pope, the birthrate in Italy is declining'.
Ibid.

8 About ten years ago there was a famous scene in the House. Mr Jack Jones was speaking. Lady Astor entered and sat down opposite him. He stopped speaking, turned to her and said: 'I am not drunk. I have had so many insults from this lady I resent it. She does not speak to me straight. She talks under her breath'. The Deputy Speaker then said how glad he would be if the honourable lady would keep quiet. Mr Jones continued: 'It is a common thing for the honourable lady to talk under her breath about drunkenness when I am speaking. I will tell her straight in her teeth that I am a better man when I am drunk than she is when I am sober.' And the House laughed its head off.
Ibid.

9 She is always direct. If people borrow books from her, and forget to return them they must not be surprised to read in the 'agony' columns of newspapers an advertisement asking for them to be returned.
Ibid.

10 Alderman Lionel Jacobs announced that he contemplated running as an independent Conservative (against Lady Astor). Suddenly Nancy arrived on the scene and changed everything. She first set about obliterating Alderman Jacobs. The alderman, beginning tentatively to form an election organisation, found to his surprise that all the meeting halls and committee rooms available had been booked for Nancy. Without a place from which to speak one cannot fight an election. The Jacobs machine was stopped before it had begun.
Geoffrey Bocca, Sunday Express 29 *Jan* 1956

11 She denounced in round terms the nurseries she had seen in Russia. 'Send a good sensible woman to me in London,' said Nancy, 'and I will take care of her and show her how children of five should be handled.' A gleam came into Stalin's merry eye. He pushed forward an envelope and asked for her address . . . Some weeks later a group of buxom Russian nurses presented themselves before Nancy in London, sent by Stalin. Nancy saw them and screamed, but duly arranged for them to be given courses at various London nurseries.
Ibid. 5 *Feb* 1956

1 I followed Lady Astor into the Lords. She had barged in, with the usual jangle of bracelets, and I happened to see Lord Astor's tired face light up, as he smiled at her with infinite tenderness; and I realised that that mad witch is still loved by her husband, after nearly forty years of marriage.
Sir Henry Channon, DIARY 23 *Mar* 1944

2 The State Opening of Parliament was magnificent. That ghastly Nancy Astor looked magnificent, but haggard. Looking at the incredibly romantic and moving scene she announced: 'I hate the Peerage — it ought to be abolished' and then looking at me she added rudely, 'And the Beerage, too'. 'You are lucky, Margaret', I said sweetly to Margaret Case. 'You are seeing the Opening of Parliament, and I have introduced you to the most unpopular woman in England.' The horrid old girl winced and I saw the withered bosom redden with rage. Our acrimonious exchange continued and she said, 'I can fill a Hall, anyway.' 'So can George Robey.' I replied. I knew that I had the upper hand, as I always do with her; nobody else has ever dared to be rude or to answer back, and she is always uneasy and disconcerted by me. 'In America I was the toast of everybody.' she boasted. 'Is that why they tried to extradite you?' I asked, and she walked away, quivering with rage.
Ibid. 26 *Oct* 1949

3 Nobody who saw her, as I did, when Plymouth was being bombed almost out of existence, could feel anything but profound and affectionate admiration. I remember in 1942 walking with her through the devastated streets of the town one morning after a bad blitz, and her effect on the weary people was electrifying. She indulged in no facile sentimentality; she was cheerful, friendly, aggressive, and at moments even a little governessy. She dashed here, there and everywhere encouraging, scolding, making little jokes. In the sitting room of one pathetic little house, the roof and kitchen of which had been demolished, she ordered a pale young man to take the cigarette out of his mouth . . . told him he would ruin his lungs and morals with nicotine, slapped him on the back, and on we went.
Noël Coward, FUTURE INDEFINITE 1954

4 Her uncompromising Protestantism was tenuous but unyielding, like a strand of barbed wire in a hedge.
Walter Eliot

5 Aunt Nancy had charm, attraction, wit and great family feeling but she demanded priority in her relationships and that may be why she seemed to resent one's other friendships outside the family. The particular crime was to marry into another family. She could never *quite* like her relations-in-law. 'I can't think what you see in them — they're so boring. *Everyone* says so.'
Joyce Grenfell, JOYCE GRENFELL REQUESTS THE PLEASURE 1976

6 As a child I was afraid of Aunt Nancy's sharp tongue. She had an uncanny knack of knowing just where to put the salt in the wound. She teased me for being too fat, crying too easily, and for my cowardice about riding.
Ibid.

7 Her hostility to Roman Catholicism and liquor was obsessional. Yet Hilaire Belloc was a close friend; and one of her admirers was a prosperous gin manufacturer in Plymouth of whom she said: 'Of all good men he was one of the best'. She was never a humbug, just inconsistent.
William Haley, The Times 5 *Oct* 1972

8 Edwin Lee, her butler, was with her for 50 years. Only once did Mr Lee threaten to leave owing to some 'unreasonable demands' by her ladyship. Lady Astor, quick as a flash, replied, 'In that case, Lee, tell me where you are going because I am coming with you.' And they ended up laughing.
Rosina Harrison, ROSE: MY LIFE IN SERVICE 1975

9 In battle her qualities were shown: her courage, flashing, roystering, tempestuous courage of the Virginian, exemplified by the way she could turn cartwheels in air raid shelters to cause a diversion when things were at their worst. Not your 61-year-old Nancy Astor, Lady of Cliveden, but Nancy the wild-eyed girl who rode unbroken horses.
Ibid.

10 *Lady Astor:* You don't have to be poor to have a heart. Women who have got money are just as much interested in the welfare of mothers as are other women.
An opposition member: You are more interested in keeping your money.
Lady Astor: OH RATS!
House of Commons 1939

1 Tiresome as she is, there is something in her. A flame somewhere.
Harold Nicolson

2 Nancy and her husband were in that familiar hospitable house on the Hoe all through the week of terrible bombing that left the centre of Plymouth a devastated wreck. People were numbed, their spirits crushed, and thousands streamed out into the countryside. Waldorf told me himself that it was Nancy's own idea to start public dancing on the Hoe. She herself led off the dance with the Prime Minister of Australia. Soldiers, sailors, airmen, townsfolk all joined in, evening after evening. Plymouth's courage came back, the public spirit of the city. It was utterly characteristic of her; her courage and love were an inspiration.
A. L. Rose, The Times 6 *May* 1964

3 Nancy Astor, though popular and widely liked, was inclined to be rash — she had to be restrained from ordering Edward VIII not to mention Mrs Simpson in the court circular.
Jan Stephens, The Times, reviewing David Sinclair's DYNASTY: THE ASTORS AND THEIR TIMES 16 *Aug* 1984

4 The only Pilgrim Mother who came back.
Hannen Swaffer, SWAFFER'S WHO'S WHO FOR 1930

5 She was always a delight to the eye, small, compact, a finely drawn profile, a classic head growing more and more exquisite with the years. She was made all of one piece, a perfect working model, always well dressed.
The Times, Obituary 4 *May* 1964

6 Her energy was extraordinary. After a long day in the House she would return to Cliveden about seven, change into tennis clothes and play two or three sets of singles with one of her nieces; then down to the river (before the war) in her cream coloured car, driven at speed; she would swim across the Thames talking all the time about God, or advising someone on the bank about the way to live his, or usually her, life, touch the bottom on the far bank, tell the swans to go away, and swim back, still talking.
Ibid.

7 She wasn't courageous, if by courage is meant mastery of fear, for she did not know about fear. She was fearless of physical danger, of criticism, of people.
Ibid.

KEMAL ATATURK

Born 1881. Turkish soldier and statesman. Defender of the Dardanelles, 1915. Expelled Greeks from Turkey 1922. President of Turkey 1923–38. Died 1938.

8 High up on the hill above Golden Horn, in the centre of the European residential quarter, stands one of the world's most depressing monuments. It represents the struggle for Turkish freedom under the leadership of the Gazi — now known as Kemal Ataturk. On one side of the monument there is the Gazi in uniform, leading his men in battle. On the other side the battle is won. There he is, in a neat European frock-coat, in front of all his frock-coated ministers. On nearly every photograph — even on the postage stamps — he is portrayed in evening clothes with a white tie. Was it necessary, I ask myself, for him to have a war and a revolution in order to dress himself and his people in clothes that do not suit them?
Vernon Bartlett, THIS IS MY LIFE 1937

9 During the war, as British troops who fought against him at the Dardanelles learned to their cost, this young officer, Mustafa Kemal, showed very unusual ability, but he was uncompromising and unpopular, and never received the credit he deserved.
Ibid.

10 An alert, upright man in an ordinary dark blue suit. A man with yellowish hair, deep-set grey-blue eyes, prominent cheek bones and very thin lips.
Ibid.

11 Kemal Ataturk horrified the orthodox, not only by encouraging people to go unveiled, but even by dancing with an unveiled girl at a big public function.
Ibid.

12 A man who, though he abhorred political assassination, was not above judicial murder.
Lord Kinross, ATATURK: THE REBIRTH OF A NATION 1964

13 He was a democrat by conviction but an autocrat by temperament. There was in him a clash between mind and temperament which caused him to think like an Occidental but act like an Oriental.
Ibid.

CLEMENT (RICHARD) ATTLEE, FIRST EARL ATTLEE

Born 1883. Prime Minister in two successive Labour governments 1945–51 after serving as deputy to Churchill 1942–5. Made an earl in 1955. Died 1967.

1 He looks like a black snail and is equally ineffective.
Sir Henry Channon, DIARY 19 *Dec* 1935

2 Mr Attlee combines a limited outlook with strong qualities of resistance.
Winston Churchill, Speech 27 *Apr* 1951

3 He it was who established the idea that the proper leader of the Labour Party should be a sphinx; if he gave no wink to the Left the same stony reproach was bestowed on the Right.
Michael Foot, Observer, The dangers of diaries 1 *Mar* 1981

4 'Are you good at gardening?' I asked him once. 'Good rough weeder. Look at the number of things in the bed, chuck out the majority. They'll be the weeds.' Two puffs of his pipe. 'One of the things I learned in politics.'
Kenneth Harris, The Times 15 *Oct* 1967

5 He came down from Oxford a Tory Imperialist, quite sure that 'Only gentlemen are fit to govern'. 'You've changed your mind about that' I said to him once. 'Only in the sense that everybody must have the chance to become a gentleman.'
Ibid.

6 His natural language was always prep school: 'Rotten', 'Piffle', 'Tripe', 'A good egg'. He nearly always referred to people by nicknames.
Ibid.

7 Possibly because of the importance to him of his own happy marriage he had opinions about the wives of practically every politician I ever discussed with him. 'He needed a sedative, she was a stimulant' he said of one famous political leader whose career he thought had been adversely affected by his marriage. And of another more successful, equally famous colleague: 'Very fortunate in his wife. Married well. Pretty, doesn't care much about politics. Fond of children.'
Ibid.

8 He is a bourgeois who is strangling the British bourgeoisie out of existence with a smile.
Peter Howard, Daily Mail 28 *May* 1947

9 On the evening when Attlee's sensational victory over Churchill was announced an old Tory friend, rocking and reeling under the blow, said to me of the new Prime Minister, 'I've not felt this way since I saw Dr Crippen. Such a nice fellow he looked, so respectable, so quiet, so much one of us. I simply couldn't believe he had done that terrible thing.' Then with a shake of his head he added, 'But by heaven, he *had*.'
Ibid.

10 I was sitting directly opposite Attlee. He was sitting hunched up like an elf just out of its chrysalis.
Nigel Nicolson, letter to Harold Nicolson 3 *Mar* 1952

11 Mr Attlee's strength comes from a peculiar form of disciplined independence . . . He has successfully ridden every revolt in his party, chiefly by remarkable timing — by knowing when to remain quiescent and when to bring the issue to a climax. Those who have challenged him are never quite sure just how they have been defeated.
Observer, Profile 9 *Jan* 1949

12 Attlee was the only man, apart from Churchill, who sat in the war cabinet from the first day to the last.
A. J. P. Taylor, ENGLISH HISTORY 1914–1945 1965

13 Both his opponents and his more impatient colleagues were prone to underrate him as a political force. He was devoid of those external marks which Aristotle thought necessary to men of consequence — sincere and quietly impressive was the most that could be said of his public personality.
The Times, Obituary 9 *Oct* 1967

14 In his dealings with his political colleagues he was both inhibited and shrewd. Faced with revolt, he would often maintain silence: obliged to rebuke, he would frequently do so in a stilted schoolmasterly manner: faced with a decision, he would take it with a total disregard for the feelings of all those who might be injured by it.
T. E. Utley, Daily Telegraph 9 *Oct* 1967

15 He is a man of complete and utter integrity, single-minded in his passion for social justice, with a clear, logical, essentially practical brain, considerable administrative ability, a very shrewd talent for politics, and no personal ambition or vanity of any kind. It is a strange combination, and an unusual one in politics, where even the most

idealistic usually mix their idealism with personal ambition and a taste for self-dramatisation.
Francis Williams, 1948

FIELD MARSHAL SIR CLAUDE JOHN EYRE AUCHINLECK

Born 1884. Commander-in-Chief Middle East 1941–2. Last British Commander-in-Chief in India 1943–6. Died 1981.

1 Auchinleck was a most impressive figure: dignified, commanding, and apparently completely self-confident. Only those who knew him well realised that he was shy and sensitive. He was as much an introvert as his political chief was an extrovert.
Lord Ismay, MEMOIRS 1960

2 The real barrier between Auchinleck and Churchill was psychological; Churchill, ingrainedly prejudiced against India and Indians; and Auchinleck with a love of the country and its people greater even than for his own.
Colin Legum, Observer 29 *Mar* 1981

3 The Auk's make-up did not allow him to put up with what his very close friend Field Marshal Lord Ismay described as Churchill's 'moods of a child of nature, as variable as an April Day'.
Ibid.

4 Those who know the general insist on his modesty. They relate that when he became known as 'The Auk' in England his officers came to him with the suggestion that their corps should henceforth bear the insignia of that ancient, ungainly bird. Ridiculing the idea of this personal build-up, he chose the elephant instead.
Alan Moorehead, Daily Express 1942

5 He laid the basis from which Britain's eventual strategic victory was achieved. However, his political master at the time failed to perceive this and responding more to fashionable currents than military analysis, decided to change the command in North Africa. Auchinleck was sacked and spent the best part of a year kicking his heels in the hills of India before he was allowed to return to the Indian task he understood so thoroughly.
The Times, Obituary 25 *Mar* 1981

6 He had to endure a crushing defeat. Yet after that defeat he saved Egypt from being over-run and held up an opponent in full course for Alexandria and the Nile delta.
Ibid.

W. H. (WYSTAN HUGH) AUDEN

Born 1907 in England. 1939 emigrated to US, became a naturalised American. Poet and dramatist. Wrote *The Ascent of F6* in collaboration with Christopher Isherwood, 1937. Published his first volume of poems 1930. Was Professor of Poetry at Oxford University 1956–61, in succession to C. Day Lewis. Died 1973.

7 If ever a poet was, he was the spokesman of his generation; he gave it its voice and its vocabulary.
Walter Allen, Daily Telegraph 19 *Jan* 1967

8 He has always been a generalising, moralising poet, but whereas he once lectured, and sometimes hectored, his tone is now that of the urbane, civilised essayist. His poems seem to exist at the level of conversation, witty, erudite, grave in matter, but light in manner.
Ibid.

9 His views were summed up in a statement he made to a group of physicians in Brooklyn. 'I like to think', he told them, 'that if I hadn't become a poet I might have become an Anglican bishop. Politically liberal, I hope, theologically and liturgically conservative, I know.'
Walter Allen, Daily Telegraph 6 *Mar* 1980

10 He became an old man too early, one can't help thinking. He was, after all, not 70 when he died, and he had cossetted himself like an old man for years, wearing carpet slippers at all times, going to bed at nine o'clock every night. He drank far too much, he had always chain-smoked, and, always a sloven, he became more and more a slob, to use the American word.
Ibid.

11 He developed many of the minor economies of our father — one of which was not to waste toilet paper, and he would observe the diameter of the roll in the guest room.
John Auden, W. H. AUDEN, A TRIBUTE (Edited by *Stephen Spender*) 1975

12 Auden, sitting at the head of the table, would preface a meal by saying: 'We've got a roast and two veg., salad and savoury, and there will be no political discussion.' He had enough of the don about him to keep us all in order; quite rightly he would not tolerate argument or bickering during meal time.
Paul Bowles, of Auden in New York in 1940

1 A poet who never wrote an original line.
Robert Graves, BETWEEN MOON AND MOON: SELECTED LETTERS 1984

2 Auden is something of an intellectual jackdaw, picking up bright pebbles of ideas so as to fit them into exciting conceptual patterns.
Richard Hoggart, W. H. AUDEN 1951

3 There Auden was, playing his favourite hymns at the piano with large pudgy hands, and dribbling ash on the keys from a large volcano-like pipe.
Christopher Isherwood. Quoted Roy Perrott, Observer 28 *Jun* 1970

4 He is all ice and woodenfaced acrobatics.
Percy Wyndham Lewis, BLASTING AND BOMBARDIERING 1937

5 Someone said of Auden that he didn't love God, just fancied him.
John Mortimer, IN CHARACTER 1983

6 Mr Auden is read widely, idolises language, understands from experience the vagaries of the human heart, and the processes, including luck, that shape a poem. I do not know of any other living critic who is so well equipped.
Raymond Mortimer, Sunday Times, reviewing THE DYER'S HAND 21 *Apr* 1963

7 Mr Auden's brand of amoralism is only possible if you are the kind of person who is always somewhere else when the trigger is pulled.
George Orwell, INSIDE THE WHALE 1940

8 Auden has described his character-type as Punctual, man 'one who doesn't know whether he is hungry unless he looks at the clock'. The minute-hand gives form to the day: the master-versifier does not care for the shapeless.
Roy Perrott, Observer 28 *Jun* 1970

9 Auden, a real and often powerful poet even though apt to keep his cleverness showing, was sometimes obscure because his poetry used private references, private jokes, so that at these times the reader seems the only outsider at a party of old friends.
J. B. Priestley, LITERATURE AND WESTERN MAN 1960

10 The thirties produced a school of poets deeply concerned with social and political questions and it is tempting to regard their leader, W. H. Auden, as the characteristic voice of his time in the way that, say, Tennyson had once been. Maybe Auden expressed in poetic form what many Englishmen were thinking. This does not mean that they read his poems or had even heard of him.
A. J. P. Taylor, ENGLISH HISTORY 1914–1945 1965

B

FRANCIS BACON

Born 1910 in Dublin. British painter. Developed a distinctive and controversial style, making use of lurid colour, distorted figures, and photographs.

1 When he paints the themes of crucifixion, it is as a commentator on the beastliness of man, and not as a believer in Christianity, yet his paintings have all the conviction of passionate Christian belief.
Brian Sewell, Radio Times 10 *Nov* 1984

2 It is all pure paint, and the length, breadth, loading and pressure of a single brush stroke contains all the information about the structure, character and movement of the thing painted, as well as its more obvious colour and texture.
Ibid.

3 Paired figures on a bed are not seen in any affectionate contiguity, but in the attitudes of erotic violence; they stem from photographs of footballers, boxers and wrestlers, but Bacon brings them close to hard-core pornography and then elevates them with his vision and technique into abstract allegory on which he makes a savage shuddering, visceral comment.
Ibid.

4 Bacon turns to Popes, presidents, businessmen and the tormented nude to make comments on our day — astute, perceptive and horrifying.
Ibid.

5 Bacon works in the tradition of a Renaissance master and is only a painter — no etchings, lithographs, finished drawings or designs for the theatre. His subjects are not pretty things for the drawing room, and the scale of his work suggests that he makes no concessions to the private patron.
Ibid.

6 He deals with Renaissance themes of religious and temporal power, authority, corruption, conflict and lust, and has compiled his own pantheon of superhuman images with which to demonstrate them.
Ibid.

ROBERT STEPHENSON SMYTH BADEN-POWELL, FIRST BARON BADEN-POWELL OF GILWELL

Born 1857. British soldier, defended Mafeking (1899–1900) during the Boer War. Founder Boy Scout movement. Died 1941.

7 Throughout his life B-P never slept more than four or five hours a night; on active service two were enough. Only his secretary, who found a huge pile of work (and sometimes a few trout as well) on her doorstep with the morning milk, knew how many hours of toil he put in while most people were asleep.
Jack Cox, Radio Times 22 *Feb* 1957

8 He went to Russia with his brother, entered a closely-guarded fort and climbed into a balloon car during the lunch-hour to sketch the dials of the instruments. B-P studied new searchlights at night under the noses of Russian officers. When arrested later for questioning, he still bluffed his way out, and was en route to London before his escape was discovered.
Ibid.

9 Disguised as the nephew of the skipper he went to the Dardanelles in a grain ship and arranged for the engines to break down near the vital defences. As they were being 'repaired' he went 'fishing' in a small boat and found out all he needed to know.
Ibid.

10 The story of B-P's exploits as a master spy may never be fully told. He went on a sketching holiday in the Austrian Alps as mountain warfare troops tested new equipment, and was given breakfast by unsuspecting Austrian staff officers. In the evening B-P taught them how to do the hula-hula.
Ibid.

11 Amateur theatricals were his outstanding hobby. On the stage B-P did solo comic turns, sentimental ballads and superb clowning acts. He spent seven months learning how to dive through a paper hoop right across the stage from one wing to the

other. He designed costumes and painted scenery; there was always a clock-face on it through which he would dive sooner or later.
Ibid.

1 In India he heard a young subaltern named Winston Churchill shouting angrily across the polo field: 'Don't talk to me. Talk to the Umpire!' That night B-P used the phrase time and again in his concert act. Soon it was a catch-phrase in India.
Ibid.

2 Baden-Powell founded the Boy Scout movement almost by accident. When he wrote his famous *Scouting For Boys* he intended it to be used by branches of other youth organisations, not a movement in its own right. It was only when the Boy Scouts themselves asserted their independence that Baden-Powell retired from the Army to devote his whole time to the movement.
William Hillcourt and Olave Lady Baden-Powell, BADEN-POWELL: THE TWO LIVES OF A HERO 1964

3 He and his wife are proverbially happily married, though she is nearly half his age and was chosen in a preposterous manner. He saw her walking in Knightsbridge and liked her walk, but did not see her face. In the best Scout manner he recognised that walk two years later in a liner, saw the face, spoke to the owner — and married her.
C. A. Lyon, Sunday Express 28 *Jan* 1934

4 His mind is far above politics. He killed an invitation to stand for parliament by answering obligingly: 'Yes, certainly! On which side?'
Ibid.

5 He sleeps in the open every night of his life except when in town, having a camp bed on the verandah of his house. Even recently when he was ill he caused his wife distress by fishing up to his knees in water for hours on end.
Ibid.

6 He was the first man to enter Buckingham Palace in shorts. He wrote specially to the King for permission. It was granted — a revolution in Court etiquette.
Ibid.

ENID BAGNOLD

Born 1889. English novelist and playwright. Most popular novel *National Velvet*. Best known play *The Chalk Garden*.

7 Lady Jones is a buxom, vital blonde, who writes books and plays under her maiden name of Enid Bagnold. She is highly social, and full of fire and energy.
Sir Henry Channon, DIARY 10 *Oct* 1942

JOHN LOGIE BAIRD

Born Scotland 1888. Television pioneer, inventor of a system of using a mechanical scanning disc. First demonstration transmission 1926. Died 1946.

8 On Thursday morning the 17th February 1938 at 10.30 a.m. Baird Television Ltd gave to the Television Society, the Press and a number of distinguished guests a special demonstration of wireless high-definition colour television on a large screen at the Dominion Theatre, Tottenham Court Road. The apparatus is the latest invention of Mr Baird, *and the first in the world to show wireless colour television*. The subjects transmitted included impersonations of a Military Officer, a Sheik, and a Turk. Ladies exhibited various coloured hats, and the programme concluded with the White Ensign and a coloured photograph of the King.
Baird Television Ltd publicity hand-out

9 Remarkable claims are made in telegrams from the United States of success for tests made on Wednesday night and the early hours of yesterday morning of television across the Atlantic. According to these reports pictures of objects and faces transmitted from a room in the heart of London were actually seen, though somewhat imperfectly, on the other side of the ocean.
Daily Telegraph 10 *Feb* 1928

10 At last the general public has been able to behold for itself an inventor's dream of making men and things visible at a distance through any intervening obstacles come true. Mr Baird's television, so often declared impracticable, has been shown at the Coliseum to be an accomplished fact . . . This is an early instalment of an invention which some day must bring, before our eyes, occurrences that are happening fifty miles or five thousand miles away . . . It sounds a complicated process, but in a year or two it will be as everyday a thing as Big Ben on the wireless.
Children's Newspaper 16 *Sep* 1930

11 The first public experimental television programme was broadcast yesterday from

the London station at the BBC. Reception of the head and shoulders of persons in the studio was good. Among them was Sir Ambrose Fleming who invented the thermionic valve now so widely used in wireless reception. Mr Baird said that at the moment only a few television receivers are in existence and probably a number of them are home made. The experiments are to be continued daily, and everything will depend on public demand.
Morning Post 1 *Oct* 1929

1 In March 1928 he pulled off a coup by sending a picture of Dora Selvy from London to the Berengaria, 1,000 miles out at sea. Three years later he transmitted the Derby. In 1932 he repeated the feat, and 4,000 people in London watched the race without getting nearer to Epsom than the Metropole cinema at Victoria.
Anthony Smith, Daily Telegraph 18 *Jul* 1962

2 Baird should, by rights, have gone on from strength to strength. Unfortunately, like so many inventors, Baird was just as capable of rushing up blind alleys as of opening up great new highways of technology. He put most of his faith in a system of television known as a mechanical scanner, and he made it work. But when the time came for broadcasting committees to choose a system, they chose electronic scanners.
Ibid.

3 Baird dabbled in many things. He had studied engineering and matters electrical at the university, but among the things that in turn claimed his attention from the livelihood point of view were the selling of a patent medicated undersock he had invented, a shoe-cleaner, again his own invention, jam-making in Trinidad, soap-making, and honey-selling.
William Stapley, Sunday Referee 3 *Feb* 1935

4 An empty biscuit box, discs cut out of cardboard, darning needles, odd bits of wood, a couple of old hat boxes, glasses bought from a bicycle shop at fourpence each, these were among the queer collection assembled on his bench. The apparatus was held together by glue, dabs of wax and odd bits of string. Electrical energy came from a row of pocket flash-lamps linked with metal clips. 'My one hope', he told me, 'was that the home-made apparatus would hold together long enough to give me some definite results.' It did. One night in 1924 the tiny image of a Maltese cross appeared on the screen. It had actually been transmitted a distance of two or three yards. No more than that, but it meant that Baird the dreamer had found the secret of television.
Ibid.

5 'I remember very clearly', says William Taynton 'how one Friday in October 1925 Mr Baird rushed downstairs in baggy flannels, a pair of carpet slippers and no socks. He dragged me into his workroom and sat me in front of his machine, a mass of wires and enormous electric light bulbs. He shot into the other room. I didn't know what was happening, but just as I felt I couldn't stick the heat any longer he bawled from the next room: 'Put out your tongue, William. Shut your eyes. Turn your head.' Then he returned tremendously excited saying: 'I saw you, William, I saw you.' I thought he had gone mad. A few minutes later William became the second man to see a human face on TV as he sat by the receiver watching on the screen Baird poking out his tongue and rolling his eyes.
J. P. Thomas, News Chronicle 23 *Oct* 1951

6 William Taynton worked at 22 Frith Street, Soho in 1925, for a dealer in films, below Baird's primitive workroom. 'We've got a crackpot on the premises,' said William's boss, and William was inclined to agree. For once, during the six months Baird had been working there, he had asked: 'What are you trying to do in that room full of gadgets?' and Baird had replied, 'William, I'm trying to see you through a brick wall.'
Ibid.

JAMES BALDWIN

Born 1924. American Negro author, novelist, dramatist and playwright. First attracted attention with his novel, *Go Tell it on the Mountain*, 1953.

7 Of his most famous *The Fire Next Time* (1963) Baldwin says with a laugh 'Ronald Reagan still thinks that book was responsible for the riots that came after it.' Then he adds with no trace of mirth, that two of his brothers were sacked from their jobs because of it, and are still working as taxi drivers in New York, and that not long afterwards he landed at Heathrow to find himself *persona non grata*.
James Campbell, The Times, Profile 2 *Aug* 1984

1 He looks like a wooden carving in a Gothic cathedral, not Notre-Dame, which he doesn't care for, but perhaps Chartres, which he loves.
Fern Marja Eckman, THE FURIOUS PASSAGE OF JAMES BALDWIN 1968

2 He is constantly suspicious, on the edge of withdrawal until he is convinced he is not being patronised or indulged. But then his alertness and his self-awareness make him one of the best talking writers. Like a fledgling, his eyes widen when he wishes to emphasise a point. What he has to say is not always as clear as his rhetoric is stirring.
Observer, Profile 14 *Jul* 1963

3 He talks with an incantatory kind of eloquence which reminds one that he began life as a Holy Rolling boy-preacher. His mannerisms make him an improbable prophet.
Ibid.

4 His prose style is uniquely graceful, rhetorical, ministering, feline and powerful. The style — prophetic and aware of the dangers of prophecy — is the more remarkable for its restraint, a restraint his Negro predecessors did not have and could probably, given history, never have had. It may yet undo him.
Clancy Sigal, Sunday Times 23 *Feb* 1964

STANLEY BALDWIN, FIRST EARL BALDWIN

Born 1867. Leader of the Conservative Party 1923–37. Prime Minister 1923–4, 1924–9, 1935–7. Died 1947.

5 Baldwin always seemed more at home with our people, particularly the older trade union people, than with his own lot.
Clement Attlee

6 If it hadn't been for my mother, my father would have remained quite happily where he was in Worcestershire, going daily to the office and back. He had no ambition, push or drive. My mother supplied them all: he was her first concern and she always saw he had every comfort in his library, especially in his London library, as she preferred London to the country.
Margaret Baldwin. Quoted H. Montgomery Hyde, BALDWIN 1973

7 You may be judged by History for your political actions, but you will be judged by God for the spirit which is in your heart.
Oliver Baldwin, who was a socialist, in a letter to his father

8 Everything I care for is being smashed to bits at this moment . . . I shall pick up the bits. I shall begin again.
Stanley Baldwin during the General Strike 1926

9 When I was a little boy in Worcestershire reading history books, I never thought I should have to interfere between a King and his Mistress.
Stanley Baldwin in 1936

10 Baldwin, with the solid support from the British middle class, decided to make politics dull; and succeeded beyond his most sanguine expectations. In private life the most delightful of companions, he contrived almost miraculously to invest himself in the eyes of the public with all the attributes of dullness, which soon became synonymous with respectability. Subtle, sensitive, the 'maestro' of political tactics, he set himself the task of lowering the temperature of political life to zero.
Lord Boothby, MY YESTERDAY, YOUR TOMORROW 1962

11 The first time I saw the late Lord Baldwin was on Sports Day at my private school in the year 1911, when my father beat him in the Fathers' Race by inadvertently winding him with his elbow. He took this with perfect equanimity, and I knew then what a nice man he was.
Ibid.

12 He was an introvert, with acute sensitivity. In fact, the exact opposite to the public image he deliberately created for himself — the simple friendly squire, concerned about his workmen and looking after the pigs. He wasn't Rudyard Kipling's cousin for nothing. He was an extremely complicated character; and so were at least two of his children, whom he well understood. He knew a lot about neurosis, and what caused it, and how dangerous it could be. But, at the critical moment, he was gone.
Lord Boothby, RECOLLECTIONS OF A REBEL 1978

13 All I am sure of is that if Baldwin had still been Prime Minister he would never have dreamed of flying to see Hitler. Nor would he have signed the Munich Agreement.
Ibid.

14 Baldwin always said there were two institutions you couldn't possibly fight — the National Union of Mineworkers, and the Pope.
R. A. Butler. Quoted John Mortimer, IN CHARACTER 1983

1 In the House of Commons this afternoon I saw Mr Baldwin sitting alone in the Chess Room, absorbed in *The Field*. And when, an hour later, I happened to return there he was still reading it. He often sits alone in the window seat of this room and stares out at the river.
Sir Henry Channon, DIARY 11 *Mar* 1937

2 Mr Baldwin smiled at me with one half of his face in the division lobby. His smiles are porcine but warm for all that.
Ibid. 12 *Apr* 1937

3 History may make him out a great man, half Machiavelli, half Milton.
Ibid. 30 *Jan* 1938

4 Baldwin as Prime Minister would not have behaved in the superhuman way that Chamberlain did. He would not have flown to Berchtesgaden — not he. He wouldn't have known where it was.
Ibid. 7 *Dec* 1938

5 Be honest. Be just. He has a difficult task. He is in search of a man with talents even more inconspicuous than his own.
Winston Churchill. Quoted Geoffrey Madan NOTEBOOKS 1981

6 The first impact he made on a wider audience was his surrender, under a slightly but not intentionally transparent anonymity, of one fifth of his fortune to help the post-war (World War I) financial crisis. This was greeted with a maximum of applause and a minimum of imitation.
Colin R. Coote 14 *Jul* 1967

7 Baldwin was a superb broadcaster. His voice on the air twanged the heartstrings of millions. I have sometimes wondered if he would have been so successful on television. Probably even more so, for he gave, in personal contact, an impression of deep and unforced sincerity.
Ibid.

8 His motto in the fierce crises in industrial relations was 'not to fire the first shot'. That did not prevent him from firing the last, but it was, at worst, only designed to graze.
Ibid.

9 He succeeded in thinking both too little and too much of himself.
Colin R. Coote, Daily Telegraph 15 *Nov* 1973

10 His voice, with the sob of sincerity in it, swayed the nation during the General Strike of 1926.
Ibid.

11 Baldwin had an odd coma after the General Strike, and an odd panic after the pacifists won in the East Fulham by-election in 1933 — the latter causing him to join the long list of those made mugs of by the Nazis.
Ibid.

12 The *Sunday Pictorial* reminded its readers that when the call first came to Mr Stanley Baldwin to form a government one of his first thoughts, he said, was that it should be a government of which Harrow should not be ashamed, and the newspaper added 'What damned nonsense'.
Hugh Cudlipp, WALKING ON THE WATER 1976

13 An inexperienced nonentity of the utmost insignificance.
Lord Curzon, on hearing he had been rejected in favour of Baldwin as the choice for Prime Minister

14 There has been so much ado about pipes. The new Premier was never seen without a pipe. If a photographer appeared unexpectedly Baldwin instinctively felt for his pipe. He admired those pictures which showed him in the act of lighting up.
Norman Hillson, Leader 6 *Mar* 1937

15 He turned up at Lords for the Eton and Harrow match – the one cricket function of the year when men go to watch cricket in their Sunday best and wearing silk toppers. Baldwin thought nothing of such things and a tailoring trade weekly took him to task. 'If he had come as a real Shropshire lad,' it said, 'in smock and leggings, with a red handkerchief, it would not have been so bad, but the Prime Minister looked suburban.'
Ibid.

16 At any rate Baldwin entered on his new job with characteristic humility. He went to the palace in an ordinary taxicab, kept it waiting while he was talking to the King, and then drove home in it as Prime Minister.
Ibid.

17 Baldwin was not a dull dog. Churchill's hostility to him, particularly over India, had ended normal relations. Churchill found himself standing next to a silent Baldwin in the neighbouring urinal in a lavatory in the House of Commons. As he did up his trousers to leave, Baldwin remarked 'I am glad there is still one common platform on which we can meet.'
H. Montgomery Hyde, BALDWIN 1973

1 Baldwin is one of us: he is a Celt at heart and that is why you find him difficult to understand.
David Lloyd George

2 Stanley Baldwin's second sight, realising that his great task was to educate the Labour Party; result, no one lost a night's sleep when they came in.
Geoffrey Madan, NOTEBOOKS 1981

3 Mr Baldwin suffers from a divided complex — if one may use such a term. He is a Puritan, with a Quaker–Wesleyan ancestry, leading the 'Cakes-and-ale' party. He is an intellectual attempting to ingratiate himself with democracy. He is a shy, retiring sort of man forced into the limelight by the exigencies of political life. He is a genial reformer, anxious to be friends with everybody, leading a party fundamentally opposed to change. How can any man serve so many masters?
W. H. Nicoll, John o' London's Weekly 1 *Nov* 1930

4 He was a man of little imagination and less vision, but he certainly had a gift for dealing with awkward situations. Generally his method was to evade them. But when he was forced to tackle them, as at the Abdication crisis, he did very well. He was an agreeable, companionable man. He was really more simple than he seemed. Or rather, his simplicity appeared so naïve that many thought it was put on for effect. I did not think so. He enjoyed life and had certain excellent principles.
Harold Nicolson, DIARY 14 *Dec* 1947

5 To accuse him of insensitiveness is to manifest a lack of psychological insight. Nobody could observe his odd little habits, the twitching of his nose and brow, the snapping of his finger and thumb, or his really astonishing idiosyncrasy of snuffing, almost licking, the books and papers that he read — could derive any impression other than that he was an intensely sensitive, even neurotic, person.
Harold Nicolson, Observer 2 *Nov* 1958

6 There were periods when, as Mr G. M. Young has written, 'The Prime Minister seemed to be little more than an amiable observer of events'. Some critics even asserted, unfairly, that his tendency to regard himself as 'the most English of all Englishmen' was a deliberate attitude, a pose of simplicity accompanied by a well-advertised predeliction for briar pipes, the novels of Mary Webb, broccoli, and leaning over pigsties scratching the backs of sows.
Ibid.

7 I often heard him catalogue his mistakes. He would do so in an equable voice, as if he were merely recounting how, when on his way to Aix, he had nearly missed the connection at Dijon.
Ibid.

8 It is the imperturbability of Baldwin that remains a conundrum to this day.
Ibid.

9 His personality always had a fine amber glow.
Observer, Profile 8 *Aug* 1947

10 Mr Baldwin once said his mind moves slowly. In that case the tortoise has been curiously addicted to leaps in the dark.
Ibid.

11 The paternal touch was exercised when Edward VIII renounced the Throne in 1936. A delicate and dangerous situation was handled with complete mastery. In the manner of a particularly nice Father who knows how to be stern when he must, Mr Baldwin spoke to the right people, in the right manner, at the right moments. And a constitutional nightmare disappeared overnight.
Ibid.

12 His partiality for old times and old ways has been unabashed. He looked wistfully back to the days when businessmen in Worcestershire corresponded by canal barge with their fellows in Bristol and it took ambassadors' despatches three weeks to reach Whitehall. In those days, as he properly pointed out, statesmen had time to spare for the weighing of great issues.
Ibid.

13 Oliver Baldwin was beside me at dinner. In some casual talk about politics I said that I'd never been able to have a party point of view. I can see things of value in each party. 'Ah, that's my father's trouble,' he said, 'he has never been able to make up his mind.'
Reginald Pound, THEIR MOODS AND MINE 1937

14 He presented himself as a simple country gentleman interested only in pigs. He was in fact a wealthy ironmaster with distinguished literary connections. His simple exterior concealed a skilful political operator. Lloyd George, after bitter experience, called him 'the most formidable antagonist whom I ever encountered' — no mean tribute.
A. J. P. Taylor, ENGLISH HISTORY 1914–1945 1965

1 Baldwin played politics by ear. He read few official documents, the newspapers not at all. He sat on the treasury bench day after day, sniffing the order paper, cracking his fingers, and studying the House of Commons in its every mood.
Ibid.

2 He had in his mind a picture, no doubt imaginary, of the patriarchal relationship between masters and men at his father's steel works, and aspired to establish these relations with labour on a national scale. Mr MacDonald said of him as early as 1923; 'In all essentials his outlook is very close to ours.' It is hard to decide whether Baldwin or MacDonald did more to fit Labour into constitutional life.
Ibid.

ARTHUR JAMES BALFOUR, FIRST EARL BALFOUR

Born 1845. Prime Minister 1902. As Foreign Secretary drew up the Balfour Declaration, assuring British protection for the Jewish settlement of Palestine. Died 1930.

3 The only quick mind in an ill-bred crowd.
H. H. Asquith. Quoted Roy Jenkins, ASQUITH 1964

4 Balfour has an advantage over the rest of us insomuch as he is half a head higher than we are, both physically and intellectually.
H. H. Asquith. Quoted Lord Riddell, John o' London's Weekly 19 *Jul* 1930

5 Balfour's much criticised aloofness wasn't understood. It was deliberately cultivated. He took up an unemotional attitude to many things including his friends' misfortunes, because he didn't trust his own emotions. He was a very highly-strung and nervous man.
John Buchan. Quoted Reginald Pound, THEIR MOODS AND MINE 1937

6 His government lived on tactics and died on tactics.
H. Campbell-Bannerman. Quoted J. A. Spender, Daily News and Westminster Gazette 20 *Mar* 1930

7 A lay priest seeking a secular goal.
Winston Churchill, GREAT CONTEMPORARIES 1937

8 He had an unconscious air of great distinction invested by the tall figure, rather thickened since the days of his slender youth, the broad shoulders, a little rounded, but vigorous and giving none of the old impressions of languor. His hair was now quite white and was never cut very short. The foreigners beheld in him the living model of an Elder Statesman in the aristocratic British tradition.
Blanche E. C. Dugdale, ARTHUR JAMES BALFOUR VOL. 2 1937

9 In the days of horse-drawn carriages he was driving with his sister to a dinner party. They were immersed in conversation when she interrupted by remarking that she thought the coachman had taken a wrong turning. 'Well,' said Balfour, 'that is his business, not ours.'
Ibid.

10 'Gentlemen,' said Clemenceau as Balfour entered the conference room at Versailles in 1919, 'let me introduce you to the Richelieu of the conference.' It was a superb compliment, the greatest a Frenchman could offer. 'What, then, may I call you, M. le President?' said Balfour, somewhat taken aback for the moment. 'Call me your friend,' said the Tiger, laying his hand on the other's arm.
J. B. Frith, Daily Telegraph 15 *Apr* 1936

11 He had an unusually strong, though carefully concealed, love of office, and complete faith in his own ability to look fastidious in any company.
Roy Jenkins, ASQUITH 1964

12 Delicacy of constitution and of mind, elegance of phrase and supple decisiveness of execution, feline charm exercised over an adoring, mainly female family, and wider social circle were Balfour's most obvious characteristics.
Roy Jenkins, Observer 15 *Jun* 1980

13 His short three-and-half-year reign, during which ministers resigned under him like leaves falling in November, ended in a Conservative holocaust. He lost his own Manchester seat as well as those of 200 of his supporters.
Ibid.

14 No one foresaw the long shadow that the Declaration [to create a Zionist national home in Palestine] was soon to start casting over British Middle East policy, and Balfour went to his grave thinking it 'the most worthwhile thing' to which he had ever set his hand.
Elizabeth Monroe, The Times 2 *Nov* 1967

15 His role, attractions and shortcomings are

epitomised in Lord Lloyd's *mot* that he might 'in a gust of mirth let slip a British interest'.
Ibid.

1 When Balfour's American host pointed out a huge skyscraper to him, telling him enthusiastically that it was fireproof, he replied, 'What a pity'.
Gerald Moore, AM I TOO LOUD? 1962

2 He wins by force of character. His speech at the beginning of the war was a most remarkable effort — probably the most historic speech that has been made in 100 years. It was a speech which will alter the map of Europe.
Lord Riddell, John o' London's Weekly 5 *Apr* 1930

3 He always used the right word. He never used the word that is worth ten words, but he frequently used the word that is worth one and a half.
Ibid.

4 Throughout his life he had a personal quality which enabled him to do rather ruthless things without giving offence.
J. A. Spender, Daily News and Westminster Gazette 20 *Mar* 1930

5 Clemenceau called him 'cette vieille fille'.
A. J. P. Taylor, ENGLISH HISTORY 1914–1945 1965

6 Of course, one purpose of the Balfour Declaration was to put a barrier between the French in Syria and the Suez Canal. This was an aspect not aired in public.
Ibid.

7 The National Home for Jews was intended by Balfour to provide security for British control of the Suez Canal.
A. J. P. Taylor, Observer 11 *Aug* 1968

8 Balfour's last contribution to Imperial affairs was his definition of the Commonwealth in 1926. It was largely meaningless, and where it had meaning, wrong. However, it is still much admired. Hertzog is said to have remarked, 'Of course, if one has someone like Balfour to explain things, they become easy to understand.' This, though flattering, was not precisely Balfour's intention.
Ibid.

9 Balfour had the advantage that at the opening of his political career Imperialism had already begun and that by the time he died it had almost ended.
Ibid.

10 A fragile philosopher who often stayed in bed for much of the day in order to sustain his delicate health, but who none the less lived on vigorously to 82.
Kenneth Young, ARTHUR JAMES BALFOUR 1963

11 He was one of the few men at the top who encouraged science at a time when most of the ruling class regarded it as a matter for common artisans. Yet he was hardly practical himself, lavishing a great deal of his vast, inherited fortune (worth £4,000,000) on futile schemes for using powdered peat as fuel.
Ibid.

TALLULAH (BROCKMAN) BANKHEAD

Born 1903. American stage and film actress. Died 1968.

12 Eddie Foy Jr confided to Tallulah that he had always longed to be a cover boy. 'Magazine or manhole?' she asked.
Bennett Cerf, SHAKE WELL BEFORE USING 1948

13 This distinguished daughter of the South inspired publicist Richard Maney to remark 'The screen had just started talking when Miss Bankhead interrupted in 1930.' She is invariably polite, and seldom fails to ask visitors questions about their own pursuits. Unfortunately, however, she never gives them time to answer. Meeting a fellow thespian who had been desperately ill for months she commanded, 'Tell me *all* about your sickness.' 'It really was pretty rugged.' began the actor, 'I was on the operating table for seven hours and — .' 'Stop being such a blasted hypochondriac.' snapped Tallulah, 'I want to tell you about my new play.'
Ibid.

14 She was always a star, but only intermittently a good actress.
Brendan Gill, The Times 4 *Aug* 1973

15 She would bet on anything — horses, the toss of a card, the match game, the colour of a stranger's eyes — and she was a good loser. But with regard to investments she took good care not to lose: she put her money into IBM and Eastman Kodak.
Ibid.

16 Her role in *Conchita* was that of a dark-skinned Cuban dancer. She wore a black wig over her golden bob and carried on her arm a tiny monkey. On opening night the monkey panicked, grabbed Tallulah's wig,

pulled it off, and darted to the footlights, whirling it like a lariat. The audience started to titter, and Tallulah, for want of anything better to do, threw a cartwheel. The audience roared with laughter and approval. She had learned in childhood and again in school, that when things go wrong the safest way out is to play the clown.
Ibid.

1 New York remained her base — towards the end the dark cave in which she crouched, with death often quite cheerfully in mind, an ageing woman reluctant to go out, unwilling to exercise, unwilling to eat, and, though suffering from emphysema and forbidden to smoke, smoking her 150 Kents a day.
Ibid.

2 She flailed about in paroxysms of disguised bewilderment, drinking and clowning and cursing and showing off. She was valiant and silly, and she knew it. But she was not rubbishy, and she knew that too.
Ibid.

3 The violent scatological energy of her speech and the celebrated speed and frequency with which she shucked off her clothes and prowled about naked, long after her body had grown ugly with age, were intended to convey an impression of untrammelled emotional freedom, and it was not so.
Ibid.

4 No doubt hundreds of people made love to Tallulah and scores of people loved her, but as a marriage prospect she was, even in her youth and beauty, intimidating: a number of eligible young men circled her warily and backed away.
Ibid.

5 It was more sad than funny when someone asked her 'Are you really the famous Tallulah Bankhead?' and got the reply, 'What's left of her'.
Leslie Halliwell, THE FILMGOER'S BOOK OF QUOTES 1978

6 Few actresses can portray more convincingly than Miss Bankhead the difficult part of a pretty girl.
Percy Hammond, Tribune, of her role in The Exciters 1922

7 Tallulah was crowding seventeen when she arrived from Alabama, stage-struck, sultry-voiced, and brimming with a roseleaf beauty which she determinedly hid under the then fashionable mask of white powder, blue eye-shadow and beef-coloured lipstick. She fondly believed that this made her look like Ethel Barrymore, who was her idol.
Margaret Case Harriman, THE VICIOUS CIRCLE

8 She was an open, wayward, free, cosmopolitan, liberated, sensuous human being. In thus systematically invading her own privacy she was the first of the modern personalities.
Lee Israel, MISS TALLULAH BANKHEAD

9 The first woman I saw stark naked was Tallulah Bankhead (aged about nine). I was taken backstage to meet her. Roland knocked on her door and a voice said 'Come in', and there was Miss Bankhead smiling and nude. She was not put out, but we moved out fast.
Michael Pertwee, NAME DROPPING

10 The Girl Who Gives Electric Shocks. She will go down to Southampton at midnight to take a bible or something to Beatrice Lillie.
Hannen Swaffer, SWAFFER'S WHO'S WHO FOR 1930

11 Tallulah Bankhead arrived at Wyndham's, a smouldering, pouting young woman with a voice like hot honey and milk, a face like an angry flower, eyes of violet-blue, hair in a waving ash-blonde mane. The newcomer had some fierce little scenes that she acted with resolution and the magnetism that could all but draw her audiences upon the stage.
J. C. Trewin of her performance in The Dancers 1922

SIR JOHN BARBIROLLI

Born 1899. British conductor. First attracted attention when succeeding Toscanini with the New York Philharmonic Orchestra 1936, but achieved greatest fame as conductor of the Hallé Orchestra, Manchester 1943–1968. Died 1970.

12 People either adore me or I nauseate them.
Barbirolli. Quoted Michael Kennedy, BARBIROLLI—CONDUCTOR LAUREATE 1971

13 He did not learn his job before a looking-glass but before an audience as a cellist in the Queen's Hall Orchestra — the finest of all training . . . One never feels that Barbirolli thinks in terms of set lengths of bar lines; he conceives each movement or work as an organic unity.
R.H., Radio Times 4 *Feb* 1944

1 When he died the NPO received a charming letter from a high school student in Japan ending: 'and the enclosed 1000 yen is my just gratitude to Sir Barbirolli. Would you kindly offer flowers on his tomb for this?'
Paul Jennings, Sunday Times 25 *Jul* 1971

2 In his early days he earned his living in theatre pits, cinemas and cafés. 'I have played everywhere except in the street.' he says, 'I even played in pantomime at the old Surrey and I don't regret a moment of it.'
Observer, Profile 6 *Jul* 1947

3 His habit of borrowing a family violin and wandering all over the flat while scraping it exasperated his grandfather Antonio Barbirolli who one day took a hansom to a fiddle shop and came back with a half-size 'cello. 'Play that instead.' he told the boy. 'You have to sit down to the 'cello.'
Ibid.

4 Family photographs show John playing the 'cello at eight or thereabouts, in a sailor suit (he always refused to wear the velvet jacket and lace collar traditional to boy prodigies); at 14 in knickerbockers, white waistcoat and Eton collar; at 25 in the spats and tailcoat of incipient fame.
Ibid.

5 Though he first began to play the violin it was as a cellist that he made his name years ago. At eleven he played a concerto at the Queen's Hall.
C. B. Rees, Radio Times 16 *Jul* 1937

6 When the BBC conductorship offer came up in 1948 he made no effort to use it as a lever towards his personal betterment in Manchester. He told the Halle Concerts Society, 'I will stay on, at the old terms, if you will increase the rank-and-file minimum wages from £10 to £13 a week.' Very prudently, the society agreed.
Charles Reid, Illustrated 29 *Jan* 1949

7 Pavlova threw a lily from her bouquet to the young cellist in *The Swan*. It was found pressed between books in Sir John's library 50 years later.
Ibid.

8 Dear Master, I feel always that my work is in the hands of a master when you are conducting.
Sibelius, letter to Barbirolli

BRIGITTE BARDOT

Born 1935 in France. Film actress. Began her career as a model. Appeared on the cover of the magazine *Elle*, May 1950, and attracted the attention of film director Marc Allegret. After small parts she reached stardom with *And Woman Was Created*, 1956

9 She has the same dominant traits as James Dean; the fever of living, the passion for the absolute, the sense of the imminence of death.
Simone de Beauvoir in 1959

10 A vegetarian, she now lives with 60 cats and 11 dogs, most of them abandoned strays which she has taken in; a goat from a market where they were being sold strung up by their hind legs, and a foal saved from the slaughter house. The local children call her 'The Animal Fairy'.
Diana Geddes, The Times 28 *Sep* 1984

11 With her unmistakable and jutting breasts she looks down on many a dull town hall meeting, immortalised as Marianne, the emblem of post-revolutionary France. Brigitte Bardot was more than just a goddess. For a war-weary generation she came to personify a new, liberated sun-soaked, care-free France. The powers that be accepted that and gave their permission for her to be used as the model for the new Marianne.
Ibid.

12 On her 40th birthday she said 'I'm a woman who has undoubtedly made a success of her career but not of her life. The myth of Bardot is finished, but Brigitte is me.'
Malcolm Macalister Hall, TV Times 20 *Oct* 1983

13 Her cascading blonde hair, her pout and her blatant sexuality led a gasping film critic of *And Woman was Created*, in 1956, to describe it as 'the most flagrant, suggestive, near-the-knuckle picture I have ever seen anywhere'.
Ibid.

14 She spends her days sunbathing, lazing, looking after her menagerie of animals, going shopping in shorts in St Tropez. The thought of appearing in another film fills her with dread.
Ibid.

15 She has made 40 films, attempted suicide at least twice, married three men and has shared passion with many more. Her rampant sexuality made her a fantasy figure for men world-wide.
Ibid.

1 During the shooting of *And Woman Was Created* (1956) the Press was informed that the love scenes were the most realistic ever filmed — so much so that they continued after the cameras stopped. Miss Bardot's flirtation with her leading man, Jean-Louis Trintignant, and her estrangement from her husband, Roger Vadim, were exploited to give substance to the publicity. A running commentary on difficulties with the censors kept the film talked about.
Observer, Profile 27 *Sep* 1959

2 The Bardot child-woman is never sentimental or mysterious. She has no time for the tantalising wiles of Cleopatra. She is a frank man-hunter and her methods of seduction are forthright — she lifts her skirt or bites her partner's shoulder to indicate what she has in mind.
Ibid.

3 B.B. on the screen is not simply a selfish delinquent. She has freshness, charm and a touch of mischievousness. She is irresponsible and immoral, but not deliberately cruel.
Ibid.

MAURICE BARING

Born 1874. English journalist and author, best known for his autobiography *The Puppet Show of Memory* (1922). Died 1946.

4 Maurice Baring showed little respect for the printed page. Whenever a passage in a book struck him Baring simply cut it out and stuck it in one of his notebooks.
Catherine Caufield, THE EMPEROR OF AMERICA AND OTHER MAGNIFICENT ECCENTRICS 1981

5 Baring was quite unconcerned with material possessions. A friend, accompanying him on a train journey through Germany, was astonished to see him, having failed to fit a new overcoat into his holdall, throw it out of the window without pausing in his conversation.
Ibid.

6 An Indian pursued him down the street crying, 'Hello, old chap'. On finding that he had accosted a total stranger he excused himself by saying that he thought Baring was 'Mr Godavari.' 'But I *am* Mr Godavari,' said Baring, and swept on.
Antonia Fraser, The Times 27 *Apr* 1974

7 As Laura Lovat put it, Maurice Baring had 'a genius for admiration', and that, surely, is the secret of his success as an anthologist.
Ibid.

8 For him, the idealism and simplicity of mind which led at last into the Roman Church were sufficient reality. However full it may have been of fun and melancholy, his writing always makes one think of an imaginative child adding lovely words together in reverie.
Paul Horgan, MAURICE BARING RESTORED 1970

9 He belongs to that class of writers who scatter largesse on their way; he is a serious writer who does not think it necessary to be always serious.
Desmond MacCarthy. Quoted Dame Ethel Smyth, MAURICE BARING 1938

10 He had a good way of spelling his name on the telephone. 'B for Beastly, A for Apple, R for Rotten, I for England, N for Nothing, G for God' — all rattled off at top speed.
Edward Marsh, A NUMBER OF PEOPLE 1939

11 One of his audacities was to ask for some stamps at the post office in Florence. When they were given him, he sniffed them with an air of suspicion. '*Sono freschi?*' he asked. 'Are they fresh? They must be very fresh. They are for an invalid.'
Ibid.

12 Time may perhaps confirm the judgement of those who see in him one of the subtlest, profoundest and original of recent English writers.
The Times, Obituary 1946

SIR J. M. (JAMES MATTHEW) BARRIE

Born 1860. Scottish novelist and playwright. Most famous plays include *The Admirable Crichton*, 1902, *Peter Pan*, 1904 and *Dear Brutus*, 1912. Died 1937.

13 A wealthy American woman tried to get in touch with him, but he eluded her. In desperation she went to H. G. Wells and asked him for a letter of introduction. 'It would be more than my life is worth,' answered Wells, 'but I'll tell you what. Go and sit on his doorstep and make a noise like a crying child. That will fetch him down quicker than anything.' The woman, it is reported, followed Wells's joking instructions and the trick actually worked.
Leo Condon, Sunday Referee 20 *Jun* 1937

14 During the war he established in France a hospital for children wounded by enemy guns. His inventive mind constantly discovered new games that would give cripples an equal chance with the children who were whole. He would steal lint from

the surgery, roll it in a tight ball, and organise cricket, a crutch being used for a bat.
Ibid.

1 Melancholy had marked him for her own.
W. A. Darlington, Everybody's Weekly Jun 1943

2 He had, in sober earnest, wished a fatal wish — Peter Pan's wish, never to grow up. His wish was granted and in receiving that gift he lost all joy and benefit that should have come to him from his great good fortune.
Ibid.

3 He avoided whenever possible sight of himself in a mirror and has referred again and again to the fact that women either did not notice him at all, or decided that he was 'harmless' and therefore uninteresting.
Ibid.

4 Constantly, all his life, he was falling down in worship at the feet of one beautiful woman after another, but of equal love between husband and wife he nowhere shows much comprehension. The only relation between the sexes which stirs him to deep feeling is the parental one.
Ibid.

5 He warned Charles Frohman, the manager, that *Peter Pan* would be immensely expensive to produce and probably a failure, but Frohman's faith in his author was so great that he accepted the play without even reading it.
Ibid.

6 There is a revealing passage in *Tommy and Grizel* when Tommy Sandys has finally failed Grizel's love by revealing that he, the famous literary authority on women and their ways, is in fact terrified of marriage. Barrie turns to the reader with a direct appeal for pity, rather than contempt for 'the boy who was so fond of games that he could not with years become a man'.
Ibid.

7 When a famous literary agent had a nervous breakdown during which he sent out no cheques to his clients, the accumulated payments due to Barrie amounted to over £15,000 [equivalent in 1985, to about £200,000] — and Barrie never even noticed that the money had not arrived.
Ibid.

8 He made a fortune by pretending to shrink from publicity because he knew that was the best way of obtaining it.
James Fairlie, Sunday Express 20 *Jun* 1937

9 When J. M. Barrie addressed an audience of one thousand girls at Smith College during his American visit, a friend asked him how he found the experience. 'Well,' replied Barrie, 'to tell you the truth, I'd rather talk one thousand times to one girl, than one time to a thousand girls.'
Edmund Fuller, ANECDOTES 1942

10 George Bernard Shaw is a noted vegetarian. At a dinner he had before him on his plate the special concoction that was always provided for him, consisting of some greens with a mixture of salad oils. Sir James Barrie, his neighbour at the table, bent over to him and asked, 'Have you eaten that, or are you going to?'
Ibid.

11 The critics were apt to be worried by his disregard of the common theatrical usage. They did not all like his novelties, his surprises. So he came to the Critics' Circle one evening and defined a critic as 'a man with a wee foot-rule, who measured plays with it, and if it was five by fo'er it was a play, and if it was no' five by fo'er it was no' a play'.
Hamilton Fyfe, John o' London's Weekly 2 *Jul* 1937

12 Barrie had the knack, and was proud of it, of making an article out of anything he saw or heard. He claimed that he once read, on a bookstall (but did not buy), a treatise on bridge-building, then wrote *How I Built My Bridge Over the Ganges*, and got it published. That was Barrie's fun, but it got into the *Times* obituary notice.
Ibid.

13 Everyone who knew him liked Barrie. His small size, his shrinking manner, his shy smile, appealing irresistibly for sympathy, for protection. He had a way of throwing himself on your mercy.
Ibid.

14 Barrie is quite out of favour now. Although his plays are beautifully constructed, there is a chocolate-box side to them which is embarrassing to the modern public, but which people adored when they were written.
John Gielgud, AN ACTOR AND HIS TIME 1979

15 At public dinners he had a habit of speaking with a cigar in his mouth which, with his Scottish accent and his way of dropping his voice at the end of a sentence, made it difficult for those who were not his immediate neighbours to hear him. His

gravity too, puzzled some of his audiences, especially when he was indulging in one of his wild flights of make believe.
Robert Lynd, News Chronicle 21 *Jul* 1937

1 When the solitary Act I of J. M. Barrie's *Shall We Join the Ladies* was given its dazzling first performance at the Royal Academy of Dramatic Art it naturally made a sensation, and everybody went about speculating why he hadn't finished the play. Did he know himself how the story ended, or had he found that he couldn't untie his own knot? Long afterwards Barrie told me himself that he had made a complete scenario of the play and fully meant to finish it, but so many strangers wrote to volunteer their own solutions that he grew sick of the whole thing and put it aside for good.
Edward Marsh, A NUMBER OF PEOPLE 1939

2 Seven years ago he announced his last speech in public. He has been making them ever since.
Passing Show 23 *Apr* 1932

3 His only club is the Athenaeum. He is rarely there. On his first visit he asked an octogenarian biologist the way to the dining room. The biologist burst into tears. He had been a member of the club for fifty years. No one had ever spoken to him before.
Ibid.

4 Barrie seeks isolation. His telephone number is in the directory under his butler's name. His telephone is in the coal bucket.
Ibid.

5 Shaw, agreeing with Max Beerbohm's view that *Peter Pan* was an artificial freak that missed its mark completely and was foisted on children by grown-ups, confessed: 'I wrote *Androcles and the Lion* partly to show Barrie how a play for children should be handled.'
Hesketh Pearson, BERNARD SHAW 1942

6 The story is that Barrie is still in love with his wife, who left him for another author just after the war. There is at times a noticeably desolate look in his face.
Reginald Pound, THEIR MOODS AND MINE 1937

7 I have actually taken to go to the theatre to see Barrie's plays; and I not only stand them without discomfort, but enjoy them.
George Bernard Shaw, Letter to Forbes Robertson 21 *Dec* 1903

8 He cheerfully assumes, as the public wishes him to assume, that one endearing quality implies all endearing qualities, and one repulsive quality, all repulsive qualities, the exception being comic characters, who are permitted to have 'weaknesses'.
George Bernard Shaw, Saturday Review 13 *Nov* 1897

9 His wife's elopement and the deaths of some of his adopted children in the war, were the only events in his life I knew of. Though he seemed the most taciturn of men he could talk like Niagara when he let himself go as he did once with Granville Barker and myself on a day which we spent walking in Wiltshire when he told us about his boyhood. He said that he had bacon twice a year and beyond this treat had to content himself with porridge. He left me under the impression that his father was a minister; but this was probably a flight of my own imagination. Actually, I believe he was a weaver.
George Bernard Shaw. Quoted Hesketh Pearson, BERNARD SHAW 1942

10 I was always on affectionate terms with Barrie, like everyone else who knew him; but though I lived for many years opposite him in the Adelphi and should, one would have supposed, have met him every day, we met not oftener than three times in five years in the street. It was impossible to make him happy on a visit unless he could smoke like a chimney (mere cigarettes left him quite unsatisfied): and as this left our flat uninhabitable for weeks all the visiting was on our side, and very infrequent.
Ibid.

11 I fancy Barrie was rather conscious of the fact that writers have no history and consequently no biography, not being men of action.
Ibid.

12 When I played Captain Hook in *Peter Pan* Barrie said he expected me to give a new reading of the part, so I asked him if he would give me a hint or two. 'Always remember,' he said, 'that Captain Hook was educated at Balliol.'
Ernest Thesiger, PRACTICALLY TRUE 1927

13 This humbly-born, mother-fixated Scotsman sought to tie three beautiful women to him in turn in an intense, close and entirely asexual relationship. What pain this vast, tough web of sentimentalism, generosity and selfishness brought to the three graceful Edwardian ladies caught in its skein, as well as to the little gnome-like spider himself, who sat lonely and unappeased at its centre.
Angus Wilson, Observer 20 *Sep* 1970

JOHN BARRYMORE

Born 1882. American stage and film actor, famous for his profile. Brother of Ethel and Lionel Barrymore. Died 1942.

1 I like to be introduced as America's foremost actor. It saves the necessity of further effort.
John Barrymore to journalists

2 There are lots of methods. Mine involves a lot of talent, a glass and some cracked ice.
John Barrymore

3 He moved through a movie scene like an exquisite paper-knife.
Heywood Broun. Quoted Leslie Halliwell, A FILMGOER'S BOOK OF QUOTES 1978

4 During a rehearsal of a John Barrymore play, the leading lady aroused the star's ire, an incautious procedure, to say the least. Barrymore gave a pungent lecture on her paternity and nocturnal pursuits. 'Kindly remember,' interpolated the actress, 'that I am a lady.' 'Madam,' snapped Barrymore, 'I will respect your secret.'
Bennett Cerf, TRY AND STOP ME 1947

5 John Barrymore once confounded an audience in New York, at the height of the run of *Redemption*. There was an epidemic of coughing throughout the first act. When it broke out again in the second Barrymore was all set. He suddenly yanked a five-pound sea-bass from under his coat and flung it over the footlights. 'Busy yourselves with *this*, you damned walruses,' he bellowed, 'while the rest of us proceed with the libretto.'
Ibid.

6 John Barrymore, at the height of his fame, went into the shop of a swanky men's clothier in Hollywood. He left an order and started to leave. 'Your name please?' the clerk asked. The Barrymore brows arched high. 'Barrymore' he replied coldly. 'Which Barrymore, please?' Coolness turned to solid ice. 'Ethel', he said.
Edmund Fuller, ANECDOTES 1942

7 Even John Barrymore, whose Hamlet I admired very much, cut the play outrageously so that he could, for example, play the closet scene all out for sentiment with emphasis on the 'Oedipus complex' — sobbing on Gertrude's bosom.
John Gielgud, AN ACTOR AND HIS TIME 1979

8 J.B., answering the call of nature, went through the wrong door. A lady entered and protested, 'Mr Barrymore, this is for ladies.' He turned round just as he was, and answered, 'And so, madam, is this.'
Leslie Halliwell, A FILMGOER'S BOOK OF QUOTES 1978

9 He was a match for co-stars like Katherine Hepburn, who at the end of the shooting of *A Bill of Divorcement* said 'Thank goodness I don't have to act with you any more.' He cooed in reply, 'I didn't know you ever had darling.'
Ibid.

BÉLA BARTÓK

Born 1881. Hungarian composer and pianist. Composed the opera *Bluebeard's Castle*. Died 1945.

10 The fourth movement took me straight back to the noises I made myself, on wet days indoors, at the age of six, by stretching and plucking a piece of elastic.
Alan Dent, letter to James Agate 26 *Nov* 1945

11 Béla Bartók is a composer whose music is apt to raise extremes of feeling in the listener. This is not because it is ultra-sensational but because of its undiluted intensity. I cannot imagine anyone 'quite liking' Bartók's music, as a pleasant background to a game of bridge. Either his works give you the biggest thrill that contemporary music has to offer, or you will have absolutely nothing to do with the fellow.
A.F., Radio Times 30 *Sep* 1938

12 His achievement as a folklorist was of inestimable value to musicology, and it provided him with the data for his fascinating and ultimately life-enhancing investigations of asymmetrical metre and rhythm, and of melodic construction in terms of small chromatic intervals as well as in peculiar modes and scales. But the same studies also tempted him into a flabby pastoral manner, initially heart-easing, but soon palling.
The Times 1 *Oct* 1965

BERNARD (MANNES) BARUCH

Born 1870. American financier who became economic adviser to successive presidents. Represented the US on the United Nations Atomic Energy Commission 1946–7. Died 1965.

13 One of Baruch's foibles was his fondness for

park benches. He would sit on a bench in Lafayette Square, Washington, just across the road from the White House, and dispense advice to officers of government.
The Times, Obituary 22 *Jun* 1965

1 President Wilson had a particular admiration for Baruch's detailed and comprehensive knowledge of American industry, naming him 'Dr Facts'.
Ibid.

2 His public utterances are usually sensible, but never arresting. They carry weight, not because they are original or startling or vividly expressed but because even a platitude dropped from a sufficiently great height can sound like a brick.
Peregrine Worsthorne, Daily Telegraph 14 *Apr* 1958

3 Starting from nothing he made an immense fortune on the Stock Exchange. Yet, as he is the first to admit, his success sprang only from speculation. He has never manufactured so much as a tintack.
Ibid.

4 His political interest coincided with the cotton panic of 1914. Wilson wanted a bankers' loan of 135 million dollars. When he was 3 million short Baruch took the balance. When he exploited this conspicuous but rather amateur beginning by making a striking success of the War Industries Board he graduated from being a celebrated eccentric to an eccentric celebrity.
Ibid.

SIR ARNOLD (EDWARD TREVOR) BAX

Born 1883. British composer. Master of the King's Musick 1942. Was also a writer under the name of Dermot O'Byrne. Died 1953.

5 I became, when still quite young, so closely identified with Eire that a part of me underwent a distinct Irish metamorphosis and was reborn as 'Dermot O'Byrne', a writer of stories and poems.
Bax, in an interview, Illustrated 12 *May* 1945

6 There are Irish pretexts for much of his music but the Celtic quality in this is merged in the more comprehensive twilight of Romanticism.
Basil Maine, Morning Post 21 *Aug* 1930

7 I was sitting next to him at a chamber concert at the Chenil Galleries. He was leaning forward hiding his face and quietly laughing. I looked round to discover the cause; but after a time I realised he was deriving amusement from his own thoughts. In the interval he turned to me to say 'Punch can be very funny now and then.' We laughed together, he at the known, I at the unknown. It occurred to me that this was a very special kind of humour.
Ibid.

SIR CECIL (WALTER HARDY) BEATON

Born 1904. English photographer, noted for his innovative portraits of the famous, including royalty. Designer for the theatre and cinema. Published several volumes of his diaries. Died 1980.

8 Some of Cecil Beaton's duller contemporaries disapproved of what they thought of as his effeminacy but he proved to be tougher in the battle of life than most of them. By his own unaided efforts he has made himself a unique figure in the modern scene.
Earl of Birkenhead, Daily Telegraph 21 *Jul* 1961

9 Sir Cecil is remarkable because, though groomed to stardom by a long line of fashion editresses, a man of the theatre, even more a creature of *Vogue* and *Harpers*, the sanctuaries to which he retires when threatened, his sensibility rises above the shiny paper and is not unworthy of the poets and painters he admires. That is his strength.
Cyril Connolly, Sunday Times 28 *May* 1972

10 There have been times when it has been almost impossible to open one of the smarter women's magazines without encountering that ever-boyish profile side by side with a pronouncement ('simply enchanting', 'gorgeous', 'so bold and exciting'), on some new mode or taste in fashion. There have also been times when the nation's only sight of royal infants has been through the delicate, if slightly pale and washed-out medium of Mr Beaton's lens.
Percy Howard, Sunday Express 16 *Jul* 1961

11 For over 30 years a figure with gleaming eyes and gossamer hair has flitted to and fro like a bright fly among the world's very best people. The name is Mr Cecil Beaton. It is a name of importance to the social historian.
Ibid.

12 A modern version of the Court poet. In

return for a place high above the salt he tells the mighty that they are even mightier than they had hoped.
Simon Raven, Observer 16 *Jul* 1961

(WILLIAM) MAXWELL AITKEN, FIRST BARON BEAVERBROOK

Born 1879 in Canada, where he became a wealthy newspaper proprietor. Came to England, bought the *Daily Express* and *Evening Standard*, and founded the *Sunday Express*. Became a member of Churchill's war cabinet. Died 1964.

1 He was unique. It would be absurd to say of anyone, 'He reminds me of Beaverbrook'.
Robert Blake, Sunday Times 25 *Jun* 1972

2 He was a connoisseur of old champagne, one of the best wines in the world — and one of the most expensive. I can still see the strangely shaped bottles from which a dark gold and slightly sparkling liquid of delicious flavour flowed like water at his dinner table.
Ibid.

3 Lord Northcliffe assured him that to assume the ownership of the *Daily Express* was to court disaster. 'I don't know how rich you are,' said Northcliffe, 'but whatever your fortune is, you will surely lose it all.' I reminded Beaverbrook of this and he replied: 'Yes — of course Northcliffe's advice was quite sound. In fact if I had known then what I know now about journalism I should never have had the audacity to take on such a venture.'
Lord Castlerosse, Sunday Express 19 *May* 1940

4 I once had the impertinence to ask Bonar Law point blank why he placed such tremendous store in Max Aitken's judgement. He replied: 'Because he is a wise man and knows the law of cause and effect, of action and reaction in an altogether uncanny manner.'
Ibid.

5 Bonar Law told me that Max Aitken arrived in his office for an interview. Bonar Law saw to it that it was short. But he did disclose that he was going up to Manchester the next day on the 9.10 train. When on the morrow he looked up from his newspaper in the railway compartment he found Aitken grinning at him. Before the train arrived in Manchester Max Aitken had become a candidate for parliament. He won the Ashton-under-Lyne seat. It was in 1910.
Ibid.

6 On two occasions, when a searching question was under discussion, he said 'Hugh, bring your chair over here. Not there — here.' We sat immediately opposite each other, with knees touching, and Lord Beaverbrook peered silently into my eyes. It was the loyalty test, or was it mesmerism? I peered silently back; there was no alternative.
Hugh Cudlipp, WALKING ON THE WATER 1976

7 An audience of one was sufficient for the Beaver to put on his act; probably no audience was necessary at all. When I arrived on my first visit to his top-floor apartment in Arlington House, above the *Caprice* restaurant and near the Ritz Hotel, overlooking Green Park, he was bawling into the telephone. 'No. No. No. No. No. No. No. No. No.' He replaced the handset and walked slowly around the room, his hands on his hips. He then returned to the instrument, picked up the handset and, as he jumped six inches into the air, he delivered one final thunderous '*No!*' That was the end of the matter. It wasn't on. He was agin it. And that was final.
Ibid.

8 Hearing that Lloyd George was fond of hymns, he invited him round to Stornoway House one evening. The latter was Prime Minister at the time and suspected some deep-laid political plot. When he arrived, however, it was to find the room full of Salvationists. Beaverbrook made him join in.
Edgar Middleton, BEAVERBROOK: THE STATESMAN AND THE MAN

9 The first impression was of a gollywog itching with vitality. Unlike the nursery variety this golliwog was always leaping from one telephone to another. Men were being threatened with outer darkness or offered prospects of dizzy glory. One had the impression that this animated little person with his orchestra of telephones was breaking up the universe.
Observer, Profile 29 *May* 1949

10 'Strange man', Bonar Law is reported to have murmured, when, in his last coma, he found Beaverbrook sitting by his bed.
Ibid.

11 At Stornoway House, St James's, seeing Beaverbrook, ennobled gnome. He was lying on a sofa on a verandah overlooking

Green Park, his soft black hat over his face, his small boots untidily laced, as if he couldn't be bothered.
Reginald Pound, THEIR MOODS AND MINE 1939

SAMUEL BECKETT

Born 1906 in Ireland. Settled in France in 1936. Wrote novels and plays in both English and French. Best-known play *Waiting for Godot*, 1954. Nobel Prize for Literature, 1969.

1 It would seem only fair to make a very careful distinction between the artist, the work of art and the person who admires or recommends it. But the fact is that a minimalist like Beckett of the later plays is trading upon his reputation. Everything he does, or refuses to do, compounds the mystery of his position as an artist. Just as a certain type of recluse draws attention to himself by his reclusiveness, so the minimalist arrogates for himself a good deal by way of status.
James Fenton, The Times, reviewing Samuel Beckett's COLLECTED SHORTER PROSE 1945–1980 9 *Aug* 1984

2 The play *Breath* is not presented to the world as any old work by any old chap; it comes at a particular moment in the career of a particular guru — and one does not become a guru by accident.
Ibid.

3 Just before the war a *clochard* to whom he had refused money stabbed him in the street. The wound put him in hospital with a perforated lung. Discharged, he went to see his assailant in gaol. He asked the tramp why he had done what he did. The unhappy *clochard* said he didn't know. One could make much of this.
Observer, Profile 9 *Nov* 1968

4 He smoked French cigarettes and drank stout. He was thin, brown-faced, beaky, the pale blue eyes not deepset but well lodged under frontal bone, a wide mouth stretched across the teeth, the hint of a dimple. His hair was not all grey and must have started fair. The voice was light and not without edge, but friendly, recognisably Irish. He would talk about anything else, not his work.
Ibid.

SIR THOMAS BEECHAM

Born 1879. English conductor. Founded London Philharmonic Orchestra 1932, and Royal Philharmonic Orchestra 1947. Died 1961.

5 At a festival performance of a Mozart opera in pre-war days the little man with the goatee beard was seen to drop off to sleep. 'But we thought, Sir Thomas, that you loved Mozart' they said to him. 'So I do love Mozart,' he replied, 'but only when I conduct him.'
Leslie Ayre, Evening News 28 *Apr* 1949

6 I have been very much helped by the invention of the gramophone, by listening to records, frequently records of other musicians. It has been of great use to me. Knowing what to avoid.
Beecham. Quoted Lord Boothby, MY YESTERDAY, YOUR TOMORROW 1962

7 When he was conducting *Siegfried* at Covent Garden he gave a superb performance of the first two acts but conducted the third at breakneck speed, so that the singers could not keep up. Next time I saw him I asked him what happened. He stroked his beard and said, 'Wagner was apt to go on too long. I knew that many of my audience were commuters with last trains to catch. So at the beginning of the last act I said to myself, "I'll get the buggers home. And I did."'
Lord Boothby, RECOLLECTIONS OF A REBEL 1978

8 'Great music' he said, 'is that which penetrates the ear with facility and leaves the memory with difficulty. Magical music never leaves the memory.'
Lord Boothby, Sunday Times 16 *Sep* 1962

9 Beecham was deeply rooted in provincial England. In this respect, and in others, he resembled Arnold Bennett. Both enjoyed being thought of as 'cards', which indeed they were.
Ibid.

10 A cosmopolitan, a man of the world, a musician of taste and intermittent lapses from taste, a man of fine arts and yet — always a man from Lancashire. Music in itself could not contain him. He was a British institution.
Neville Cardus, Guardian, Obituary 9 *Mar* 1961

11 Beecham was rehearsing Chaliapin in *Don Quichotte*. The girl who was singing the part of Dulcinée came in too late on three occasions, so Beecham called her up to the footlights. 'My dear Miss Nelis, three times Mr Chaliapin has died with the most

affecting realism; three times you have come in too late. Why?' 'Oh, Sir Thomas, it is n-n-not my fault. And I am sure it is not your fault. I think it is Mr Chaliapin's fault. He died too soon.' Beecham made this historic reply: 'My dear Miss Nelis, no opera singer ever died too soon.'
Neville Cardus, CONVERSATIONS WITH CARDUS

1 He was not a wit, but a wag.
Neville Cardus

2 Bravura led to an active disregard of conventional deportment. It was said that when walking one day in Piccadilly in a fur-lined coat, and finding the day sultry, he hailed a taxi, threw his coat in the back and told the driver: 'Follow me about, it may turn cool again.'
Observer, Profile 7 *Jan* 1951

3 Recently his advice to modern composers was that they should have their works performed in the Albert Hall, as that alone would assure them of a second hearing — referring, of course to the hall's celebrated echo.
Ibid.

4 When his braces parted under violent symphonic strain at Carnegie Hall he ignored entirely a disaster which became steadily more apparent to his audience.
Ibid.

5 He was exactly the kind of card that our countrymen love. Amateurish when it pleased him, professional in streaks, rude, vain, noisy, an untidy mixture of porcupine and marshmallow, of Lupin Pooter (whom he greatly resembled) and an early Medici, he now takes his place in the long, tiresome gallery of the English Eccentrics.
Allan Pryce-Jones 1961

6 Recording the *Messiah* Tommy obviously thought the band wasn't happy enough, so he suddenly produced two bottles of Scotch for the coffee break at 11.15 in the morning. We loved him very much.
An unnamed musician. Quoted Robin Ray, WORDS ON MUSIC 1984

7 The splendid tyrant Sir Thomas Beecham was rehearsing the Delius Piano Concerto with his wife Betty. It was not a happy event and Lady Beecham made many mistakes. As she left the platform the hall attendant asked whether or not the piano should be moved before they began the next work. 'Don't worry,' crowed Sir Thomas, 'I expect it will slink off by itself'.
Robin Ray, WORDS ON MUSIC 1984

8 Beecham hated sharing the platform and Heifetz, of course, was no more interested in conductors than Tommy was in soloists, so they didn't get on very well together. On one occasion, when they were appearing at the Festival Hall, Beecham decided on some sabotage. In the cadenza of the concerto first he had a prolonged fit of coughing, then he produced a tin of cough sweets and spilt them all over the platform.
Ibid.

9 With Beecham music is an adventure. You feel it is going to be as he makes his way to the platform. You know it when he raises his baton. You remember that it was, long after the concert. Whatever is lovely you will not be allowed to miss.
C. B. Rees, Radio Times 12 *Jul* 1946

10 The beard gives an extra sharp edge to life, to music, to you. There is an intensity in the dark, luminous eyes that burns. The bland utterance has in its studied carelessness the quality of a lash. 'Ladies and gentlemen,' he said to an applauding audience, 'we will now play you the work you think you have just heard.'
Ibid.

SIR MAX (HENRY MAXIMILIAN) BEERBOHM

Born 1872. English caricaturist, essayist and critic. Wrote only one novel *Zuleika Dobson*, 1911, which achieved lasting fame. Died 1956.

11 Like Brummell, he carefully fashioned the exterior he was to present to the world, at once an adornment and a rampart. The image of a dandy was formed, and the clothes were carefully devised.
Second Earl Birkenhead, Daily Telegraph 5 *Nov* 1961

12 He was at heart a conventional moralist, and a man of strong family loyalties, but we have a feeling that he did not wish these bourgeois virtues to be recognised.
Ibid.

13 As Max came out of the Abbey after Meredith's memorial service a girl approached him. 'Oh Mr Barrie,' she said 'can I have your autograph?' 'I felt a devil rising in me that I could not resist', relates Max. 'I took her book and wrote in it: 'Aye lassie, it's a sad day the noo. J.M.B.'
David Cecil, MAX: A BIOGRAPHY 1961

14 We sat down to a delicate tea of wafer-thin cucumber sandwiches, tiny cakes and weak china tea. Beerbohm's eyes were red-

MENACHEM BEGIN

rimmed and watery, and, I thought, very forlorn. He was such a sad, sad little man, really. He regaled me with anecdotes; rather automatically, it seemed to me, as though he had told them many times before and was sick to death of them. He was like a poor old performing dog at a circus, wearing its little faded skirt, and still able to get on its hind legs — just; then looking around in the apologetic, melancholy way old animals do.
Malcolm Muggeridge, TREAD SOFTLY FOR YOU TREAD ON MY JOKES 1966

1 At times, as when he deals with Kipling or Edward VII, he surrenders to malice. 'Scratch me,' he writes, 'and you will find the caveman. But the scratch must be a sharp one; I am thickly veneered. Outwardly I am as gentle as you, gentle reader.'
Harold Nicolson, Observer 20 *May* 1962

2 His remarkable gifts for caricature and for parody were based on a most sensitive awareness of proportions. His skill in parody was not unrelated to his eccentric habit of defacing photographs. He would spend hours tampering with portraits. These were not soft-hearted pastimes. He chuckled over the degradation he imposed with sable brush and Indian ink.
Ibid.

3 He was a keen Latinist. It is from his knowledge of Latin vocabulary that he derives so many of his unexpected words, such as 'comprimend', 'rident', 'unguentarians', 'unisonant', 'hubility', 'rasure' or 'octoradiant star'.
Ibid.

4 He still surveys the English literary scene as his later caricatures (which depict a paunchy Shaw and therefore lose realism) proclaim. The elegant have grown malicious and factious; he distils them for amusement. His old loves are dead or dreary; he dwells courteously upon their past grandeurs.
Ibid.

5 He possesses that priceless gift of making the person on whom he has lavished his brilliant conversation feel that it was not Max, but his listener, who was being witty.
Ernest Thesiger, PRACTICALLY TRUE 1927

6 He is described as 'the irrepressible, the light of touch, the inimitable, the insouciant, the impertinent'. And he says about himself, 'My gifts are small. I've used them very well and very discreetly, never straining them, and the result is that I've made a charming little reputation.'
World's Press News 29 *Jun* 1931

MENACHEM (WOLFOVITCH) BEGIN

Born 1913 in Brest-Litovsk. Israeli politician. After serving in the Polish army came to Israel to take command of the Jewish liberation group Irgun. Elected to the Knesset as leader of the right-wing Harut party. Became Prime Minister 1977. Resigned 1983.

7 I believe Judea and Samaria [the West Bank] are an integral part of sovereignty. It is our land. It was occupied by Abdullah against international law, against our inherent right. It was liberated during the Six Day War when we used our rights of self-defence. You annexe foreign lands. You do not annexe your own country.
M. Begin. Speech 1977

8 The former terrorist won a Nobel Peace Prize for his peace deal with Egypt's Anwar Sadat. He has secured Israel's frontiers as never before — but the cost is still to be paid. His population of the West Bank of the Jordan ensures that Israelis will not sleep easily in their beds for many years to come.
Daily Star 29 *Jul* 1983

9 The collapse and loss of will-power of this remarkable fighting Jew might have been written as a political allegory of the state of the country at the end of his period of autocratic power.
Colin Legum, Observer 12 *Feb* 1984

10 Begin's rule will, I believe, come to be seen as an unfortunate interlude in Israel's political evolution.
Ibid.

11 Not a fiend in human shape, but a hard, narrow-minded man, ultra-sensitive to Jewish suffering, virtually indifferent to that of non-Jews.
Edward Mortimer, The Times 15 *Mar* 1984

12 A tall angular man with the thin lined face of a fanatic, jet black hair and myopic eyes behind thick lenses, he is the type of irresponsible, uncompromising rebel, thirsting for personal power.
Palestine Police description 1946

13 He redrew the map of Palestine but did not solve the problem of the Palestinians. He left behind an Israel in his own image, more narrowly Jewish, more aggressive and more isolated.
Eric Silver, BEGIN 1984

14 He angrily refuses to accept the description of terrorist, despite a campaign which

included the blowing up of the King David Hotel, the hanging of two British sergeants in 1947 and the Deir Yassin massacre in which more than 200 Arab men, women and children were killed.
Christopher Walker, The Times 31 *Aug* 1983

BRENDAN BEHAN

Born 1923. Irish playwright, known for his black comedies, *The Quare Fellow*, 1956, *The Hostage*, 1959, and his autobiography *Borstal Boy*, 1958. Died 1964.

1 Last night Brendan was out late. I left the key in the door for him. But neither himself nor his pal could manage it. So they smashed down the side door. At least the man came around this morning to apologise. We needed a new door anyway.
Beatrice Behan, Sunday Express 16 *Sep* 1962

2 He let no one down in a real sense. He lived a gay, wild, extravagant, loud life. He never counted the cost. He died a far too early death. But who will cast the first stone? Is it better to die an early death, having lived a full life and leaving behind *Borstal Boy* and *The Quare Fellow*, than to die quietly at four score leaving a handful of dust?
Kathleen Behan, AUTOBIOGRAPHY 1984

3 I remember, in the Middlesex Hospital, waiting guiltily for last words for a newspaper. 'Brendan,' I whispered, 'do you never think about death?' He sat up, like an enormous Pooh bear in a sheet like a toga. 'Think about death?' he shouted, 'Bigod, I'd rather be dead than think about death.'
Alan Brien

4 The literary proof of Behan's tragedy was that he was able to *write* nothing after the instant success of *Borstal Boy* and the *Hostage* in 1958. For the last six years of his life he spoke into a tape recorder loyally controlled by Mrs Jeffs. Three books emerged, all disappointing.
Stephen Fay, Observer 13 *Nov* 1966

5 The nightmarish element of his story is that in the less lucid moments which eventually dominated his life he actually began to believe the grandiose myth his behaviour had helped to create. The most serious aspect of his second visit to America, in 1962, was that he now believed that his behaviour, however unworthy, should be condoned, and he both demanded and expected adulation and acceptance.
Rae Jeffs, BRENDAN BEHAN: MAN AND SHOWMAN 1966

6 The only time he voluntarily committed himself to a cure for his alcoholism was when he was groping his way to a friend's house before the pubs opened on a Sunday morning, and rang the wrong doorbell. It was a nursing home which specialised in a particularly rigorous alcoholic cure; one look at Behan and the nurses had him under sedation in minutes. But like all other cures he began, he could not complete it.
Ibid.

7 He came to crave publicity and to despise himself for it. Even while he was playing the roaring boyo to the gallery he would turn aside to lament the death of the genius he had been born with.
Iain Hamilton, Daily Telegraph 23 *Jul* 1970

8 From the wild depths of his nature he had made a grotesque mask that was to stifle him. It was Behan the Wild Bowsie from the Dublin slums that was promoted by television and the gossip columnists.
Ibid.

9 Behan, when not acting Brendan, was the sage and even saint that his best work would suggest him to have been.
Colin MacInnes, Observer 13 *Nov* 1966

10 Brendan was incapable of speaking coherently, which perhaps, in the circumstances, was just as well. He took off his boots and muttered something about 'wanting a leak'. I decided to take the risk. When the cameras came on us I put my first question and, allowing Brendan to mumble a little, answered it myself. All television interviews are really like this. Brendan's was simply an extreme case.
Malcolm Muggeridge, TREAD SOFTLY FOR YOU TREAD ON MY JOKES 1966

11 Drunkenness with him was more a state of mind than a physical condition. He had to be drunk in order to carry with an air of insouciance the load of phoneyness he had piled on his own back.
Malcolm Muggeridge, Observer 25 *Jul* 1970

12 He stumps and staggers through life proclaiming the glories of the bottle, hitting policemen and other interfering citizens, knocking the lard out of three languages and hurling words at strangers that would blister the hide off a Dublin docker.
Liam Robinson, Sunday Express 16 *Sep* 1962

1 In 1959 Behan announced that his doctor had said that he would die unless he turned away from the drink. 'I never turned to it.' he confided to Eamonn Andrews, 'it seemed to turn to me.'
Hilary Spurling, Observer 23 *Jan* 1983

2 What really made Behan a household name in 1956 was being the first person to appear drunk and incapable on television.
Ibid.

3 It seems to have been a passion with him to be like his fellows and to do as they did; and he could gratify this most readily by mingling with them wherever they foregathered, to drink, gossip, play darts, and drink again. To have a reputation as a drinker meant, as Behan saw it, to be accepted as a man like others, only more so.
The Times, Obituary 21 *Mar* 1964

GERTRUDE (MARGARET LOWTHIAN) BELL

Born 1868. English writer and traveller in the Near East, had considerable influence in the creation of modern Iraq. Best known works *The Desert and the Sown*, 1907, *The Arab of Mesopotamia*, 1917. Died 1926.

4 She worked as a man among men, who were all younger than herself and nearly all less knowledgeable, yet her judgments of them are invariably generous.
Elizabeth Burgoyne, Editor of GERTRUDE BELL, PERSONAL PAPERS 1914–1926

5 A solitary Englishwoman in her tent in the central Arabian desert, chattering with fever, menaced by marauding bedouin and gazing up at the white Asian stars, asking them whether the sullen camel-men mean to murder her before dawn and hide her body in the sand.
Elizabeth Burgoyne, GERTRUDE BELL 1968

6 When crossing the Jebel Shamar in Central Arabia she donned a tea gown for her evening meal. After spending the night on the summit of the Finsteraarhorn she would come down to lunch in a lovely Liberty dress of mauve velvet decorated with a wide collar of *broderie anglaise*.
Ibid.

7 Not the least of England's advantages during the War were the services of two people who possessed enormous influence over many of the Asiatic nations. They were T. E. Lawrence and Gertrude Bell. The new map of Asia is largely of their making.
John o' London's Weekly 12 *Sep* 1931

8 She was no blue-stocking. When engrossed in Oriental studies she still displayed an interest in dress. On one of her returns from her travels she was earnestly discussing Arabian affairs with a friend on an afternoon walk when, glancing at a shop-window in Sloane Street, she exclaimed, 'That's the hat I've been looking for!' dashed in, came out with it on her head, and continued the discussion.
Ibid.

9 The midwife to a Kingdom.
Martin Moore, Daily Telegraph 18 *Aug* 1961

10 Above the turmoil and confusion we see her sharp little nose, indomitably inquisitive, indomitably brave.
Harold Nicolson, Observer 30 *Jul* 1961

11 She was the most zestful human being that I have ever known and it is not surprising that wearied statesmen should find relief in her unfailing effervescence. Whether shooting black grouse, bathing in the Tigris, riding across the sands at dawn, or indulging in Cabinet making or arranging court ceremonial she was always the same, neat, feminine, bossy and amused.
Ibid.

12 The spell of Arabia became for her the central focus of her romanticism. When, in the evening of her life, the doctors told her that she must return to Europe, she just laid herself down and died.
Ibid.

13 For all its inspired busyness hers was a curiously unfulfilled life. Arabia, on which she wrought so much well-meaning damage, was perhaps no more than a symbol. What it really stood for is something that none of her biographers have yet begun to explain.
Jonathan Raban, Sunday Times 15 *Oct* 1978

HILAIRE (JOSEPH HILARY PIERRE) BELLOC

Born 1870 in France. English essayist, biographer, novelist and verse-writer. Died 1953.

14 I was constantly expecting Belloc's mind to

explode and burst through his skull. Such a flow of words I have never listened to.
Gertrude Atherton. Quoted A. N. Wilson, HILAIRE BELLOC 1984

1 At dinner, preceded by much drink, Hilaire Belloc sang Provençal lyrics and recited Ronsard and du Bellay, and Jacobite songs and early English ballads. A riveting evening which almost became a bore as we sat clustered about the great man who looked for all the world like a French-Canadian priest, and applauded while he chanted. It was a unique experience, but not to be repeated.
Sir Henry Channon, DIARY 18 *Jul* 1936

2 He failed to turn up when Chesterton was received into the Church. He did, on the other hand, attend the Requiem for Chesterton in Westminster Cathedral; and in the course of the Mass he managed to sell his exclusive obituary of his friend to four different editors.
John Gross, Observer 22 *Apr* 1984

3 He is out of fashion, out of print and in most cases out of mind, not because of the quality of his literary output, but very largely because of the nature of his political and religious beliefs.
A. N. Wilson, HILAIRE BELLOC 1984

4 It is not wholly absurd to see in his last years the work of sanctification and grace in progress.
Ibid.

5 He turned up at his agent's dressed typically in a well-fitting black fustian suit, dripping with soup, dandruff, grease and fishbones and bulging at the pockets with newspapers and bottles of white port.
Ibid.

6 A dirty, noisy figure. An opinionated super-tramp.
Ibid.

SAUL BELLOW

Born 1915 in Canada. Novelist, author of *Herzog*, 1964. Nobel Prize for Literature, 1976.

7 He once told a prospective biographer (who wrote a whole book on his failure to write a book on Bellow) 'What can you reveal about me that I haven't already revealed about myself?'
Martin Amis, Observer 11 *Dec* 1983

8 Bellow is 68. His hair is white and peripheral, but the eyes are still the colour of expensive snuff. Generous, yet combative, the mouth is low-slung, combining with the arched eyebrows to give his face an animated roundness. In repose the face is squarer, harder.
Ibid.

9 Bellow's technique isn't flamboyant, and his world is not one of total loss. He is always the humane artist. But he still *is* the artist, the man who seeks, severely and fully, to find amid historical and biological necessities, that world of free play where the human being can be.
Malcolm Bradbury, Daily Telegraph 13 *Feb* 1969

10 His protagonists all believe themselves to be privileged to inhabit a sphere of intellectual and spiritual freedom and regard those who occupy roles or defend boundaries with bewilderment, fascination and contempt. The comedy of Bellow's writing stems from the ironic contrast between their personalities, usually childish, sulky and ingenuous, and their pretensions to the cherished values of the Western intellectual tradition.
David Corker, MAKERS OF MODERN CULTURE (*Edited by Justin Wintle*) 1981

TONY (ANTHONY WEDGWOOD) BENN

Born 1925. Labour politician. When first elected to Parliament was Labour's youngest MP, aged 25. Harold Wilson appointed him to the newly created post of Minister of Technology, 1969. Son of the first Lord Stansgate, renounced the title in order to remain in the Commons.

11 Benn has an aristocratic disdain for British workers which he skilfully camouflages with empty rhetoric. He knows what's best for them and never tires of instructing them in what they ought to seek. He dismisses the views of the great bulk of workers and shop stewards and blames the media for brainwashing them.
Frank Chapple, SPARKS FLY 1984

12 It is a measure of how far the popular press has moved to the right, and only to a lesser extent how far Benn has moved to the left, that he should have been transformed in so short a time from Fleet Street protégé to folk devil.
James Curran, The Times 1 *Dec* 1982

ARNOLD BENNETT

1 A middle-aged tearaway.
Daily Express.

2 Not only is he a teetotaller, he is also a total tea drinker — consuming at least 18 pints a day. I once asked a doctor about the effects of drinking such huge amounts of caffeine, tannin, and tiny black leaves. He reeled off an alarming catalogue of ailments adding, 'and if Mr Benn was a racehorse he would foam at the mouth'.
Peter Hillmore, Observer 27 *Feb* 1983

3 Popular worries about Mr Anthony Wedgwood Benn appear to be less that he is a leftie than that he may be a loonie.
Peter Jenkins, Guardian

4 Mr Benn is no doubt less of a wild-eyed European Trot than a very English phenomenon: a descendant of the Puritans and the nonconformists and, despite his doubts about the Almighty, of the clean-living, nineteenth-century Christian Socialists.
John Mortimer, IN CHARACTER 1983

5 I remember telling him, on the steps of St Matthews, that I thought the major difference beween us was his weak hold on the doctrine of original sin. I suspect that he believes man is basically good, whereas I think he is prone to evil. This is more than teleological hair-splitting as it has political implications. If man is good he will presumably sacrifice himself for the well-being of society. If he is prone to evil he is motivated by selfishness.
Mervyn Stockwood, CHANCTONBURY RING 1982

6 When he first took a ride in his official car he sat on the floor; the point being that he not only didn't like the trappings of office, but didn't want to be seen enjoying them.
Ivan Yates, Observer 12 *Oct* 1969

(ENOCH) ARNOLD BENNETT

Born 1867. English author, best known for his novels set in the Staffordshire potteries. Died 1931.

7 How I loved my Arnold Bennett, and how Arnold loved my champagne!
Lord Beaverbrook. Quoted A. J. P. Taylor, BEAVERBROOK 1972

8 This year I have written 304,000 words: one play, two films, one small book on religion and 81 articles. Also, I lost a full month on rehearsals, and a full month, no six weeks, on holidays.
Arnold Bennett, DIARY 31 *Dec* 1928

9 Arnold Bennett had a disconcerting habit at literary gatherings. He would select a chair in the middle of the festivities, settle himself comfortably, and promptly fall asleep. He had been dozing happily one evening all through a bitter argument on current trends when a particularly vehement declaration woke him up with a start. 'Isn't it time to be going?' his wife asked in some embarrassment. 'Not at all,' said Bennett. 'It would be extremely rude to leave so early' — and promptly went back to sleep.
Bennett Cerf, SHAKE WELL BEFORE USING 1948

10 Bennett was like a conjurer who takes ten minutes doing the tricks and half an hour explaining them. If only he hadn't been so insistent on his craftsmanship and professionalism . . . the world might have remembered him as a masterly novelist, and not a kind of literary saggar-maker's bottom knocker.
Bevis Hillier, Sunday Times 24 *May* 1970

11 Arnold Bennett said to me, the most tremendous compliment ever paid to him was Lord Beaverbrook saying, 'Arnold, you're a hard man.'
Geoffrey Madan, NOTEBOOKS 1981

12 That Arnold should have spent the last of his energy and determination in the description of a hotel seems to me to have a symbolical significance. For I feel that he was never quite at home in the world. It was to him perhaps a sumptuous hotel, with marble bathrooms and a sumptuous cuisine, in which he was a transient guest.
W. Somerset Maugham, John o' London's Weekly 24 *Jun* 1933

13 His stammer was torture to him. It may be that but for the stammer which forced him to introspection Arnold would never have become a writer. But I think it is not the least proof of his strong and sane character that notwithstanding this impediment he was able to retain his splendid balance.
Ibid.

14 Arnold was good company and I always enjoyed spending an evening with him, but I did not much like him. He was very cocksure and bumptious and he was rather common.
Ibid.

15 I caught a glimpse of Bennett once in a theatre when I was in my early twenties. He was wearing what seemed to me the most elaborate evening dress I had ever seen off

stage; full of unexpected frills and furbelows. I read afterwards somewhere that it cost him a pound every time he put on evening dress.
Malcolm Muggeridge, Observer 19 *Jun* 1966

1 I met Arnold Bennett turning the corner into the Savoy, his bowler hat well on the side of his head; he looked just a trifle ridiculous, I thought. A sort of deliberately manufactured appearance. His blue Melton overcoat was waisted a shade too noticeably and I would bet that it was through his own lack of judgment rather than his tailor's.
Reginald Pound, THEIR MOODS AND MINE 1937

2 I saw him practising his efficiency gospel in one particular on a lot of occasions. He used the Reform Club a great deal, sometimes with Wells alone, mostly with a group that assembled after lunch in the smoking room. Whatever the company, however animated the talk, Bennett always got up, I noticed, on the stroke of half-past two, with just a touch of cockiness, as if he wished it to be announced this was a demonstration of his superiority.
Ibid.

3 He did a fair amount of writing for me, and if an article came to, say, fifty more words than the length we had agreed on, he would want to be paid his fifty extra florins.
Ibid.

4 Someone said that he had never been quite the same man since hearing that every bedroom in the Ritz had its own bathroom. Someone else [G. K. Chesterton] called him 'The man who came up for the Cup Final and never went back'.
Edward Shanks, Arnold Bennett's obituary, John o' London's Weekly 18 *Apr* 1931

5 One of the few English novelists to portray ordinary people in realistic terms and not as caricatures.
Alan Sillitoe

6 His grey topknot, his features, a few slightly protruding teeth, the backward tilt of his body as he sat in his chair listening, above all the expression in his eyes, all presented an appearance of irremediable obstinacy, while his stutter, even in its very beginning, rejected every plea put forward.
Osbert Sitwell, LAUGHTER IN THE NEXT ROOM 1949

7 I met Arnold Bennett only once at a friend's house where the children were to perform the Toy Symphony. He stood in the dining-room, a bored look on his face, the heavy-lidded eyes half shut. A lady came up to him, hustling forward a shy schoolgirl. 'Oh Mr Bennett, this is my daughter, she is so anxious to meet you.' Bennett turned, faintly raising one eyebrow. He looked at the lady, then at the girl. He held out his hand and drawled a word or two. Then suddenly his eyelid flickered, and he gave the girl one of the most delightful smiles I have ever seen. A few moments later, without warning, the symphony began. Bennett broke off short. 'Good God!' he exclaimed and stood up on a chair to see better.
L. A. G. Strong, John o' London's Weekly 21 *Mar* 1936

8 He knew his own powers and could not resist a secret feeling of glee that he had so successfully hoodwinked the world into giving him such celebrity and such enormous sums of money — and could not help despising it for being imposed upon.
Ibid.

9 'The Old Wives' Tale' after Dickens is perhaps England's first record of ordinary people's lives. It is a work of genius. I cannot imagine its author writing, as he does, such drivelling journalism — 'How to Get Thin' and that sort of thing — at £100 a time. Still, the rich must live, I suppose.
Hannen Swaffer of Arnold Bennett's contributions to the Evening Standard. Quoted L. W. Needham, FIFTY YEARS IN FLEET STREET

10 Great men are usually inordinately modest about their real achievements but quite grotesquely vain about the little things they do as sidelines. I am sure that Arnold is much more proud of his efforts at the piano — which really ought to be seen as well as heard — than he is about, let us say, *Riceyman Steps*.
Ernest Thesiger, PRACTICALLY TRUE 1927

11 His writing is a thing of which Arnold Bennett has every right to be proud, and by his writing I mean his calligraphy. The MS of *The Old Wives' Tale* is a work of art in itself — an exquisitely penned affair, with illuminated initial letters at the beginning of each chapter, and scarcely a single erasure throughout the whole wonderful book. I wonder where that manuscript will ultimately rest, and how many dollars some American will have to pay to possess it?
Ibid.

1 I cannot bear anyone not to like Arnold Bennett.
Ibid.

2 Is Dickens of no value to the world any more because Mr Arnold Bennett has found it impossible to finish one of his novels?
Hugh Walpole, 'Literary Dogmatists', T.P.'s and Cassell's Weekly 6 *Aug* 1927

3 He had a trick of closing his eyes and holding his mouth open for a moment before he said the vital word in the sentence.
Rebecca West

4 He would look at his chosen prey with a fierce flat eye and the air of a man refusing to finance a tin-mine.
Humbert Wolfe. Quoted Geoffrey Madan, NOTEBOOKS 1981

5 He can make a book so well constructed and solid in its craftsmanship that it is difficult for the most exacting of critics to see through what chink or crevice decay can creep in. And yet — if life should refuse to live there?
Virginia Woolf, THE COMMON READER 1925

JACK BENNY

Born 1894. Stage name of Benjamin Kubelsky, American comedian. Went into vaudeville at the age of 15 as a violinist — a talent which he exploited for comic effect throughout his subsequent career in the theatre, films, radio and television. Died 1974.

6 He was neither a mean man nor a mean violinist, although when he played his first serious concert one critic did note that the New York Philharmonic seemed to be out of tune with him and another added simply 'Last night Jack Benny played Mendelssohn, and Mendelssohn lost '
The Times, Obituary 29 *Dec* 1974

7 To his audiences he was the archetypal miser. He was also vain, sour, an awful violinist, and for several decades remained thirty-nine years of age.
Charles Van Doren, WEBSTER'S AMERICAN BIOGRAPHIES 1974

8 Jack's show did a lot for the image of the black people in America. Before Jack came along everybody thought blacks were only fit to be shoeshine boys and railroad porters. The Jack Benny programme proved that they could also be chauffeurs, dishwashers and houseboys!
Desmond Wilson on American radio Feb 1974

E. F. (EDWARD FREDERIC) BENSON

Born 1867. English author who wrote a number of light novels, immensely popular in their day, which went out of favour for a period after his death, but enjoyed a revival of interest when reprinted in 1984. Died 1940.

9 E. F. Benson's idea of a good conversation is when neither party remembers a word of what was said afterwards.
Geoffrey Madan, NOTEBOOKS 1981

10 E. F. Benson never lived his life at all, only stayed with it and lunched with it.
Ibid.

11 The question is, why did he disappear so completely when he is English literature's sole heir to the Thackeray of *Vanity Fair*? There is only one convincing theory. Benson went out of vogue after the war because we could not face an author mercilessly mocking the English way of life that everyone had just been fighting to defend.
Stephen Pile, Sunday Times 11 *Mar* 1984

12 While his father, Queen Victoria's stern unsmiling Archbishop of Canterbury, sat in Lambeth Palace writing his endless biography of St Cyprian, Fred — as the family called E. F. — was writing a stream of witty, bitchy, camp, often savage and distinctly unepiscopal novels mocking English provincial life and manners.
Ibid.

BERNARD BERENSON

Born 1865 in Lithuania. American art critic and art historian. Adviser to dealers, collectors and galleries. His authentications were regarded as infallible. Died 1959.

13 I wanted to become a work of art myself, and not an artist.
Bernard Berenson, SUNSET AND TWILIGHT 1964

14 Berenson was a genius — not as a creative artist but as a kind of tactile computer, a combination of judgment, flair, knowledge and aesthetic perception which has never before been met with and which was fed the appropriate sense-data all his life.
Cyril Connolly, Sunday Times 19 *Jun* 1966

15 I remember him telling me how, on his first

visit to the Prado he emerged with a clear image of every picture in his mind which was never to forsake him. So, perhaps does an eagle memorise a whole mountainside on its first flight.
Ibid.

1 He had a devastating effect on the art world and by the time he had achieved his full stature as a critic a word from B.B. was sufficient to add or subtract thousands of pounds from the value of a work of art.
Paul Levy, Observer 17 *Jul* 1979

2 He won my admiration as the most cultivated human being I had ever met, but what I came to love him for was his warmth — a quality seldom conspicuous in Anglo-Saxons of the educated class.
Raymond Mortimer, Sunday Times 9 *Feb* 1964

3 I was present at a luncheon once when the director of an American museum was complaining that 'some idiot' had claimed that the antique statue he had just purchased at a fabulous price for his museum was a forgery. B.B. said, without a moment's hesitation: 'But it is!'
Benedict Nicolson, Observer 11 *Oct* 1960

4 I remember him once, on a walk in the Tuscan hills, gazing enraptured, as Proust used to do, for minutes on end at an ordinary tree.
Ibid.

5 On one occasion — he was a mere seventy-three then — we sat watching a boy playing at our feet in the library of his villa near Florence, looking, he pointed out to me, like one of the children in Bellini's *Allegory* in the Uffizi. Gravely B.B. addressed him: 'I wish I were as young and beautiful as you.' He *was*, at that moment.
Ibid.

6 He invented a painter he called *Amico di Sandro* around whom he grouped a number of pictures which bore a certain resemblance to Sandro Botticelli but were not quite up to standard. He published his findings in an article and forthwith these rather dim Madonnas went up considerably in value. Later B.B. ceased to believe in his *Amico di Sandro*, having reached the conclusion that the group was made up of works by different followers and imitators of Botticelli, and redistributed them accordingly. American collectors were furious to find they had been cheated of their esoteric labels.
Ibid.

7 How curious that this pernickety little person, who took such delight in trivial social gossip, should in the end have succeeded in inspiring such reverence, such awe, such terror, that even kings and queens would rise instinctively when he entered his own drawing room.
Harold Nicolson, Observer 27 *Mar* 1960

8 How odd it was that he would reject with sulky scorn the considered compliments of scholarly men, yet lap with zest huge bowls of gush when served to him by intrusive women!
Ibid.

9 He was as curious, persistent and imaginative as a child, agile as a chamois, as sensitive as a poet and as learned as a sage.
Iris Origo, Cornhill Magazine 1960

HENRI BERGSON

Born 1859 in France. Philosopher and author. Propounded anti-nationalist views based on the theory that knowledge comes from intuition, expounded in *Creative Evolution*, 1907. Awarded Nobel Prize for Literature, 1929. Died 1941.

10 True reality, in Bergson's view, is an endless becoming, an unceasing flow and flux, that can be perceived and understood only by intuition, and not by the inferior function of intellect, compelled to halt the flow, to abstract something static from it, in order to analyse it.
J. B. Priestley, LITERATURE AND WESTERN MAN 1960

11 It was an act of extraordinary boldness for a then obscure professor in a provincial French university to come forward and violate the great taboo by asking, in effect: 'And this reason of yours — is it really as almighty as you make out? What precisely is it good for? and just how much does it give you to know? And what connexion has it with that other magic word of yours, evolution?'
Esme Wingfield Stratford, GREAT CONTEMPORARIES: HENRI BERGSON 1935

12 The universe of Bergson's vision is not mechanical but poetic. Creative energy, the informing spirit is at work first, last, and without ceasing. Subtract that from the universe and you abolish time. Not even chaos is left — you are brought up against a blank wall of negation.
Ibid.

IRVING BERLIN

Born Israel Baline, 1888 in Russia. Emigrated to America to become a famous composer of songs, e.g. *I'm Dreaming of a White Christmas*, and musical shows, e.g. *Annie Get Your Gun*.

1 At one of the first performances of *Annie Get Your Gun* Dick Rogers, the producer, stood in the lobby during the intermission with Berlin, composer of the hit-studded score. Berlin moved away and a stout lady standing nearby obviously recognised him. She nudged her husband and Dick heard her say wonderingly, 'Sam, to look at him, who would think?'
Bennett Cerf, SHAKE WELL BEFORE USING 1948

2 Mr Churchill gave a Downing Street lunch to Irving Berlin the ragtime king under the belief that he was Isaiah Berlin, the eccentric genius who at that time was watching the American scene for Winston from the top window of our embassy in Washington. The creator of *Alexander's Ragtime Band* doubtless felt flattered by the Premier's keen interest in his political views, and we are told that he kept his end up magnificently, even if it involved a bit of swift syncopation now and then.
Ian Mackay, News Chronicle 3 *Jan* 1946

3 In 1925 Allin Mackay's father, appalled at the possibility of family entanglements with a song writer, said to Irving, 'What will you do if I cut my daughter off without a cent?' Said Berlin, 'In that case I'll have to settle a million on her myself.'
News Chronicle 25 *Jul* 1936

SARAH BERNHARDT

Stage name of Rosine Bernard, born 1844 in France. Became world-famous as an actress. Died 1923.

4 Mr Zukor, you have put the best of me in pickle for all time.
Bernhardt, of her performance, in 1912 *in the film Queen Elizabeth*

5 If the Gods punished *hubris*, they punished it in Sarah's case by putting her in impossible positions. For instance there was the man with the dead whale who, on her Boston tour, somehow inveigled her into posing on the back of the unsavoury object: whereupon a joyful and hysterical Press proclaimed that Madame Bernhardt had pulled out one of the mammal's bones with her own hands, to reinforce her stays.
Pamela Hansford Johnson, John o' London's Weekly 13 *May* 1949

6 It is fair to say of Sarah Bernhardt that she saw life as a grandiose performance with herself in perpetual lead.
Joanna Richardson, SARAH BERNHARDT 1959

7 She carried herself lightly and with dignity, even in old age, when she would lean on her chair, or on someone's shoulder, as if the absence of a limb were an indispensable asset to a graceful bearing.
Suze Rueff, I KNEW SARAH BERNHARDT 1951

8 In that frail body will-power took the place of physical stamina, and self-pity she kept for the casual annoyance. When her leg was amputated she, of all the world, gave no sign that this might be a disaster, and worked on.
Ibid.

9 She never had a bank, but carried her entire fortune about with her in a chamois bag . . . the treasure exhausted, she set out on another world tour.
Ibid.

10 Every year Madame Bernhardt comes to us with a new play in which she kills someone with a hairpin or a hatchet and intones a great deal of dialogue as a sample of what is called 'the golden voice' to the great delight of our curates who all produce golden voices by more or less the same trick.
George Bernard Shaw

11 The indefatigable actress went off after lunch to play one act of *La Tosca* at the Coliseum. In the evening she appeared there again, after which she attended a large supper party in her honour and then finished the day by motoring to Folkestone, en route for Paris. The following week she was to sail for America where, she told me, she was to produce eleven new plays. Not a bad achievement for an invalid of seventy!
Ernest Thesiger, PRACTICALLY TRUE 1927

12 A great friend of mine, then seventeen, and I went together to the Coliseum where Bernhardt was doing one act from *Phèdre*. For what seemed an interminably long time the actress stood on the stage supported by the handsome Lou Tellegen, and whispered long, dull speeches. The audience got restless; I could see that my young friend was

getting bored and I regretted having brought him. Suddenly she became galvanised into life and with that one line, '*Venus toute entière à sa proie attachée*', electrified the whole theatre. As for my blasé young friend, he burst into tears, and cried, 'Oh God! I had no idea it was going to be like this!'
Ibid.

1 She fell deeply in love with an undertaker's assistant but refused to marry him when he would not permit her to be present at an embalming. Between the hours of her rehearsals she visited the cemeteries of Paris and sat among the tombstones like a sister of the departed.
Henry and Dana Lee Thomas, LIVING BIOGRAPHIES OF FAMOUS WOMEN: SARAH BERNHARDT

2 You are too stupid to be much of an actress, but it will keep you out of mischief.
Her mother, Julie Von Hard, on entering her as a pupil at the Paris Conservatory

3 I have played Hippolyte to many Phèdres, and with all the others I felt that when the Queen had declared her passion there was no reason why I should stay to hear the rest of the speech except that I was paid to do so. With Sarah it was different. She hypnotised me — I couldn't move. It was only when she took her eyes off me that I recovered the use of my limbs.
Jean Yonnel

4 The air seemed to vibrate round us as Sarah began to speak and I remember the fruit and flowers all over her huge hat danced and trembled in time with our excitement.
Jean Yonnel, The Times 22 *Jan* 1965

SIR JOHN BETJEMAN

Born 1906. English poet. His *Summoned by Bells*, 1960, is his autobiography. An enthusiast for the preservation of Victoriana. Appointed Poet Laureate 1972. Died 1984.

5 John Betjeman came round the other day and went around saying, 'Very nice, very nice.' One room especially got him going. 'Unique work,' he said, 'Absolutely beautiful. Nothing like it today.' He wasn't talking about the really vintage stuff, it turned out. What he liked was the wall moulding. 1930, he said, was a very good year.
Kingsley Amis. Quoted Philip Oakes, Sunday Times 28 *Sep* 1969

6 By appointment: Teddy Bear to the Nation.
Alan Bell, The Times 20 *Sep* 1982

7 I always make a point on aeroplanes to travel in the smoking compartment because there won't be any kiddies there.
John Betjeman, Radio Times 28 *Aug* 1976

8 He was the only boy in the house who brought his golf clubs to school (Marlborough).
Arthur Byron, The Times 22 *May* 1984

9 His eccentricities and idiosyncrasies make him memorable and lovable: his admiration for his teddy bear, his baggy trousers and bicycle clips, his interest in Victoriana, gaslights, trams and canal pumping stations, and his zeal for rooting out the guidebooks which pander to the corporation.
Tim Devlin, The Times 11 *Oct* 1972

10 His wildly heterogeneous world of farce and fury, where sports girls and old nuns jostle with town clerks and impoverished Irish peers, is as remote from the common reader as remorse and religion, architecture and Archibald, and the rest of his favourite subjects. Yet the common reader, and his children after him, have lapped it up.
Philip Larkin, Observer 13 *Mar* 1983

11 Suddenly comes the uproarious back-of-the-pit horse-laugh, wide open, all teeth and creases. And above it the extraordinary powerful skull, like a Roman bust, or a phrenologist's model waiting to be marked into 33 sections, labelled with Superior Sentiments and Reflective Faculties.
Ibid.

12 Betjeman appeared in a pair of eccentric bedroom slippers and said he hoped I didn't mind them as he had a blister. He seemed so pleased with himself that I couldn't help saying that I had no objection to *his* wearing them — a view which I believe surprised him. He had been very idle over the Old English, and I told him it wouldn't do.
C. S. Lewis, Diary 1925, *when Betjeman was an undergraduate at Magdalen*

13 Because he is an excellent clown it would be easy to mistake him for one of those harmless English eccentrics whose prophetic utterances can be dismissed as an elaborate joke.
Observer, Profile 8 *Feb* 1959

14 He shows considerable expertise in the English social system; he knows whether Mavis is a higher class name than Doreen,

and what it means if you shop at the Home and Colonial.
Ibid.

1 His zest for his chosen occupations and companions was irresistible. He was also precocious, whimsical, perhaps self-regarding, totally impractical, prone to sudden boredom and melancholy, and troubled with guilt. He could so easily have remained what he was in his Oxford days, the last of a few. But he became a public figure, a mascot almost.
Myfanwy Piper, The Times 30 *Oct* 1984

2 Like Blake he feared both pretension and learning (as opposed to knowledge) seeing them both as destructive of feeling, as substitutes for the eye, the ear and the heart.
Ibid.

3 Betjeman abandoned English at Oxford in favour of Welsh, causing a don to be imported from Aberystwyth twice a week.
Patrick Taylor-Martin, JOHN BETJEMAN: HIS LIFE AND WORK 1983

4 At Oxford he went out with an Eton-cropped waitress called Olive Sparks.
Ibid.

5 He is a poet whose response to experience, both visual and emotional, is direct and spontaneous. He says what he feels without self-consciousness. He is frightened of death and says so; he feels guilty about neglecting his parents and says so; he does not want his son to die and says so.
Ibid.

ANEURIN BEVAN

Born 1897 in Wales. Labour politician, Minister of Health 1945–51, responsible for inaugurating National Health Service. Died 1960.

6 For Health I chose Aneurin Bevan whose abilities had up to now been displayed only in Opposition, but I felt that he had it in him to do good work.
Lord Attlee, AS IT HAPPENED

7 Bevan has resigned over the budget. He made his traditional explanation to the House but it was not a success and pleased nobody, for he was savage, vindictive and long-winded. He in turn assailed Gaitskell, insulted the Tories and railed against the Government and Attlee. Twice during his harangue the Speaker half rose to silence him, but lacked the guts. At the end of 32 minutes he sat down exhausted and defeated — temporarily. It may be that his bubble has burst, but I think it more likely that he has run away to fight another day.
Sir Henry Channon, DIARY 23 *Apr* 1951

8 I can think of no better step to signalise the inauguration of the National Health Service than that a person who so obviously needs psychiatric attention should be among the first of its patients.
Winston Churchill, House of Commons Jul 1948

9 He was wise and balanced. He taught me how to become resolutely anti-communist without becoming a cold warrior, and how to wish the Americans out of Europe without becoming anti-American.
Richard Crossman, Sunday Times 7 *Oct* 1973

10 He struck me, not as a case-hardened Labour leader but a lovely human being, a warm-hearted, boisterous, creative, exasperating personality.
Ibid.

11 The Ministry was the making of him. By a tremendous effort he got to the office punctually, worked regular hours, controlled his tongue, never bullied his civil servants and read all the papers in his red boxes. For the first time his political genius matured because his life and his work were regulated by a discipline which controlled his wilfulness. This discipline was removed with disastrous consequences when he resigned.
Ibid.

12 He could have been the greatest orator of our time, but never disciplined himself to prepare a speech, preferring to think aloud on his feet in a way which was unreportable.
Ibid.

13 How often he told me that the time to work out your plans is not when you are in opposition but after you have won the election and all the government experts are at your disposal.
Ibid.

14 Aneurin was on his way to join Jennie at George Strauss's home in Kensington Palace Gardens while London was being blitzed, and was nearly hit by an explosion in Oxford Street. He saved himself from splinters by the miner's habit of falling to the ground in the presence of danger. When he arrived, still brushing the glass from his shoulders, he remarked, 'I could have loved London tonight.'
Michael Foot, LIFE OF ANEURIN BEVAN 1962

1 'We might be brother and sister,' said Jennie Lee the first time they really talked together. 'Aye,' replied Nye with an appraising, mischievous grin, 'but with a tendency to incest.'
Ibid.

2 Nye hated acrimony. He loved good fellowship. If his aim in life had been personal advancement, if he had chosen to disarm his critics by abandoning his principles, the leadership of the party was his for the taking.
Jennie Lee, MY LIFE WITH NYE 1980

3 His laugh rang out like the shout of a great woodpecker.
Reginald Pound, THEIR MOODS AND MINE 1937

4 The National Health Service was, for Bevan, one of those political creations which justify a life-time of politics.
William Rees-Mogg, The Times 8 *Oct* 1973

5 A friend of Nye's wanted me to baptise his child with Nye as godfather. I was told he was an atheist with no liking for parsons. While I was hesitating he wrote to me. With characteristic integrity he asked me to send him a copy of the service in order that he might read for himself the promises he would make. I was moved by his honesty but felt it inadequate and suggested an additional godfather to make the orthodox answers, allowing Nye to remain silent at the appropriate moments. Thus began a friendship that was to endure until many years later as Bishop of Southwark I preached his memorial sermon in Westminster Abbey.
Mervyn Stockwood, CHANCTONBURY RING 1982

WILLIAM HENRY BEVERIDGE

Born 1879 in India. British economist and civil servant. Supervised the establishment of labour exchanges, and of food rationing during the First World War. Director of London School of Economics 1919–37. Produced a report for the founding of a Welfare State, 1942. Died 1963.

6 I have spent most of my life most happily making plans for others to carry out.
Beveridge, writing in 1953

7 He is a pleasant, earnest, professional little man, obviously capable of immense work. He explained the report which, surprisingly enough, irritates the Socialists more than it does us. I think it should be adopted.
Sir Henry Channon, DIARY 2 *Dec* 1942

8 The Beveridge Report has been made public. It will revolutionise life in England — but at first glance I am in favour of it.
Ibid.

9 Beveridge raised the committee to the level of a crusade. One day, looking pleased, he put before me a list of five words: Want, Disease, Squalor, Ignorance and Unemployment — the five giant evils he had set himself to conquer.
Sir Norman Chester, secretary to the Beveridge committee, The Times 1 *Dec* 1982

10 Beveridge became a household word. One of the most popular figures in the country. In university and Whitehall circles he was respected but not greatly liked; certain ministers, including Churchill, had doubts and reservations.
Ibid.

11 He once complained that I was not critical enough but some time later when I suggested some drafting amendment he said, 'Chester, you are gilding the lily.'
Ibid.

12 Beveridge refused to accept the argument that subsistence must take into account not only what was essential, but what was customary. He included nothing for beer or tobacco, for neither was essential.
Ibid.

13 The main theme of his life starts with the never-to-be-forgotten advice Edward Caird, then Master of Balliol, gave the young undergraduate at the turn of the century: 'When you have learnt all that Oxford can teach you, go and discover why, with so much wealth in Britain, there continues to be so much poverty, and how that poverty can be cured.'
The Times, Obituary 18 *Mar* 1963

ERNEST BEVIN

Born 1881 in England. Labour politician and Trade Union leader. Minister of Labour 1940–45, Foreign Secretary 1945–51. Died 1951.

14 Ernest Bevin's position in his own country, his influence with Parliament, the TUC and the Cabinet, the devoted respect with which he was regarded by the Foreign Office and

ERNEST BEVIN

the Foreign Service rendered him the authentic voice of Britain.
Dean Acheson, SKETCHES FROM LIFE 1961

1 Bevin was so forthright and so rational he seemed to have cornered the market for common sense. His broad and rollicking gaiety disarmed the antagonism of his opponents and riveted the affection of his supporters.
Ibid.

2 He pleaded the case of the dockers in 1920 in a most dramatic manner. He put ten plates before the Court. They contained the tiny proportion of cabbage, potatoes and meat which the employers considered adequate to sustain the strength of a docker hauling seventy-one tons of wheat a day on his shoulders. This was when he became known as 'The Dockers' KC'.
Lord Attlee, Observer, The Bevin I knew 13 *Mar* 1960

3 Bevin was among several prominent Labour politicians who in the 1945 election had promised that Anglo-Russian relations would be better with a left-wing British Government: 'Left can speak to left in comradeship and confidence', he had claimed. In office he proved a man big enough to eat his own unguarded words, and will rank high in history as one of the chief organisers of Western resistance against the advance of revolutionary Communism from the East.
Lord Butler, THE ART OF THE POSSIBLE 1971

4 Not only was our private relationship friendly but on the major public issues arising from the Cold War there was rarely much between us save a difference of emphasis on detail. I remember his taking me into the Smoking Room one evening and saying, ''Ave a beer, Rab, I'm worried about the A-rabs.'
Ibid.

5 All day the Government Front Bench was crowded and old Bevin, sallow and shrunken, looked as if he had been kissed by death.
Sir Henry Channon, DIARY 20 *Mar* 1951

6 Bevin's solicitude for his wife was immense. He would leave important discussions with his officials during an international conference if she sent for him to sit on the suitcases when she couldn't get them shut.
Nicholas Henderson, THE PRIVATE OFFICE 1984

7 Ernest Bevin loved talking and drinking late into the night, yanking me out of my bedroom. 'Let's have one more drink and a chat before we turn in'. 'Poor humanity,' was a favourite aside as he dealt with some problem affecting not just frontiers, but people's lives.
Ibid.

8 'What you have got to do in foreign affairs,' he announced in Bevinese on one occasion, 'is not to create a situation.'
Ibid.

9 Had he to choose at any time up to the outbreak of war, between the slaughter of the Labour Party and that of the Transport and General Workers' Union, there can be no doubt that it would have been the Labour Party, reluctantly but unhesitatingly, that he would have sent to the abattoir.
Roy Jenkins, LIFE OF ERNEST BEVIN 1971

10 He was the man who battered the Labour Party Conference into shape from the floor. He was the prototype of the union leader without whose intervention few major debates were complete. And he behaved in a more arrogant (or, according to taste, self-assured) fashion than anyone does today.
Ibid.

11 Bevin always treated the Soviet Union as if it were a breakaway faction of the Transport and General Workers' Union.
Kingsley Martin, HAROLD LASKI

12 David Scott tells me that the Foreign Office are delighted with Bevin. He reads with amazing rapidity, remembers what he reads, cross examines the experts, and having once mastered his brief, acts with vigour.
Harold Nicolson, DIARIES 8 *Aug* 1945

13 He always seems to get the last laugh on his opponents. There is something in him that makes mere cleverness look silly.
Observer, Profile 23 *May* 1948

14 What distinguishes his career from others of this kind is its steadiness and the absence of luck. It is a slow, sure progression, step by step, merit coming before recognition, recognition before power, power before fame.
Ibid.

15 Ernest's mother died when he was eight. He left school at 11 and began work as a farmhand at 6d a week. His work did not stop at dusk. In the evening he was expected to read out articles from the Bristol papers to the farmer's family in the kitchen.
Robert Pitman, Sunday Express 13 *Mar* 1960

1 Like Churchill, he seemed a visitor from the eighteenth century — of the company of Chatham and Samuel Johnson, men of strong hearts and strong opinions.
The Times, Obituary

F. E. (FREDERICK EDWIN) SMITH, FIRST EARL OF BIRKENHEAD

Born 1872. British politician and lawyer, led Conservative opposition to Irish home rule. As Attorney General (1915–19) prosecuted Roger Casement. Lord Chancellor 1919–22. Died 1930.

2 No one will controvert me when I say that Lord Birkenhead had a first-rate intellectual equipment. But I think what I said of him some years ago — that his brains had gone to his head — was true; because, like many men of mark, he exaggerated the value of cleverness.
Margot Asquith, News Chronicle 1 *Oct* 1930

3 A most fluent and plausible bounder.
Raymond Asquith

4 Lord Birkenhead was not merely an ex-President of the Oxford Union. He was the embodiment of the Oxford Union manner. With his wit and his irony and his majestic Johnsonian periods, he has become the model of successive generations of Oxford undergraduates.
Robert Bernays, News Chronicle 4 *Nov* 1932

5 When he finally gave up hunting, his decision was made in characteristic fashion. He had been shivering by the covert side in a bitter east wind for several hours in futile expectancy when he was heard to say, 'In future this vermin may pursue his way unmolested by me.' Then he rodc home, and the Bicester hounds knew him no more.
Second Earl of Birkenhead, BIRKENHEAD: THE FIRST PHASE 1933

6 When Judge Willis once, after a long squabble with F. E. Smith on a point of procedure, asked, 'What do you suppose I am on the Bench for, Mr Smith?' 'It is not for me,' F.E. answered gravely, 'to attempt to fathom the inscrutable workings of Providence.'
Ibid.

7 Lloyd George told of a ten-minute statement made by Birkenhead at the Peace Conference on some question which involved issues of international law. 'At the end of it you felt there was nothing more to be said. Clemenceau turned to me and said "How wonderfully clear!" I asked him to let us hear what the French jurist — a lawyer of great distinction — had to say. Clemenceau replied: "It is quite unnecessary. The Lord Chancellor's statement has settled the question."'
J. B. Frith, Daily Telegraph 5 *Mar* 1935

8 He spoke for an hour and put the House in his pocket.
J. L. Gavin. Observer, of F. E. Smith's maiden speech.

9 Judged by the essentials of manhood, intellect, courage, kindness and loyalty, Lord Birkenhead was a great man
D. Lloyd George. Quoted J. B. Firth, Daily Telegraph 5 *Mar* 1935

10 He held the record for the walk from Oxford to London. A great athletic figure. One of those natural athletes who require no training — in fact who seems to thrive in spite of indulgence.
Oliver St John Gogarty, AS I WAS GOING DOWN SACKVILLE STREET 1937

11 Lord Birkenhead brought home the news of a lucrative contract for a series of articles to be called *Milestones of My Life*. His family asked him what incidents he proposed to use, and when he told them Lady Birkenhead said 'You might have put in your marriage' and Lady Eleanor Smith added, 'and the birth of your first child.' F.E. answered 'I said milestones, my dear, not millstones.'
Edward Marsh, A NUMBER OF PEOPLE 1939

12 His early success in the House was meteoric. When, as Mr F. E. Smith, he made his first speech there he took the house by storm. 'Who is he?' nearly everyone was asking when the slim, youthful figurc rose immediately behind Mr Balfour (who was then leading the Opposition) and a torrent of clever argument and biting sarcasm — which lost little of its effectiveness because it was delivered in the mincing tone which some young men from Oxford affect — was directed against the Government and its supporters. When Mr Smith resumed his seat his reputation as a Parliamentary orator was made.
Morning Post, Obituary 1 *Oct* 1930

13 It was rightly said of him that he could see no good in an enemy, no bad in a friend. He was harsh, sentimental, emotional and controlled. He hated as passionately as he loved. He adored beauty but was pitiful of

ugliness. He was impatient, intolerant and irritable. He very often hurt people's feelings without knowing in the least that he had done so.
Lady Eleanor Smith, LIFE'S A CIRCUS 1939

1 He had three cars, painted buttercup yellow, and his stables were filled with horses, some of which he had never ridden. He seldom went to bed before two o'clock, and would be called again at eight. He would cross the Channel in a storm, play baccarat all night at Deauville Casino, and next afternoon be seated, inscrutable and stern upon the Woolsack — the Woolsack, insignia of his high office as Lord Chancellor, on which he allowed his children to bounce up and down, to the horror of the officials.
Ibid.

2 What can one say of a man who derived exquisite pleasure from taking his small daughter to Willie Clarkson's where, after putting a flaxen wig on her head, he caused her cheeks to be grotesquely painted, then escorted her, gravely, upon a series of solemn legal calls?
Ibid.

3 'F.E.' was intellectually fit to be a great statesman, a great judge, even a great journalist. His tragedy was that he never really knew what he wanted to be.
H. A. Taylor, SMITH OF BIRKENHEAD 1931

LOUIS BLÉRIOT

Born 1872. French aviator and inventor. Designed monoplane in which he made the first flight across the Channel in a heavier-than-air machine, 1909. Died 1936.

4 Twenty minutes after I have left the French coast I see the green cliffs of Dover, the Castle, and away to the West the spot where I had intended to land. Avoiding the red building on the right I attempt to land; but the wind catches me and whirls me round two or three times. At once I stop my motor and instantly my machine falls upon the land from a height of 20 metres.
Louis Blériot

5 I was Northcliffe's official timekeeper. The sky was grey but, officially, the sun was rising. The moment had come. 'Now,' I said, 'off you go. Good luck and au revoir.' It was then that Blériot put that staggering question to Leblanc, 'Where is Dover?' Leblanc waved his hand seaward. 'It's over there,' he said. Blériot nodded, then gave his head mechanic the signal to turn the propeller. The engine started.
Hamilton Fyfe, News Chronicle 20 *Jul* 1934

6 In the midst of this odd throng I saw what appeared to be a cripple directing the mechanics as they tuned up the engine of the little monoplane. He pointed here and there with his crutch. The cripple was Blériot. Some days previously he had badly burned his foot when the engine of his aircraft caught fire. He turned to me and said 'I cannot walk, *but I can fly*.'
George Mumford, Evening News 25 *Jul* 1949

7 While we waited, I talked to M. Blériot. He was the coolest person present. He oozed confidence. 'My machine is good for an hour and a half,' he told me. 'And by that time — ' He gestured towards the invisible English coast.
Ibid.

SIR ARTHUR BLISS

Born 1891. British composer. Master of the Queen's Music 1953–75. Died 1975.

7 In the latter part of his life Bliss turned more and more to illustrative music, the prop of a story or situation apparently kindling his imagination more readily than the abstract manipulation of themes in sonata, quartet or symphony. Thus his three ballets, *Checkmate*, 1937, *Miracle in the Gorbals*, 1944, and *Adam Zero*, 1946, are all first rate.
Ernest Chapman, DICTIONARY OF COMPOSERS (*Edited by Charles Osborne*) 1977

8 His elaborate film scores, such as *Things to Come* and *Men of Two Worlds* constitute a pioneering achievement in their field.
Ibid.

9 Sir Arthur Bliss headed a party of English musicians on a short tour of Russia in April 1955. A special distinction was attached to the Bliss Violin Concerto by the presence on the rostrum of the composer himself. In fact Bliss was a winner all along the line — unless I except the few games of chess in which he indulged with some of the members of the Soviet Orchestra.
Gerald Moore, AM I TOO LOUD? 1962

10 The first English composer to compose an opera specifically for television.
Henry Raynor, Daily Telegraph 29 *Jul* 1961

EDMUND (CHARLES) BLUNDEN

Born 1896. English author, poet and literary critic. Gained wide attention with his *Undertones of War*, 1928. Died 1974.

1 One of my aims will be to decrease the number of people who hate poetry.
Edmund Blunden on being elected Professor of Poetry at Oxford University 5 *Feb* 1966

2 He ransacks the past, watching with agony the decaying of it as each familiar thing 'whirls on nor understands God's freezing love'. As we read we begin to perceive that strain of madness in the work, as of a child who sees his toys, symbols of a larger life, being consumed with his burning home in a midnight conflagration.
Richard Church, John o' London's Weekly 7 *Feb* 1931

3 In his youth he had been a great cricketer at village level. He was one of the members of the first side ever fielded by Sir John Squire, the Invalids — the team immortalised by A. G. Macdonell in *England Their England*.
David Holloway, Daily Telegraph 22 *Jan* 1974

4 Imagine this reader and lover of nature being called from his books and cottage to deliver death to those he had no wish to harm! He no doubt wore his khaki with a difference. But while *Undertones of War*, which is written in fine prose without ornament, is plainly the work of one who was not born for soldiering, it is equable in spirit.
Frank Swinnerton, THE GEORGIAN LITERARY SCENE 1935

WILFRID SCAWEN BLUNT

Born 1840. English author, poet, diplomat and explorer. His travels in the Near East made him a fierce anti-imperialist. Died 1922.

5 He was, in essentials and in detail, a poor man's Byron. He was very conscious of the parallels in his life. His father had been Byron's fag at Harrow. He married Byron's grand-daughter, Lady Anne King-Noel.
Paul Johnson, Observer 16 *July* 1979

6 Like Byron, he was good-looking and was vain about it; would dress up at the roll of a turban (he had himself buried rolled up in his favourite Oriental carpet), enjoyed wild gallops and saw himself as a pure-blooded stallion servicing fortunate mares (one reason why he bred bloodstock).
Ibid.

7 He was remembered as a minor poet, a Sussex squire, a distinguished breeder of Arab horses, an early anti-Imperialist who went to jail for his convictions in Ireland and who publicised the cause of Indian and Arab nationalism. To insiders he was also known as a notorious womaniser.
Ibid.

8 Being an adherent of the Establishment I do not really admire Englishmen who assure backward peoples that the British Government is invariably treacherous, cruel and mistaken. My father, who had experience of Blunt in Constantinople and Egypt, would always refer to him as 'that conceited ass'.
Harold Nicolson, Observer 11 *Jun* 1961

9 I always suspect Englishmen who admire Arabs and who put on fancy dress when enertaining parties in Sussex. I have the impression that Scawen Blunt was a man of very unusual talents, who wasted his gifts owing to vanity and a streak of ostentation.
Ibid.

10 When Lady Anne died she did not leave her share of the stud to Blunt as he had expected while certain horses he wanted to keep were claimed by his strong-willed daughter. The scenes that took place, Blunt being nearly 80, were worthy of King Lear.
Anthony Powell, Daily Telegraph 12 *Jul* 1979

11 Once when he was bent on seducing a vegetarian peeress she did not turn up and he had to eat a solitary dinner of spinach, cauliflower and sago pudding by himself in his Mount Street flat.
Ibid.

12 Blunt was brought up a Roman Catholic, married according to the Anglican rite, spent considerable stretches of his life as an atheist, and was at times a devout Mohammedan. He liked having affairs with Catholic ladies, preferably relations, as these kept him in touch with the Church, offering more chance of repentance.
Ibid.

13 Blunt was an interesting type, but always, to my mind, wrong-headed — saw things wrongly and was, I should say, capable of misrepresenting facts to establish his case. And I think he had a touch of malignity in his constitution.
Lord Rennell, letter to Harold Nicolson, 1941

1 Moral courage was certainly required of a man who consistently upheld, as Blunt did, 'my country always wrong'.
H. D. Ziman, Daily Telegraph 9 *Jun* 1961

HUMPHREY (DE FOREST) BOGART

Born 1899. American film actor. Specialised in 'tough' roles. One of his most famous films was *The African Queen*, in which he co-starred with Katherine Hepburn, 1952. Died 1957.

2 He cried at all his own weddings — and with reason.
Lauren Bacall. Quoted Nathaniel Benchley

3 Bogart's a helluva nice guy till 10.30 p.m. After that he thinks he's Bogart.
David Chasen

4 He and I only had one major confrontation. His taste for Scotch was famous: one day when we'd just started *To Have and To Have Not* he got back from lunch unsteady on his feet. I said to him 'Bogie, you're not that good an actor that you can cope when you've got a few drinks in you.' 'Too bad.' he said, 'I like my drink.' 'Right,' I said, 'then either I need a new actor or you need a new director.' He never drank at lunch again.
Howard Hawkes, Radio Times 23 *May* 1974

5 The vanity of some of the old Hollywood stars was incredible, but Bogart didn't care about all that rubbish. 'You can't do much with this mug of mine, Jimmy,' he used to say. 'So you look after the women.'
James Wong Howe, cameraman, Radio Times 23 *May* 1974

6 He was playing Bogart all the time, but he was really just a big sloppy bowl of mush.
Stanley Kramer

7 I don't recall ever having had a long conversation with him, and my strongest impression of him was of a man always on his guard.
Michele Morgan, Radio Times 23 *May* 1974

8 I admired him dearly in so many ways, and so did my husband. He was a rare human being. Very intellectual, very intelligent. I don't think that came across in his screen personality. He was an awful tease. He could really upset people, turn them upside down and make them cry. But it was usually deserved. He came out and said what he felt. He knew phonies, and he hated phonies.
Claire Trevor, Radio Times 14 *Jun* 1973

9 The young man identified on the programme as Humphrey Bogart was not only mediocre. He was terrible.
Alexander Woollcott. Quoted Glyn Roberts, Film Weekly 3 *Jul* 1937

MARGARET GRACE BONDFIELD

Born 1873. British politician and trade unionist. First woman to be a British cabinet minister, as Minister of Labour 1929–31. Died 1933.

10 By 1923 she was the first woman to preside over the General Council of the Trades Union Congress. She would have been the first to preside over its Annual Conference had not her election as an MP been immediately followed by her appointment as Parliamentary Secretary to the Ministry of Labour. In 1929 she was herself Minister of Labour and sworn of the Privy Council, thus making history for her country and her sex.
Mary Agnes Hamilton, John o' London's Weekly 20 *Jan* 1950

11 She is one of those precious characters who care greatly and toil ceaselessly to get things done — and stop there. She does not care a button whether she gets the credit for their doing, providing the job is done.
Ibid.

12 I thought Maggie Bondfield was like a robin redbreast, busy and cheerful, but with nothing much of a song — apt to be a little chirpy.
Naomi Jacob. Me — A Chronicle About Other People 1933

DIETRICH BONHOEFFER

Born 1906. German Lutheran pastor, theologian and author. Led the German church's opposition to Hitler, accused of being involved in the plot to assassinate him, arrested and sent to concentration camp, 1943. Hanged 1945.

13 At the place of execution he again said a short prayer and then climbed the steps to the gallows, brave and composed. In the almost fifty years that I worked as a doctor I have hardly ever seen a man die so submissive to the will of God.
The camp doctor at Flossenburg. Quoted Eberhard Bethge, DIETRICH BONHOEFFER: A BIOGRAPHY 1970

1 When he presented his thesis for doctorate at 21, Karl Barth described it as a miracle.
Lord Longford, Sunday Times 12 *Apr* 1970

2 If he were still alive — and he would only be 64 — he could hardly have exceeded the total impact on Christian feeling to which his martyrdom contributed so largely.
Ibid.

3 Bonhoeffer died on his gibbet when he was 39. His real contribution (to theology) was that only a suffering God can be the answer to our problems. 'Man is challenged to participate in the sufferings of God at the hands of a heartless world.'
Ernest Raymond, GOOD MORNING, GOOD PEOPLE 1970

4 He was hanged, at the same time as his brother-in-law, on April 9. On April 23 his brother and another brother-in-law would be shot; his uncle, the military commandant of Berlin, had been executed earlier. His twin sister lived in exile. All had committed high treason. He himself had volunteered to personally kill Hitler.
Gudrun Tempel, The Times 11 *Apr* 1970

5 The irony of his posthumous reputation is that he has been claimed as the pioneer of that absurdity Theology without God, whereas the great achievement of his prison years was his discovery of God without Theology.
Philip Toynbee, Observer 17 *Nov* 1968

ROBERT BOOTHBY, BARON BOOTHBY OF BUCHAN AND RATTRAY HEAD

Born 1900 in Scotland. British politician, author, radio and television personality. Elected MP for East Aberdeenshire 1924 and held the seat for 34 years until raised to the peerage.

6 He always gave an exciting impression of being on the brink of disaster.
Susan Barnes, Sunday Times Magazine 1 *Apr* 1973

7 I was very precocious. I was very pleased with myself. I thought I was very good looking and I thought I was very clever — and I was.
Lord Boothby, Daily Express 6 *Feb* 1968

8 I was a precocious little boy: and it gave me pleasure to reduce the old girls in the front pews to tears in the solo part of 'Oh for the wings of a dove' and then go back to suck a bullseye.
Lord Boothby, Sunday Times 16 *Sep* 1962

9 Mr R. Boothby is a man who is always about to achieve success.
Tim Heald, Daily Express, quoting an earlier commentator 6 *Feb* 1968

10 My first memory in life was a holiday with the Boothby family. I lost my temper and hurled a toy engine at Bob. Most adults would have said 'Naughty little boy'. Bob picked it up and hurled it back.
Ludovic Kennedy (a younger cousin). Quoted Susan Barnes, Sunday Times Magazine 1 *Apr* 1973

11 When the radio *Any Questions?* team were asked what they would do if they woke up and found they had changed sex, Lord Boothby boomed; *Go for a walk and see what happened.*
Graham Lord, Sunday Express 15 *Oct* 1978

12 He could make the most ridiculous statements sound as if they'd been inscribed on tablets brought down from the mountain. Then if Alan Taylor or Michael Foot confuted him chapter and verse Bob would intone in that booming voice: 'That's right' and the public thought Bob had won.
Edgar Lustgarten, producer of the BBC TV *progamme In the News*

13 You weren't built by God to be a henchman. One day you will disagree with Winston, and when you do he will think it disloyalty. The best thing you can do is to keep your independence always.
Oswald Mosley to Boothby when he became Churchill's PPS 1926

HORATIO BOTTOMLEY

Born 1860. Editor of *John Bull*. Independent MP 1918–22. Convicted of fraudulent conversion, 1922. Died a pauper, 1933.

14 In a few days' time I shall send you the most remarkable article I have ever written, and indeed that has appeared in recent years. Its title is to be *How I Found God* and it tells of a process of spiritual revelation which came to me as I was lying at death's door, and which has continued and developed ever since. It is all gospel truth though many will at first doubt it, but it is only the beginning of a story which cannot be unfolded all at once.
Bottomley, letter to Reginald Pound, features editor of Daily Express

SIR ADRIAN BOULT

1 Whatever his self-deception, whatever his crimes, Bottomley was a tower of strength in the war and had he been less of a gambler, had he been capable of a simplicity of motive, had he been a man of honour, he might — in the turmoil that followed the war — have become a parliamentary dictator.
Daily Express 27 *May* 1933

2 He gambled heavily in the City, on the Stock Exchange, and on the Turf. Time after time he went through the Bankruptcy Court and emerged to carry on his financial ventures. In eight years — between 1903 and 1911 — he disposed of more than 200 bankruptcy petitions.
Ibid.

3 Bottomley had been a Member of Parliament, a newspaper owner, an editor, a journalist, an author, a theatrical impresario, a racehorse owner. He had been twice a millionaire and yet, when his life was nearly ended he sought — and was refused — an old age pension.
Ibid.

4 Here was a man, the record of whose birth is lost in obscurity, who became such a demagogue, who rose to such power that in the first years of the war he was second only to Kitchener in the eyes of the public. The newspapers called the troops 'Kitchener's Army', but he called them 'Bottomley's Boys'.
Ibid.

5 The fall of Bottomley had in it elements that perplexed me. His personality is strong enough even in his senility to suggest he had been wronged, not by society, but by life. You felt that it may all have begun in something infinitely trivial in his boyhood, that some youngster may have stolen his cricket bat and started the ossification of his emotions. Looking into his tired old eyes, it seemed to me impossible that he had ever been criminally callous or that he had *wanted* to rob poor widows. If you are born to be Horatio Bottomley it is difficult to see what you can do about it.
Reginald Pound, THEIR MOODS AND MINE 1937

6 Bottomley's leonine head has been remarked often enough. What hasn't is his extraordinary habit of contracting his nostrils and sniffing — if that isn't a leonine tic, I don't know what is. Absurd to say so, but it was very nearly fascinating. Also, of course, there was his intemperate likeness to Bradlaugh, whose illegitimate son he was said to be.
Ibid.

7 The poor people trusted you, and you robbed them of £150,000 in ten months. The crime is aggravated by your high position, by the number and poverty of your victims, by the trust which they reposed in you.
Mr Justice Slater, sentencing Bottomley to seven years' penal servitude 29*May* 1922

8 A prison visitor found Bottomley sewing mail bags. 'Ah, Bottomley, sewing I see'. 'No,' said Bottomley, 'reaping.'
Julian Symons, HORATIO BOTTOMLEY

9 During the run of a play in which I took part — a dull affair and a failure, I used to notice a rather large man hovering in the wings, and as he seemed on the point of speaking to me I asked who he was. 'Oh, that's one of the backers,' I was told, 'Horatio Bottomley.' When I knew who he was I avoided him carefully, but at a supper given to the company one night we were introduced, and I confess I succumbed at once to his charm and intelligence. He was really a delightful companion, one of his most disarming characteristics being that he always appeared to be saying, 'I'm really a thoroughly untrustworthy blackguard,' which even then I thought to be true.
Ernest Thesiger, PRACTICALLY TRUE 1927

SIR ADRIAN (CEDRIC) BOULT

Born 1889. British conductor, formed BBC Symphony Orchestra 1930 and continued as its principal conductor until 1949, then conducted London Philharmonic Orchestra until 1957. Died 1983.

10 At the end of the BBC Symphony Orchestra's first season Reith said to me, 'Well, they all tell me the orchestra plays better for you than for anyone else. You'd better be the Chief Conductor. Do you want to go on being Director of Music as well?' I said I did, and then began those hectic years of trying to do both jobs — making policy decisions down the telephone in the break between rehearsals.
Sir Adrian Boult. Quoted Nicholas Kenyon, Observer 8 *Apr* 1979

11 I first saw him in the Maida Vale studios when I was 15, and I realised how the music was mirrored by the point of his stick. Most conductors end at the wrists, but he trusts his

fingers almost as an instrumentalist does. I thought, Ah, *that's* how it works.
Vernon Handley. Quoted Paul Jennings, Radio Times 7 *Apr* 1979

1 Peter Beavan tells the charming story of the Walton Violin Concerto. 'Gentlemen, it gets a little complicated here,' said Sir Adrian. 'I'll keep a steady two; you'll have to fish about for yourselves'.
Paul Jennings, Radio Times 7 *Apr* 1979

2 A man on a bus once said to Sir Adrian Boult 'I know you quite well, don't I? I see you often at Lords,' and although Sir Adrian replied that well, he didn't have much time for that, the man went on, 'Oh yes, I know. You are one of the policemen there.'
Ibid.

3 I had written to Sir Adrian Boult, asking him if I could talk to him about the BBC Symphony Orchestra. He was on the telephone at nine the next morning. 'I say, I hope you realise I'm very old. We'd better start immediately.' The precision, self-effacement and wry humour were all absolutely characteristic.
Nicholas Kenyon, Observer 8 *Apr* 1979

4 He has what amounts to a genius for mastering new music however forbidding its idiom. He will soak himself in a music score, usually on a long train journey, until he is certain he has the root of the matter in him. He is gently critical of conductors who rely on getting a first impression of a new work from the preliminary run-through at rehearsal.
Observer, Profile 24 *Jul* 1949

5 Simplicity and economy of gesture are basic to his teaching and to his practice. The conductor is not there to be watched by the audience. It is the players who must do the watching, an audience should be all ears. (As a concert-goer, Sir Adrian habitually leans back and closes his eyes.)
Ibid.

6 Boult has never encouraged any exploitation of his personality. The music's the thing. Personal triumphs are at best an irrelevancy and in any case he often finds applause aesthetically inept. He considers the great 'sunsets' of music (e.g. the end of Brahms' Third Symphony, or of Elgar's *Falstaff*) should be followed by at least two minutes' silence. It is for this reason that he is fond of conducting in cathedrals.
Ibid.

7 He is the apotheosis of the music-making that demands to be heard and need not be seen.
C. B. Rees, Radio Times 1 *Nov* 1946

BRENDAN BRACKEN

Born 1901 in Ireland. British politician. Entered Parliament as the member for Paddington 1929. Parliamentary Private Secretary to Winston Churchill. Youngest man ever to be appointed Privy Councillor, 1940. Minister of Information 1941.

8 A good name, with its br br suggesting partly a Bren gun and the plant that grows wildly on the moors. An unfailing joke in Parliament. I remember the Duchess of Atholl once asking what steps the Minister of Agriculture was taking to 'reduce bracken'. His reply was that the committee appointed to control the spread of bracken (laughter) by improved methods of cutting (ha ha) and of spraying (No!) had failed to decide on the appropriate method (Shame!) and would renew their experiments in the coming year (Hear! Hear!).
William Barkley, Daily Express 21 *Jul* 1941

9 Brendan Bracken, bombastic, imaginative and kindly, with his teeth blacker than ever and his red hair greying.
Sir Henry Channon, DIARY 20 *Apr* 1942

10 The 1922 Committee was addressed by Brendan Bracken, the kind-hearted, garrulous, red-headed gargoyle, whom I have always considered a fraud, au fond; he is an indifferent Minister, promising all and doing little — inoperative, in fact, and prejudiced.
Ibid. 3 *Feb* 1943

11 Brendan Bracken was part of our life at Chartwell. Sunday become known as 'Brendan Day'. A red-haired Irishman, of booming character and voice, he would instil and embrace all with his warm-hearted energy. He talked like a fountain without pause, a considerable achievement in our household.
Sarah Churchill. Quoted Charles Edward Lysaght, BRENDAN BRACKEN 1979

12 Though I never till then hated anybody I took on sight such a loathing to this man and felt such nausea, that my instinct was to put as much of the country between him and me as my legs could manage.
David Green, one of his pupils when he was a master at Sedbergh. Quoted Andrew Boyle, POOR DEAR BRENDAN 1974

1 In the midst of a by-election Clemmie Churchill heard that Brendan was putting about the story that he was Winston's son. She rang Winston in exasperation. 'I do not think Brendan is my son, but I suppose he could be,' he teased. 'I shall, however examine the matter and let you know the result of my enquiries.'
Charles Edward Lysaght, BRENDAN BRACKEN 1979

2 A journalist told him 'I don't believe a word you say, Brendan. Everything about you is phoney. Even your hair, which looks like a wig, isn't.' Unwittingly the journalist got him just right. He liked to pretend he was a sham, whereas in everything important he was real. Much of the play-acting was conducted solely for his own satisfaction.
A. J. P. Taylor, Observer 11 *Sep* 1979

DON (SIR DONALD GEORGE) BRADMAN

Born 1908. Australian cricketer. Played for Australia 1928–48, was captain from 1936.

3 [Don Bradman] was enclosed in a legend that grew bigger daily, like a gigantic indestructible crystal.
Philip Larkin, REQUIRED READING 1983

4 He began, reasonably enough, with only 131 in the first Test at Nottingham, in 1930. He followed with 254 at Lords, 334 (a new record) at Leeds, and 232 in the deciding match at the Oval. He had set a new standard of arithmetic. Once, batsmen, even in Test matches, had tended to depart, decently or with a flourish somewhere between the first and second century. But Bradman batted on.
Observer, Profile 1 *Dec* 1946

5 To the connoisseur the most exquisite duel in cricket was between Bradman and the left-handed Verity; the back-chatting urchin versus the Professor of Logic. Don against don. The last time it was fought was in 1938 between the Australians and Yorkshire at smoky Bramall Lane. The pitch varied from the sportive to the cantankerous. Verity used every trick of spin and flight; stuff that might have won two matches in a day, and Bradman played him for over after over in the middle of the bat.
Ibid.

6 The Don was playing his final Test match innings. He was given a rapturous welcome by the spectators and treated to three cheers by the English players. He was promptly bowled by Eric Hollies for a duck, which reduced his overall Test average to just under 100.
E. M. Wellings, VINTAGE CRICKETERS 1983

7 I never played cricket with the Don, but I did play golf with him, and that gave me a clue to his make-up. During the 1965 tour we were spending Christmas in Adelaide. The English players and press arranged a Christmas Day golf competition among themselves and we invited Bradman to join us. It was a light-hearted affair. Denis Compton was his partner. But he played the round with the utmost seriousness, and was, of course, the winner. To the Don the least important event had considerable significance. He was incapable of not taking it very seriously. He strove to do well on that trivial Christmas afternoon outing as if playing in a Test match.
Ibid.

8 His batting produced a most favourable impression among the onlookers. Though he is not polished by any means he makes most of his scoring strokes correctly, and bats with plenty of freedom. He gets across to the ball nicely and watches it well. His footwork is exact but clumsy, but with a little tuition he should develop into a batsman of class. Too much must not be expected of him for the present.
A Sydney journalist reporting Bradman's first appearance for New South Wales 1926

(EULEN FRIEDRICH) BERTOLT BRECHT

Born 1898. German dramatist, best known for his Marxist dramas *The Threepenny Opera* 1928, *Mother Courage and Her Children* 1939, and *The Caucasian Chalk Circle* 1945. Died 1956.

9 Brecht spoke for the eternal little man, for the underdog, and only when all dogs are permanently equal will his work lose its force.
D. J. Enright, Observer 12 *Feb* 1984

10 I think Brecht was a great lyric poet, but a second-rate dramatist.
Ibid.

11 Incidents drawn from his schooldays suggest that he sprang fully armed from his mother's womb. In discussing the romantic theme, 'What draws us to mountain peaks?' he was practical and succint: 'Funicular railways.'
Ronald Hayman, BRECHT: A BIOGRAPHY 1983

1 Where conventional theatre tries to unite the audience into an emotional unity Brecht seeks to divide it, by forcing its members to react as individuals.
Kenneth Tynan, Observer 31 *May* 1964

2 He envisages a theatre as a sort of public laboratory where artists build working models of human behaviour to find out its causes and effects, just as scientists use models to study the behaviour of molecules.
Ibid.

3 In 1927 he absorbs Marx and announces: 'When I read *Das Kapital* I understood my plays.'
Ibid.

4 The great Marxist magpie who brought science, poetry, politics, music, economics, dance and sociology to the service of his art, and compelled us by his example to redefine the form and function of twentieth-century drama.
Ibid.

5 Not the least remarkable aspect of his prodigious output is that it welled rather than slackened during the Hitler years when he was exiled and virtually unperformed.
Ibid.

LEONID (ILYICH) BREZHNEV

Born 1906. Soviet leader. President of USSR 1960 until he succeeded Khrushchev as First Secretary in 1964. Formally recognised as head of state after changes in the Soviet Constitution, 1974. Died 1982.

6 He is eagerly gallant with women, kissing as many hands as he can grab . . . One woman who had some contact with him said he had all the charm of a St Bernard.
William Shawcross, Sunday Times 31 *Oct* 1971

7 He has come a long way since 1966 when De Gaulle met him in Moscow. In answer to some suggestions by De Gaulle on Berlin Brezhnev had then replied simply by reading from a previously prepared paper. When De Gaulle tried to comment Brezhnev, unable to conduct any sort of dialogue, just picked up the paper and began to read it through again. 'I heard you the first time,' said De Gaulle.
Ibid.

ROBERT (SEYMOUR) BRIDGES

Born 1844. English poet. His *Testament of Beauty* attracted adverse criticism for its experimental spelling. Appointed Poet Laureate 1913. Died 1930.

8 Bridge's anthology *The Spirit of Man* is vomit after a rich meal.
A. C. Benson. Quoted Geoffrey Madan, NOTEBOOKS 1981

9 In his lifetime Robert Bridges was described by a friend as being 'Somewhat shy, somewhat austere, fastidious, difficult'. He was also a man of fortune and culture, educated at Eton and Oxford, at one time a physician, a scholar and experimentalist in technique, a grammarian and exponent of something called 'Pure English', and finally a poet. I mention all his other qualifications because I believe them to be handicaps to a poet. I think they were handicaps to Bridges.
Frank Swinnerton, THE GEORGIAN LITERARY SCENE 1935

10 Doctor Bridges dwelt in the rarefied air of Oxford; and as he seemed to make no effort to come down, as it were, to us, we made no effort to go to him.
Wilfred Whitten, John o' London's Weekly 27 *May* 1938

(EDWARD) BENJAMIN BRITTEN, BARON BRITTEN OF ALDEBURGH

Born 1913. English composer of mainly operatic and vocal music. Among his main works are *Peter Grimes, Billy Budd* and *The Young Person's Guide to the Orchestra*. Died 1976.

11 'My only complaint with the work (Peter Grimes)' I said, 'is that you never give one a second chance to hear some of the melodies again. Verdi isn't so spiteful.'
Ronald Duncan, The Times 8 *Jun* 1968

12 He is not the least concerned to write music that expresses his personality. His sole concern is to write music that shall be apt and engrossing in its own terms.
Observer, Profile 27 *Oct* 1946

13 Britten's primary workshop is his head, which remains as unflurried and as active as a gyroscope amid the comings and goings of an agitated physical existence. He is perpetually rushing off to catch trains. The business of musical creation goes on serenely among the bustle and the baggage. Looking unseeing through train windows he composes as fluently as if he were sitting in

a sound-proofed cell with piles of manuscript paper before him and a grand piano at his elbow.
Ibid.

1 Unlike many contemporaries, he never writes paper music; everything has first been vividly heard by an inner ear of amazing acuteness. This faculty explains the speed at which he composes. The processes of trial and error take place mostly in the head.
Desmond Shaw-Taylor, Sunday Times 17 *Nov* 1963

RUPERT (CHAWNER) BROOKE

Born 1887. English romantic poet. Died on Dardanelles campaign 1915.

2 As I was driving Cathleen Nesbitt to the station I asked her whether she would have married Rupert Brooke. 'Yes, I suppose we would have married had it not been for the war. I only knew him for three years and during two of those he was in America. When he was studying for some Naval Reserve course at Dartmouth, I went down there to see him and sometimes he came to see me when I was touring. We read poetry to one another. I read Donne to him, he read his poems to me.'
Cecil Beaton, DIARY 1970

3 His life has closed at the moment when it seemed to have reached its springtime.
Winston Churchill

4 We must look upon the death of Rupert Brooke as the passing away of a charming and gay young spirit. To talk of a severe loss to English poetry is all sentimental cant and humbug. There is not the least sign in the work of Rupert Brooke to justify us saying he would have become the first poet of his age.
W. H. Davies

5 Leonard Woolf, meeting him at the age of twenty-two, thought to himself, 'This is exactly how Adonis must have looked in the eyes of Aphrodite.'
Christopher Hassall, RUPERT BROOKE 1964

6 Splendid Rupert, to be the soldier that could beget them on the Muse, and lucky Muse, no less, which could have an affair with a soldier and yet not feel herself guilty of the least deviation.
Henry James, LETTERS 28 *Mar* 1915

7 My friendship with Rupert Brooke was certainly one of the most memorable things in my life. In his combination of gifts, of body, character, mind and spirit, he was nearer completeness and perfection than anyone I have known; intellect and goodness, humour and sympathy, beauty of person and kindness of heart, distinction of taste and 'the common touch', ambition and modesty, he had them all: and there is no telling what he might have done, had he lived.
Edward Marsh, A NUMBER OF PEOPLE 1939

8 A poet who flings himself with his full force and passion, and with a wild unscrupulous gaiety, into and out of each mood that offers. Mr Brooke can write in every tone, reverent, gross, grim, cynical or tender. Now he sees the fullness, now the hollowness of life. He is several kinds of philosopher, and *enfant terrible*.
Edward Marsh, POETRY REVIEW *Apr* 1912

9 The legend lingers on, but his gifts are now generally under-rated or forgotten except by readers under eighteen or over fifty.
Raymond Mortimer, Sunday Times 10 *May* 1964

10 One of his closest friends said to me, when the legend was at its height, 'Rupert wasn't nearly so nice as people now imagine; but he was a great deal cleverer.'
Ibid.

11 He was a hypochondriac who fainted under stress and took to his bed at the slightest sniffle. He was a bit of a sponger, always ready to exploit his youth and good looks; a Narcissus who was proud even of the prehensile qualities of his feet and who surprised a photographer by suddenly stripping to the waist during a portrait session so that the lens might not miss his torso.
Robert Pitman, Sunday Express 10 *May* 1964

12 Rupert Brooke, whom I knew fairly well, was beautiful and vital, but the impression was marred by a touch of Byronic insincerity and by a certain flamboyance.
Bertrand Russell, UNPOPULAR ESSAYS, *Eminent Men I Have Known* 1950

13 Brooke is so handsome that I find myself staring.
Edward Thomas

14 *The Sphere* pronounced him the only considerable English poet to have died for his country since Philip Sidney at Zutphen. Which, since Brooke died of a gnat bite, was piling it on somewhat.
Christopher Wordsworth, Observer 1 *Oct* 1967

1 People do not buy Rupert Brooke because they feel they ought to have such a book in the house, as they ought to have Shakespeare. They buy him because his poems give them pleasure, which some modern critics would consider a poor excuse.
H. D. Ziman, Daily Telegraph 8 *May* 1964

GEORGE (ALFRED) BROWN, BARON GEORGE-BROWN

Born 1914. British politician. Deputy leader of the Labour Party 1960–8. Foreign Minister 1966–8. Died 1985.

2 George Brown's flight in and around and through British politics has been gay and erratic as a parakeet's.
Michael Hilton, Daily Telegraph 29 *Mar* 1971

3 A major factor in George Brown's career as deputy leader was his relationship with Harold Wilson. For much of his period in the Labour Government the Prime Minister and his most senior Cabinet colleague nursed a near total contempt for each other.
Richard Marsh, The Times 29 *Mar* 1971

4 No one who ever knew George Brown could possibly regard Jekyll and Hyde as more than a pair of well-meaning amateurs. At his best he is brilliant, at his worst he is unbearable.
Ibid.

5 George Brown is one of the most outrageous, impossible yet strangely attractive personalities in British public life. I have seen highly intelligent civil servants reduced to a neurotic hatred of the man, and heard the same men extolling his virtues for hour after endless hour.
Ibid.

6 Life with Brown is apt to be a succession of blazing rows, never mild tiffs or cold disagreements, but always followed, on his part at least, by reconciliation and the accolade of being addressed as 'Brother'.
Observer, Profile 18 *Dec* 1960

7 At the Labour Party dinner for Bulganin and Khrushchev at the House of Commons in 1956 Khrushchev's rambling, unscripted speech included the phrase: 'You threw the Germans at our throats.' Brown, filling his pipe, said softly, 'May God forgive you.' There was a shocked silence. Khrushchev asked him to repeat the words. Brown hesitated and Khrushchev taunted him with lacking the courage to say it again. Brown thereupon said loudly: 'It doesn't require any courage. I said "May God forgive you"' and went on to lecture Khrushchev about the Ribbentrop agreement, and the number of Brown's friends killed before Russia was attacked . . . 'It was,' Brown disarmingly explains, 'the kind of thing you would do at a branch meeting.'
Ibid.

JOHN BUCHAN, FIRST BARON TWEEDSMUIR

Born 1875 in Scotland. Novelist, biographer, politician, Governor-General of Canada 1935–40. His best-known works include *The Thirty-Nine Steps*, 1915 and *Greenmantle* 1916. Died 1940.

8 He was a romantic Tory who thought Toryism better than it was.
Clement Attlee. Quoted Janet Adam Smith, JOHN BUCHAN 1965

9 One of the main reasons for enjoying Buchan is because he is so preposterous. The tuppence-coloured rhetoric and the bluff characterisation are an essential part of the appeal.
John Gross, Observer 19 *Sep* 1965

10 There is something which faintly repels about his commitment to the ethic of success, something watchful and thin-lipped.
Ibid.

11 He was entirely too self-contained for the rough and tumble of the Parliamentary arena and the cadences of his oratory were liturgical rather than combative.
Thomas Jones, Observer 24 *Aug* 1947

12 His world is a clean-cut public school one of cold baths, stiff upper lips and sexless living.
Allan Massie, Observer 9 *May* 1962

13 His mind ranges widely, his talk moves smoothly, a bit pedantically, from one topic to another. Voice not unlike Sir Samuel Hoare's. 'I was with Milner, you know, in South Africa.' 'I was badly shaken up in the war.' . . . Buchan is first-rate company, but in an undefinable way he puts an edge on one's class consciousness.
Reginald Pound, THEIR MOODS AND MINE 1937

14 He seems to like to bring Dukes into his talk. 'I went deer-stalking with the Duke of

Sutherland' could just as well have been 'I went stalking with a friend.'
Ibid.

1 John Buchan came to lunch with me, our first meeting. He isn't so explicitly Scots as I had imagined, though there is a tightness of the mouth. One eye droops. A little more robust and thick-set and he would be Cromwell.
Ibid.

RICHARD BURTON

Born 1925 in Wales. Stage and film actor. First attracted attention by his performances in plays by Christopher Fry 1949–50, and added to his reputation in Shakespearean roles 1952–4. After a highly successful period in films his career went into a decline in the 1970s, when his private life began to draw more attention than his acting. Died 1984.

2 There has been an element of the defrocked saint in most of his best work. At Stratford a fellow actor described him as 'bringing his own cathedral on with him'. That is apt and impressive and also a tribute to the transforming powers of art and ambition. For Burton himself, of course, was strictly chapel.
Robert Cushman, Observer, Burton's farewell 12 *Aug* 1984

3 He was the greatest actor of the postwar generation. But there was a lot about being an actor which a part of him despised. He was certainly not a dedicated actor in the way that some are. The key to Burton was that he was following a career that he was brilliant at, but which he felt would never gain him respect from the people of his own origins. When he was looking back on his career he would say that he should have been an academic at Oxford.
James Fenton, The Times 6 *Aug* 1984

4 'I get increasingly disenchanted with acting,' he told a friend in London in 1972. 'I'll be 47 in November. As the years totter past I find it ludicrous, learning some idiot's lines in the small hours of the night so that I can stay a millionaire.'
Paul Ferris, RICHARD BURTON 1981

5 The head has the imperiousness of a Roman emperor's bust. The wide-set eyes penetrate, perhaps intimidate. Some of this may have been learned; most of it is an accident of birth. All of it has been worked on.
Ibid.

6 He was a born actor but a bit wild and chose a rather mad way of throwing away his theatre career.
Sir John Gielgud, The Times 6 *Aug* 1984

7 I think Richard a great figure. There was something enormously aristocratic about his attitude. When one met his brothers there was something extraordinary about *them*, too. None of them was the cavalry leader that Richard was, but they all had amazing dignity.
Robert Hardy. Quoted Paul Ferris, RICHARD BURTON 1981

8 His career veered crazily — between great peaks — in the early 1950s he was regarded by many as the finest Shakespearean actor of his generation — and troughs. His various marital breakdowns coincided with several lapses into alcoholism.
Rupert Morris, The Times 6 *Aug* 1984

9 Emlyn Williams remembers Burton aged 17 auditioning for a part in one of his plays. 'We spoke Welsh when we first met, and he had to speak some Welsh in my play. I remember asking him what his last part had been at school and he said it was Professor Higgins in *Pygmalion*. I was amused to think of someone obviously Welsh in that part.'
Ibid.

10 What he achieved was both moving and powerful; it promised an unachieved greatness which must always be lamented.
The Times, Obituary, 6 *Aug* 1984

11 A shrewd Welsh boy shines out with greatness.
Kenneth Tynan. Quoted Paul Ferris, RICHARD BURTON 1981

SIR MATT BUSBY

Born 1910, in Scotland. International footballer, who played for Manchester City and Liverpool. Became manager of Manchester United, creating the successful side, known as 'Busby's Babes', which was almost wiped out in the Munich air crash of 1958; he immediately set about rebuilding it, with great success.

12 At Munich, where eight of United's players died in the snow, and a gifted ninth, Jackie Blanchflower, was put out of football for ever, Busby himself came near to death. That he should have recovered was itself a tribute to his will power and constitution.

That he should have survived to build another team capable of bestriding English football was almost unbelievable.
Brian Glanville

1 In 20 years he built the club to world proportion. In that period Manchester United's impact on the crowds who follow the game was equivalent to that of the Beatles on the pop scene.
Geoffrey Green

2 In public, after a defeat, Busby is immaculately good-mannered with the stiffest of upper lips. In private, though, he is said to have wept at big disappointments.
Observer, Profile 27 *Apr* 1958

3 At Old Trafford they call him 'The Boss'. You ask the players in the dressing room 'Where's Matt?' and they look at you reprovingly and say, 'You mean the Boss.'
Michael Parkinson, Sunday Times 26 *Nov* 1967

4 Matt Busby is a symbol of everything that is best in our great national game.
Harold Wilson

RAB (RICHARD AUSTEN) BUTLER, BARON BUTLER OF SAFFRON WALDEN

Born 1902. British politician. Minister of Education 1941–5. Chancellor of the Exchequer 1951–7. Foreign Secretary 1963–4. Died 1984.

5 Rab Butler is a scholarly dry-stick but an extremely able, cautious, canny man. I must cultivate him.
Sir Henry Channon, DIARY 26 *Feb* 1938

6 Rab is fundamentally male, endowed with great intelligence and judgement and even some charm; but the lighter graces are certainly not his; he has no superficiality, no social sense.
Ibid. 27 *Sep* 1938

7 Rab dined at No. 10 with the PM to meet Sumner Welles and I helped to dress him for the occasion at the office. He is completely devoid of any personal vanity and dressed 'dry' in 10 minutes, and, I must add, looks it. He has no time or use for the frivolities of life; with such a brain he does not need them.
Ibid. 12 *Mar* 1940

8 I went to the House of Commons and listened to Rab make a shrewd speech to the 1922 Committee. He was clear, concise and convincing about his Education Bill. It has made him known to the country as a whole, and may well make him Prime Minister one day.
Ibid. 2 *Feb* 1944

9 In spite of having a legion of admirers Butler has always managed to raise doubt, suspicion and dislike wherever he has gone.
Patrick Cosgrave, R. A. BUTLER: AN ENGLISH LIFE 1981

10 He is unwilling to be decisive about anything. Did he really have to go to a National Day cocktail party at the Moroccan Embassy? I assured him three times that it was unnecessary before he left the office. When he got home Rab rang for another reassurance that there was no need for him to go. The next morning we asked him whether, as a matter of courtesy, he ought not to write to the Moroccan Ambassador to apologise for unavoidable absence the night before. 'Oh, I went' he said.
Nicholas Henderson, THE PRIVATE OFFICE 1984

11 I think I learned more in one year from Rab about political life than I did from anyone else I have served, however long.
Ibid.

12 His great failing is that he likes to be a don among politicians and a politician among dons.
Ian Macleod. Quoted Patrick Cosgrave, R. A. BUTLER, AN ENGLISH LIFE

13 He lacked the dash, the vulgarity, and the smoking-room popularity which have often been important characteristics of Tory leaders. Like oysters or gulls' eggs, he was an acquired taste.
Christopher Patten, The Times 23 Apr 1981

14 The greatest of the Might-Have-Beens.
Enoch Powell, Daily Telegraph 12 *Jul* 1971

C

(LEONARD) JAMES CALLAGHAN

Born 1912. British politician. Chancellor of the Exchequer 1964–7. Foreign Secretary 1974–6. Succeeded Harold Wilson as Prime Minister 1976.

1 He has always enjoyed the role of international statesman. Sometimes, indeed, he has enjoyed it too much. It was his confidence after a particularly good international summit in Guadalupe early in 1979 that made him make the celebrated and uncharacteristic faux pas on returning to a strike-paralysed Britain: 'Crisis? What crisis?'
Ian Bradley, The Times 16 *Oct* 1980

2 As one ex-colleague puts it 'he epitomises the decency of social democracy, perhaps slightly dull, but standing essentially for social cohesion, for justice, for stability'. His image in public life of the benign, matter-of-fact avuncular figure, is on the whole a true representation of his character.
Ibid.

3 In Barbara Castle's diaries he is cast as a snake-in-the-grass, disloyally manoeuvring for his own advantage. His friends, however, maintain that Mr Callaghan opposed *In Place of Strife*'s proposals because he did not believe that legal restraints were the way to deal with trade union power.
Ibid.

4 To his critics Mr Callaghan's career has been an example of mediocrity triumphing through opportunism. While no intellectual he has been a wily political operator and tactician. As one ex-colleague put it, 'If Mr Hugh Gaitskell's motto was "Fight, fight and fight again", then Jim's is manoeuvre, manoeuvre and manoeuvre again.'
Ibid.

5 When I am shaving in the morning I say to myself that if I were a young man I would emigrate. By the time I am sitting down to breakfast I ask myself 'Where would I go?'
James Callaghan, at a Cabinet meeting. Quoted Barbara Castle, THE CASTLE DIARIES 1974-76 1980

6 I would like to have built St Paul's Cathedral. I would like to have written Beethoven's symphonies. I would like to have been Mervyn Davies and captained Wales as a rugby forward.
Callaghan to Kenneth Harris, Observer 3 *Dec* 1976

7 I like a simple game of chess or Scrabble. I love reading biographies, and seeing how other people handled some of the problems similar to mine.
Ibid.

8 I think Jim Callaghan is the most disloyal and damaging member of the whole Government. Frankly, I believe he is capable of anything.
Barbara Castle, THE CASTLE DIARIES 1964–70 1980

9 He was one of the best Prime Ministers we have had since the war but he was certainly the worst Chancellor of the Exchequer we have had in the same period.
Len Murray, The Times 2 *Sep* 1984

MRS PATRICK (BEATRICE STELLA) CAMPBELL

Born 1865 née Tanner. English actress. Among many famous performances she created the role of Eliza Doolittle in Shaw's *Pygmalion*. Died 1940.

10 I attribute this great player's failure to stay the course to the fact that she came to resemble the things she said. To them she sacrificed her material, her art, and finally herself. Gloriously witty things burned her mouth as money burns my pocket.
James Agate, EGO 4 1940

11 In appearance Mrs Campbell seems a prototype of a stage duchess. But after the hot lights had played on her face for a while, she began to disintegrate. There was something ghastly about her dirty white gloves, her fallen chins and the tragic impediments of age. She began to bellow like a sick cow, throwing her hands to the skies. 'Oh why must I look like a burst paper bag? Why must I have these dewlaps? Why can't I be a beauty?'
Cecil Beaton, DIARY 1938

1 Mrs Pat is a great woman, triumphing over the sordid difficulties of poverty and age by a resolute sense of beauty and poetry. For today's sitting she wore black velvet and artificial pearls. She brought with her the white pekinese dog to which she is so inordinately devoted that she will not return to England (because of it having to remain in quarantine).
Ibid.

2 After a dull weekend Mrs Patrick Campbell took pen in hand and wrote in the hostess's elaborate visitors' book, 'Quoth the raven'.
Bennett Cerf, SHAKE WELL BEFORE USING 1948

3 A taxicab driver once demurred at transporting her and a disagreeable pooch named 'Moonbeam', but she swept into the vehicle commanding, 'The Empire Theatre, my man, and no nonsense.' The dog, never housebroken, misbehaved en route, and the driver gave Mrs Campbell a furious I-told-you-so look as she descended. 'Don't blame Moonbeam,' she informed him loftily. '*I* did it.'
Ibid.

4 *Pygmalion* may cause a sensation. Mr Shaw introduces a certain forbidden word. It is a word which the *Daily Sketch* cannot possibly print. And this evening the most respectable audience in London is to hear this appalling word fall with bombshell suddenness from Mrs Pat's lips.
Daily Sketch 11 *Apr* 1914

5 She thrived in a period when fashion and art treated women extremely well. Hairstyles were glorious, throat and neck were liable to cause sensation, glimpses of ankles made men deliciously uncomfortable and a crowd could gasp as Mrs Campbell climbed into a carriage wearing pink stockings from one of her plays. (They thought they had just seen her bare legs.)
James Fenton, The Times, reviewing Margot Peters' LIFE OF MRS PATRICK CAMPBELL 2 *Aug* 1984

6 The year 1928 was the centenary of Ibsen's birth, and I was asked to play in a revival of *Ghosts* with Mrs Patrick Campbell. I had seen her years before on tour in Croydon in *Mrs Tanqueray* and she had a tremendous effect on me, although she was fat and middle aged. I saw her again in *Pygmalion* with my aunt Marion as Mrs Higgins. She could sulk on the stage in a way that was perfect for Eliza Doolittle and for Hedda Gabler as well. She could be beguiling, sensual, wayward, petulant, and disagreeable, yet manage to be glamorous at the same time.
John Gielgud, AN ACTOR AND HIS TIME 1979

7 When I was playing Hamlet in New York I asked my director to invite her to the party after the performance and she behaved with appalling tactlessness. She went up to Judith Anderson, who was playing the Queen, and said 'Why do you sit on the bed? Only housemaids sit on the bed.'
Ibid.

8 I was in New York with her the day Edward VIII abdicated. We had just seen Charles Laughton in the film *Rembrandt*. When we came out the famous abdication speech from Fort Belvedere was being broadcast. We went into the Plaza Hotel to hear it. Mrs Campbell burst into tears and said 'Let's send him a telegram.' I suggested as we did not know the ex-King and in any case he would have left Fort Belvedere by this time, it was not a good idea. 'Oh yes, we must, we must' she said. So we rushed to a post office. She said to the clerk, 'Isn't it wonderful? The greatest thing since Anthony gave up his kingdom for Cleopatra.' The woman took a piece of gum out of her mouth and replied, 'Oh I guess he just wanted to go play ball.' I finally persuaded her to send a telegram to Charles Laughton instead, saying how much we had enjoyed his film.
Ibid.

9 I once took months trying to find a play for her and thought I had succeeded. The part was tailor-made for her, an ex-opera singer who took pupils in a mountain chalet. In the third act there was a scene in which her daughter was being stoned because she had had an affair with a peasant and went into a church for refuge. She put on the Madonna's robe and apron and the peasants thought she was the Mother of God come to life and knelt down and worshipped her. In the next act the daughter returned home and her mother had to say 'I salute my genius in you', and fall on her knees. I thought this would be the most marvellous scene for Mrs Campbell but she only said sulkily 'I suppose you want me to play the daughter.' She was then about seventy and extremely fat. It was preposterous, but typical of the way she cut the ground from under your feet, so you could not help her or advise her.
Ibid.

10 She could be wise and even affectionate, and why she had to be so ill-behaved, sometimes even common and rude, it was difficult to tell. A kind of demon seized her and she

MRS PATRICK CAMPBELL

could not resist being unkind to people, making cheap jokes at their expense. Yet she could also be witty, very lady-like and gracious.
Ibid.

1 It was agreed that Shaw should call on Mrs Campbell (for whom he had written *Pygmalion*) to talk things over. Before entering the room in which she received him he felt calm, business-like, hard as nails, insolently confident of his superiority to 'a dozen Delilahs'. But nobody could resist Mrs Campbell when she was out to capture. To his astonishment he presently found himself head over ears in love with her, 'and dreamed and dreamed and walked on air all the afternoon and the next day as if my next birthday were my twentieth'. Business was banished from his mind.
Hesketh Pearson, BERNARD SHAW 1942

2 Her second marriage was a failure. To love Stella was inevitable, to live with her was impossible.
Ibid.

3 When Mrs Campbell was duly married again she wrote her memoirs and promised the publisher such an incomparable collection of love-letters — from a well-known duke, from a famous painter with illustrations, from James Barrie, from Shaw and hosts of others whom she had enchanted — that he advanced £2000 on it. But she had reckoned without the Copyright Act. The executors of the letter-writers absolutely refused to authorise such an exhibition of infatuation. Mrs Campbell was left with nobody to extricate her but Shaw and Barrie. They had to allow her a few edited samples and thus save the situation for her.
Ibid.

4 Mrs Campbell did not know how to use the front of the stage, at which Shaw was an adept. She wanted too much limelight on the front of her face, not knowing she was making it look, as Shaw said, like a dinner plate with two prunes on it, instead of the beautifully modelled head it actually was.
Ibid.

5 I could think of nothing but a thousand scenes of which she was the heroine and I was the hero. And I am on the verge of 56. There never has been anything so ridiculous, or so delightful, in the history of the world. On Friday we were together for an hour; we visited a lord; we drove in a taxi; we sat on a sofa in Kensington Square; and my years fell from me like a garment. I was in love for nearly 35 hours; and for that may all her sins be forgiven her.
G. B. Shaw. Quoted Hesketh Pearson, BERNARD SHAW 1942

6 If Mrs Campbell hardly ever said a kind thing, she never failed to do one. Once when she came to tea with my sister [Edith] in her flat in Bayswater Mrs Campbell made a great disturbance about not being given a silver teaspoon. 'Why haven't I got one?' she kept on enquiring. 'Because I am poor and can't afford it', my sister said at last. This quieted Mrs Campbell, who herself was earning little money at the moment. But when a few months later she scored a great success in a long run in *The Thirteenth Chair*, one of the first things she did in her new affluence was to send my sister a dozen silver teaspoons.
Osbert Sitwell, LAUGHTER IN THE NEXT ROOM 1949

7 My witty, bubble-pricking friend Mrs Patrick Campbell materialised in the deck chair next to mine with a little the air of a luminous-faced seal. Since the ocean had undoubtedly tamed her inexhaustible mischief, she sat very low in her chair and, turning her lustrous eyes on me, so as to watch every expression on my face, contented herself with narrating to me in considerable detail the plot of a play she was determined I should write for her. It was a very, very long play about a noble scientist who had discovered something or other — I never could quite make out what; nor, I think, could she.
Ibid.

8 What she most enjoyed in conversation was to see how far she could go, like a child playing Tom Tiddler's Ground, without being caught — without being hurt. Sometimes, however, she hurt others in the process. One had to know how to treat her, and the technique to apply was one of surprise, best obtained by agreeing with her in a manner she would not expect. Thus, when she said to a friend of mine, looking at her earnestly, 'Norah, were your eyes *always* so far apart as that?' she received the reply, 'No, Stella, didn't you know? They had to be *dragged* apart.'
Ibid.

9 One night, when she went to the stage door to see whether her conveyance had arrived she found a small knot of people hanging round the entrance. 'There are thousands of people waiting to see me come out,' she exclaimed excitedly, and settling her hat at a more becoming angle, and draping her

cloak carefully, she posed by the carriage door so that everyone could see her well, and then said to me in deep stagey tones, 'You get in first.' I replied in a high cockney voice, 'Ow now, you get hin first, Hauntie', and this time it was the great actress who was deflated.
Ernest Thesiger, PRACTICALLY TRUE 1927

1 One day we were at tea and a servant came in to say that Herbert Trench was waiting downstairs. He had just taken the Haymarket Theatre and was full of his own importance. He had also written a poem called *Apollo and the Seaman*, which had been set to music by Joseph Holbrook. When admitted he showed quite plainly that he considered it an affront to have been kept waiting. So Mrs Campbell said in her sweetest voice, 'Oh Mr Trench I am so sorry to have kept you downstairs, but I thought you were a newspaper reporter. Now I must make amends and introduce you to all my interesting friends' — she named us all — 'and this,' she exclaimed, pointing to the infuriated poet with a magnificent gesture, 'is Mr Herbert Trench who wrote the beautiful music for that appalling poem, *Apollo and the Seaman*.'
Ibid.

2 Her opening lines [in *Electra*] I shall never forget, 'Alone, alone, always alone', and each time the word 'alone' was prolonged into a deep booming note — like a foghorn preceding a shipwreck, though that sounds less complimentary than it is meant to be.
Ibid.

3 I wept solidly through the play [*Electra*] — not excepting the one moment, when, taking advantage of a long speech from Orestes, Electra walked to the side of the stage and snatching a glass of stout that appeared miraculously from the wings, gulped it down in full view of the audience.
Ibid.

ROY (DUNACHIE) CAMPBELL

Born 1901 in South Africa. Poet whose work emphasised aggressive masculinity. Fought in the Spanish Civil War on Franco's side. Died 1957.

4 Campbell's extraordinary life as a man of action led him to earn his living as a Provençal jouster and bullfighter; his literary targets were the more easily wounded members of the Bloomsbury group.
Alan Bold, MAKERS OF MODERN CULTURE (*Edited by Justin Wintle*) 1981

5 In 1918 he fell under the influence of Wyndham Lewis whose argumentative style and provocative manner he adopted. In Campbell's case the aggression was not confined to books and he became known as a hell-raiser who was as quick with his fists as he was with his wits. Campbell, who fancied himself as a skilful boxer, played the tough-guy role to perfection.
Ibid.

6 We would always try to persuade him, when he came to see us, to say a few words in Zulu for the clicking sounds were fascinating and required a true virtuosity to render them.
Osbert Sitwell, LAUGHTER IN THE NEXT ROOM 1949

7 Roy Campbell, then eighteen or nineteen years old and only lately arrived at Oxford from South Africa, exhibited in his appearance a curious mixture of strength and delicacy. He also was inclined to be rather silent at first, but the unusual intensity of his appearance, his pallor, the clearness of his eyes and gaze, and their suggestion of tautness and of an interior life as well as his evident passion for poetry, set him apart as a strong personality.
Ibid.

AL (ALFONSO) CAPONE

Born 1899 in Italy. Emigrated to America. During the Prohibition period organised a crime syndicate in Chicago. Despite involvement in many violent crimes he evaded conviction until the FBI charged him with tax-evasion in 1932, for which he was sentenced to 11 years in prison. Died 1947.

8 Prohibition brought the gangs opportunities of acquiring vast wealth. The illegal trade in liquor was worth 75,000,000 dollars a year. It was for this huge prize that gang warfare was ruthlessly waged daily, with revolvers, sawn-off shotguns, bombs and machine guns. Al Capone was victorious, thanks to his organising ability and the admirable training of his army of gunmen.
Morning Post *Jan* 1931

9 Fred D. Pasley humorously sub-titled his life of Al Capone 'the biography of a self-made man' so as to relieve the Creator from an unpleasant responsibility.
Ibid.

1 He is Neapolitan by birth and Neanderthal by instinct.
Fred D. Pasley, AL CAPONE: THE BIOGRAPHY OF A SELF-MADE MAN 1931

2 A pleasant enough fellow to meet socially, in a speakeasy, if the proprietor were buying Capone beer; a fervent handshaker with an agreeable, ingratiating smile, bearing a gleaming expanse of dental ivory. Facile conversationalist, fluent as to topics of the ring, the stage, the gridiron, and the baseball field.
Ibid.

3 Al Capone's brief career was the interval between the last of the robber barons of crime and the age of the business man of crime. He used both the tommy-gun and the accountant to gut society.
Andrew Sinclair. Quoted ibid.

4 Al Capone was to crime what J. P. Morgan was to Wall Street; the first man to exert national influence over his trade.
Ibid.

TRUMAN CAPOTE

Born in America, 1924. Novelist, achieved fame with *Breakfast at Tiffany's*, 1958. Developed a style of 'documentary fiction' with *In Cold Blood*, 1966. Died 1984.

5 It is surprising to find that much of contemporary life, and many of the interests of civilised people, pass him by. Whereas it is unexpected that he knows about finance, and has admiration for those in big business, he is totally uninterested in painting, works of art, classical music or architecture. Wild horses won't drag him into a museum.
Cecil Beaton, DIARY 1949

6 At twenty-six years old, Truman still looks so young that bartenders are likely to consider him under age and to refuse his request for 'a martini — very dry and very cold'; here the Arab urchins treat him as a child and are apt to taunt him.
Ibid.

7 When I first became friends with Truman two years ago he was fluttery and wraith-like. Now he has become comparatively rugged. For days he will go without shaving, for months he lets his toenails grow; his rooms become untidier, the dogs make messes on the floor; he will never send his suit to the cleaner. He reserves all his energies for his creative work.
Ibid.

8 I feel anxious lest Truman shall not survive to make old bones. I am slightly scared that someone who lives so intensely, so warmly, so generously, may be packing into a short span more than many people are capable of enjoying or experiencing in a long lifetime. Truman seems to attract drama; he has violent reactions to everything, and the moment comes when total fatigue takes over. Then he sinks into a death-like sensual sleep from which you feel he will never recover.
Ibid. 1953

9 I'm about as tall as a shot-gun and just as noisy. If you looked at my face from both sides you'd see they were completely different. It's sort of a changeling face.
Capote, writing of himself in 1956

10 He had little formal schooling and claims to be unable to recite the alphabet to this day.
John Daniel, MAKERS OF MODERN CULTURE (*Edited by Justin Wintle*) 1982

11 For much of his literary career he combined critical recognition with celebrity status. Acclaimed as 'the most discussed novelist of the day' in 1948 with the publication of his first novel *Other Voices, Other Rooms* he rapidly gravitated towards the wider sort of fame conferred by membership of New York's café society. He became famous for his bizarre clothes, for his slightly camp wit, and for the lavish parties which he gave or frequented.
The Times, Obituary 27 *Aug* 1984

12 He trained himself to record conversations and looked for an appropriate subject for a non-fiction novel. The opportunity came in 1959 when he read a brief account in the *New York Times* about the apparent motiveless slaughter of the Clutters, a respectable family of Kansas farmers. For the next six years he interviewed anyone and everyone concerned with the crime, including the two young ex-convicts who were arrested, found guilty and eventually executed in 1965. The result was *In Cold Blood*, published in 1966, from which Capote is estimated to have made more than two million dollars.
Ibid.

13 His collection of paperweights and hats became the preoccupation of gossip columnists, and his bizarre sense of style — a refined labourer's dress, a Jaguar convertible, and an English bulldog — made him into a cult figure.
Ibid.

1 I would say that Capote is now absolutely immortal. At least for a generation . . . It is quite possible that no one will ever read a book of his again, but it is impossible that everyone will not be reading *about* him until the end of the century.
Gore Vidal, Obituary comment

ANDREW CARNEGIE

Born in Scotland in 1835. Emigrated to Pittsburgh and made a fortune in steel. In 1901 sold out to US Steel Corporation, and thereafter devoted himself to philanthropy. Died 1919.

2 As I lie in my swimming pool thinking over my possessions the conviction comes to me that if a commission were sent down from heaven to assess what I have, I should be deprived of a great part of it.
Carnegie. Quoted Burton J. Hendrick, LIFE OF ANDREW CARNEGIE 1933

3 He found an America of wood and iron, and turned it into steel.
Burton J. Hendrick, LIFE OF ANDREW CARNEGIE 1933

4 The cynics smiled when Andrew Carnegie, asked by an Industrial Commission what his business was, replied: 'My chief business is to do as much good as I can in the world — I have no other business.' But he meant it, this little emperor of steel. His creed was that the man who dies rich dies disgraced, and he toiled as hard to get rid of his millions as he had done to amass them.
Philip Morton, Sunday Express 2 *Oct* 1949

5 He inspired, directed, drove, but not always on the spot where the sweat and toil were. 'No. 8 furnace broke all records today', an executive once wired triumphantly. 'What were the other ten furnaces doing?' Carnegie wired back.
Ibid.

6 He rarely carried money. He left that to his secretaries. Once he was turned off a London bus because he had not got the fare.
Ibid.

7 Carnegie adopted a formula, 'Put all your eggs in one basket, and watch the basket.' The basket was steel.
Ibid.

8 On the publication in 1900 of his book *The Gospel of Wealth*, Carnegie resolved to stop accumulating and begin the infinitely more serious and difficult task of wise distribution, thereby living up to his precept that wealth in the hands of private individuals is a trust for the community from which it is gleaned.
Radio Times 22 *Nov* 1935

EDWARD HENRY CARSON, BARON CARSON

Born 1854. Irish politician who opposed home rule and, during First World War, was an advocate of Ulster's support of the British Government. Died 1935.

9 My only great qualification for being put in charge of the Navy is that I am all at sea.
Carson, in 1916. *Quoted Montgomery Hyde,* CARSON

10 Early in 1914 Asquith's back-benchers were urging him to have Carson prosecuted. Long afterwards Asquith told Carson that he had never intended to prosecute because he feared that he could not procure a conviction. 'You need have had no fear,' said Carson to Asquith's astonishment. 'I should have pleaded guilty. I should have said, "My Lord Judge and gentlemen of the jury, I was born under the British flag, a loyal subject of His Majesty the King. If to fight so to remain, like yourselves, a loyal subject of His Majesty be a crime, my Lords and gentlemen of the jury, I plead guilty." And where would you have been then?'
Ian Colvin, LIFE OF LORD CARSON 1934

11 Carson stands out as one of the men who was absolutely disinterested. He was not even ambitious. He stood quite alone. Not a single colleague of his on the Front Bench, with the fitful exception of Bonar Law, stood by him, however much they sympathised, when he organised a 'Provincial Government' in Ulster to resist, by force of arms if necessary, the enforced inclusion of the province in a separation from Great Britain.
Ibid.

12 All his life he suffered from ill-health and some of his mightiest forensic triumphs were won when he was in acute physical pain. Once when he had won a great victory, in an Irish case, against Tim Healy the latter said to him as they went out of court: 'That was a wonderful speech you made, Ned. You must have had a grand breakfast to have done it. What did you have?' 'A bottle of medicine,' was the gloomy reply.
Edward Marjoribanks, LIFE OF LORD CARSON 1932

13 He was the greatest cross-examiner of his

time, a master of traps, terse, imperturbable with a gift of deadly iteration never so forcibly exhibited as in his famous cross-examination of Oscar Wilde.
Ibid.

1 The public knows Carson as a man who has spent most of his life fighting in the Courts and in Parliament, who has raised an army of a hundred thousand men, and sent by his advocacy many men to prison. They picture him perhaps as a grim personage, as 'Coercion' Carson, an embodiment of the unbending spirit of Ulster. How false is such an impression. He is the gentlest of men.
Ibid.

2 What the world does not know is that after Carson's victory over the flippant, brilliant and resourceful Oscar Wilde and Wilde lost his case for criminal libel against Queensberry, when the Crown decided to prosecute him to the bitter end, Carson went to one of the Law Officers and in merciful intercession suggested that they should stay their hand. 'Hasn't he suffered enough?' pleaded Carson. In those words you have the secret of him who his biographer Edward Marjoribanks rightly describes as 'the gentlest of men'.
J. H. Morgan, John o' London's Weekly 16 *Jul* 1932

3 Dangerous in opposition, he was ineffectual in office.
A. J. P. Taylor, ENGLISH HISTORY 1914–1945 1965

JIMMY (JAMES EARL) CARTER

Born in America 1924. Governor of Georgia, 1970–4. As Democratic candidate defeated Gerald Ford in 1976 presidential election. Was himself defeated by Republican candidate Ronald Reagan in 1980.

4 He was very interested in the arts and I suspect that to some degree his eagerness to immerse himself in culture reflected his small-town origins. After Horowitz had given a recital in the White House, Carter told me that during the entire concert Horowitz missed only one note.
Zbigniew Brzezinski, POWER AND PRINCIPLE: MEMOIRS OF THE NATIONAL SECURITY ADVISER 1977–1981 1983

5 He is the only man since my dear husband died to have had the effrontery to kiss me on the lips.
Queen Elizabeth, the Queen Mother. Quoted Peter Hillmore, Observer 13 *Feb* 1983

6 I don't know what people have got against Jimmy Carter. He's done nothing.
Bob Hope. Election campaign speech for Reagan. 2 *Nov* 1980

7 A man of high moral worth, tested in great affairs, and utterly destroyed, in part as a consequence of his own failings, even his own virtues.
Geoffrey Hodgson, *Observer* 19 *Dec* 1982

8 Honest to a fault, the religious Jimmy was haunted by a *Playboy* magazine interview in which he admitted he 'lusted after women in his heart'. He was haunted by family indiscretions, too.
TV Times 20 *Oct* 1984

ENRICO CARUSO

Born 1873 in Italy. Achieved world fame as an operatic tenor. At an early stage in its development saw the huge potential of the gramophone and successfully exploited it. Died 1921.

9 Beecham once said to me that there has never been a voice to approach Caruso's. As a boy I heard him sing *Che gelida manina*. It remains the most unforgettable experience of my life. The world stood still. I can hear it now; *Aspetti Signorina*. He had the sob in his voice that Italians alone have. Gigli had it, and Gobbi. So have the gondoliers in Venice, and the fishermen in the Bay of Naples.
Lord Boothby, RECOLLECTIONS OF A REBEL 1978

10 There is not a voice to approach Caruso's. The volume of the voice and the quality of the voice are pre-eminent. When he was young he had all the top notes you want in the world, and the middle-range register of a light baritone. It was unique.
Sir Thomas Beecham. Quoted Lord Boothby, Sunday Times 16 *Sep* 1962

11 Singing at Brooklyn in 1921 a blood-vessel burst in his throat. With a supreme effort of will he regained control and sang on for another twenty minutes though his wife begged for the curtain to be lowered. Handkerchiefs were passed out to him and with these he tried to staunch the flow of blood. At last, choking and with tears in his eyes, he had to stop. The audience applauded as never before.
John Fisher, Everybody's Weekly 3 *Sep* 1938

1 He had a passion for picture postcards and when on tour would buy them in ten-shilling lots, have them addressed to himself and forwarded to his next stopping place.
Ibid.

2 A strange result of his death was that the following day another obituary appeared in the papers. Carl Numan of Copenhagen, it read, died an hour after he had eaten twenty-six hard-boiled eggs, a feat he had undertaken to accomplish if the report of Caruso's death was confirmed.
Ibid.

3 What a child he was, that man with his broad shoulders and enormous chest.
Lou Tellegen, WOMEN HAVE BEEN KIND

BARBARA CASTLE

Born 1911, née Betts. English Labour politician. Elected MP for Blackburn, 1945.

4 I have never consciously exploited the fact that I am a woman. I wouldn't dare try that, even if I knew how to. I have too much respect for my male colleagues to think they would be particularly impressed.
Barbara Castle to Kenneth Harris, Observer 5 *Oct* 1969

5 Ted [Castle] was very impressed by my speech at the Labour Party Conference, in 1943. He was night editor of the *Mirror* and suggested they put a picture of me on page one, which they did. You might say we began courting on the front page of the *Mirror*.
Ibid.

6 It has always been an endless worry as to whether I would ever have a whole garment and an unladdered pair of stockings to wear. Poor old Ted pointed out to me that his jacket was torn. My riposte was to pull out my winter coat, whose lining is falling apart for want of a stitch, and tell him how embarrassed I was when people at functions insisted on helping me into it.
Barbara Castle, DIARIES 1974–78 1980

7 No one ever saw Mrs Castle cry except once, and then they were tears of anger when a group of civil servants at Overseas Development were trying to put paragraphs into a White Paper and Mrs Castle didn't want them.
Peter Dunn, Sunday Times 2 *Jul* 1967

8 She is sometimes called the Lady Astor of the Left for her ebulliently organising ways. If she bawls out a civil servant she takes the sting out of her anger by clutching his arm — 'a disarming gesture' one of them remarked.
Ibid.

9 When she left the Ministry for Overseas Development it was as though someone had switched off the current.
Ibid.

10 Her total commitment, combined with her warmth, spontaneity and fearlessness, were the secrets of much of her success. And a very considerable success it was.
Roy Jenkins, Observer 11 *Nov* 1984

11 All Mrs Castle's sacrifices, her puffing, her striving and hustling, were to no avail at all. At the end her political career was snuffed out by heartless Jim like a spent candle.
Paul Johnson, Sunday Telegraph, In face of strife 28 *Nov* 1980

12 She was the ablest Labour politician of her generation. On grounds of ability alone she ought to have become Britain's first woman Prime Minister. But there is no justice in politics.
Ibid.

13 Coming down from Oxford she became, by accident and in desperation, a sales demonstrator in a Manchester store. 'The most miserable year of my life' she calls it, hard on the feet, draughty and unrewarding. When she chose she would break sales records with her tins of coffee and boxes of cheap crystallised fruits. But often she didn't and the cold, comfortless insecurity of the shop-girl's working conditions reinforced her Socialism and made it still more real and personal.
Observer, Profile 16 *Nov* 1958

14 To the Tories she is an evil emblem of shrill, waspish, underhand Socialist opposition, which actually enhances her position in her own party.
Ibid.

15 She was a fighter with a limited vision; though she did wonder whether it was possible for a social democratic government to run capitalism. Her nostrums were mainly unimaginative relics of the past, apart from her unsuccessful attempt to stop the trade unions strangling the economy. But she brought colour and style to politics.
Woodrow Wyatt, The Times 8 *Nov* 1984

FIDEL CASTRO

Born in Cuba, 1927. Organised revolutionary campaign which overthrew Batista in 1958, and set up a communist regime which collectivised agriculture and expropriated industry to the state.

1 Castro has, for the last 25 years, kept a thick curtain of discretion round his private life. In 25 years he has never escorted a woman to a public function. None of the women alleged to have been graced with his favour has ever chosen to make the subject public.
Isabel Hilton, Sunday Times Magazine 8 *Jan* 1984

2 When he arrives at a reception he is invariably accompanied by a butler-cum-bodyguard who solemnly carries a large black bag containing the president's whisky, rum, cigars and glasses. It is regarded as a matter of self-congratulation if Castro shows enough confidence in his host to accept a drink.
Ibid.

3 Physically he was harder then [in 1959] than he is now, handling a machine-gun as if it were made of plastic, humping a 50-lb pack without trouble. He was as springy as an athlete. And his life was disorganised madness.
Observer, Profile 23 *Apr* 1961

4 Pale beneath the beard and usually hoarse from speech-making, Castro was soon surprising visitors who found an enthusiastic self-confident amateur instead of the doctrinaire fanatic they read about in the newspapers.
Ibid.

5 A bespectacled lawyer then aged 32, Castro burst into Havana in January 1959, trembling with excitement, obviously exalted, riding an armoured car through delirious, jam-packed streets. Distinguished features included a rich black beard, peaked cap, green battledress and Colt revolver; he played marbles, suffered with his lungs, and read poetry.
Ibid.

EDITH CAVELL

Born 1865. English nurse, matron of a nurses' training hospital in Brussels where, during World War I, she secretly helped Allied soldiers to escape into neutral Holland until caught and shot by the Germans, 1915.

6 Of the risk of arrest she once remarked: 'If we are, we shall all be punished, whether we have done much or little. So let us go ahead and help these men as much as possible.'
A. E. Clark-Kennedy, lecture to the London Hospital League of Nurses 8 *May* 1965

7 A fragile, middle-aged little woman, grey eyes that could be tender or critical, a mouth of masculine firmness, a woman to cling to her standards at all costs.
Ibid.

8 She was introspective, deeply religious, possessed by a sense of duty and with neither inclination nor capacity to make friends; a solitary, withdrawn figure, who loved suffering humanity as a whole, rather than a particular member of it.
Ibid.

9 I handed to General Sauberzweig, military governor of Brussels, the appeal for a reprieve drawn up by the American representative of British prisoners of war. He pushed the appeal to the floor and said 'I shall not receive this appeal. Our conversation is at an end.' I could not control myself any longer. 'This woman's blood be upon you and your children!' He answered, 'I was brought up to accept responsibility gladly.' With that he withdrew.
Baron von der Lancken-Wackenitz, MY THIRTY YEARS OF OFFICE 1930

10 At the unveiling of the statue — not a very great likeness — that stands opposite the National Portrait Gallery in London, the artist James Pryde exclaimed 'My God, they've shot the wrong person.'
Nigel Rees, SAYINGS OF THE CENTURY 1984

11 Edith Cavell was a British Red Cross nurse who, without question, broke the rules of war by using her job to help Allied prisoners escape from German-occupied territory. Her message to the world 'Patriotism is not enough . . .' was not in the form of 'last words' spoken before a firing squad, but was said the previous day to an English captain, the Revd Stirling Gahan, who visited her in prison.
Ibid.

FEODOR IVANOVICH CHALIAPIN

Born 1873. Russian bass singer. His most famous role was as Boris Godonov in Mussorgsky's opera. He also, in his recitals, popularised *The Volga Boatman*. Died 1938.

12 The standard bass of today is as different

from Chaliapin as Euston Station is from Westminster Abbey.
Sir Thomas Beecham. Quoted Lord Boothby, Sunday Times 16 *Sep* 1962

1 Before he had reached wealth Chaliapin was singing in an opera which had a ballet. One of the dancers was an Italian who seemed sad and friendless. Chaliapin guessed she was homesick and longed to cheer her up with the sound of her native language, but the only Italian words he knew were allegro, andante, moderato. He went up to her and said them. She guessed his kindly intention and fell in love with him. Soon afterwards they were married.
Children's Newspaper 22 *Oct* 1927

2 Infinitely vain in his cloak of fame — at the same time working like a hero and a galley-slave to put across his own inspired idea of what opera should be — learning every part, the better to sing his own.
Edward Crankshaw, Observer 3 *Dec* 1967

3 Chaliapin was the admiration and despair of his friends, the scourge and joy of his enemies, causing scandal whenever he opened his mouth, drinking and womanising, spurning and cherishing — one moment pouring his talents into the sand, the next feverishly, compulsively acquiring riches.
Ibid.

4 How pugnacious a man Chaliapin is may be guessed from his story of how he knocked down a member of the chorus behind the scenes at Covent Garden when, at a performance before the King and Queen, the chorus struck for more pay and refused to go on.
Robert Lynd, News Chronicle 31 *Oct* 1932

5 I took Kennard Bliss to the Russian Opera, *Boris Godunov*, which is splendid. The *most* glorious Russian man called Chaliapin does Boris — gorgeously tall and handsome, marvellous singer and supreme actor. I'm told he drinks like a fish, and when his friends say, Please don't you'll spoil your beautiful voice, he says, Hooray, then I shall be able to act instead of singing.
Edward Marsh, letter to Rupert Brooke 29 *Jun* 1913

6 With the revolution his fortune — more than £1,000,000 — was lost. But even the revolution and the changing economic order did not end the fascination his voice held for the people. He was made an Artist of the People by the Bolsheviks. He was paid in food. For one of his concerts he was paid — six months afterwards — by 10 lbs of flour, one ham, 5 lbs of sugar and a selection of weird potatoes.
Sydney Morrell, Sunday Express 5 *May* 1935

7 'Ma cheri, I wish I could 'ave a baby by you.' This Chaliapin to Evelyn Laye at the Savoy. 'He says that to all of them, doesn't he Evelyn?' said Hannen Swaffer, calling across to that lady, who was looking suitably and attractively confused by this Russian pleasantry.
Reginald Pound, THEIR MOODS AND MINE 1937

8 There have been great actors who have not been singers, great singers who were mediocre actors, some even who could not act at all. Chaliapin is unique among the greatest singers of his age insofar as he, alone among them, is one of the most gifted and remarkable actors in the history of the theatre.
W. J. Turner, GREAT CONTEMPORARIES: *Chaliapin* 1934

AUSTEN CHAMBERLAIN

Born 1863. British politician. Son of Joseph Chamberlain. Chancellor of the Exchequer 1903–6, 1919–21, Foreign Secretary 1924–9. Instrumental in the setting up of the Locarno Pact, 1925, guaranteeing the German frontiers, and was awarded Nobel Peace Prize. Died 1937.

9 I lunched with Emerald (Cunard) and was next to Sir Austen Chamberlain; he talked too much and his frosty eyes stared. I asked him what in life had given him his greatest aesthetic thrills; he named them in this order: his view of the sunlit Parthenon, his first view of the Velasquez in the Prado, the Rubens in the cathedral at Antwerp. Then a conversation followed about the present lack of great men. Austen said that great men were like high mountains; one had to be away from them to appreciate them.
Sir Henry Channon, DIARY 2 *Mar* 1935

10 Old Austen Chamberlain, the doyen of the House of Commons donkeys, made a really stupid speech in which he attacked Germany

with unreasoning violence. He is ossified, tedious, and hopelessly out of date.
Ibid.

1 Austen Chamberlain has held high office but he never carried much weight. He was always a coming man, but he never arrived.
Bruce Clavering, Sunday Referee 10 *May* 1936

2 No one knew that he had once climbed a lamp-post — in 1915, to get a better view of an air raid. Had they known, they might have cared for him more. A railway porter at Victoria said, 'Oo's that? Chamberlain? Oh, that's the bloke Briand kisses.'
Ibid.

3 He held his seat in the Liberal landslide of 1906 and went into Opposition. He was useful. He was put up to speak, always had something to say, always said the right thing — and never caught either the imagination or the fancy of the electorate.
Ibid.

4 He visited an old nurse. He told her he was in politics. She said: 'Why? There are enough of the family in politics already. I always hoped you'd do something useful.'
Ibid.

5 A centenarian confused him with Joe. She said: 'Very glad to see you, sir. What a pity you have such a stupid son.'
Ibid.

6 Unlike his lamented father he does not know how to give his political opponents the rough edge of his tongue. He 'ventures to suggest' or he is 'compelled reluctantly to express the view'. He has all the intolerable verbal clichés of British politics as well as the mental clichés of his party and class.
A. J. Cummings, News Chronicle

7 I am sure a shiver of fastidious loathing runs down his spine every time Mr J. H. Thomas slaps him on the back and calls him 'Austen'.
Ibid.

8 The eye-glass is a great protection to its owner. It fortifies the lizard-like stare with which he repels a too-familiar advance.
Ibid.

9 He is a gentleman. He means well. Europe has suffered for fifty years from well-meaning gentlemen.
Gustav Stresemann, in 1925

(ARTHUR) NEVILLE CHAMBERLAIN

Born 1869. British politician, half-brother of Austen Chamberlain. Prime Minister 1937–40. Was responsible for the appeasement policy which lead to the signing of the Munich Pact. Resigned as Prime Minister 1940, and died the same year.

10 You have sat too long for any good you have been doing. Depart, I say, and let us have done with you. In the name of God, *go.*
L. S. Amery, House of Commons May 1940

11 After his meeting with Hitler Bob Boothby told Chamberlain, 'You're dealing with a madman, a destructive genius almost without parallel in history.' Chamberlain replied, 'I'm afraid I don't agree with you.'
Susan Barnes, Sunday Times Magazine 1 *Apr* 1973

12 He rashly believed that he could ride the tiger, and was staggered and outraged when the animal bit him.
Earl of Birkenhead, Daily Telegraph 2 *May* 1974

13 Oliver Stanley once said that to Baldwin Europe was a bore, and to Chamberlain a bigger Birmingham.
Lord Boothby, MY YESTERDAY, YOUR TOMORROW 1962

14 'I like,' he said, 'to stick at things even after there seems no chance of success.' That, and a quite unreasoning optimism, was his undoing. Even after war was declared he thought that Hitler had missed the bus and that it would be over before the spring. The final phase of his life, when he passed, within the space of a few months, from the dizziest heights of apparent success to the depths of public and personal disaster, had something of the nobility of Greek tragedy.
Ibid.

15 He was a first-class municipal administrator who well understood and radically changed the structure of British local government; and he was the first prominent politician to grasp the power of the political machine in the modern age, which he reanimated and subsequently used for his own purposes. There it ended.
Ibid.

16 In private life Neville Chamberlain was affectionate and sensitive, with a great love and knowledge of country pursuits and the music of Beethoven. These are endearing qualities which were rewarded by the complete devotion of a small and intimate

family circle. In public life he was aloof, arrogant, obstinate and limited. He was also a failure. 'Everything I have worked for,' he told the House of Commons, with absolute truth in September 1939, 'has crashed in ruins.'
Ibid.

1 On the Good Friday of 1939, which Mussolini chose for the invasion of Albania, I hurried up from the country and at once called at No. 10 for instructions. I was led into a small room upstairs, overlooking the garden, which the Prime Minister used as a study. The window was partly open, showing a table for bird food suspended outside. Neville seemed irritated at my intrusion and surprised that I was perturbed. He said 'I feel sure Mussolini has not decided to go against us.' When I started to talk about the general threat to the Balkans, he dismissed me with the words, 'Don't be silly. Go home to bed', and continued to feed the birds. At least he did not tell me, as he had once advised Anthony Eden, to take an aspirin.
Lord Butler, THE ART OF THE POSSIBLE 1971

2 The Prime Minister's broadcast on the outbreak of war was pathetically moving, but scarcely a tocsin ringing to arms.
Ibid.

3 Why is it so hard to be nice about Neville?
John Campbell, The Times, reviewing David Dilke's NEVILLE CHAMBERLAIN VOL 1 22 *Nov* 1984

4 Baldwin said I always gave him the impression, when I spoke in the House of Commons, that I looked on the Labour Party as dirt.
Neville Chamberlain, DIARY 19 *Jun* 1927

5 I went to Edward Stanley's memorial service. Chamberlain arrived and took his seat in the first stall, and prayed a long time. I watched him throughout the ceremony; he looked very alive and sad, and when a sunbeam fell on him, he seemed what he is, a saint.
Sir Henry Channon, DIARY 20 *Oct* 1938

6 Old Brolly got back from Rome — his stature enhanced, his prestige increased. He is winning through and will probably be Premier for years to come. He was well received in London.
Ibid. 15 *Jan* 1939

7 That old town clerk, looking at foreign affairs through the wrong end of a municipal drain pipe.
Attributed to Winston Churchill, after Munich, by R. L. Taylor in THE AMAZING MR CHURCHILL; *but also attributed to D. Lloyd George by Leon Harris in* THE FINE ART OF POLITICAL WIT

8 In the depths of that dusty soul there is nothing but abject surrender.
Winston Churchill

9 For him, the dictators of Germany and Italy were like the Lord Mayors of Liverpool and Manchester, who might belong to different political parties and have different interests, but who must desire the welfare of humanity and be fundamentally reasonable, decent men like himself. This profound misconception lay at the root of his policy and explains all his mistakes.
Duff Cooper, OLD MEN FORGET 1953

10 Chamberlain had many good qualities but he lacked experience of the world, and he lacked also the imagination which can fill the gaps of inexperience. He had never moved in the great world of politics or finance, and the continent of Europe was for him a closed book.
Ibid.

11 Neville Chamberlain's egocentric notion that he, of all men, could chat up the dictators and maintain peace in Europe on honourable terms was a confidence trick which diverted public attention from the real issue, but only fleetingly.
Hugh Cudlipp, WALKING ON THE WATER

12 Fundamentally the difficulty is that Neville believes he is a man with a mission to come to terms with the dictators.
Anthony Eden, DIARIES 18 *Jan* 1938

13 An unremarkable figure; gaunt, with bushy eyebrows and old-fashioned moustache, but no democratically endearing features.
Robert Graves and Alan Hodge, THE LONG WEEK-END 1940

14 Chamberlain's great fault was that he sneered at people. He sneered at the Labour members and they never forgave him.
Lord Halifax. Quoted Harold Nicolson, DIARY *Jun* 1954

15 They start bloody wars they can't afford . . . Chamberlain . . . didn't give a thought to the cost of it — didn't enter his head to get an estimate — soppy old sod.
Johnny Speight, BBC TV, Till Death Us Do Part

16 A few hours before proclaiming 'peace for our time' he allegedly said to Halifax among the cheering crowds: 'all this will be over in three months'. Chamberlain was not being

dishonest or two-faced. He reflected the muddle in most English minds. Munich sprang from a mixture of fear and good intentions. In retrospect, fear predominated.
A. J. P. Taylor, ENGLISH HISTORY 1914–1945 1965

1 He believed that Hitler and Mussolini were rational statesmen like himself, or at any rate must be treated as such, and that their discontents could be appeased by rational discussion.
Ibid.

2 Chamberlain's asset was his sharp rationalism. He beat down critics with the question: What is the alternative?
Ibid.

3 Chamberlain has turned all four cheeks to Hitler.
The Week, after the Munich crisis

4 In any list of British prime ministers Neville Chamberlain is the odd man out, history's greatest misfit — which indeed he looked — the most improbable Prime Minister of all.
Harold Wilson, A PRIME MINISTER ON PRIME MINISTERS

5 Praise be to God and to Mr Chamberlain. I find no sacrilege, no bathos, in coupling those two names.
Godfrey Winn, Daily Express, after Munich

RAYMOND (THORNTON) CHANDLER

Born 1888. American detective story writer. A prolific writer, his best-known character was Philip Marlowe, and among his most successful novels *The Big Sleep*, 1939 and *Farewell, My Lovely*, 1940. Died 1959.

6 If my books had been any worse I should not have been invited to Hollywood, and if they had been any better I should not have come.
Raymond Chandler. Quoted F. MacShane THE LIFE OF RAYMOND CHANDLER

7 What greater prestige can a man like me (not too greatly gifted, but very understanding) have than to have taken a cheap, shoddy, and utterly lost kind of writing, and have made of it something the intellectuals claw each other about.
Raymond Chandler, letter to Charles Norton

8 I write in a sort of broken-down patois which is something like the way a Swiss waiter talks, and when I split an infinitive, God damn it, it stays split.
Raymond Chandler, letter to Edward Weeks, editor of Atlantic Monthly

CHARLIE (SIR CHARLES SPENCER) CHAPLIN

Born in London 1889. Emigrated to America in 1910 to become the first and most internationally famous of film comedians. His first full-length film was *The Gold Rush*, 1914. Left the States to live in Switzerland 1958. Remained a British citizen. Died 1977.

9 I have no further use for America. I wouldn't go back there if Jesus Christ was President.
Chaplin on leaving the US

10 At a dinner in Hollywood to celebrate his birthday, Charlie Chaplin entertained the guests throughout the evening by imitating people they knew: men, women, and children, his chauffeur, his Jap servants, his secretaries. Finally he sang at the top of his voice an aria from an Italian opera — sang it superbly. 'Why Charlie, I never knew you could sing so beautifully,' said someone. 'I can't sing at all,' Charlie rejoined, 'I was only imitating Caruso.'
Edmund Fuller, ANECDOTES 1946

11 Chaplin's genius was in comedy. He had no sense of humour.
Lita Grey, ex-wife. Quoted Richard Lamparski, WHATEVER BECAME OF—? 1983

12 He pitied everything that stumbled or whimpered or wagged a tail, particularly he pitied himself. There has never been a portrait of self pity so vivid or so shocking as Charlie with a rose in his hand.
Robert Hatch, reporter 25 *Nov* 1952

13 Charlie has become tubby and white and gap-toothed. I ask him whether he is recognised now in tubes and buses. He says not if he wears glasses. But sometimes he forgets to put them on, and sees a startled look coming over the faces of people sitting opposite.
Harold Nicolson, DIARY 8 *Dec* 1953

14 That obstinate, suspicious, egocentric, maddening and lovable genius of a problem child.
Mary Pickford

15 He will die as he has lived an unregenerate classicist who believes in making movies he can feel in his frayed lace valentine heart.
André Sarris

1 His gospel is like Mary Pickford's; the hope of a little child.
Hannen Swaffer. Quoted Leslie Halliwell, THE FILMGOER'S BOOK OF QUOTES 1978

2 When he found a voice to say what was on his mind, he was like a child of eight writing lyrics for Beethoven's Ninth.
Billy Wilder. Quoted ibid.

CHARLES (PHILIP ARTHUR GEORGE), PRINCE OF WALES

Born 1948. Heir to the British throne.

3 Happily summoned to the Palace to take the first long-awaited photographs of the heir to the throne. Prince Charles was an obedient sitter. He interrupted a long, contented sleep to do my bidding and open his blue eyes to stare long and wonderingly into the camera lens, the beginning of a lifetime in the glare of public duty.
Cecil Beaton, DIARY *Dec* 1948

4 The Prince is a simple, nice, cheerful adolescent of nineteen years. He has a gentle regard, a disarming smile and the tip of his nose is delicately modelled like a Gainsborough. He has obviously no flair — is badly dressed but at any rate his hair is long — and that is a triumph of independence over the influence of his father and others at court.
Ibid. 4 *Nov* 1968

5 At dinner I was next to Prince Charles and I am afraid I rather monopolised him. Again I realised what we impose on our royal family. When I asked him if there was any way he could continue to do the history work he loved, he replied quietly: 'No, I'm afraid not. There won't be time. One has to be available.'
Barbara Castle, DIARY 3 *Apr* 1968

6 On an Australian tour Prince Charles decided to take a dawn surf at St Kilda, near Melbourne. On returning to the beach he declared 'It's been like swimming in undiluted sewage'. One local mayor suggested the Prince deserved 'a good thump under the ear'. The mayor of St Kilda said 'when that young crank came here, he didn't have the brains to tell us he was going to St Kilda or we would have cleaned the place up.'
Noël St George, ROYAL QUOTES 1981

G. K. (GILBERT KEITH) CHESTERTON

Born 1874. English novelist, essayist and poet. Created the priest detective Father Brown. Died 1936.

7 Chesterton was a late developer, not talking much before three, only learning to read in his ninth year, though henceforth at it all day long, 'for the mere brute pleasure of reading — the sort of pleasure a cow must have in grazing'.
Dudley Barker, G. K. CHESTERTON 1973

8 Chesterton's championship of Christian dogma sticks in my throat.
Arnold Bennett 1909

9 He had an excessive literary taste for duels and battles and wars of all kind without having the faintest idea what the real thing would be like. Hence the odious nonsense in *The Napoleon of Notting Hill* about blood running 'in great red serpents that curl out into the main thoroughfare and shine in the moon'.
Bernard Bergonzi, Observer 26 *Apr* 1970

10 He was led forth to see the nightly spectacle of Broadway ablaze with those myriad glamorous lamps. 'How beautiful!' exclaimed Chesterton. 'How beautiful it would be for someone who could not read.'
Bennett Cerf, TRY AND STOP ME 1947

11 The late G. K. Chesterton was over six feet tall and weighed upwards of 300 pounds. When he tried his hand at the drama with the unusual comedy called *Magic*, Bernard Shaw referred to it as Fatty's First Play.
Ibid.

12 When he gave his first lecture in America Edwin Markham, author of *The Man With the Hoe*, was in the chair. The distinction of introducing so distinguished a visitor obviously unhinged Markham's reason; he embarrassed the speaker of the evening with a eulogy that went on indefinitely. Chesterton was red with embarrassment. He heaved himself to his feet, shuffled to the centre of the platform, looked plaintively around him, and murmured, 'After the whirlwind, the still, small voice.'
Ibid.

13 In the most unlikely places he would suddenly say, 'I think we'll do a little work, if you don't mind.'
Dorothy Collins, his secretary, in G. K. CHESTERTON: A CENTENARY APPRAISAL (*Edited by John Sullivan*) 1974

14 Gilbert and his wife were looking for a house

CHIANG KAI-SHEK

in the country. Gilbert had no idea where to look, so they arrived at Paddington one morning and took tickets to the destination of the first train that left. It went to Slough. They got out and strolled through the lanes all day. At night they came to Beaconsfield, stayed at the White Hart, and bought a house there. That was Gilbert for you.
Dorothy Collins, Sunday Times 2 *Jun* 1974

1 Ever since his schooldays at St Paul's Chesterton has always seen life as to a large extent as a high-spirited debating society.
Christopher Hollis, THE MIND OF CHESTERTON 1970

2 In the days before the Great War, a huge shambling man, six feet four inches tall, with long chestnut-coloured hair, and weighing about 20 stone, could often be seen wandering down Fleet Street. Dressed in a black cloak and sombrero hat, with pince-nez perched incongruously on his nose, he carried a sword-stick and his pockets bulged with 'penny dreadfuls'. From time to time he stopped to read a book or write something down, or paused in the middle of the road, while the traffic whirled about him, apparently struck by an important thought. Most of the time he seemed to be chuckling over some secret jokes of his own.
Richard Ingrams, Telegraph Magazine 24 *May* 1974

3 He grew up from manhood into boyhood.
R. A. Knox. Quoted Geoffrey Madan, NOTEBOOKS 1981

4 Chesterton believed in religious and political causes of medieval futility and revolting sentimentality.
Simon Raven, Spectator 24 *May* 1974

5 The Immense Champeroon; the fellow of infinite vest.
G. B. Shaw

6 If all my Atheology turns out wrong and your Theology right, I feel I shall always be able to pass into Heaven (if I want to) as a friend of G.K.C.'s. Bless you.
Ibid.

7 He made a great number of books but he rarely wrote them *as* books. They are rather accumulations of perceptions, placed together like uncemented bricks, making up a wall but never a building.
Times Literary Supplement 17 *Apr* 1974

8 When his first published book *Greybeards at Play* appeared in 1900 he told his future wife Frances that he felt 'a humbug'. 'To publish a book of my nonsense verses seems to be exactly like summoning the whole of the people of Kensington to see me smoke cigarettes.'
Ibid.

9 When he looked back he did so in the spirit of a joker. 'I have a notion that the real advice I would give to the young journalist is to write an article for the *Sporting Times* and another for the *Church Times* . . . it is the only theory upon which I can explain my own undeserved survival.'
Ibid.

10 Chesterton was adult by inspiration at great moments; hardly wholly so.
Charles Williams, letter to Raymond Hunt 31 *Jul* 1942

CHIANG KAI-SHEK

Born in China 1887. Political and military leader. Became president following the death of Sun Yat Sen in 1925. After the invasion by the Japanese, and a long struggle against the Communists under Mao Tse-tung, was driven from the mainland to set up a Nationalist government on Taiwan. Died 1975.

11 Chiang, sitting bolt upright on his chair, remained courteous, but embarrassingly cold and remote. His lack of charm, or any attempt to charm, was all the more striking in contrast with the attractive volubility of his famous wife.
Vernon Bartlett, News Chronicle 21 *Jan* 1949

12 His courage is flawless. During his famous kidnapping in Sianfu in 1936, when his life hung by a hair, he disdained the slightest concessions to his captors. Indeed he lectured them on their improper conduct as if they and not he were the prisoners.
O. M. Green 1949

13 It is a bit rough on Chiang Kai-Shek to call him 'the man who lost China'. He might equally well be called 'the man who nearly saved China' or 'the man who made Taiwan prosperous'.
Woodrow Wyatt, Sunday Times, reviewing Brian Crozier's THE MAN WHO LOST CHINA 8 *May* 1977

14 Chiang's character was something of a muddle . . . [His principles] developed into a strange amalgam of socialism, Boy Scouting, muscular Christianity, Confucianism, tinged with Communism or Fascism according to personal prejudice. There was much stress on the need to wash and do one's buttons up — aims not distant

from those of Mao Tse-tung and company. Like his Communist enemies Chiang also believed in discipline and was a raving xenophobe.
Ibid.

1 Chiang believed in obedience. He was apt to order random executions to emphasise the point. He was also quixotic. When he saw a small boy smoking in the street he demanded to be taken to the parents. They were sharply reprimanded for allowing such a shocking thing.
Ibid.

2 What a remarkable place Taiwan is. Between Chiang's arrival in 1950 and his death in 1975 the income per head rose to be second only to Japan in all Asia. It is a queer little monument to him that he should have succeeded in establishing, from Peking's point of view, a maddeningly successful free enterprise island just off the mainland of China — a model of what he might have made China but for the Communists and the Japanese.
Ibid.

AGATHA (MARY CLARISSA) CHRISTIE

Born 1891. English author, specialising in intricate detective novels. Wrote the long-running play *The Mousetrap*, first staged in 1952. Died 1976.

3 Outsold only by the Bible and Shakespeare and translated into over 100 foreign languages, writer of the longest-running play on the British stage, the most popular entertainer the world has ever known.
Robert Barnard, A TALENT TO DECEIVE 1980

4 Each of her characters is surveyed, analysed, dissected as murderer-potential without an ounce of involvement. And it is because the non-involvement is total that the puzzle remains paramount, stands at the centre of the reader's interest loud and crystal clear.
Ibid.

5 She is a comely, ample woman with no outward traces of brilliance.
Sir Henry Channon, DIARY 14 *Feb* 1944

6 An archaeologist is the best husband any woman can have; the older she gets, the more interested he is in her.
Agatha Christie, of her own second husband Max Mallowan 1954

7 Her plots were assembled on principles picked up in childhood from paper games, and puzzle books, acrostics, letter and figure charades, inversions, rebuses, enigmas, arithmorems, chromograms, cryptographs and the like.
Janet Morgan, AGATHA CHRISTIE: A BIOGRAPHY 1984

8 Her books are stylistically unpretentious but intellectually interesting.
Ibid.

9 'I am of the same belief as Dorothy Sayers,' she told a correspondent, 'that the detective story is the direct successor of the old Morality Play. It is the triumph of good over evil — the deliverance of the innocent from the aggressor — that is what makes it exciting.'
Ibid.

10 She wanted a detective of a type that had not been used before and eventually decided that he should be a Belgian refugee. Torquay was full of Belgian refugees, bewildered and suspicious, who wanted to be left alone. The detective was to be clever, meticulous, with an impressive name and some knowledge of crime and criminals. Agatha made Hercule Poirot a retired Belgian police officer.
Ibid.

11 She changed nightly for dinner in the desert with her second husband, the archaeologist Max Mallowan, whose finds she punctually recorded. Writing fitted into any odd time left over from assembling pottery fragments which she cleaned with orange sticks and face cream; 'quiet moments' in the single year 1933 netted 'two detective stories, two collections of short stories, and a novel'.
Hilary Spurling, Observer 23 *Sep* 1984

12 Where other people make do with a medicine cupboard Agatha Christie set aside a whole room in her house for keeping medicines, installed a market garden in the grounds solely to supply produce for her ample table, and ordered a car that could seat 11 solely for picnics.
Ibid.

13 Her housekeeping was on the hospitable Edwardian scale passed down by a grandmother from whom, she admitted, Miss Marples took a tip or two.
Ibid.

14 Materially generous, morally prudent and emotionally secure, she managed her inordinate success prudently and well, disbursing funds with energy and discrimination on family, friends and foreign travel.
Ibid.

15 Poirot's creator was the epitome of modesty

and moderation in everything except her sales which, by the time she died in 1976, were reckoned at roughly four hundred million copies (current annual turnover is thought to be over a million pounds, and still rising).
Ibid.

1 The deception in these Christie stories is like the conjurer's sleight of hand. She shows us the ace of spades face up. Then she turns it over but we still know where it is, so how has it been transformed into the five of diamonds?
Julian Symons, BLOODY MURDER FROM THE DETECTIVE STORY TO THE CRIME NOVEL: A HISTORY

WINSTON (LEONARD SPENCER) CHURCHILL

Born 1874. British statesman and author. First Lord of the Admiralty 1911–15, until discredited by the failure of the Dardanelles campaign. Chancellor of the Exchequer 1924–9. Prime Minister 1940–5 and 1951–5. Nobel Prize for Literature for his *The Second World War*, 1953. Died 1965.

2 He is quite the most difficult man to work with I have ever struck, but I would not have missed the chance of working with him for anything on earth.
Viscount Alanbrooke. Quoted Arthur Bryant, THE TURN OF THE TIDE 1955

3 He spoke as George III might have done, had he been endowed with the tongue of Edmund Burke.
Stanley Baldwin. Quoted Lord Butler, THE ART OF THE POSSIBLE 1971

4 I am suddenly aware of how much I hated serving under Winston.
Gertrude Bell, PERSONAL PAPERS 1922

5 The Prime Minister wins debate after debate, and loses battle after battle. The country is beginning to say that he fights debates like a war and a war like debates.
Aneurin Bevan, House of Commons 2 *Jul* 1942, *after the fall of Tobruk*

6 I arrived at the conclusion that his chameleon-like character in politics is founded upon a temperamental disability. He fills all the roles with such exceeding facility that his lack of political stability is at once explained.
Aneurin Bevan. Quoted Michael Foot, LIFE OF ANEURIN BEVAN 1962

7 His ear is so sensitively tuned to the bugle note of history that he is often deaf to the more raucous clamour of contemporary life, a defect which his Conservative upbringing and background tend to reinforce.
Aneurin Bevan. Quoted Leon Harris, THE FINE ART OF POLITICAL WIT

8 He always refers to a defeat as a disaster as though it came from God, but to a victory as though it came from himself.
Ibid.

9 He had to think aloud. Solitary reflection was alien to his nature. And this imposed a certain strain on his staff and, still more, upon the Chiefs of Staff in the Second World War. In his drawing-room, the bedroom, the bathroom, the dining-room, the car, an aeroplane, a sleeping berth on a train or in his room at the House of Commons, the flow of his *private* oratory never ceased. I remember on several occasions being commanded to attend him when he was having a bath and to make suitable notes of what he said. At intervals he turned a somersault, exactly like a porpoise, and when his head reappeared at the other end of the bath he continued exactly where he had left off.
Lord Boothby, RECOLLECTIONS OF A REBEL 1978

10 He would cry over the death of a swan or a cat; for human life he had little regard, least of all for his own. He enjoyed danger. But I have never disguised from myself the fact that this element of cruelty might have been essential for what he had to do. When he sacked or broke people, and he broke many, he never thanked them and seldom saw them. He simply didn't care. And in some cases he did it with relish.
Ibid.

11 I think that one of the reasons he hated television was that he couldn't do it himself. He had to read. This is all right on radio, but no good in front of a camera. He once referred to me, in the House of Commons, as 'The Hon. Member for Television'. He said it, not with a smile, but with a snarl, and the House didn't like it.
Ibid.

12 If he sometimes enjoyed hauling up under-dogs, he had no use for top-dogs other than himself. The truth is that his egotism, derived not only from his Churchill but his American blood, prevented him from tolerating any kind of personal challenge to his own supremacy.
Ibid.

13 In his final year of office, when the mind was

beginning to fade, he became obsessed with the idea that he, and he alone, could make peace with Stalin; and this came to dominate all his thoughts and actions.
Ibid.

1 He was by far the most egotistical man I have ever known. He saw and lived life in terms of himself, against the background of history which he both made and wrote.
Ibid.

2 I never really liked Churchill. Although Keynes rightly described *The World Crisis* as one of the most powerful tracts against war ever written, war was his element and Power his objective. In my heart I hated both. I could never take the streak of cruelty in his nature, detected in his portrait by Graham Sutherland, who once said to me in Venice 'I painted the man I saw'. This, I am convinced, is why the picture 'preyed on his mind'.
Ibid.

3 He had the necessary brutality in him. 1940 was his finest hour. Once Field-Marshal Alanbrooke asked me 'Have you ever known a bigger cad than Churchill?' I replied that Lloyd George once said to me, 'Winston has behaved to you like the cad he is.' But it required a *tremendous* cad to beat Hitler.
Lord Boothby. Quoted Susan Barnes, Sunday Times Magazine 1 *Apr* 1973

4 One of the last memories I have of working with Halifax and Churchill was when we were invited to march up and down in the garden of No. 10 while Winston was rehearsing his speech, 'We shall fight on the beaches'. There we were, lanky Edward, the stocky Winston, and myself. As Winston declaimed he turned to us and said 'Would you fight in the streets and on the hills?' Pacific as we were we warmly agreed, saying, 'Yes, certainly Winston' and then continued to march up and down with him.
Lord Butler, THE ART OF THE POSSIBLE 1971

5 He never eats his words to save his face.
Violet Bonham Carter. Quoted Geoffrey Madan, NOTEBOOKS 1981

6 I watched Winston while Bevan was speaking. He sat grinning and dangling his watch chain. He looked like a plump naughty little boy dressed as a grown-up.
Sir Henry Channon, DIARY 23 *Apr* 1951

7 I watched Winston today, with his hand to his ear, listening to a fellow MP in the Division Lobby. He has this trick of wants to shed a bore, or protect himself from importunities.
Ibid. 2 *Jul* 1951

8 It took me all my time to keep up with him. I never had anything left over.
Lady Churchill. Quoted Mary Soames, CLEMENTINE CHURCHILL 1979

9 Already in 1900 I could boast I had written as many books as Moses.
Winston Churchill, Observer, Sayings of the week 9 *Jul* 1950

10 It took Armageddon to make me Prime Minister. But now I am there I am determined that Power shall be in no other hands but mine. There will be no more Kitcheners, Fishers or Haigs.
Churchill to Robert Boothby. Quoted Lord Boothby, RECOLLECTIONS OF A REBEL 1978

11 To have been alive with him was to have dined at the table of history.
Sir William Connor (Cassandra), Daily Mirror

12 It was early in 1913 that I met Winston Churchill for the first time. As a public figure he was probably more disliked by the Tories than any other member of the Government. That he had been elected first as a Conservative, that his language was as brilliant as it was provocative, and that he seemed to be on the left rather than on the right of his more respected colleagues, were the reasons, no doubt, combined with his innate pugnacity, why he made so many enemies.
Duff Cooper OLD MEN FORGET 1953

13 Lloyd George said to me of Churchill 'He was a very bad picker of men.' He suggested Churchill would pick men he liked, and not worry about their actual ability.
Hugh Cudlipp, WALKING ON THE WATER 1976

14 Churchill had no objection to us kicking poor old Chamberlain, but he didn't like being hurt himself.
Ibid.

15 That boy can't have gone through Harrow. He must have gone under it.
Capt. James, who tutored Churchill for his third attempt to qualify for Sandhurst Royal Military College

16 By the violence of his speeches and the exaggeration of his images he had grievously debased the coinage of alarmism.
Robert Rhodes James, CHURCHILL, A STUDY IN FAILURE 1900–1939

17 *Stanley Baldwin:* Where shall I put Winston?
Thomas Jones (Secretary to the Cabinet in 1924): Shove him in the Army or the Navy.

WINSTON CHURCHILL

It doesn't matter which. Give him the one with the most work.
Thomas Jones, WHITEHALL DIARY 1919–1925 1969

1 For a very short period in history Churchill was a necessary shit. He didn't like the upper classes and the upper classes didn't like him. He managed to combine tremendous egalitarianism with being a roaring old snob.
Osbert Lancaster. Quoted Duncan Fallowell, Times profile 11 *Oct* 1982

2 Winston Churchill, after brandy, like a tortoise.
Geoffrey Madan, NOTEBOOKS 1981

3 Winston Churchill in conversation, like an old ironclad, not easy to turn or manoeuvre, not answering the helm.
Ibid.

4 Sir William Joynson-Hicks made some statement in the House to which Winston gave signs of demurring. 'I see my Right Honourable friend shakes his head,' said Jix, 'but I am only expressing my own opinion.' 'And I,' answered Winston, 'am only shaking my own head.'
Edward Marsh, A NUMBER OF PEOPLE 1939

5 Winston took a little house near Godalming called Hoe Farm, and there on a Saturday morning his sister-in-law Lady Goonie, who had come to stay for the weekend, established herself in the garden with her paraphernalia and began to sketch. Winston had never seen anyone paint before; a planet swam into his ken, and on the Monday morning he bought up practically the entire contents of Robertson's colour-shop in Piccadilly — easels, palettes, brushes, tubes and canvases. Lavery and Orpen let him paint in their studios, and Sickert gave him wrinkles.
Ibid.

6 Winston Churchill's proofs were of course for many years part of my official duties, and he has kept me on in their service to this day. In one of the *World Crisis* volumes he used a coinage of his own 'choate' to signify the opposite of 'inchoate'. I knew quite well that the word had no right to exist, and it was my clear duty to warn him; but I thought it expressive and pleasing, and there is no stint of shaky words in English, so I let it pass, and though he forgave me I have never forgiven myself for the obloquy it brought on his head.
Ibid.

7 For a man as human and humorous and audacious as Churchill had been, to be turned into a totem, serving to protract illusions of grandeur, was a sad end to a splendid career.
Malcolm Muggeridge, TREAD SOFTLY FOR YOU TREAD ON MY JOKES 1966

8 Churchill seems to do much better waving his hat than talking through it.
New Masses (USA). Quoted News Review 14 *Nov* 1946

9 Violet Bonham Carter says he is enormously influenced by words. A thing pungently expressed seems to him truer than wisdom dully expressed. I think that this is true.
Harold Nicolson, DIARY 29 *Oct* 1947

10 Winston hates being alone, is happy with his painting and his History of the English Speaking Peoples, awaits death with fortitude, loves his ducks, his budgerigars and his poodle Rufus, and is a resigned and happy man. He told her [Vita Sackville-West] that at his last audience with the Queen she had said to him, 'Would you like a Dukedom, or anything like that?'
Ibid. 29 *Aug* 1955

11 A big man, a very big man indeed — the only man big enough to get us out of the mistakes he makes; and it must be added in fairness, out of the mistakes that others, less great, make as well.
Osbert Sitwell, LAUGHTER IN THE NEXT ROOM 1949

12 What will he become? Who shall say? At the rate he goes there will hardly be room for him in Parliament at thirty, or in England when he is forty.
G. W. Stevens, Daily Mail 1898

13 We cannot congratulate Mr Churchill on his wedding outfit. It was not a success. The sleeves are too short and too backward hanging, and consequently creased badly when the arms were brought forward. It was too long and heavy for a morning coat, and too skimpy for a 'frock'.
Tailor and Cutter 1908

14 It is said that Churchill, when offered the post of chancellor [of the exchequer], thought he was being invited to become chancellor of the duchy of Lancaster, and accepted gratefully.
A. J. P. Taylor, ENGLISH HISTORY 1914–1945 1965

15 Churchill often wore the uniform of air commodore, complete with honorary

'wings' — the only prime minister, not excluding Wellington, to wear military uniform while in office.
Ibid.

1 His speeches succeeded, to the surprise of the experts. They were rhetorical and cheeky at the same time; Macaulay and contemporary slang mixed together much as Churchill sometimes wore a Victorian frock-coat and more often an extremely practical siren-suit reminiscent of a child's rompers. He was an eccentric, which exactly matched the mood of the British people.
Ibid.

COUNT GALEAZZO CIANO

Born 1903 in Italy. Married Mussolini's daughter Edda, 1930. Officer in Italian air force during the Abyssinian invasion. Foreign Minister 1936–43. Involved in a plot to depose Mussolini, 1943. Arrested and shot, 1944.

2 Ciano has been shot. He was forty-one and nobody has ever risen so high, and fallen so low. I knew him, and always found him cordial, gay, fashionable and pain-staking; he was pro-Fascist, certainly, but not anti-English. He three times invited me to lunch and once I went, a grand affair at the Palazzo Barberini. He was shot on Mussolini's orders, and I find it rather shocking to shoot one's son-in-law.
Sir Henry Channon, DIARY 11 *Jan* 1944

3 Mortimer Durand was sitting at his typewriter in Asmara, Abyssinia, typing his dispatch to a London newspaper. Some jovial company was having a good time in the neighbouring partition where the Italian journalists usually dined. He was struggling along undecided whether or not to get up and ask the Italians to sing lower when suddenly one of them appeared and shouted; 'Captain Ciano requests you to stop pounding your typewriter. You disturb his singing.'
Henri Gris, Sunday Referee 25 *Apr* 1937

4 Asked by his son-in-law, the comedian Vic Oliver, to name the greatest name in World War II, Winston Churchill retorted peremptorily, 'Mussolini. He at least had the courage to kill his son-in-law.'
Samedi Soir, Paris 1946

GEORGES CLEMENCEAU

Born 1841. French politician. Prime Minister 1906–9, 1917–20. Died 1929.

5 Clemenceau was the peasant, as close to the soil and the people as man can be, earthly, shrewd, suspicious.
Bernard M. Baruch, THE PUBLIC YEARS 1961

6 I visited Clemenceau in his home at 8 Rue Franklin whenever I was in Paris. There the old Tiger would be sitting, in his grey gloves and his grey skull cap, usually wearing large grey slippers. He looked like a grey cat.
Ibid.

7 An excited supporter burst into the chambers of the old Tiger Clemenceau and cried 'Your son has just joined the Communist Party'. Clemenceau regarded his visitor calmly and remarked, 'Monsieur, my son is 22 years old. If he had not become a Communist at 22 I would have disowned him. If he is *still* a Communist at 32 I will do it then.'
Bennett Cerf, TRY AND STOP ME 1947

8 An Englishman who met him eight years ago in India tells how, after he had been shown the splendid stables of a rajah he asked whether the purdah system was observed among horses too, and if the mares had to veil their faces when they were out of doors. 'No,' replied the official who was showing him round. 'Then,' said the Tiger, 'in India mares are better treated than women.'
Children's Newspaper 14 *Dec* 1929

9 Clemenceau is going over to America to whimper and sentimentalise like the old dotard he is. Clemenceau lost the peace. His apologia would have but little success in France; he is hoping to have more success with it in the United States. This journey is a piece of personal publicity. It is devoid of any practical value.
Marshal Foch. Quoted M. Raymond THE MEMORIAL OF FOCH 1930

10 He had only one illusion — France, and only one disillusion, mankind.
J. Maynard Keynes, THE WORLDLY PHILOSOPHERS

11 On the writing table in his study stood a charming little nude torso of a Greek female figure. The Tiger told A. J. Balfour that a lady had recently been to call on him, and reproached him for not remembering her. 'How can I forget you,' he replied pointing to the statuette, 'when I have this portrait always before me.' The lady never returned.
Sir Ian Malcolm, LORD BALFOUR 1930

CLAUD COCKBURN

1 Manet painted him as a Tartar in repose, brow alert for danger, arms uneasily folded, the whole effect a striking anticipation of Lenin.
Michael Ratcliffe, The Times 11 *Apr* 1974

2 I am reminded of a remark of Clemenceau, 'I am an old man. I have lost most of my friends. I have been treated with ingratitude. But I still have my teeth. I can still bite!'
Lord Riddell, John o' London's Weekly 19 *Apr* 1930

3 I see him at Versailles, when Count von Brockdorff-Rantzau standing in what Clemencau described as 'stiff insolence' came to receive the draft peace treaty and began his observations, 'You are at last about to slake your hatred.' Lloyd George whispered to Clemenceau, 'What are you going to reply?' To which the old man answered, 'I am going to stick my piece of paper under his nose and say "This is what you've got to sign."'
Ibid.

4 Clemenceau was rather high-handed with the smaller powers. '*Y-a-t-il d'objections? Non? Adopté.*' Like a machine gun. He reminded Wickham Steed of an express train.
David Robin Watson, GEORGES CLEMENCEAU: A POLITICAL BIOGRAPHY 1974

5 During the Versailles Peace Conference of 1919 Balfour was asked his opinion on a proposal. He spoke at some length, carefully balancing the arguments on each side, until Clemenceau drily cut in: 'Pour ou contre?'
Sydney H. Zebel, BALFOUR: A POLITICAL BIOGRAPHY

CLAUD COCKBURN

Born 1904 in China. British author and journalist. Was foreign correspondent for *The Times*, but on becoming a communist left the paper for the *Daily Worker*. His several volumes of autobiography were collected under the title of *I Claud*, 1967. Died 1981.

6 In order to dispense the extra-special bits of political news which he picked up on his rounds he founded a small, mimeographed private news letter called *The Week*. It had a circulation of only a few hundreds, but it was read by influential people. In 1938 it ran the story having world-wide sensational significance about what Cockburn christened the Cliveden Set. It said that Cliveden had become Britain's second Foreign Office, that statesmen under the chairmanship of Lady Astor debated shifting foreign policy there, that Eden's downfall was plotted there. The story crashed and reverberated across two continents. The Cliveden friends found themselves at the white hot core of a great international uproar.
Geoffrey Bocca, Sunday Express 12 *Feb* 1956

7 Claud Cockburn was a journalist and an oddity even among the oddities of Fleet Street. He was a shaggy-haired, tweedy, somewhat eccentric young man with an agonising sense of humour. He was a product of Oxford, joined the *Times* editorial staff and was appointed by Geoffrey Dawson first to the Berlin and afterwards the Washington office of the paper. Then Cockburn, as he succinctly put it himself, 'turned red' and he became political correspondent for the *Daily Worker*, working under the name of Frank Pitcairn. Communism had little effect on Cockburn's way of life. He maintained a butler, and his wife rode to hounds.
Ibid.

8 Claud is a progressive who enjoys Kipling and Wodehouse, a materialist who distrusts Freud, a libertarian who regrets the existence of homosexuals, an atheist who believes in luck, a drinking man who never has a hangover, an exercise-hater for whom walking is the extreme penalty of poverty.
Alan Brien, Sunday Times 26 *May* 1968

9 Cockburn is known to have associations with many far from desirable elements in the lower walks of journalistic life. It is only reasonable to state that Cockburn is a man whose intelligence and capability, combined with his left-wing tendencies and an unscrupulous nature, make him a formidable factor.
MI5 report to the Prime Minister, 1934. *Quoted Patricia Cockburn*, THE YEARS OF THE WEEK 1968

10 Cockburn's basic and correct notion is that news exists only when a journalist envisages it, in the same way that history exists only in the minds of historians, or as faith exists only in the souls of the faithful.
Malcolm Muggeridge, Observer 24 *Sep* 1967

11 The notorious headline *Small Earthquake in Chile; Not Many Dead* with which Claud Cockburn claimed to have won a competition for dullness among sub-editors on *The Times* during the 1930s has proved

impossible to trace despite an exhaustive search. It may just have been a smoking-room story.
Nigel Rees, SAYINGS OF THE CENTURY 1984

1 The cap and bells of a jester sat more easily on him than the hammer and sickle of a commissar; in his most earnest ideological phase he remained nearer to P. G. Wodehouse than to Karl Marx.
The Times, Obituary 17 *Dec* 1981

2 He became a master of the fine art of letting cats out of bags, and, if there were no cats he cheerfully and resourcefully invented them. Cocking snooks at the Official Secrets Act, in constant peril of libel action, he led a journalistic charmed life.
Ibid.

3 'If you go on like this' Sir John Wheeler-Bennett once said, 'you'll soon be either quite famous or in jail', to which Cockburn replied 'Lots of people have been both.'
Ibid.

JEAN COCTEAU

Born in France 1889. Novelist, playwright and film director. Died 1962.

4 He became ill. For several days he could not sleep, eat or smoke opium. His throat was completely constricted. At last someone puffed opium smoke into his mouth; and like a galvanised corpse he staggered from his bed, and gave a virtuoso performance that was full of ideas, wit and poetry.
Cecil Beaton, DIARY *Spring* 1936

5 A fakir-thin body is held up by legs as thin as a sparrow's; yet curiously, he has flat feet. His hands seem so brittle you are afraid a sharp blow may break them off. The fingers taper, can bend backwards. The nails are discoloured and slightly dirty (a sign of the dope addict's *laisser-aller*).
Ibid.

6 The dilated pupils of his bulging fishy eyes, anguished and tortured, aghast and helpless, seem to be looking into another existence.
Ibid.

7 Looking like cheese, Jean came out to the ruins of the Paris Exhibition to be photographed. It was very cold. His nose turned purple, making the rest of the face seem even more grey, green and yellow. But the low temperature did not chill his volubility. Indeed, I could hardly persuade him to stop talking long enough for exposures to be made.
Ibid.

8 Perhaps the most surprising thing about him was that despite his fashionable eccentricities he was such an able organiser of the talents of others. He managed to head a school of composers without ever writing music and to put on ballets with little knowledge of the dance. Much of his best work was done in the cinema — essentially a collaborative art.
David Bradbury, MAKERS OF MODERN CULTURE (*Edited by Justin Wintle*) 1981

9 He turned from the Establishment without looking back lest he become 'a pillar of sugar'.
Cyril Connolly, Sunday Times 22 *Nov* 1970

10 He let opium choose his friends.
Cyril Connolly

11 In 1915 when Picasso was in his 'harlequin' period Cocteau came to see him having previously garbed himself in a harlequin costume under his trench coat to facilitate the interview. It was in every sense a Coctelian master-stroke — of mirror theatre, of chameleon art, of aesthetic hero-worship. Briefly, the master purred.
Richard Holmes, The Times 11 *Nov* 1970

12 With Cocteau we are at once in a world of eternal mirrors, of reflections which kiss each other, fantasies that become realities, poets that become statues, autobiography that becomes myth, sinuous obsessions that become crystalline cinema, corpses that become angels and men that become women.
Ibid.

13 In his time Cocteau embraced an enormous number of art forms, from pipe-cleaner sculpture and necktie design, via pottery, posters, tapestry, costume jewellery, drawing and murals to choreography, scenarios, journalism, plays, criticism, travelogues, novels, poems and film making, as well as playing the bongos and managing the bantamweight boxer Panama Al Brown.
Ibid.

14 A friend once said that Cocteau discussed his own colds as if they were railway disasters.
Ibid.

15 His marginal gifts were perhaps best summarised by his observation on the sight of Proust lying dead in his bedroom with the manuscript of *A La Recherche du Temps Perdu* piled on the mantelpiece: 'that pile of paper on his left was still alive, like watches ticking on the wrists of dead soldiers' — a

characteristic spasm of elegant but somehow chilling wit.
Ibid.

1 If Cocteau belonged to no party but his own, his own was the intersecting point of everybody else's.
Elizabeth Spriggs and Jean-Jacques Kihm, COCTEAU: THE MAN AND THE MIRROR 1968

2 Maurice Goudeket, Cocteau's schoolmate, Colette's widower, in his seventies, newly remarried and the father of a small son whose godfather was Cocteau, told me about boasting to him of the boy's precocity: 'He's been walking since he was six months old.' Cocteau's retort: 'Where is he now?'
Francis Steegmuller, COCTEAU 1970

3 Everyone knew how chimerical and unmarriageable Cocteau's 'proposals of marriage' could be.
Ibid.

4 He tried to turn everything into self-advertisement, including his death.
Stravinsky. Quoted Frederick Brown, AN IMPERSONATION OF ANGELS 1969

5 Because he was not martyred by others — like Wilde — or by himself — like Brian Howard — this dancing Peter Pan of the Ecole de Paris does arouse envious or moralistic reactions; more often, both.
Philip Toynbee, Observer 24 *Jan* 1968

6 He once described himself as being on the extreme Right of contemporary letters, joining the circle with the extreme Left, and therefore finding himself within easy earshot of his opposites.
John Wain, Observer 22 *Nov* 1970

7 We might almost apply to him his own epigram on Victor Hugo and say Jean Cocteau was a madman who thought he was Jean Cocteau.
Ibid.

8 I met a young man of nineteen or twenty who at that time vibrated with all the youth of the world . . . It is one of the regrets of later years to have watched the fading of that light.
Edith Wharton. Quoted Elizabeth Spriggs and Jean-Jacques Kihm, JEAN COCTEAU: THE MAN AND THE MIRROR 1968

9 It may well be that behind the silliness, the go-getting and the tinsel there was, after all, a touch of genius. As somebody has said, there are phoney phoneys and genuine phoneys. If Cocteau was a phoney he was on such a grand scale that he made a career of it.
John Weightman, Observer 21 *Sep* 1969

10 He was one of those homosexuals who boost their young men; two of them at least, Raymond Radiguet and Jean Marais, achieved fame, and perhaps would not have done so but for him.
Ibid.

MARCUS (COOK) CONNELLY

Born 1890 in America. Playwright who, in 1930, attracted great attention and aroused considerable controversy with *The Green Pastures*, a re-enactment of Bible stories in terms of the lives of the Negroes of the Deep South, and which presented God on the stage.

11 Isabel Leighton, the writer, aspired to be an actress and landed a bit part in *Deburau*. She reported triumphantly to the crowd at the Round Table: 'All I do is walk once across the stage, but it's a start.' 'What theatre do you open at?' asked Marc Connelly. 'The Belasco.' 'Too bad it isn't the Hippodrome,' said Connelly, 'your part would have been twice as big.'
Bennett Cerf, TRY AND STOP ME 1947

12 Harold Ross, editor of the *New Yorker*, once complained 'Thurber's women don't have any sex appeal.' Marc Connelly reminded him 'They do for Thurber's men.'
Ibid.

13 Seated one afternoon at the Round Table the puckish, uninhibited and entirely bald Connelly felt a man run his hand from his forehead to the back of his head. 'That feel's just like my wife's behind,' the fellow said. Marc waited just a split second before replying, 'So it does,' he said.
Howard Teichmann, SMART ALECK 1976

14 Returning from Europe Connelly was presented in the press next day as 'A sun-tanned Marc Connelly has come back to New York with a new three-act play.' Speculation arose immediately at the Algonquin. 'Knowing Marc,' a Round Table member said, 'I'll bet he doesn't have a full three-act play.' 'I doubt that he has two acts,' replied a second. Woollcott looked around the assembled group. 'I say he doesn't even have a sun-tan,' he pronounced conclusively.
Ibid.

15 The 'sensation' of the play [*Green Pastures*] — it has caused 'a greater sensation in New York than any other play of the century' — is that God Himself is one of the chief

characters. He, too, is a Negro and wears a white shirt, bow tie, black alpaca coat, black trousers, and Congress gaiters. He smokes ten-cent cigars, and drinks custard, calls the Archangel Gabriel 'Gabe', has an office with a roll-top desk, and works miracles accompanied by crashes of thunder.
Frank Whitaker, John o' London's Weekly 24 *May* 1930

1 He is an infuriating blend of poet, peacock and procrastinator.
Alexander Woollcott. Quoted Howard Teichmann, SMART ALECK 1976

CYRIL (VERNON) CONNOLLY

Born 1903. English essayist, critic and novelist. From 1940–9 he ran the magazine *Horizon*. His best-known work is *The Unquiet Grave*, which when it originally appeared in 1945 was published under the pen-name Palinurus. Died 1974.

2 Of all the boys at St Cyprian's Cyril Connolly was certainly the strangest, most fascinating character to me. He seemed so grown up. Even his face was dotted with adult moles. I got a bit of a shock when I discovered how much he knew about life. A few of us vaguely realised that someone's parents were titled, or had a large motor-car. But Cyril knew which of the masters had a financial interest in St Cyprian's, and which were only there on sufferance. He said it helped you to know how to behave towards them.
Cecil Beaton, DIARIES 1922–1939

3 Writers like Connolly gave pleasure a bad name.
E. M. Forster. Quoted Geoffrey Grigson, Guardian 30 *Sep* 1976

4 Egoism alone remains constant, and his journal throughout reveals the ingenuity and contrivance with which he managed to explain it away to himself. Blame was for other people.
David Pryce-Jones, CYRIL CONNOLLY: JOURNAL AND MEMOIR 1983

5 I suppose that none would dispute that the key to his behaviour was self-indulgence, which he made almost a rule of life.
Stephen Spender, Observer 10 *Jul* 1983

6 Connolly's famous description of the thin man imprisoned in the body of a fat man, signalling wildly to be let out, is after all a metaphor of punishment from Dante's *Inferno*. He makes this doubly clear in a letter written to his first wife in 1938: 'My own fat is to me the outward symbol of moral and mental fat and that is why I dislike it.'
Ibid.

7 His friend Peter Watson, who paid for *Horizon*, used to call him 'Squirrel' — a very good name, really, for a man so much of whose life was spent in a circular argument in which he used his gifts to explain his failure to use his gifts — Squirrel revolving in his cage.
Ibid.

JOSEPH CONRAD

Born in Poland, 1857. Original name Teodor Jozef Konrad Nalecz Korzeniowski. Wrote novels and short stories in English, his successes including *Lord Jim*, 1900 and *Typhoon*, 1902. Died 1924.

8 Conrad did nothing significant in the second half of his life except write.
Jocelyn Baines, JOSEPH CONRAD 1960

9 At first, through inexperience, he painted in strident primary colours. His sentences were enfeebled by a clinging burden of epithets. After a letter from H. G. Wells with a sting in the tail — 'You have everything it takes to become a splendid novelist except skill, but that comes with practice' — the style became sparser and more sinewy.
Second Earl of Birkenhead, Daily Telegraph 27 *Jul* 1957

10 He seems to write books about the sea, the Malay archipelago, and the Congo, but he is really writing about the desperate, convoluted hopeless heart of man.
Anthony Burgess reviewing Frederick R. Karl's JOSEPH CONRAD: THE THREE LIVES, *Observer*, 6 *May* 1979

11 I sit down for eight hours every day — and the sitting down is all. In the course of that working day of eight hours I write three sentences which I erase before leaving the table in despair.
Conrad, letter to Edward Garnett

12 It is a curious fact that Joseph Conrad to the day of his death retained a weatherbeaten complexion, and this after over thirty years ashore, and after leading, almost without exception, an indoor life. From his table to his bed, for days and days on end, those few

steps would be the only physical exercise he could be induced to take.
Mrs Joseph Conrad, CONRAD AS I KNEW HIM 1927

1 Although he manipulated situations, combined them for dramatic effect, piled agony on agony by putting a single character through a series of situations in real life shared more modestly by a number of different men, his inventive faculty was as incapable of fabricating wholly imaginary situations as wholly imaginary characters.
Edward Crankshaw, JOSEPH CONRAD 1936

2 He had just finished his story *The End of the Tether* when the lamp on his work table exploded and burnt up his manuscript — from which little 'private disaster' he was rescued by a grant from the Royal Literary Fund, secured for him by Edmund Gosse and Henry James.
Malcolm Elwin, Daily Telegraph 14 *Jul* 1959

3 The secret casket of his genius contains a vapour rather than a jewel.
E. M. Forster, ABINGER HARVEST

4 I read you as I listen to rare music — with deepest depths of surrender, and out of those depths I emerge slowly and reluctantly again to acknowledge reluctantly that I return to life.
Henry James, letter to Conrad 1 *Nov* 1906

5 Conrad's stories, so strangely diverse in scenery and skill, are a unique archipelago in the ocean of fiction. They are often steep and (in the nautical sense) foul; but there are many of us, the old backroom boys of literature, who would rather be marooned there than almost anywhere else.
Christopher Morley, John o' London's Weekly 15 *Aug* 1949

6 He thought of civilised and morally tolerable human life as a dangerous walk on a thin crust of barely cooled lava that might break and let the unwary sink into fiery depths.
Bertrand Russell. Quoted Norman Sherry, CONRAD AND HIS WORLD

(JOHN) CALVIN COOLIDGE

Born 1872. President of United States 1923–9. Died 1933.

7 There is a famous anecdote about a Sunday when Mr Coolidge attended church without his wife. When he returned to the White House she asked what the subject of the sermon had been. 'Adultery' said the President. 'What did he say about it?' she persisted. Coolidge thought for a moment. 'He was against it,' he reported finally.
Bennett Cerf, TRY AND STOP ME 1947

8 One of his famous statements referred to war debts. 'They hired the money, didn't they?'
Daily Telegraph 6 *Jan* 1933

9 As he grew into public life he became known as 'Honest Cal', and later as 'Cautious Cal', but from first to last he was 'Silent Cal'.
Ibid.

10 At one of the White House press conferences reporters were vainly firing their questions at Coolidge. 'Have you anything to say about Prohibition?' 'No.' 'About the forthcoming senatorial campaign?' 'No.' The meeting broke up and the reporters began to file out of the room. 'And,' called the President, 'Don't quote me.'
Edmund Fuller, ANECDOTES FOR ALL OCCASIONS 1942

11 Two Massachusetts senators got into an angry debate and one told the other he could 'go to hell'. The man thus consigned called on Governor Coolidge and asked him to do something about it. Coolidge replied: 'I have looked up the law, Senator, and you don't have to go there.'
Ibid.

12 A newspaper correspondent visited Coolidge at Plymouth, watched the automobiles rolling by and said 'It must make you proud to see all these people coming by here, merely to look at you sitting on the porch. It shows that although you are an ex-President you are not forgotten. Just look at the number of those cars'. 'Not as many as yesterday,' replied Coolidge 'There were 163 then.'
Ibid.

13 Silent Cal Coolidge was an undoubted mediocrity, but as funny in his way as Buster Keaton.
Philip Howard, The Times 10 *Dec* 1981

14 Mr Coolidge's genius for inactivity is developed to a very high point. It is far from being an indolent activity. It is a grim, determined, alert activity which keeps Mr Coolidge occupied constantly. Inactivity is a political philosophy and a party programme with Mr Coolidge.
Walter Lippmann, MEN OF DESTINY

15 He looks as if he had been weaned on a pickle.
Alice Roosevelt Longworth

1 How could they tell?
Dorothy Parker, on being told that Coolidge had died

2 'You must talk to me Mr Coolidge,' said a woman at a party. 'I've made a bet that I can get more than two words out of you.' 'You lose', he answered, poker-faced.
Isabel Ross, GRACE COOLIDGE AND HER ERA

3 A runty, aloof little man, who quacks through his nose when he speaks.
William Allen White. Quoted C. M. Fuess, CALVIN COOLIDGE

(ALFRED) DUFF COOPER, VISCOUNT NORWICH OF ALDWICK

Born 1890. British politician and author. First Lord of the Admiralty 1937–8. Resigned in opposition to the Munich Pact. Joined war cabinet under Churchill. Appointed ambassador to France 1944–7. Wrote biographies of Talleyrand and Haig. Died 1954.

4 A noted lecher, he began seeking extramarital diversions even during his honeymoon and procuring suitable partners for him became one of his wife's occupations.
John Carey, Sunday Times 20 *Sep* 1981

5 Duff is considered by men who have a better knowledge of his potential than I do to be one of the most remarkable men of his generation; he has political foresight, courage and wisdom that are unique. Behind his shyness there is a force that could make him worthy of leading the country.
Cecil Beaton, DIARY *Sep* 1944

6 He has perhaps the most civilised mind of any man I know; his intelligence, erudition and general knowledge make me feel inadequate. There is no subject — even photography or design — about which he does not know more than I; even after all these years I am shy with him.
Ibid. 1947

7 At dinner at Emerald's Duff was in a violent, vehement, tipsy mood, and attacked everybody and everything, particularly Mr Chamberlain. He still harps on that and finally I gently asked him how long he had served under him. Duff, rather nettled, went red in the face. He can be so difficult and opinionated.
Sir Henry Channon, DIARY 12 *Dec* 1942

8 Emerald tells me that Duff Cooper, who is in the gentlest of moods these days, remarked to her that all his life he had tried to make people like him and always failed. He cited me as an example, praised me and added that he knew I only tolerated him because of Diana. This is, of course, true, though I do like him better of late.
Ibid. 28 *Jan* 1943

9 The Conservative opponents of appeasement got few rewards (from Churchill); Duff Cooper, the true hero of Munich, only got the ministry of information.
A. J. P. Taylor, ENGLISH HISTORY 1914–1945 1965

DIANA COOPER, VISCOUNTESS NORWICH OF ALDWICK

Born 1892. Daughter of the Duke of Rutland. Briefly pursued an acting career in 1920s. Married Alfred Duff Cooper and from then devoted herself to supporting him in his political career.

10 Diana's main faults are that she takes money from men and spends her day powdering her face until she looks like a bled pig.
Margot Asquith. Quoted Philip Ziegler, DIANA COOPER 1981

11 What a pity that Diana, so pretty and decorative, should let her brain rot.
Ibid.

12 Lady Diana Cooper appeared, wearing an enormous apricot-coloured garden hat. Surely she must be the most beautiful Englishwoman alive today. I stared in awe. Her face was a perfect oval, her skin white-marble. Her lips were japonica red, her hair flaxen, her eyes blue love-in-the-mist.
Cecil Beaton, DIARIES 1922–1939

13 Although Diana takes her own unconventionality with her wherever she goes, awe of the British Embassy is obviously paramount in the minds of the Parisians. Little wonder that an elderly Frenchman, arriving unexpectedly early, was surprised when Diana, unbuttoning her trousers to change into a skirt, asked him point blank 'And what can I do for you?'
Ibid. 29 *Oct* 1944

14 Diana sends me a wire to come to Bognor. Although the sirens sound thirty times day and night, it is a comparatively peaceful existence running the place as a farm. She has always been attuned to the time and circle she adorns. Today she is beautiful in

GARY COOPER

the only way she could be admired at the moment. Wearing dungarees of blue canvas, flecked and splashed in many colours, her head tied up in a kerchief over which she wears a straw hat, she manages artlessly to look as beautiful as she did in *The Miracle*.
Ibid. *Dec* 1940

1 She hates fuss. Arriving to spend the night in a strange town she never seeks the best hotel. She says: 'Charm is what we're after — not revolving doors.'
Ibid. 29 *Oct* 1944

2 It was as an actress that she made her biggest hit. Improbably cast as a statue of the Virgin Mary in Reinhardt's *The Miracle* she toured the USA and Europe to world acclaim in the 1920s. Since the part entailed standing mute in a stone niche it did not test her to the full, but devotees agreed that her aristocratic poise distinguished her gratifyingly from the mere professionals.
John Carey, Sunday Times 20 *Sep* 1981

3 A blank helpless sort of face, rather like a rose just before you drench it with DDT.
Ibid. (*of a photograph of Diana Cooper*)

4 Men of every age flocked around her like gulls round a council tip.
Ibid.

5 I called on the Coopers who came back last night from Cairo via Malta. Poor Diana, who loathes flying, and is always terrified, has flown right around the world, in itself almost a record. She was looking lovely, slim and glamorous and embraced me affectionately.
Sir Henry Channon, DIARY 17 *Feb* 1942

6 This morning I Christmas-shopped with Diana Cooper. What an amazing character she is, with her energy, her beauty, and her wit; her broad-mindedness is staggering and she is still startlingly beautiful, with her wide, rather vacant, staring eyes; no detail of life is too much trouble for her; her interest in everything is acute, operative, and her taste exquisite and flawless. She reminds me of Obsidian or Onyx, shiny and metallic.
Ibid. 19 *Dec* 1934

7 Last night on my return home from the House I was surprised to hear what I thought was quacking coming from my Amalienburg dining room. On investigating I found twelve ducks in a basket in the blue and silver banqueting room, left 'to rest' there by Diana Cooper, who this morning fetched them and took them with her to Paris.
Ibid. 3 *Jun* 1949

8 Brilliant, brittle and blonde, with the palest watery blue eyes.
Sefton Delmer, Daily Express 1925

9 Diana will be no good at all [as Ambassador's wife in Paris]. She will be rude to the bores and she will wear trousers because they are comfortable and offend everyone. Only if there is an earthquake or a revolution will she show her true metal. But who knows? There may be both.
Lady Bridget McEwen, letter to her husband 1945

10 Even at the age of 18 she could not enter a room without being noticed or leave it without causing a sense of loss. And at 88 she can still command the attention of a crowded room.
Philip Ziegler, DIANA COOPER 1981

GARY COOPER

Born 1901 in America. Real name Frank James Cooper. Film actor. Began his career in 1925 in a silent film *The Winning of Barbara Worth*. Received Academy awards for his roles in *Sergeant York*, 1941, and *High Noon*, 1952. Died 1961.

11 Until I came along, all the leading men were handsome, but luckily they wrote a lot of stories about the fellow next door.
Gary Cooper

12 The understandably popular Gary Cooper underacts more completely than any other player within memory.
New York Herald Tribune 1930

13 There is something about the sadness in Mr Cooper's eyes which reminds the middle-aged observer that Mr Cooper has been at it a long time.
New York Times 1950

14 One of the best-loved illiterates this country has ever known.
Carl Sandburg. Quoted Leslie Halliwell, THE FILMGOER'S BOOK OF QUOTES 1978

15 So solid was his box office appeal that producers hardly bothered finding him good scripts. Instead they used him to prop up movies that otherwise would never have been made. The unfortunate result was films that are worth seeing for his performance but are otherwise fairly mediocre.
Bob Smyth, Radio Times 13 *May* 1971

16 His command of his craft was so easy and unobtrusive that it often went unnoticed, but any lingering doubts about his acting ability

SIR NOËL COWARD

can hardly be sustained after the most cursory glance at a list of his performances.
The Times, Obituary 15 *May* 1961

1 I watched him stumble and stutter his way through a scene for *The Fountainhead*, the first film we made together. Imagine my amazement when I watched our first day's work on the screen and observed and heard a performance that overflowed with charm and personality.
King Vidor

2 He got a reputation as a great actor just by thinking hard about the next line.
Ibid.

3 You could never put Coop in a small hat and get your money back.
Richard Zanuck

SIR NOËL COWARD

Born 1899. English actor, playwright, composer, film director. Among his best-known plays are *Private Lives*, 1930 and *Blithe Spirit*, 1941; his best-known film script *Brief Encounter*, 1945. Died 1973.

4 Noël Coward told me how to avoid hostility. That, he explained, was why he studied his own 'façade'. Take his voice; it was definite, harsh, rugged. He moved firmly and solidly, dressed quietly. 'You should appraise yourself,' he went on. 'One would like to indulge one's own taste. I myself dearly love a good match, yet I know it is overdoing it to wear tie, socks and handkerchief all of the same colour.'
Cecil Beaton, THE WANDERING YEARS 1962

5 There was a famous fun-fair at Margate to which we often used to go in the evenings, and I shall never forget the excitement in my office in the City when one day a telegram arrived: 'Meet me in Dreamland tonight at ten o'clock. Noël Coward'.
Lord Boothby, RECOLLECTIONS OF A REBEL 1978

6 I was a talented child, God knows.
Noël Coward, PRESENT INDICATIVE 1937

7 Mr Coward excites and titillates by shovelling up the ordure of an unprincipled smart set.
James Douglas, Sunday Express

8 The younger generation is knocking at the dustbin.
Sir Gerald du Maurier 1924

9 I went [in 1924] to see Noël at the Royalty Theatre in Dean Street. His dressing room was full of bottles of Chanel No. 5, with twenty dressing gowns in the wardrobe.
John Gielgud, AN ACTOR AND HIS TIME 1979

10 A very ugly man. He has moreover a thin, flat behind which implies shallowness of character.
James Lees-Milne, DIARIES: 1946–7 1983

11 It is proof of Mr Coward's adroitness that he has managed to disguise the grimness of his comedy, and to conceal from the audience that his conception of love is desolating and false.
Desmond MacCarthy, HUMANITIES

12 I thought Noël Coward the most electric person I ever met. I hear that in addition to writing plays, acting, composing music, he also paints. I shouldn't be surprised; one would never be surprised at anything Noël Coward did.
Ethel Mannin, CONFESSIONS AND IMPRESSIONS 1930

13 I shall always carry in my mind a picture of Noël Coward in George Doran's sitting room at the Savoy one night after a party. 'The distinguished American publisher' had just made a remark about being 'ware of women with loose hips because it generally went with loose lips. Noël leapt up and did a *pas seul* round the room with his coat-tails flying, chanting like a revue catch number 'Loose about the hips, loose about the lips'. He said what marvellous words they would make for a fox-trot song.
Ibid.

14 Meeting him several years after my first encounter he appeared quite unchanged, the same gushing manner; everyone is 'darling' and he used it a great deal years before it became fashionable; the same droll way of saying 'my deah!' when he is amused or pained; the same impression that he only stays still by force of will, and that if he let himself go he would be doing a step-dance round the room the whole time, chanting amusing couplets, rhyming flagellation with adulation, and things like that.
Ibid.

15 I found the music of *Bitter-Sweet* the essence of all the musical comedy staleness and all the *Blue Danube* sentimentality ever orchestrated.
Ibid.

16 By the time of his great theatrical coup in 1925 with four shows running simultaneously in the West End, Coward could arrive (late) in an ordinary suit at a

Bloomsbury party where everyone else wore evening dress, call for silence and announce magnanimously, 'I don't want anyone to feel embarrassed.'
Sheridan Morley, A TALENT TO AMUSE 1969

1 His first London appearance was in *The Goldfish* at the Little Theatre in 1911, 'a boy with elfin ears and a foul temper' who slapped June Howard-Tripp with a ballet slipper and subsequently proved his professional aplomb by stealing her one and only line when she was immobilised by a chocolate eclair.
Ibid.

2 Mr Coward, like Miss Dietrich, is his own invention and contribution to this century. Anyone who cannot see that should keep well away from the theatre.
John Osborne. Quoted Sheridan Morley, A TALENT TO AMUSE 1969

3 I passed Noël Coward by the National Gallery and argued with myself whether I should go and give him the one on the chin I owe him. I had been to see him in his dressing room at the time of *The Vortex*. He was lying on a sofa, washed out. When I left I found the door wouldn't open. I fumbled with the key, but it wasn't that. I heard giggling. That made me still more flustered. I then discovered it was a trick. There was an iron plate on the bottom of the door, and I was standing on it so that the door held fast. In my confusion, when I did get out, I fell down three stone steps and sprawled in a passage. I thought it a mean sort of trick, but no doubt it is time I got over disliking Coward because of it. I shall go on disliking his clipped way of talking instead.
Reginald Pound, THEIR MOODS AND MINE 1937

4 He was once Slightly in *Peter Pan*, and has been wholly in Peter Pan ever since.
Kenneth Tynan. Quoted on BBC Radio 4 'Quote, Unquote' 15 *Sep* 1979

JOAN CRAWFORD

Original name Lucille le Sueur. Born in America 1906. Film actress. Died 1977.

5 Joan Crawford was the perfect image of the movie star, and, as such, largely the creation of her own indomitable will.
George Cukor. Quoted Alexander Walker, JOAN CRAWFORD: THE ULTIMATE STAR 1983

6 Joan Crawford drank 120-proof vodka all the time she was filming and *still* managed to block the lighting and cast dark shadows on her co-stars' faces.
Sheila Graham, MY HOLLYWOOD 1984

7 Joan Crawford is the only actress to read the whole script. Most actresses just read their own lines to find out what clothes they're going to wear.
Anita Loos, KISS HOLLYWOOD GOODBYE

8 Nobody suffered on screen quite as she did, the great eyes brimming with manfully-fought-back tears, the wide pillar-box gash of a mouth quivering before some frantic contortion brought the impregnable teeth into play to signify an invincible will rising above adversity.
John Russell Taylor, The Times 18 *Nov* 1967

9 The war years gave her no new image; somehow the idea of a Crawford helping the Resistance in her mink did not catch on.
Ibid.

10 A light-red-haired, Slav-jawboned, and million-volt-eyed woman of thirty-eight, named, in chronological order, Lucille LeSeuer, Joan Fairbanks, Joan Tone, Joan Terry and Joan Crawford. There may be another name soon, but in reality it has always been Joan Crawford.
Roland Wild, Illustrated 3 *Aug* 1946

11 A producer said: 'I saw her at the Opera, and believe me, when the audience spotted Joan, with star sapphires and ermines, and that air she has of bugles blowing and banners flying, nobody cared whether Tristan and Isolde ever got together again or not.'
Ibid.

12 When La Crawford tries her lines for the first time she says to the director, 'That stinks, ya? You want me to show a little enthusiasm when I say I love him?' When the piece goes right she says, 'That's IT.' So far as I know, no living director has yet said in reply, 'That's NOT it.'
Ibid.

13 Joan Crawford is now trapped in the cycle of pictures which show amnesia, split minds, alcoholism and other interesting psychopathic maladies in interesting succession.
Ibid.

14 She is much given to good works once they have been glamourised, and would not step on the hands of another girl grasping at a straw except under exceptional circumstances. Nobody with a life such as

that lived by the Queen of Hollywood today would do anything different.
Ibid.

DR (HENRY HAWLEY) CRIPPEN

Born 1861 in America. English murderer, the first criminal to be captured by the use of wireless. Executed 1910.

1 Crippen was a nasty little creature. Marie Lloyd used to call him 'The Half Crown King'. He used to wear a red-spotted waistcoat, and had goggly eyes behind gold-rimmed glasses. His favourite trick was to ask someone to have a drink with him. Then to order one for himself as well, then to discover he had left his money at the office, or at home, or some other excuse. In the end the other fellow paid and Crippen got the drink.
Naomi Jacob, ME, A CHRONICLE ABOUT OTHER PEOPLE 1933

2 Crippen's wife Belle Elmore was a ballad singer. She wasn't a good artist; in fact she was a quite remarkably bad one. When she failed to attend two meetings of the Music-hall Ladies Guild Mrs Coborn and Miss Lottie Albert called at Crippen's office. Crippen said she had gone to stay in the country, and generally hemmed and hawed a great deal. Two days later he sent them a letter to say that his wife was dead. They again called at his office so that the Guild might send a wreath. His whole manner made them both so suspicious that they left the office and went round to Bow Street.
Ibid.

3 I remember at the trial, Crippen's counsel worked up a most ingenious defence for this unpleasant little creature, but he was convicted. Poor Belle Elmore — who people told me was a kindly creature, given to taking rather more alcohol than was good for her, but that was all — was drawn as a frightful harridan who had made Crippen's life a burden to him.
Ibid.

4 Inspector Dew, disguised as a pilot, came aboard to arrest him. His nerve broke. Emotionally overcome, hopes dashed in destruction, the guilty man was inclined to sob his grief, and sank back on the settee while Dew still held his hand. Then did Dr Crippen throw down his defence in one single utterance. 'Thank God it is all over. The suspense has been too great. I couldn't stand it any longer.'
Captain H. K. Kendall, ADVENTURES ON THE HIGH SEAS 1939

5 He was well mannered, the very essence of politeness, a great reader, a non-smoker and (so far as I could see) a total abstainer. He came into my cabin one day with a book. 'I have brought you this to read,' he said. 'It will just suit you, a detective story by Edgar Wallace. It is called *The Four Just Men*. All about a murder in London, and £500 reward.' Pretty callous for one who had murdered his own wife.
Ibid.

6 Anyone sitting on the *Montrose*'s deck could tell by the crackling electric sparking that words were being sent forth. Well do I remember Crippen sitting in a deck chair, looking aloft, listening to this noise and remarking: 'What a wonderful invention!' Little did he realise that this 'wonderful invention' was to bring him to the scaffold.
Ibid.

7 The *Montrose* had not long left Antwerp before I became suspicious of two of the passengers. I immediately sent off a wireless message: 'Have strong suspicion that Crippen, London cellar murderer, and accomplice are among saloon passengers. Moustache taken off. Growing beard. Accomplice dressed as boy. Voice, manner and build undoubtedly girl. Travelling as Mr and Master Robinson.'
Ibid.

SIR (RICHARD) STAFFORD CRIPPS

Born 1889. British politician. Expelled from the Labour party in 1939 for advocating formation of a Popular Front with the Communists. Served in Churchill's war cabinet. Readmitted to the Labour Party in 1945, and was Chancellor of the Exchequer 1947–50. Died 1952.

8 Cripps had a heart of gold, but he was an ascetic, a vegetarian, a teetotaller, and by nature a schoolmaster.
Lord Boothby, RECOLLECTIONS OF A REBEL 1978

9 I dined with a curious collection of guests, including Sir Stafford Cripps, who has charming manners, and is honest, if demented, but agreeable to meet and to talk to. He ate three scraped carrots, some salad

BING CROSBY

and an orange, nothing cooked. He only drank orange juice.
Sir Henry Channon, DIARY 8 *Mar* 1944

1 The Steel Nationalisation Bill. Cripps in a particularly nauseous glib speech wound up for the Government, and made some startling statements. All through he was barracked, heckled and interrupted by the rightly indignant Opposition, led by Winston. Cripps lost his temper for a second and made a damaging admission 'If we cannot get Nationalisation of steel by legal means we must resort to violent methods.' This ill-timed threat of Revolution threw the House into an uproar.
Ibid. 15 *Nov* 1949

2 In the lobby I passed Cripps and the air chilled. I felt as if I had breathed the dark, fetid atmosphere of beyond the tomb.
Ibid. 14 *Jun* 1950

3 The trouble is, his chest is a cage in which two squirrels are at war; his conscience and his career.
Winston Churchill. Quoted Lord Moran, DIARY

4 He delivers his speech with an expression of injured guilt.
Winston Churchill

5 Sir Stafford Cripps, if he continues, is more likely to be the architect of British Fascism, based on the fears of a frightened middle class, than Sir Oswald Mosley.
Manchester Guardian 1932

6 Sir Stafford Cripps, known abroad as Sir Scrapps, among his friends as Scrappy, and among the ungrateful proletariat as Cripes.
Morning Post 1932

7 Only one thing seems to be lacking among his many talents. 'He is not at home,' Fenner Brockway noticed, 'among the working class, and workers do not feel at ease with him.'
Observer Profile 5 *Oct* 1947

8 Perhaps if Stafford could for once say 'I don't know the answer' or 'Yes I was wrong' the barriers would disappear and Elijah would stand forth, glittering in his glory and visible to us all.
Ibid.

9 Oliver Baldwin mentioned that Cripps is half-Jewish, which helps, I suppose, to 'explain' him.
Reginald Pound, THEIR MOODS AND MINE 1937

(HARRY LILLIS) BING CROSBY

Born 1904. American singer and actor. Became the world's most successful singer in terms of records with his 'crooning' style. Made many popular films, particularly in partnership with Bob Hope. Died 1977.

10 A gentleman who took success casually but elegantly.
President Carter

11 When I first started in movies they said my ears stuck out too far. They said I looked like a taxi with both doors open. Know what they did? Before every scene they glued them to my head. Then I looked like a whippet. Trouble was, when I got on the set the hot lights melted the glue and half way through the scene my ears would spring back again.
Bing Crosby. Quoted Michael Parkinson, Sunday Times 16 *Oct* 1977

12 He told me last year that he still sang everywhere; in the shower, taking long walks, writing letters — but never on the golf course, which is where he died. 'That would be conspicuous. At golf, I only allow myself to whistle.'
Derek Jewell, Sunday Times 16 *Oct* 1977

13 He gave all Walter Mittys something to aspire to — including his singing. I did two shows with Bing Crosby in recent years and I came to the conclusion that of all the stars I have met, he was the one whose private personality came closest to his public image.
Michael Parkinson, Sunday Times 16 *Oct* 1977

14 A slightly built man in a battered hat who walked towards us as if he was about to break into a dance. He had, like Astaire and Wayne, a totally inimitable way of moving.
Ibid.

15 He carried a hat box under his arm. 'This here's my rug. Where's the gal who's gonna fix my rug?' 'Rug?' I said. 'My toop,' he said, pointing to his skull.
Ibid.

16 There was once a famous thing that he did while on a television show; he was asked by the interviewer why it was he had this calm about him, and a sort of unruffled air? He reached into his pocket and pulled out an enormous wad of dollar bills and said, 'that helps'.
Stefanie Powers. Quoted Charles Thompson, BING

(EDWARD) ALEISTER CROWLEY

Born 1875. English poet and author of books on magic and the occult. Notorious for his celebrations of Black Magic rites. Died 1947.

1 He bridged the gap between Oscar Wilde and Hitler.
Cyril Connolly. Quoted John Symonds, THE GREAT BEAST 1972

2 I met Crowley two or three times in 1939. His presence at lunch was announced several seconds before his arrival by a pungent reek as of an operating theatre. This came from his daily eye-opener, a toothmug of ether.
Maurice Richardson, Observer 26 *Oct* 1969

3 He demanded triple absinthes in his high quacking voice, then devoured snails, wild duck, venison and Camembert washed down with torrents of Burgundy, topped off with grappa and black Mexican cigars strong as fireworks. He had, as I believe is not unusual with heroin addicts, a hearty appetite.
Ibid.

4 His appearance, with that huge naked face and bulging eyes, was so arresting that it was hard not to stare. He was dressed like a duke in a musical comedy, in a tail coat and spongebag trousers and the period effect was increased by dated slang expressions like 'old top'.
Ibid.

5 It is always difficult with megalomaniac cranks to sort out fantasy and trickery from genuine delusion. It is particularly difficult in Crowley's case because he was not only manic and paranoid and often drugged to the eyes, but also an accomplished con-man, reminding one at moments a little of W. C. Fields.
Ibid.

GEORGE CUKOR

Born 1899. American film director. After an early career directing successful plays on Broadway went to Hollywood in 1929, and was responsible for more than fifty productions, his forty-seventh being *My Fair Lady* in 1964. Died 1983.

6 It is doubtful if either the stage or screen will ever see a more loving portrayal of Edwardian England, or for that matter a better musical, than *My Fair Lady*.
The Times, Obituary 26 *Jan* 1983

7 He had the considerable asset of being able to handle temperamental female stars as he revealed during the often turbulent days when he was making *The Women*, with a cast which included Norma Shearer, Rosalind Russell, Joan Crawford and Paulette Goddard.
Ibid.

8 Hollywood's cleverest director of beautiful stars.
Kenneth Tynan

GEORGE NATHANIEL CURZON, FIRST MARQUIS CURZON OF KEDLESTON

Born 1859. British politician. Viceroy of India 1899–1905. Foreign Secretary 1922–3. Died 1925.

9 My name is George Nathaniel Curzon/I am a most superior person.
Anon, THE BALLIOL MASQUE

10 Many qualities, but not quality; a prose mind, though its ardour prevented it from being commonplace.
Margot Asquith

11 I met Curzon in Downing Street, from whom I got the sort of greeting a corpse would give to an undertaker.
Stanley Baldwin, after being chosen Prime Minister in preference to Curzon, May 1923

12 One of his friends remarked that 'it was his misfortune to have the manner of a minor royalty without its habitual incapacity'.
David Dilkes, CURZON IN INDIA VOL 2 1970

13 The ex-Viceroy was treated shabbily. Both the Prime Minister and St John Brodrick, the Secretary of State for India, made excuses so there was no official reception for Curzon when he arrived at Charing Cross. The following day the roof of the station fell in. 'How like St John,' said Lady Curzon, 'to bring it off a day late.'
Ibid.

14 He would bore the Cabinet by endless discourses and when asked for his policies would look disconcerted and astonished.
H. A. L. Fisher. Quoted Harold Nicolson, DIARY 11 *Oct* 1933

15 He belongs to that class of clever men which has every gift except the gift of common sense.
Lloyd George, House of Commons 1909

16 In Parliamentary life, he was to be one who stayed to get his feet wet before deciding the ship was sinking.
Leonard Mosley of Lord Curzon in THE GLORIOUS FAULT

1 Like most politicians, Curzon burst into tears at the drop of a hat, was easily wounded, and carried about with him a load of vanity as big as the Ritz.
Malcolm Muggeridge, Observer 16 *May* 1965

2 He was a frightful man. I find his caddish treatment of Elinor Glyn more reprehensible than his partition of Bengal for which, as a matter of fact, there was quite a lot to be said. The famous authoress of *Three Weeks* was his mistress for a number of years, and then, in the most heartless way, he abandoned her to marry a second rich wife.
Ibid.

3 On first entering his room as the Secretary of State in the Foreign Office on January 6 1919, 'How ghastly!' he murmured, and pointing, asked, 'And what, Mr Clerk, may I ask is that?' 'Your writing table, sir.' 'I was not referring to the writing table, Mr Clerk. I was referring to the object on its surface.' 'Well sir, that is your inkstand.' 'I am dumbfounded. You assure me that this is the inkstand of the Secretary of State? It must be replaced immediately. When I was at the Privy Council Offices I was furnished with an inkstand of crystal and silver. This contraption, if I may say so, is merely brass and glass.'
Harold Nicolson, CURZON, THE LAST PHASE: 1919–1925 1934

4 The best criticism I heard of his maiden speech was from Walter Long. 'He is overtrained.' The same may be said of nearly every oration he delivered. He could be very direct, very lucid, but he could not get on his legs without uttering some phrase of resounding and somewhat challenging eloquence; the air of the man, too, made even the simplest sentence sound grandiloquent.
T. P. O'Connor, T.P.'s Weekly 13 *Oct* 1928

5 Even when he sat down to his meal at a cure resort in France he would sit almost in the lonely grandeur of a dictator and would issue his order for the dishes on a menu with an air of arrogant command.
Ibid.

6 As I was leaving his spacious house in Carlton House Terrace I saw him being placed by his retinue of servants on a couch — probably necessary to him in his weakening health. As I saw him lying wearily there, I thought it was one of the most pathetic and eloquent lessons I ever saw of the futility of great ambition.
Ibid.

7 Curzon, seeing soldiers bathing, was surprised that the lower orders had such white skins.
A. J. P. Taylor, ENGLISH HISTORY 1914–1945 1965

8 Curzon was unpopular in the Conservative party — disliked both for his pompous arrogance and his weakness. Curzon lacked resolution, despite his rigid appearance. He was one of nature's rats. He ran away over the Parliament bill; he succumbed to women's suffrage. He promised to stand by Asquith and then abandoned him. He did the same with Lloyd George. Beaverbrook has called him 'a political jumping-jack'.
Ibid.

D

SALVADOR DALI

Born 1904. Spanish painter who became famous for his surrealist, dream-world style, influenced by Freudian psychology. Collaborated with Luis Buñuel in surrealist films.

1 Dali has always behaved like the Mephistopheles of art, and at 69, his face a mass of wrinkles accentuated by startling eyebrows and the trade-mark, the lion-tamer's waxed moustache, he looks it.
Colin Bell, TV Times 1973

2 Every day Dali receives masses of press cuttings from all over the world. Harty asked him if he read them. 'Dali never reads,' said the maestro in his usual adoring third-person. 'Dali weighs them. If they heavy, Dali happy.'
Ibid.

3 Naïve souls who think that publishers are allowed to keep Dali's originals may be interested to know that he sold the *Don Quixote* set to a private collector for about ten times the fee he received for their use in book form.
Bennett Cerf, SHAKE WELL BEFORE USING 1948

4 For the 1939 World's Fair he cooked up a sideshow of diving mermaids in suggestive costumes that brought the censorship squad on the double. They were told that this was Dali's 'surrealist art', and were so mystified that they allowed the exhibition to continue.
Ibid.

5 Critics, disregarding Dali's personal eccentricities, agree that from a technical standpoint he is one of the greatest artists of all time. The master himself sees to it that he is publicised properly. He delivered one lecture about his art in a diving helmet. He designed a window display for a Fifth Avenue department store and carefully biding his time until the police, press and camera crew hove in view, smashed the plate-glass window in a frenzy of what might be called spontaneous combustion.
Ibid.

6 Dali, a dark, sinister, Bloomsbury-looking man, joined us for dinner. He told us that the anarchists had burnt his house. His conversation had a disastrous effect on Diana Cooper's night. She dreamed of women with flies coming out of their nipples and babies with piano instead of human legs.
Sir Henry Channon, DIARY 17 *Feb* 1938

7 I have Dalinian thought; the one thing the world will never have enough of is the outrageous.
Salvador Dali, DIARY OF A GENIUS 1966

8 I do not paint a portrait to look like the subject, rather does the person grow to look like his portrait.
Ibid.

9 Sooner or later everyone is bound to come to me. Some, untouched by my painting, concede that I draw like Leonardo. Others have discovered in me literary gifts superior to the skill which I reveal in my pictures. Others proclaim that I have a unique gift for the theatre. It is difficult to avoid coming under my sway in one way or another.
Salvador Dali, in the preface to his novel HIDDEN FACES

10 The only animals I really like are the rhinoceros and fillet of sole.
Salvador Dali. Quoted Colin Bell, TV Times 1973

11 Salvador Dali is reported to carry with him at all times a portrait of Lenin.
George A. Dondero. Speech to US Congress 10 *May* 1949

12 Dali's soft watch is a symbol for a lolling tongue, and a lolling tongue is a symbol for a fat penis.
Marcel Jean, THE HISTORY OF SURREALIST PAINTING 1960

13 At his best Dali is like someone dressed up as Siegfried who suddenly winks at the audience in the middle of an aria.
Philip Toynbee, Observer 26 *Jun* 1966

TAM DALYELL

Born 1932 in Scotland. Labour politician. Elected MP for West Lothian 1962. After the Falklands War conducted a long campaign concerning the circumstances surounding the sinking of the Argentinian battleship *Belgrano*.

1 In an Aberfoyle hotel, he got into a heated debate about disarmament with a Young Socialist. Several minutes after it had ended he suddenly lunged at the girl with a fork, stabbing her in the arm. She spun round, grabbed it, and hurled it across the room. 'Aha!' cried the empiricist, 'so you *do* believe in defence.'
Observer, Profile 27 *Aug* 1984

2 A gangling, physically disorientated man, with tufted hair and a slightly sepulchral voice; his foibles delight dedicated Tam watchers.
Ibid.

3 Four years at King's where he read history and economics, left him with a touching faith in academic wisdom. Not long ago a reporter entered the press gallery at the Commons to witness Dalyell, pale as a candle, shouting at an astounded William Waldegrave, Junior Minister and a fellow of All Souls. 'What on earth did Tam say?' the reporter enquired of a colleague. 'He said,' was the grave reply, 'You are a disgrace to All Souls.'
Ibid.

4 His hilltop family seat, The Binns, stands on 260 acres overlooking his mining constituency. It is now owned by the National Trust for Scotland. The Dalyells live in a flat in the house. The Labour MP Eric Heffer was once woken at 2 a.m. by blood-freezing screeches coming from the upper reaches of the house. It sounded like the first Mrs Rochester having one of her turns. *Heffer:* I think this house is haunted, Tam. I heard a ghost last night. *Dalyell:* No, Eric, you did not hear a ghost. Those were our peacocks.
Ibid.

5 He has a passion for eggs, which he carries around with him. In the BBC's Glasgow canteen he was offered a cup of tea. 'Thank you,' said Tam, producing two fresh eggs from his pocket, 'and I'll have these lightly boiled, please.'
Ibid.

6 You can't really understand Tam unless you met his mother. She used to stride around West Lothian in yellow stockings, referring to Cromwell as *that man*.
An unnamed friend. Quoted ibid.

7 In a properly ordered universe Tam Dalyell, Labour MP for Linlithgow, would be one of Margaret Thatcher's most dedicated supporters instead of being the scourge of her South Atlantic policy. Not only can he lay claim to the title of Sir Thomas Dalyell, tenth baronet of the Binns, but he was educated at Eton and Cambridge, and continues to live in a 17th century castle through which thousands of visitors troop (at £1.05 a head).
George Rosie, Sunday Times 26 *Aug* 1984

8 Although it is Tam Dalyell's two-year-long campaign of unceasing parliamentary questions to ferret out the facts behind the sinking of the *Belgrano* that has brought him to the fore, in fact he has been demanding answers of successive governments with badger-like persistence ever since he became an MP. 'It's parliamentary technique,' he says. 'I am a great believer in facts, and not generalisations.'
Ibid.

9 With the help of a band of friendly experts Dalyell has run campaigns on, among other things, the future of Diego Garcia (the Indian Ocean naval base) and the promotion of kidney transplants.
Ibid.

GABRIELE D'ANNUNZIO

Born 1863. Italian novelist, playwright, poet and patriot. Held Fiume for Italy after World War I (1919–20). A supporter of Mussolini. Died 1938.

10 The poet used to have his favourite motto 'Who shall keep me chained' engraved on all objects he presented to women.
Tom Antongini, D'ANNUNZIO 1938

11 He had an inordinate affection for scent, and used, on an average, a pint of eau de Coty daily.
Ibid.

12 The sad fact is that out of uniform or formal dress he was an unimpressive figure.
Ibid.

13 The stuff he was made from was nine-tenths tinsel — but a great deal may be done with tinsel, provided the limelight is bright enough.
John Brophy, John o' London's Weekly 29 *Apr* 1938

14 The fifty-year-old aesthete, with a long record of rhetorical poetry and perfumed amours behind him, suddenly became a man of action. He was a brilliant warrior, fighting

on land and sea and in the air by turns. No one can be sceptical about his physical bravery.
Ibid.

1 After the war he plunged again into active service as a rebel, risking his fame and his life in the quixotic adventure at Fiume . . . making half hourly orations from balconies, kissing the coffins of victims, having his bed decorated by girls with flowers thrice daily, seizing a sword and slashing up his sky-blue cloak and handing pieces to his officers.
Richard Church, John o' London's Weekly 16 *Nov* 1935

2 While D'Annunzio was living in France, a letter was addressed to him simply with the words 'To Italy's Greatest Poet'. He declined to accept it, saying that he was not Italy's greatest poet — he was the world's greatest poet.
Edmund Fuller, ANECDOTES 1942

3 He had the moral code of a barn-fowl and the sense of family responsibility of a cuckoo. One could almost forgive him if he had merely deserted the women who gave themselves to him; but he did worse. A Moral Bluebeard, he dissected the souls of his dead loves and buried the remains in his pornographic novels.
Gerald Griffin, GABRIELE D'ANNUNZIO 1935

4 All his servants are dressed like monks, and a church bell summons them to prayers and announces mealtimes.
John o' London's Weekly 4 *Apr* 1931

5 Before he was twenty-one he had eloped with a young Duchess and they were united in marriage. He had the magnetic power to attract attention, irresistible to certain types of women, with his elegancies, audacities, and his sensuous, voluptuous and flamboyant verse. He entered the free-living Italian world of luxury and fashion, a somewhat vulgar Don Juan.
P. Nardelli and Arthur Livingston, D'ANNUNZIO: A PORTRAIT 1931

6 Mussolini created a feudal estate for him on the shores of Lake Garda, and gave him title as Prince of Montenevoso — Prince of Snowy Mountain.
Ibid.

7 D'Annunzio affected many peculiarities to impress his few visitors. He would offer them occasionally a cocktail which he would describe as the actual potion presented by Hermes to Ulysses, to protect him from the snares of Circe.
News Chronicle, Obituary 2 *Mar* 1938

8 He became preoccupied by death and dwelt at length on how he wanted to die. Recently he conceived the idea of borrowing an Italian Air Force plane and flying to the Arctic, not forgetting to take little jars of honey for the polar bears who would be his last companions on earth.
Ibid.

9 A year ago he declared that when he felt death was near he would take a bath of acid in which his body would dissolve. 'Disdaining to die agonised between sheets,' he wrote, 'I am now testing my last invention.'
Ibid.

W. H. (WILLIAM HENRY) DAVIES

Born 1871. Welsh author and poet, best known for his *Autobiography of a Supertramp*, 1907. Died 1940.

10 One day his wooden leg was broken and Davies was anxious to obtain another, but had a morbid dread of any of the villagers knowing about it. So under Davies's guidance Edward made a drawing of an appliance which he asked the village wheelwright to make without telling him its purpose. He made it perfectly and when the bill came in it was for: 'Curiosity Cricket Bat — 5s', the joke of which Davies enjoyed as much as we did.
Helen Edwards, The Times 27 *Mar* 1963

11 Our children were very fond of him and he of them. His wooden leg intrigued them greatly and on one occasion when we were walking with him down a lane and he called the children to the side of the path of an oncoming wagon, my daughter said to him: 'It would not matter if it ran over you, would it, Sweet William, because you are made of wood.'
Ibid.

12 I made my first acquaintance with W. H. Davies near the end of 1918 and was delighted with the man — my feelings a strange mixture of admiration and amusement. He was curiously naïve and simple, though into his primitive make-up went a good deal of wiliness and worldly wisdom. He was super-sensitive and a little vain, too, and even jealous of his contemporaries when he thought they were getting more than their money's worth of praise and sales.
Herbert Palmer, John o' London's Weekly, 11 *Oct* 1940

1 He was intensely jealous of Walter de la Mare. Angered by what he regarded as gross overpraise of him in the press he bought a target pistol of some sort and practised shooting at a portrait of de la Mare which he tacked up on the landing of his boarding house.
Richard Stonesifer, W. H. DAVIES 1963

BETTE DAVIS

Original name Ruth Elizabeth Davis. Born 1908. American film actress. Known for her intense, highly dramatic roles in such films as *Dark Victory*, 1939, *Now Voyager*, 1942 and *Whatever Happened to Baby Jane?*, 1962.

2 Surely no one but a mother could have loved Bette Davis at the height of her career.
Brian Aherne, in 1937

3 If Hollywood didn't work out I was prepared to be the best secretary in the world.
Bette Davis, THE LONELY LIFE 1963

4 I was the first star who ever came out of the water looking wet.
Ibid.

5 Not only was I made up for the *Cabinet of Dr Calgari*, but I was dressed by a man who evidently had read his instructions in Braille.
Ibid.

6 I have eyes like a bullfrog, a neck like an ostrich and long limp hair. You must have to be good to survive with that equipment.
Bette Davis. Quoted Robert Ottaway, TV Times 17 *Aug* 1972

7 I think I can throw a tantrum better than most actresses around, in public and in private.
Ibid.

8 Whatever Bette had chosen to do in life she would have had to be the top or she couldn't have endured it.
Gary Merrill (her husband)

9 She would probably have been burned as a witch had she lived two or three hundred years ago. She gives the curious feeling of being charged with power which can find no ordinary outlet.
E. Arnot Robertson

10 The kid might be all right for certain roles, but what audience would ever believe that the hero would want to get *her* at the fade-out?
Studio report. Quoted Bette Davis, THE LONELY LIFE 1963

11 All she had going for her was her talent.
David Zinman

CHARLES (ANDRE JOSEPH MARIE) DE GAULLE

Born 1890. Leader of Free French forces in World War II. Elected first President of the Fifth Republic 1958. Resigned 1969. Died 1970.

12 He is a born gamekeeper who, even when he has been driven to snare a rabbit for the pot, has done it so majestically that rabbits scamper in begging to be caught, and other gamekeepers steal away on tip-toe for fear of disturbing him.
Vernon Bartlett, I KNOW WHAT I LIKED

13 He was maddening, arrogant, occasionally treacherous and extremely unattractive, but he was also authentically great.
Second Earl of Birkenhead, Daily Telegraph 8 *May* 1969

14 Within hours of the French capitulation Louis Spears invited me to lunch to meet what he called 'a French brigadier whom I have just brought over from Bordeaux'. The brigadier was De Gaulle. When Spears took him to see Churchill the latter said 'Why have you brought this lanky, gloomy brigadier?' Spears replied, 'Because no one else would come.'
Lord Boothby, RECOLLECTIONS OF A REBEL 1978

15 Walking in St James's Street after lunch I met de Gaulle, strutting along insolently, and crossed over to avoid him. His intolerable swagger and conceit aggravate everyone.
Sir Henry Channon DIARY 20 *Oct* 1942

16 The 'Anglo-Saxons' (as Le General used to call us) have always had some difficulty in appreciating the grandeur that was De Gaulle. The first question that the United States Press corps asked the head of the Free French in 1940, was 'What colour pyjamas do you wear?'
Richard Holmes, The Times 2 *Dec* 1982

17 I said 'But General, the proposition is preposterous. If we succeed you have arranged for the French to take all the credit, and if we fail you will say "I told you so!" You are trying to get the best of both worlds.' To which his reply was, 'Yes, my boy, and what is wrong with that?'
Lord Home, LETTERS TO A GRANDSON 1983

1 In his later years he became reckless. The cry of '*Vive le Québec libre*' on his visit to Canada was pure and irresponsible mischief.
Ibid.

2 Whil Pétain kept presidential state in the Hôtel du Parc at Vichy, De Gaulle, with two spare pairs of trousers and a photograph of his wife, occupied a three-roomed flat behind Oxford Street. Destiny seemed to promise him very little, perhaps not even a better address.
John Keegan, Observer, review of François Kerraudy's CHURCHILL AND DE GAULLE 4 *Oct* 1981

3 When his mongol child — on whom he unfailingly lavished such tender care — died, he remarked, '*Maintenant elle est commes les autres.*' How exquisite!
Malcolm Muggeridge, Observer 4 *May* 1969

4 Soustelle was complaining to De Gaulle that all his friends in Algeria detested the General's changed attitude. '*Alors, mon vieux,*' De Gaulle replied, '*changez vos amis*'.
Ibid.

5 He had the hands of a leader; the hands almost, of a messiah.
Diana Vreeland, D.V. 1984

FREDERICK DELIUS

Born 1862. English composer. Best-known works include *On Hearing the First Cuckoo in Spring* and *Brigg Fair*. Died 1934.

6 The picture of a feeble, blind, paralysed old man, perpetuated in James Gunn's famous portrait, has led to a popular misconception of Delius as an etiolated Chopinesque dandy who lolled on couches and suffered from wretched health all his life.
Sir Thomas Beecham, FREDERICK DELIUS 1959

7 There is in him so much melody that you have to keep a tight hold on the melodic line in order to control it. But if you do that he is *unique* (this with a crash of clenched fist on the table); his music, once he found himself, was underivative. He described himself as a conservative anarchist. He owed very little to his predecessors. His musical ancestry was lost somewhere in the mists of the past. His vein of inspiration lasted for about ten or twelve years, say from 1901 to 1914, just as it did for Debussy.
Sir Thomas Beecham. Quoted Lord Boothby, MY YESTERDAY, YOUR TOMORROW

8 Delius contrived whenever possible to take his holidays in Norway. Before he took a cottage overlooking the hills he usually walked and climbed above. Once Beecham went with him, who he never forgave for forgetting the sandwiches the day they lunched on a glacier.
Eric Fenby, DELIUS AS I KNEW HIM 1936

9 When Elgar paid a visit to Delius at *Grez-sur-Loing*, Delius began the conversation by saying that he thought it a great pity that Elgar had wasted so much of his time and energy by writing long-winded oratorios. 'That,' said Elgar, 'is the penalty of my English environment.' 'Well anyhow,' replied Delius 'you're not as bad as Parry. *He* would have set the whole Bible to music, had he lived long enough.'
Ibid.

10 Delius's house was a fortress, impregnable to the outside world; and it was ruled over by an invalid whose slightest word was law. His face would turn to stone if the soup had been insufficiently salted. He would be wheeled out into the garden, to sit in the sun, and seem to blame his attendant for the very clouds that conspired to hide it.
Ibid.

11 When he was in pain, meals had to be eaten in silence. The slightest rattle of a cup or clatter of a spoon was sufficient to lash him to fury, and if one forgot oneself and found oneself saying, 'Mrs Delius, may I pass you so-and-so' it was certain to be met with his, 'Will you please be quiet!' One day I tactfully suggested to his wife that his illness excused such behaviour but was told, 'You ought to have known Fred when he was well. He is not half so hard as he was in those days.'
Ibid.

12 He would hear no music but his own so I was sometimes driven for sanity's sake, to go off to my own room and tune in to some favourite composition to be greeted in the morning with: 'Did you like the music you were listening to last night?' 'Yes.' 'Well, I didn't.'
Ibid.

13 Delius, at the age of 22, had gone to Jacksonville to buy a piano. He was trying one when an organist called Ward passed the open door. Impressed by the beauty of what he heard Ward went in and introduced himself. It is not too much to say the whole of Delius's technical equipment is derived

CECIL B. DE MILLE

from the instruction he received from Ward during his six months' sojourn on the orange plantation.
Philip Heseltine, DELIUS 1929

1 Delius found that he possessed the wonderful faculty of thinking, not only horizontally of melody, but vertically of a succession of chords, in a way that nobody had ever thought of before.
Ibid.

2 Of well-marked melody he has but little, and nearly all his works defy technical analysis. They obey laws of structure all their own, and they have a logic all their own, which not everybody can learn.
Alfred Kalisch, Daily News 9 *Oct* 1929

3 A visit to Norway brought about a meeting with Ibsen and a narrow escape from death during a political disturbance. He had composed the incidental music for Gunnar Heiburg's play *Folkeraadet*. On the second night a revolver was discharged at Fred and he had to flee the theatre. He sought refuge in the establishment where Ibsen was accustomed to take his evening refreshment. There Fred and the famous dramatist talked and laughed while the riot continued.
Philip Page, Evening Standard 31 *Oct* 1935

4 Delius said of *Sea Drift* 'the shape was taken out of my hands so to speak, as I worked, and was bred easily and effortlessly of the nature and sequence of my particular ideas, and the nature and sequence of the particular poetical idea of Whitman that appealed to me'.
Radio Times 18 *Feb* 1947

5 A provincial Debussy.
A. J. P. Taylor, ENGLISH HISTORY 1914–1945

6 Delius in the prime of life was robust, tireless, gay, amorous and talkative, widely cultured in five languages and articulate in his discrimination.
The Times 26 *Jan* 1962

CECIL B.(BLOUNT) DE MILLE

Born 1881. American film director, pioneer in producing extravagant epics, some of which dealt with biblical subjects, e.g. *The Ten Commandments* 1923, remade 1956. Died 1959.

7 So Cecil B. De Mille is coming to London Town. That B. could stand for many things – Barnum, Ballyhoo, Box-office, Blarney, Billion-dollar, and Bathtubs. Especially Bathtubs. Wasn't he the man who put Claudette Colbert into a great bathtub full of asses' milk? But prosaically enough it stands for Blount.
Norah Alexander, Daily Mail 5 *Jul* 1947

8 He drives his people 15 hours a day and explodes at a touch. He is constantly followed by two attendants, one with a chair; the other with a microphone. Whenever he speaks the microphone is held before him. He never has to look for a chair when he wants to sit down — it's there behind him and he just sits.
Ibid.

9 The pongee sports shirt, well-tailored riding breeches, leather puttees and Napoleonic stride seemed to proclaim the fact that here was the director to end all directors. 'My God,' I thought, 'it's an American Mussolini.'
Charles Bickford, BULLS, BALLS, BICYCLES AND ACTORS

10 To suit his role he wore breeches and high boots and carried a revolver. The boots supported his legs, he explained, and protected him from the snakes so often found on his Californian ranch; the snakes inspired the revolver as well.
Kevin Brownlow, THE PARADE'S GONE BY

11 In 1913 Cecil B. De Mille with two other aspiring young men, Jessy L. Laski and Samuel Goldfish (later Goldwyn), set out westward in search of a location for filming; finding Arizona unsuitable he hit upon a barn in a little-known country suburb of Los Angeles called Hollywood, transformed a barn into an improvised studio, and made the first American feature-film, *The Squaw Man*.
Daily Telegraph, Obituary 22 *Jan* 1959

12 Having attended to the underclothes, bathrooms and matrimonial irregularities of his fellow citizens he now began to consider their salvation.
William de Mille, of his brother's decision to make Biblical epics

13 Cecil B. De Mille's *King of Kings* probably taught me more about the life of Christ than did a great deal of the Sunday School training I had as a boy.
Billy Graham, evangelist. Quoted Show, Apr 1963

14 Cecil B. De Mille's evangelical films are the nearest equivalent today to the glossy German colour prints which sometimes decorated mid-Victorian bibles. There is the

same complete lack of historical sense, the same stuffy horsehair atmosphere of beards and whiskers.
Graham Greene, Spectator 30 *Aug* 1935

1 There has always been a touch of genius as well as absurdity in this warm-hearted, sentimental salvationist.
Graham Greene. Quoted Leslie Halliwell, THE FILMGOER'S BOOK OF QUOTES 1978

2 He saw the Bible as a ready-made script factory. 'Give me a couple of pages of the Bible and I'll give you a picture.'
Leslie Halliwell, A FILMGOER'S BOOK OF QUOTES 1978

3 He made small-minded pictures on a big scale.
Pauline Kael

4 He packed the screen with impressive pageantry, supported by complex plots and sub-plots, and into each scene he measured out a careful soupçon of suspense.
Jesse Lasky Jnr, WHATEVER HAPPENED TO HOLLYWOOD

5 It did not concern him in the least that in the opinion of 'serious' film makers his works were considered as artistically significant as Barnum and Bailey's circus. He feared only one thing — that an audience might be bored.
Ibid.

6 I never met such an egotist in my life. Even if it was wrong and he knew it, once he had said it, it had to be.
Arthur Miller

7 When I saw one of his pictures I wanted to quit the business.
King Vidor. Quoted Kevin Brownlow, THE PARADE'S GONE BY

EAMON DE VALERA

Born 1882. Irish politician, born in United States. Imprisoned for his part in the Easter Rebellion, 1916. After creation of the Irish Free State, 1921, he eventually became Prime Minister for three terms 1937–41, 1951–4, 1957–9, and President 1959–73. Died 1975.

8 He is grey and dignified and looks like an unfashionable dentist.
Sir Henry Channon, DIARY 11 *Sep* 1938

9 De Valera was arrested at Ennis in the middle of a political speech. A year later he was released. He went forthwith to Ennis, and began to speak again with the words 'As I was saying when I was interrupted — '
Edmund Fuller, ANECDOTE 1942

10 The party he founded has proved unable, without him, to cope with the tensions of its heritage from him.
Conor Cruise O'Brien, Observer, Deviations of Dev 9 *Jan* 1983

11 When he was in power the rational element was firmly in control . . . When he was in opposition he was much more inclined to let his emotions rip, yet in a way that seems instinctively calculated.
Ibid.

12 De Valera's handling of Northern Ireland as a *problem* requiring statesmanship, lacks coherence. His handling of Northern Ireland as an *issue* in 26 county politics is generally masterly.
Ibid.

13 De Valera has a democratic genius as men have a genius for music or painting. Once, when asked how he knew that the course of action he was taking would be approved by the people he was representing he said simply 'My heart tells me'. There are very few statesmen who would dare to use such a phrase or who, if they did, would for a moment be believed; but in the case of de Valera I think that was the simple truth.
Francis Stuart, GREAT CONTEMPORARIES: PRESIDENT DE VALERA 1934

SERGE (PABLOVICH) DIAGHILEV

Born 1872 in Russia. Ballet impresario. Founded Ballets Russes, 1909, touring Europe and America and making the international reputations of such performers as Pavlova and Nijinsky. Died 1929.

14 In Russia his student cronies were unknown artistic youngsters like Bakst, Benois and Fokine; but in Paris he became intimate with princesses, and countesses and grand dukes. His trick was to bring the two worlds together — a feat he repeated in capital after capital.
Alexander Bland, Observer 1 *Jul* 1979

15 There is no true label for him; he invented his own genre. There is always a mystery about such solitary phenomena, like the enigma of a single exotic flower which appears suddenly on the mountainside.
Ibid.

16 He made novelty not only smart, but

culturally *de rigueur* and in so doing influenced the whole social-cultural pattern of our times.
Ibid.

1 His foibles and frailties were matched by his heroic courage, patience and resilience until overwork and diabetes wore him down.
Ibid.

2 I wouldn't boast that I knew him. None of us *knew* him. He was a great man, an autocrat, he could be incredibly kind, yet extremely unfair.
Ninette de Valois, Radio Times 16 *Aug* 1973

3 I am first a charlatan, though rather a brilliant one; secondly, a great charmer; thirdly, frightened of nobody; fourthly, a man with plenty of logic and very few scruples; fifthly, I seem to have no talent.
Diaghilev, of himself

4 He was the *grand seigneur*, and had that wonderful voice that could charm anyone. He could work up in you a creative sense, and a desire to express yourself. It can't really be put into words, but my life, through him, has been quite different. He was the greatest man I have ever met.
Marie Rambert, Radio Times 16 *Aug* 1973

5 Diaghilev was very jealous of Nijinsky, with whom I was working, and used to send his valet to spy on us. He was for ever in and out of the room, to see if the windows were open too far, or not far enough.
Ibid.

6 Once, when Ninette de Valois was eating in the cheap part of a café with two friends, Diaghilev who was sitting in the expensive part, saw them and said, 'I trust I pay my artists enough to eat in the better part of a café.'
Jenny Rees, Radio Times 16 *Aug* 1973

7 He was so difficult to approach. If you met him and said something, he would take it in silence, as if it wasn't worthy of an intelligent reply.
Lydia Sokolova, ibid.

8 I remember dancing two principal parts and being expected to dance in *Firebird* in the corps de ballet as well. I asked if I needn't do that as I needed the rest. With those veiled eyes of his, he said, 'You will dance when you are told to dance. It is an honour for you to dance in my corps de ballet.'
Ibid.

MARLENE DIETRICH

Born 1904. Original name Maria Magdalene von Losch. German actress and cabaret singer who moved to Hollywood to make films, achieving international fame with *The Blue Angel*, 1930. After the war abandoned films and returned to the stage as a solo entertainer.

9 It is entirely due to her perseverance that she is not just another old, discarded film star. She magnetises her audience and mesmerises them (and herself) into believing in her. The old trouper never changes her tricks because she knows they work, and because she invented them.
Cecil Beaton, DIARY 1973

10 Marlene has become a sort of mechnical doll. The doll can show surprise, it can walk, it can swish into place the train of its white fur coat. The audience applauds, not just the old who remember her tawdry films, but the young, too, who find her sexy. She is louche, and not averse to giving a sly wink.
Ibid.

11 I watched, on television, Marlene Dietrich's successful performance staged at Drury Lane. Aged seventy she is a quite remarkable piece of artifice. Somehow she has evolved an agelessness. All the danger spots were disguised. Her dress, her figure, her limbs, all gave the illusion of youth. The high cheek-bones remain intact, the forehead good, the deep-set eyelids useful attributes, and she does the rest.
Ibid.

12 Though we all might enjoy/Seeing Helen of Troy/As a gay cabaret entertainer/I doubt that she could/Be one quarter as good/As our lovely legendary Marlene.
Noël Coward

13 If she had nothing but her voice she could break your heart with it. But she also had that beautiful body and the timeless loveliness of her face.
Ernest Hemingway

14 Age cannot wither her nor custom stale her infinite sameness.
David Shipman. Quoted Leslie Halliwell, A FILMGOER'S BOOK OF QUOTES 1978

WALT (WALTER ELIAS) DISNEY

Born 1901. American film producer, who pioneered full-length cartoon features after original success with Mickey Mouse. His first full-length production was *Snow White and the Seven Dwarfs*, 1938. Died 1966.

1 Disney was not the inventor of the animated cartoon, but he raised it to the level of a new form of art worthy of serious criticism.
Daily Telegraph, Obituary 16 *Dec* 1966

2 Disneyland is the biggest people-trap ever built by a mouse.
Leslie Halliwell, FILMGOER'S BOOK OF QUOTES 1978

3 Disney's world was one in which violence, conflict, ruthless physical force and utter desperation were normal, accepted elements of experience . . . This was a society in which aggression paid out, inhumanity was practical, and power, being right, was always admirable.
Lloyd Morris, NOT SO LONG AGO

4 Disney made audiences roar with laughter by endowing such inanimate objects as steam-shovels and rocking chairs with human emotions . . . His pictures were pure fantasy and almost pure fable, but what they reported about twentieth-century existence afforded little warrant for optimism or complacence.
Ibid.

5 With a squawk of fury the irascible Donald Duck burst upon the scene. Although he was said to be a conglomeration of all the people Disney disliked he became a symbol of unsuppressed indignation defying the frustrations of circumstances.
The Times, Obituary 16 *Dec* 1966

6 Disneyland achieved such world-wide popularity and renown that Soviet premier Nikita Khrushchev was bitterly disappointed when security considerations prevented him visiting it during his 1959 tour of the United States.
Charles Van Doren, WEBSTER'S AMERICAN BIOGRAPHIES 1974

ALEC (ALEXANDER FREDERICK) DOUGLAS-HOME, BARON HOME OF THE HIRSEL

Born 1903. British politician. Foreign Secretary 1960–3 and 1970–4. Renounced his peerage as fourteenth Earl of Home, to succeed Macmillan as Prime Minister 1963. Created life peer 1974.

7 A prime minister reputed to do his arithmetic by matchsticks.
Leo Pliatsky, GETTING AND SPENDING 1982

8 Sir Alec Douglas Home looked like a caricature of Macmillan's paternalism, with none of his radicalism, and in parliament he was the ideal foil for Harold Wilson.
Anthony Sampson, THE CHANGING ANATOMY OF BRITAIN 1982

9 Sir Alec, having lost the election, left his party in a shambles.
Ibid.

10 A friend says, 'I still find it incredible that someone with such narrowness of mind can believe that he has an intuitive understanding of the way the world works.' To such critics of his political capacities he replies 'Those who say I am out of touch with life simply do not know what life is about.'
Hugo Young, Sunday Times 3 *Oct* 1971

11 He was an appeaser from the High Tory school, which feared the Soviets more than it distrusted Hitler.
Ibid.

12 After Nasser's funeral, a hot hectic occasion, he regained his plane at the cocktail hour. But when the steward asked him what he wanted with his ice he replied by asking what time it was in London. 'Four o'clock' said the steward. 'Very well then,' said Sir Alec. 'I'll have a cup of tea.'
Ibid.

THEODORE DREISER

Born 1871. American novelist, attracted international attention with *An American Tragedy*, 1925. Died 1945.

13 Dreiser's physical stature gives him dignity, but he has more than dignity. He has greatness. After a few minutes in his presence I was aware of an emanation of which I have been aware in the presence of only one other man — Edward Carpenter.
Thomas Burke, T.P.'s Weekly 9 *Jun* 1928

14 His figure is one of his books given human shape — large, deliberate and loose, without fire and without fatigue. He walks with the

ponderous pace of the books, and his slouch is expressive of his own prose.
Ibid.

1 In 1906 Theodore Dreiser was appointed managing editor of *The Delineator*. He celebrated his first day at the post by solemnly rejecting two of his own stories.
Bennett Cerf, SHAKE WELL BEFORE USING 1948

2 It was the ponderous battering-ram of his novel that opened the way through the genteel reticences of American nineteenth-century fiction for what seemed to be the truthful description of people's lives. Without Dreiser's treading out a path for naturalism none of us would have had a chance to publish anything.
John Dos Passos, THE BEST TIMES 1967

3 Is *An American Tragedy* a great work? It has at least one attribute of greatness — it leaves no reader unaffected. Some have praised it to the skies. It has been hailed as 'the great American novel'. (How touching it is that they should want only one.) Others have declared it to be downright bad. It has exasperated many.
Oliver Edwards, The Times 5 *Aug* 1965

4 He is a clumsy though often powerful novelist and as a courageous pioneer of realism he had a great influence on American fiction.
J. B. Priestley, LITERATURE AND WESTERN MAN 1960

5 Power, somewhat clumsily used but unmistakable, is the first characteristic of his work. Patience is the second; he goes on lumbering after his effect until he gets it. Both characteristics appear as clearly in his nature as a man.
Edward Shanks, John o' London's Weekly 22 *Apr* 1932

6 Over the luncheon table Dreiser made Lasky pay 100,000 dollars for the film rights to *An American Tragedy*, and threw a cup of coffee in his publisher's face. Accounts differ as to whether the coffee was hot or cold.
Ibid.

7 His luck as a novelist was atrocious, comparable to, but in some ways worse than, that of D. H. Lawrence.
Ibid.

8 It is unlikely that future readers will care to acquaint themselves at first hand with the work of this trail-breaker. The labour of reading Dreiser is too arduous and not sufficiently profitable. Too often, while engaged with one of his novels, one has that sense of grinding despair that comes in nightmares when one is being pursued over endless wastes of soft sand.
T. K. Whipple, SPOKESMEN

JOHN FOSTER DULLES

Born 1888. American politician. Secretary of State under Eisenhower 1953–9. Gained a reputation abroad for intransigence and inflexibility. Died 1959.

9 He invented Brinkmanship, the most popular game since Monopoly.
Richard Armour, IT ALL STARTED WITH COLUMBUS

10 J.F.D. is the woolliest type of useless pontificating American — Heaven help us!
Sir Alexander Cadogan, DIARY 15 *Jul* 1942

11 Dulles, having explained something once, was apt to forget that he had done so, and in a day or two do it all over again.
Dwight D. Eisenhower, WAGING PEACE 1966

12 He lacked in large measure the statesman's dispassionate vision and the courage to peer across the perilous divide to the bristling trenches of alien ideology, to identify there, and then to build on, the hidden elements of possible reconciliation.
Townsend Hoopes, THE DEVIL AND JOHN FOSTER DULLES

13 My cousin Oliver told me he was, in international politics, simply *the* bull in a china shop — being almost indistinguishable from that animal in face, figure, intelligence, impulsiveness and capacity for destruction.
G. W. Lyttelton, THE LYTTELTON HART-DAVIS LETTERS 18 *Jan* 1950

14 The world's longest range misguided missile.
Walter Reuther

15 Dulles is a man of wily and subtle mind. It is difficult to believe that behind his unctuous manner he does not take a cynical amusement in his own monstrous pomposities.
I. F. Stone, JOHN FOSTER DULLES: PORTRAIT OF A LIBERATOR 1953

SIR GERALD DU MAURIER

Born 1873. English actor, son of George du Maurier, *Punch* artist and author of *Trilby*. Father of novelist Daphne du Maurier. Appeared in many plays with Mrs Pat Campbell, and from 1906 when he had a big success with *Raffles* had an unbroken run as actor and actor manager in London's West End theatres almost until his death in 1934.

1 Du Maurier filled all parts of the house with his devotees while he changed the whole aspect of English acting. It might be called a revolution, but it was tranquil, gradual and seemly.
Ivor Brown, The Times 26 *Mar* 1973

2 Oh how can I act with a dreadful ugly face like that?
Mrs Patrick Campbell. Quoted John Gielgud, AN ACTOR AND HIS TIME 1979

3 Why make the effort to learn long and exquisitely written speeches when 'I love you, damn you', and 'What about a drink?' succeed even better among the public, and take less time to say? It was pleasant, this business of being charming and rather amusing and making love light-heartedly. Financially it was proving enormously profitable to all concerned, and infinitely more worth while than standing in tights before a dark curtain, and protesting to five people in the stalls that all our yesterdays have lighted fools the way to dusty death. Gerald can hardly be blamed, and if he was sneered at he was more often envied.
Daphne du Maurier, GERALD 1934

4 It was travelling in the grand manner with Gerald and an experience not to be lightly undertaken. Couriers must await him on every platform, carriages locked after him, and largesse distributed liberally and without hesitation to every official encountered from the gentleman covered in braid to the menial who tapped the wheels. A covey of porters would trail along the platform staggering under golf-clubs, tennis rackets, dispatch cases, pillows and rugs . . . It was not until the door had been closed, the engine had whistled and the guard had waved his flag that Gerald, looking out of the window and perceiving a spot of rain upon the glass, would remark in a genuine and rather wistful voice, 'Don't let's go after all. I'd much rather stay at home.'
Ibid.

5 When Gracie Fields was acting with him in *Interference* he started off by playing one of his practical jokes. Buying a fake diamond ring for ten and sixpence he wrapped it in a box from Cartier's and threw it on Gracie's lap in his careless and off-hand manner. 'Wear it for me,' he said, 'It only cost seven hundred pounds.' The poor girl blushed with anger and handed it back. 'Come on,' he said roughly, 'Don't be a silly little fool.' Furious at his insulting manner and dark insinuations Gracie Fields walked up to him and gave him a ringing slap in the face.
Ibid.

6 He did not read much and he did not like the theatre to be taken too seriously. He preferred to give the impression that the stage was just a way of earning a living on the side, though in actual fact he was not particularly happy outside the theatre.
John Gielgud, AN ACTOR AND HIS TIME 1979

7 Gerald Du Maurier was marvellous in scenes with young girls. He was able to stand away from them and express such erotic tenderness.
John Gielgud. Quoted John Mortimer, IN CHARACTER 1983

8 Gerald du Maurier really was tactless. He was deputed by the committee of the Garrick Club to tell a well-known director he had been black balled. The director looked very unhappy and finally asked, 'Were there many black balls?' 'My dear fellow,' Du Maurier said, 'Have you ever seen sheep shit?'
Ibid.

9 The offhand, slightly mocking manner of acting that Du Maurier perfected had a great vogue and can be studied at second-hand in the movies of Leslie Howard, who learned from him.
Brendan Gill, The Times 4 *Aug* 1973

10 At the height of his powers he was one of the few actors who could draw the public even to a bad play. Partly this was due to his enormous personal charm, but still more to his amazing technical ability, both as a player and as a producer.
Morning Post, Obituary 12 *Apr* 1934

ISADORA DUNCAN

Born 1878. American dancer who achieved world-wide fame for her concept and interpretation of dancing based on the art of Ancient Greece. Died tragically in a motoring accident 1927.

11 A woman who was as reckless of money as she was of her reputation, and who lived like

ISADORA DUNCAN

a princess on the income of a petty duchess.
Norman Collins, John o' London's Weekly 15 *Feb* 1933

1 Isadora Duncan probably represents the maximum possible development of emotion at the expense of intellect. She was a creature of impulse, and the impulses were usually bad ones. She drank champagne as a thirsty horse drinks water.
Ibid.

2 What a woman Isadora Duncan was, and what a warning. Nothing could be more melancholy, or more Hogarthian in its horror, than the progress of this great artist from the days when all Paris besieged the Trocadero to see her dance, and the storm-troops of the police had to be called out to control the crowds, to the time when, a drunken and flabby termagant, she had to be carried upstairs to bed, having endeavoured to polka but been too fuddled to make the steps.
Ibid.

3 In Paris in 1913 Isadora rescued a male relative from the clutches of a very notorious cinema vamp. When Isadora broke the news that she had packed off her relative the actress arose, and in a voice trembling with hate said, 'I curse you. The gods of my fathers curse you and your children for ever.' At that very instant we were on the spot where, years afterwards, the motor car with Isadora's children and nurse plunged into the Seine.
Mary Desti, ISADORA DUNCAN'S END 1929

4 She made a pitiful exhibition in Buenos Aires when she insisted on dancing in a night club when she should have been in the hands of a doctor. As a gentleman leaned out of one of the boxes and applauded she kissed her hand to him, and taking off one of her sandals, threw it up to him with a graceful gesture. The second sandal soon followed, but it was thrown in anger, at some people in another box, who had laughed at her.
M. Dumesnil, AN AMAZING JOURNEY 1933

5 As the car started from her studio in Nice Isadora was seen to throw the long fringed end of her shawl over her left shoulder. The car started forward and the shawl seemed to trail on the ground beside the wheel. Mary Desti screamed: '*Ton chale, Isadora! Ramasse ton chale!*' The car stopped. The watchers thought it was to allow Isadora to pick up the end of her shawl. They walked towards it and saw that her head had fallen forward. They ran. The driver was out of the car gesticulating, howling in Italian 'I've killed the Madonna! I've killed the Madonna!'
Irma Duncan, ISADORA'S RUSSIAN DAYS 1929

6 As a dancer she was probably one of the greatest who ever lived. Nor was she any less great as a woman — a wild, impetuous and extravagant creature of whims and what is called 'artistic temperament'.
John o' London's Weekly 5 *Oct* 1929

7 In America Isadora Duncan was propounding and demonstrating a new theory of what the dance should be. Miss Duncan did not believe in a vocabulary of steps and movements; she clad herself in flowing draperies, as depicted on Greek vases, and moved about the stage in a kind of free-fluid.
Frank Muir, THE FRANK MUIR BOOK 1976

8 At a café in Havana at three o'clock in the morning Isadora danced to morphine-maniacs, cocainists, opium smokers and other derelicts of life. The pianist woke from his morphia-trance and played as if inspired. She danced until morning and many of her strange audience wept, and as she left they all embraced her.
Con O'Leary, T.P.'s Weekly 2 *Jun* 1928

9 The curious rumour got about that sick people who watched her dancing became well. Sick people were brought into her matinees on litters.
Ibid.

10 Isadora was incapable of analysing what she did, even when teaching her pupils, and refused to make films.
Victor Seroff, THE REAL ISADORA 1972

11 In South America, in 1916, the orchestra was about to clear a space for her while she composed and rehearsed a new dance. But she told them it would not be necessary — all she needed would be a chair placed near the conductor's desk. Whispering to Wolff she asked him to play Franck's Redemption, and without taking off her cape or hat, she remained immobile in her chair, listening to the music — and she performed triumphantly on the following day.
Ibid.

12 A woman whose face looked as if it had been made out of sugar and someone had licked it.
G. B. Shaw. Quoted Hesketh Pearson, BERNARD SHAW 1961

JIMMY (JAMES FRANCIS) DURANTE

Born 1893. American entertainer, who began his career as a piano player in dance halls and nightclubs, and became a star on Broadway, in films, on radio and television.

1 His voice can only be described as a dull rasp calling its mate, or an air-raid signal blasting through two layers of gravel.
Fred Allen

2 The Riff-Raff Caruso.
Ibid.

3 He had his first cheese soufflé in an expensive French eatery recently. After one bite he registered ecstasy, and summoned the head waiter. 'Where has dis been all my life?' he demanded. The waiter looked pained. 'I don't know, sir,' he apologised.
Bennett Cerf, TRY AND STOP ME 1947

4 Many of his expressions, such as '*Everybody* wants to get into da act', and 'I got a *million* of 'em', and his puzzling signing-off line for many years, 'Goodnight, Mrs Calabash, wherever you are' (in fact an affectionate greeting to his wife) were often imitated but never duplicated. No more so was his hoarse, impish rendition of his theme song 'Inka Dinka Doo'.
Charles Van Doren, WEBSTER'S AMERICAN BIOGRAPHIES 1974

5 Through more than half a century in show business his style remained constant; his magnificent nose (for which he was known as Da Schnozz, or Schnozzola, and in regard to which he noted 'Dere's a million good-looking guys. I'm a novelty'), his battered hat and piano, and his penchant for mangling most of the longer words in the English language, all were trademarks round the world.
Ibid.

ELEANORA DUSE

Born 1859. Italian actress who achieved world-wide fame. Died 1924.

6 She tortured herself to win stage laurels, and then threw them away on the bald head of a worthless lover (D'Annunzio) who would betray her in the end.
Trevor Allen, John o' London's Weekly 3 *Mar* 1950

7 One admires that Venetian nomad, trembling with stage-fright in the wings, panicky to the point of fleeing, then going on to storm Paris in Bernhardt's theatre with Bernhardt watching from a box.
Ibid.

8 My prevailing impression is of a great egoistic force; of a woman overriding, with an air of sombre unconcern, plays, critics and public.
Max Beerbohm. Quoted William Weaver, DUSE: A BIOGRAPHY 1984

9 Her dress was always up on one side and down on the other. Her hat was always crooked. No matter how costly her garments, she never seemed to wear them, but appeared to condescend to carry them on her.
Isadora Duncan, MY LIFE 1928

10 I am a vagabond, a nomad. I was even born travelling — on the hard seat of a dingy Venice–Padua local to be precise. The child of strolling players.
Eleanora Duse. Quoted Bertits Harding AGE CANNOT WITHER 1950

11 I cannot think of more than one actress to whom I could without hesitation ascribe greatness. This was Eleanora Duse. With that one exception I have only seen actresses who could be good, sometimes very good, in certain parts.
W. Somerset Maugham

12 The furthest extremes of Duse's range as an artist must always remain a secret between herself and a few fine observers.
G. B. Shaw. Quoted William Weaver, DUSE: A BIOGRAPHY 1984

13 Nobody has ever given a clear or convincing explanation of how or why she knocked the public sideways on two continents. Other actresses are said to have wept and vowed to leave the stage when they first saw Duse playing. Audiences emerged 'stammering ecstatically, waving their arms like lunatics'. She electrified Rilke, James Joyce and Charles Chaplin. Gordon Craig believed she would inaugurate his theatre of the future and so, 20 years later, did Mussolini. She enchanted Pirandello and for the young Chekhov her acting was a revelation.
Hilary Spurling, Observer 7 *Oct* 1984

14 Duse brought off her greatest triumphs in flashy, commercial, increasingly old-fashioned vehicles, which she could never afford to trade in: she first of all played Dumas's *Dame aux Camelias* in 1882 and, for all her protests, she was still playing Marguerite a quarter of a century later.
Ibid.

E

(ROBERT) ANTHONY EDEN, FIRST EARL OF AVON

Born 1897. British politician. Foreign Secretary 1935–8. Resigned in opposition to Chamberlain's appeasement policy. Resumed as Foreign Secretary in Churchill's Cabinet 1940–5 and again 1951–5. Became Prime Minister 1955, but resigned over the Suez Crisis 1957. Died 1977.

1 In this country, being terrifically good-looking is a terrible handicap, although it's all right to be good-looking like Eden, like a stuffed tailor's dummy.
Lord Balogh. Quoted Susan Barnes, Sunday Times Magazine 1 *Apr* 1973

2 I remember talks with Anthony Eden because I like him so much and wish so much that I could admire him more.
Vernon Bartlett, THIS IS MY LIFE 1937

3 Eden was a very gallant and courageous Prime Minister, but he had to wait too long for the premiership. He was unfortunate in being PM at a time when events were moving too quickly in the direction of the dismantling of what had been British influence and power.
Sir Frederick Bishop (Principal Private Secretary to Eden), Western Morning News 7 *Aug* 1979

4 It is significant of his intellectual bent that he chose to read Persian and Arabic at Oxford, a study which required high linguistic technical skill, attention to detail and the patient unravelling of unfamiliar languages in unfamiliar scripts, but which did not need or develop ideas.
Robert Blake, Sunday Times 16 *Jan* 1977

5 He could focus a clear, narrow beam upon a particular problem. He could never illuminate a landscape.
Ibid.

6 Although Eden was a product of Eton and Christ Church, in fact the first Prime Minister for half a century to come from either of those 'nurseries of statesmen', there was nothing anachronistic about him.
Ibid.

7 Popular opinion saw him as an essentially calm, conciliatory, imperturbable middle-of-the-road figure, a contrast, not unwelcome at that time, with the grand rhetorical, if slightly anachronistic statesman [Churchill] whom he succeeded.
Ibid.

8 He was the last Prime Minister to believe that Britain was a great power and the first to confront a crisis which proved she was not.
Ibid.

9 All his life he tended to be absorbed in details and to find difficulty in delegating even such matters as the drafting of a telegram . . . This defect did not matter so much when Eden held the Foreign Office. It was more serious when he became Prime Minister.
Ibid.

10 Part of the trouble with Suez was the fact that Eden and Dulles instinctively mistrusted each other. Anthony has the habit when talking to you of calling you 'my dear'. Although sometimes not entirely convincing I have always found it engaging. But Dulles didn't. The stark puritan from New England did not wish to be addressed as anyone's 'my dear'.
Lord Boothby. Quoted Susan Barnes, Sunday Times Magazine 1 *Apr* 1973

11 At the end of March 1955 Anthony and I were invited into the Cabinet room. Winston made a slip by asking me to sit on his right, but then corrected himself and beckoned to Anthony. We all gazed out over Horse Guards Parade. Then Winston said very shortly, 'I am going and Anthony will succeed me. We can discuss details later.' The ceremonial was over. We found ourselves in the passage where Anthony and I shook hands.
Lord Butler, THE ART OF THE POSSIBLE 1971

12 . . . his unfortunate propensity to offer clichés and platitudes on a scale unusual even for a politician.
David Carlton, ANTHONY EDEN

13 I am a little uneasy that the destinies of countless millions should be in the exquisite

hands of Anthony Eden for whom I have affection, even admiration — but not blind respect.
Sir Henry Channon, DIARY 30 *Jul* 1935

1 He has had a meteoric rise, young Anthony. I knew him well at Oxford, where he was mild, aesthetic, handsome, cultivated, and interested in the East — now at thirty-eight he is Foreign Secretary. I like him, but I have never had an exaggerated opinion of his brilliance, though his appearance is magnificent.
Ibid. 23 *Dec* 1935

2 His sartorial splendour makes everyone else look shoddy.
Ibid. 25 *Jun* 1937

3 The King [George VI] is sound, and is against Anthony Eden who, in two years, has caused us more trouble than any Foreign Secretary since Palmerston.
Ibid. 22 *Jun* 1938

4 To the House, where Anthony Eden, smartly dressed, delivered a pretty travelogue which interested nobody particularly. He has not got the gift of holding the House, and there was little wit, humour or eloquence in his tedious description of the momentous meetings in Tehran and Cairo. After twenty minutes Members got up and began to trickle out.
Ibid. 14 *Dec* 1943

5 I heard Anthony Eden winding up for the government. Well dressed, hot, and with a very hoarse voice, he was gesticulating and for once managed to please the House, or at least not to annoy it. His manner of uttering platitudes as if they were world-shattering pronouncements is too irritating. I find him a man of tinsel, and yet today he was not without charm as he waved, smiled and placated. Not a brilliant parliamentary performance, but at least he talked sense.
Ibid. 23 *Feb* 1944

6 They asked for a leader and were given a public relations officer; here is the news and this is Anthony Eden reading it.
Malcolm Muggeridge, TREAD SOFTLY FOR YOU TREAD ON MY JOKES 1966

7 Here lies the fallacy of his whole career. He believed in diplomacy, a procedure as irrelevant to our present circumstances as embroidery in a factory which mass-produces bath mats.
Ibid.

8 Nothing in Eden invited either admiration or abhorrence. He was just empty of content like his television appearances in which a flow of banalities were presented in the persuasive manner of an ex-officer trying to sell one a fire-extinguisher at the front door.
Ibid.

9 Eden has lost his hold, and although he plays the right cards, he plays them in the wrong order or in the wrong manner.
Harold Nicolson, DIARY 15 *Sep* 1956

10 Equivocation was his fatal sin . . . but if he was without ideology he wasn't a very good Tory either. He was a Foreign Office man.
Michael Ratcliffe, reviewing David Carlton's ANTHONY EDEN *in The Times* 27 *Aug* 1981

11 Eden's previous record [in 1937] was not marked by resolute action. He had been the conciliator in chief, travelling across Europe with disarmament conventions and peace pacts in his bag. As foreign secretary, he had provided the idealistic smoke-screen with which to save Baldwin after the Hoare–Laval plan. He had acquiesced in the Italian conquest of Abyssinia and had deterred the French, so far as they needed it, from action in the Rhineland. He sponsored the pretences of the Spanish non-intervention committee. He relied on moral disapproval; strong words and no acts. Sooner or later, he believed, Hitler and Mussolini would come begging for forgiveness, if Anthony Eden continued wagging his finger at them.
A. J. P. Taylor, ENGLISH HISTORY 1914–1945 1965

THOMAS (ALVA) EDISON

Born 1847. American inventor, in the fields of telephony, the phonograph, the generation and distribution of electricity. His company, holding over 1300 patents, emerged as the General Electric Company. Died 1931.

12 Edison, whose inventions did as much as any to add to our material convenience, wasn't what we would call a scientist at all, but a supreme 'do-it-yourself' man — the successor to Benjamin Franklin.
Sir Kenneth Clark, CIVILISATION 1969

13 If he had invented only the electric light bulb, he would have been noteworthy, but he also gave us the microphone, the kinetoscope, the phonograph and scores of other devices, making him one of the greatest inventors ever known.
Keith Ellis, THOMAS EDISON: GENIUS OF ELECTRICITY

1 While Mr Edison and I were calling on Luther Burbank in California he asked us to register in his guest book. The book had a column for signature, another for home address, another for occupation and finally one entitled 'interested in'. Mr Edison signed in a few quick but unhurried motions. In the final column he wrote without an instant's hesitation 'Everything'.
Henry Ford, MY FRIEND MR EDISON

2 'Results!' exlaimed Edison to an assistant marvelling at the bewildering total of his failures — 50,000 experiments, for example before he succeeded with a new storage battery. 'Results! Why man, I have gotten a lot of results. I know fifty thousand things that won't work.'
Edmund Fuller, ANECDOTES 1942

EDWARD VII

Born 1841. Eldest son of Queen Victoria, whom he succeeded in 1901. Died 1910.

3 Every day he reckoned to smoke ten, twelve or thirteen cigars so large and pungent that strong men blenched when he kindly pressed them to take one. Smoking on this scale was clearly bad for anyone who suffered as he did from chronic bronchitis.
Georgina Battiscombe, QUEEN ALEXANDRA 1969

4 He was an affectionate, easy family man but on to family life he imposed his own tastes, his own interests, his own friendships.
Roger Fulford, FROM HANOVER TO WINDSOR 1960

5 . . .returning to join the ladies for luncheon at Balmoral, sitting astride a broad-backed pony, enveloped in a huge cloak, looking not unlike some ancient warrior of the Glens.
Ibid.

6 Those who believe that sovereigns should not attempt to combine their duties with the delights of social and fashionable life will condemn King Edward: he would no doubt reply that it was his recreation, his attempt to overcome that isolation and seclusion which can prove fatal to the best-intentioned kings and queens.
Ibid.

7 The King is loved because he has all the faults of which the Englishman is accused.
Lord Granville. Quoted Robert Cecil, LIFE IN EDWARDIAN ENGLAND 1969

8 Sights of London: the church in Leicester Square where Mme Navarro, between the matinée and evening performance, used to pray to be delivered from the attentions of King Edward VII.
Geoffrey Madan, NOTEBOOKS 1981

9 King Edward, who had frowned his disapproval of *Arms and the Man*, laughed so heartily over *John Bull's Other Island* that he broke the chair on which he sat.
Hesketh Pearson, BERNARD SHAW 1942

10 Edward VII, who was not quite a gentleman, but let that pass, was among the first to spread around the rumour that the young ladies of Paris threw off their clothes more readily than their English sisters and the French named a boulevard after him in recognition of his researches on that subject.
Douglas Sutherland, THE ENGLISH GENTLEMAN

11 As his mother had made respectability in itself respectable, so Edward VII made 'conspicuous waste' respectable.
Thorstein Veblen, THE THEORY OF THE LEISURED CLASS 1899

12 You cannot imagine what a Satan he is.
Kaiser Wilhelm II. Quoted Robert Cecil, LIFE IN EDWARDIAN ENGLAND 1969

EDWARD VIII (DUKE OF WINDSOR)

Born 1894. Son of George V, succeeded to the throne 1936. Abdicated in order to marry Wallis Warfield Simpson. Created Duke of Windsor. Died 1972.

13 The benefit of the King's Coronation depends under God upon the faith, prayer and self dedication of the King himself. We hope he is aware of this need. Some of us wish that he gave more positive signs of such awareness.
Dr Alfred Blunt, Bishop of Bradford. Speech at a diocesan conference which precipitated the abdication crisis 1 *Dec* 1936

14 The Duke's kingdom had shrunk to the Duchess herself. For him and her there was nothing beyond.
J. Bryan III and Charles J. Murphy, THE WINDSOR STORY 1979

15 In England Alexander Woollcott attended a small dinner given in honour of Edward VIII, then Prince of Wales. He was deeply flattered when the prince called him into private consultation after the ladies had left the room, but his elation vanished when the

reason became apparent. 'Woollcott,' said the prince, 'you've got something to do with that blasted *New Yorker* magazine, haven't you? Well, why the devil do my copies reach me so irregularly?'
Bennett Cerf, TRY AND STOP ME 1947

1 He takes up things with violence — golf, hunting, flying, drink, and latterly gardening; since Wallis's influence, Society. He is fanatically loyal while his friendships last.
Sir Henry Channon, DIARY 1936

2 For two years he has played the bagpipes, sometimes all night, and drank next to nothing and then only whisky with plain water, claret or Vichy water because Wallis drinks these things.
Ibid.

3 Walter Monckton's description of the last family farewell is poignant. It took place at Royal Lodge, Windsor and there the ex-King said goodbye to his family. His mother, Queen Mary, ever magnificent, was mute and immovable and very royal and had thoughtfully left off her mourning black for the evening so as not to cast more gloom. The brothers were sad and showed their emotion. At last he left, and bowing over his brother's hand, the brother he had made King, he said, 'God bless you, Sir. I hope you will be happier than your predecessor', and disappeared into the night, leaving the royal family speechless.
Ibid. 21 *Dec* 1936

4 Lord Queenborough told me what Queen Mary had said to him in reply to a question as to when the Duke of Windsor would return to this country: 'Not until he comes to my funeral.'
Ibid. 1 *Apr* 1939

5 As a prince, as a King, as a man, he was at his best only when the going was good.
Alistair Cooke, SIX MEN

6 It was very largely due to him that his going was not cataclysmic. His determination that what he did should not be politically upsetting was as strong as his determination to do it.
Sir Colin Coote, Daily Telegraph 29 *May* 1972

7 He had hidden shallows.
Clive James, THE CRYSTAL BUCKET 1981

8 I don't mind your being killed, but I object to your being taken prisoner.
Lord Kitchener, when Edward, Prince of Wales asked to go to the Western Front. Quoted Lord Esher, JOURNALS 18 *Dec* 1914

9 He was the golden boy who had survived his own doomed generation; steeplechasing, clearing the undergrowth at Fort Belvedere, buried beneath a Welsh Guard's bearskin on St David's Day; inspecting Grenadier veterans with his great-uncle the Duke of Connaught, cruising with Wallis Simpson in Corsica, mourning his father in St George's Chapel, talking to the unemployed in South Wales. A lost, bewildered expression on his face, gaining with the years, a kind of wincing foreknowledge of what time would bring to birth.
John Raymond, History Today, The Baldwin Age Sep 1960

10 In a rather feckless way he wanted to make the monarchy more adventurous, and the country with it.
A. J. P. Taylor, ENGLISH HISTORY 1914–1945 1965

11 He resented the staid tepidity of the 'old men', his ministers. They resented him. In the early days of the reign Neville Chamberlain drafted a memorandum of complaint, urging the king to 'settle down'. He should wear drabber clothes, work at his 'boxes' and not make public remarks about slums or unemployment. Baldwin suppressed the memorandum.
Ibid.

12 All men would have judged him worthy of the throne if he had never ascended it.
The Times leader 11 *Dec* 1936

ALBERT EINSTEIN

Born in Germany 1879, became American citizen. Physicist. Published his General Theory of Relativity 1916. Nobel Prize for Physics 1921. Died 1955.

13 As a pacifist he martyred himself on the rack of his own convictions when he wrote to Roosevelt on Aug 2 1939, warning him that the Germans might try to produce the atomic bomb and starting the fuse that led to Hiroshima.
Ritchie Calder, News Chronicle 14 *Mar* 1949

14 He keeps his sense of humour, as when he was asked to define relativity. 'When you are courting a nice girl an hour seems like a second. When you sit on a red-hot cinder a second seems like an hour. That's relativity.'
Ibid.

15 Mrs Einstein was particularly impressed by

the giant telescope at Mt Wilson Observatory. 'What do they use it for?' she asked. Her host explained that one of its chief uses was to find out the shape of the universe. 'Oh,' said Mrs Einstein, 'my husband does that on the back of an old envelope.'
Bennett Cerf, TRY AND STOP ME 1947

1 Einstein has made it possible for man to see himself in truer proportions. He has unified our laws of motion and our law of gravity and has opened the way for us to see with new clarity our universe, finite now in extent but vaster by far than has been dreamed of before his thoughts stimulated the imagination of the scientific world.
Dr Arthur Compton, UNESCO broadcast 13 *Mar* 1949

2 Isn't it strange that I who have written only unpopular books should be such a popular fellow.
Albert Einstein

3 I'm not much with people, and I'm not a family man, I want my peace. I want to know how God created this world. I'm not interested in this or that phenomenon. I want to know His thoughts, the rest are details.
Albert Einstein. Quoted Ronald W. Clark, EINSTEIN: THE LIFE AND TIMES 1973

4 Einstein a scientist? As a rational scientist Einstein is a fair violinist. Einstein is already dead and buried alongside Andersen, Grimm and the Mad Hatter.
George Francis Gilette (1929). *Quoted Chris Morgan and David Longford*, FACTS AND FALLACIES 1981

5 Einstein's name will still be remembered and revered when Lloyd George, Foch and William Hohenzollern share with Charlie Chaplin in that ineluctable oblivion which awaits the uncreative mind.
J. B. S. Haldane, DAEDALUS: OR SCIENCE AND THE FUTURE

6 Einstein — the greatest Jew since Christ.
Ibid.

7 Outside his work, his judgment was not noticeably good or stable, and whether he should have signed the letter to Roosevelt urging the making of the Bomb may remain open.
Marghanita Laski, The Times 10 *Sep* 1973

8 Einstein, a keen amateur violinist, was practising sonatas at home with his pianist friend, Artur Rubenstein. Someone walked past the door of their practice room and overheard Rubenstein as he pointed out a false entry on Einstein's part. 'Oh Albert', he was saying, 'can't you *count*.'
Steve Race, MY MUSIC 1979

9 'Exactly what did Einstein do that was so smart?'
'Einstein revolutionised physics. He proved that matter is energy. That when light goes past the sun, it *bends*. That —'
'Awright, awright,' said the old man. 'But tell me: from that he makes a living?'
Leo Rosten, HOORAY FOR YIDDISH 1983

10 Men of science, at their best, have a special kind of impressiveness, resulting from the combination of great intellect with childlike simplicity. When I say 'simplicity' I do not mean anything involving lack of cleverness; I mean the habit of thinking impersonally, without regard for the worldly advantage or disadvantage of an opinion or action. Among the men of science I have known, Einstein is a supreme example of this quality.
Bertrand Russell, UNPOPULAR ESSAYS, *Eminent Men I Have Known* 1950

11 No great man of science has ever been so swathed in myth, adulation, prejudice, and sheer fudge.
Michael Maxwell Scott, The Times 13 *Sep* 1973

12 As a child he was so backward at acquiring the normal adaptations, such as learning to talk, that his parents gravely doubted whether he was not mentally deficient. On the other hand, at four years his first sight of the compass needle's mysterious persistence made him tremble and go cold.
J. W. N. Sullivan, GREAT CONTEMPORARIES 1935

13 Entering Tom Quad one day Gilbert Murray caught sight of Einstein sitting with a faraway look on his face. The faraway thought behind that faraway look was evidently a happy one, for, at that moment, the exile's countenance was serene and smiling. 'Dr Einstein, do tell me what you are thinking', Murray said. 'I am thinking,' Einstein answered, 'that after all this is a very small star.'
Arnold J. Toynbee, ACQUAINTANCES

DWIGHT D. (DAVID) EISENHOWER

Born 1890. American general, supreme commander of Allied invasion of Europe 1944. Became President of the United States 1953–61. Died 1969.

14 I have but one career, and its name is Ike.
Mamie Eisenhower. Quoted J. B. West, UPSTAIRS AT THE WHITE HOUSE 1974

1 He possessed that most priceless quality of military qualities — luck.
Michael Howard, Sunday Times 10 *May* 1970

2 From the very beginning his mind possessed a hard cutting edge; he shouldered responsibility effortlessly; and he grew at beanstalk speed to keep pace with his job.
Ibid.

3 He was the great tortoise upon whose back the world sat for eight years. We laughed at him; we talked wistfully about moving; and all the while we never knew the cunning beneath the shell.
Murray Kempton, Esquire *Sep* 1967

4 In a nuclear world, teeming with violence on all sides, he successfully 'waged peace' for the eight years of his incumbency.
Arthur Larson, EISENHOWER: THE PRESIDENT NO ONE KNEW

5 President Eisenhower's whole life is proof of the stark but simple truth — that no one hates war more than one who has seen a lot of it.
Richard Nixon. Speech on Russian TV 1959

6 There are few peasants among his social companions.
Merriman Smith, MEET MR EISENHOWER

7 The General has dedicated himself so many times he must feel like the cornerstone of a public building.
Adlai Stevenson. Quoted Leon Harris, THE FINE ART OF POLITICAL WIT

8 Golf is a fine release from the tensions of office, but we are a little tired of holding the bag.
Adlai Stevenson. Quoted ibid.

9 He's a good man. The only trouble was, he had a lot of damn fool Republicans around him.
Harry S Truman *Dec* 1963

10 Ike had only two driving forces — he wanted to be a soldier and to play golf.
TV Times 20 *Oct* 1984

11 Television provided an effective medium for President Eisenhower. His wide smile, his proud, erect posture, his direct manner were magically carried to homes around the country. With much ado he made the first telecast from the White House ground floor broadcast room in May 1953 (thereafter, actor Robert Montgomery came to advise him on his performances).
J. B. West, UPSTAIRS AT THE WHITE HOUSE 1974

12 Every four years the American Booksellers Association sent several hundred new books for the White House library. But when it was reported that the President's favourites fell into the Western category we were flooded with paperbacks, guns blazing on the covers, most of which the President read after dinner while Mrs Eisenhower concentrated on magazines and romantic novels.
Ibid.

13 The President's pride and joy was his putting green, a gift from the American Public Golf Association, installed on the south lawn just outside his office window. Keeping that green in perfect condition became an obsession with Dwight Eisenhower. He ordered the gardeners to flick the dew off the grass with fishing poles every morning. The squirrels, that Mr Truman had almost tamed by feeding them scraps, infuriated Mr Eisenhower because they buried acorns and walnuts in the putting green. 'The next time you see one of those squirrels go near my green, take a gun and shoot it,' he thundered. The quick-thinking Secret Service talked him out of it. 'There's bound to be some fuss made, the press would get hold of it, and the humane societies would never let you forget it.' Somehow the gardeners caught most of the offending aniamls in nets. They were evicted by White House van to Rock Creek Park.
Ibid.

14 No one, however much he may 'like Ike', can prevent Eisenhower from appearing in history as one of the least inspiring presidents of the United States.
H. D. Ziman, Daily Telegraph 18 *Jan* 1968

SIR EDWARD ELGAR

Born 1857. English composer whose popularity was established with *The Enigma Variations,* 1899. Among his best-known subsequent works are *The Dream of Gerontius* and *Pomp and Circumstance.* Died 1934.

15 It was not until many years later that it dawned on Dora Penny, the original of the tenth Enigma Variation, Dorabella, that she had been as much the victim of Elgar's impish humour as had some of the other characters. She says 'I stammered rather badly at times when I was young and Elgar exploited his humour at my expense with such marvellous delicacy that no one could

help laughing with him — if they understood it.'
Michael Bell, Radio Times 19 *Jun* 1949

1 The *Enigma Variations* item was absolutely overwhelming. I saw Elgar afterwards at the Savoy Grill and congratulated him. He said he never went to hear his own music. He said also that he wrote the thing 31 years ago, when it was called 'silly', and now people talked about its 'profound psychological import'. He is now a rather silly and disgruntled old man. Even eight years ago, when I last had him to dinner, I said I would never ask him again because of his affectations.
Arnold Bennett, LETTERS TO A NEPHEW 1936

2 He was reserved, somewhat proud, and seemed on tenter-hooks. He was very kind to me in after years and one of my most precious possessions is a score of *Cockaigne* with inscription, that he sent to me in France. It arrived a few days before July 1, 1916 and bears on its pages the marks of mud from the Somme trenches.
Sir Arthur Bliss. Quoted Henry Raynor, Daily Telegraph 29 *Jul* 1961

3 When Elgar composed his violin concerto he asked Yehudi Menuhin, then a boy, to come down to the west country and play it with an orchestra conducted by himself. They played it straight through without a break. Then Elgar said, 'That'll do. Now we can go to the races.'
Lord Boothby, RECOLLECTIONS OF A REBEL 1978

4 Although he became a public figure who pretended that music was bosh and only dogs and horses worth while, he could behave like a failed poet nail-biting in York Minster.
Anthony Burgess, Observer 29 *May* 1983

5 It is a curious thing that the performances which I have hated and loathed as being a caricature of my thoughts are the very ones held up as patterns.
Sir Edward Elgar. Quoted Basil Maine, ELGAR, HIS LIFE AND WORKS 1933

6 I like to look on the composer's vocation as the old troubadours or bards did. In those days it was no disgrace for a man to be turned on to step in front of an army and inspire them with a song. I know that there are a lot of people who like to celebrate events with music; to these people I have given tunes. Is that wrong? Why should I write a fugue or something that won't appeal to anyone, when the people yearn for things that can stir them?
Sir Edward Elgar. Quoted Robin Ray, WORDS ON MUSIC 1984

7 One of Elgar's most outstanding qualities was artistic sincerity. When he played to the gallery he was undoubtedly sincere in his rather vulgar approach, but he never forgot he was a craftsman. This vein of vulgarity that is best described as Edwardian jingoism was an intellectual weakness, not a musical one.
Ralph Hill, Radio Times 18 *Feb* 1944

8 His music is something that transcends mere music and becomes part, almost, of the bloodstream; it gathers personal associations which the passing of the years makes more poignant, and although the poignancy seems at times unbearable, the music then becomes a solace, a renewing stream.
Michael Kennedy, BARBIROLLI — CONDUCTOR LAUREATE 1971

9 When he was nine years old Edward Elgar was discovered sitting on the bank of a river with a pencil and a piece of paper whereon were ruled five parallel lines. He was trying, he said, to write down what the reeds were singing.
Basil Maine ELGAR, HIS LIFE AND WORKS 1933

10 That night Lady Elgar and I sat in the drawing room next door to the study where he was at work for five hours — waiting. It was nearly 2 a.m. before the piece was finished. After a cosy meal round the fire we went into the study and he played it straight through. A nice job I had, turning over, with the music written on all sorts of odd pieces of paper, and some of it on *both* sides. I saw the words, 'The sun goeth down; Thou makes darkness and it is night — ' When I hear *The Kingdom* now how can I help remembering that evening.
Mrs Richard Powell, EDWARD ELGAR: MEMORIES OF A VARIATION

11 I had heard a number of good pianists, but I had never heard anything like this. He didn't play like a pianist, he almost seemed to play like an orchestra. It sounded full without being loud, and he contrived to make you hear other instruments joining in.
Ibid.

12 *The Apostles* places British music once more

definitely in the first place European rank, after two centuries of leather and pommels.
G. B. Shaw, Daily News 9 *Jun* 1922

1 Sir Edward Elgar, with his grey moustache, grey hair, grey top hat and frock coat, looked every inch a personification of Colonel Bogey.
Osbert Sitwell, LAUGHTER IN THE NEXT ROOM 1949

2 To me, in spite of its genius, the music of Elgar is obnoxious; so full of English humour and the spirit of compulsory games.
Ibid.

3 Great men are usually inordinately modest about their real achievements, but quite grotesquely vain about the little things they do as sidelines . . . Sir Edward Elgar nearly burst with pride at having succeeded in making a ridiculous fountain in his garden emit a feeble jet of water, whereas he spoke quite disparagingly about *Gerontius*.
Ernest Thesiger, PRACTICALLY TRUE 1927

4 To the careful observer there is nothing to occasion astonishment or require explanation in the fact that the same Elgar who produced the mystical exaltation of *Gerontius* was an enthusiastic follower of horseracing.
Sir Jack Westrup, SHARPS AND FLATS

T. S. (THOMAS STEARNS) ELIOT

Born 1885 in United States. English poet. Established his reputation with *The Waste Land*, 1922. Awarded Nobel Prize for Literature 1948. Died 1965.

5 I began to read contemporary memoirs and a quite different man emerged — a young man nervous, difficult, proud, exhibiting a kind of hypersensitivity which left him almost defenceless against the world. And there was another man — the bank clerk and later publisher who fulfilled his obligations and arranged his tasks as if by so doing they might form a carapace in which he might hide. And then there was the older man — stooped, deathly pale, ill, unable or unwilling to derive pleasure from his fame. There was also the fourth man after his second marriage to Valerie Fletcher; he became a joyful and optimistic septuagenarian, who considered taking up dancing lessons.
Peter Ackroyd, The Times, A life measured out 15 *Sep* 1984

6 Perhaps it was religion that saved him from fascism. His craving for authority and order found satisfaction at the high altar — preferably at the very high altar.
Peter Ackroyd, T. S. ELIOT 1984

7 They [Eliot and his first wife Valerie] both possessed a strong theatrical streak and the element of willed drama in their relationship was not entirely negligible.
Ibid.

8 If Mr Eliot had been pleased to write in demotic English, *The Waste Land* might not have been, as it is to all but anthropologists and literati, so much waste paper.
Anon., Manchester Guardian

9 He was but a thin and squeaking Matthew Arnold.
Bernard Berenson. Quoted Cyril Connolly, Sunday Times 19 *Jun* 1966

10 As a poet Eliot could more easily achieve intensity than extension, and the same thing was true of his prose writing.
Bernard Bergonzi, T. S. ELIOT

11 I was much impressed with the chalk-white face with the swollen purple lips and felt confident that he had been brooding all night over the Crucifixion or some other holy torture.
William Empson, of Eliot in 1930, USING BIOGRAPHY 1984

12 Tom Eliot was an extraodinary case of a man who had stepped right out of the Middle Ages.
William Empson. Quoted Stephen Spender, Observer 30 *Sep* 1984

13 He likes to look on the bile when it is black.
Aldous Huxley. Quoted Edward Marsh, AMBROSIA AND SMALL BEER

14 Eliot's besetting vice is a never wholly penetrable ambiguity about what is supposed to be happening.
Hugh Kenner, THE INVISIBLE POET 1960

15 His notorious statement that he is 'an Anglo-Catholic in religion, a classicist in literature and a royalist in politics' has earned him much foolish abuse from the political left.
Frederick Laws, News Chronicle 5 *Nov* 1948

16 Appearing at one's door, or arriving at a dinner rendezvous (I am thinking of the late thirties, not his more vernal years) his face would be haggard, he would seem at his last gasp. To ask him to lie down for a short while at once was what I always felt I ought to do. However, when he had taken his place at a table, given his face a dry wash with his

hands, and having had a little refreshment, Mr Eliot would rapidly shed all resemblance to a harassed and exhausted refugee, in flight from some Scourge of God.
Wyndham Lewis, T. S. ELIOT, A SYMPOSIUM (*Edited by Richard Marsh and Tambimuttu*)

1 On the day when the first copy of *The Waste Land* reached the family no one quite understood it, but they sensed it was somehow meant to be 'uncomfortable'. His mother staunchly defended it against family misgivings.
Roy Perrott, Observer 10 *Jan* 1965

2 When Eliot was poor and living in a London bed-sitter he lived underneath a pair of girl tap-dancers who used to practise at night and prevent him writing. On a mild complaint the landlord said 'Well, Mr Eliot, they're different from us. They're artists.'
Ibid.

3 Eliot did nothing to discourage the idea that he was a connoisseur of English cheeses. 'Let's lunch at the Athenaeum,' he would say, in the manner of a *bon viveur* of dairy products. 'They keep a good piece of cheese there.' Or, 'Ah! Wensleydale, the Mozart of cheeses!' But at home for years Eliot never complained at the regular bit of 'old Cheddar' which the housekeeper used to produce.
Ibid.

4 He did his writing standing up, working at an old typewriter set on a kind of high lectern, designed like a piece of church furniture, in his back room away from the distractions of the Thames.
Ibid.

5 His shyness, at Harvard, and his efforts to overcome it, are things that largely stayed with him. He stopped hiding in the lavatory and got out on to the dance floor. He even took boxing lessons. His coach gave him a shiner for hitting too hard.
Ibid.

6 His admiration for his contemporaries was limited and uncertain, but to James Joyce he was completely devoted, both to the writer and to the man.
Sir Herbert Read, T. S. ELIOT: THE MAN AND HIS WORK (*Edited by Allen Tate*) 1962

7 As a publisher he is not only the firm's expert on poetry, but he is also a conscientious composer of blurbs for book jackets. He finds it an exacting task. 'I don't know how to grow asparagus, or how to improve your lawn tennis, or the best diet for a six-month-old baby, but I have to write blurbs about them,' he said.
Milton Shulman, Evening Standard 8 *Aug* 1950

8 Though he was reserved, and had armoured himself behind the fine manners, and the fastidiously courteous manner, that are particularly his own; though too, the range and tragic depths of his great poetry were to be read in the very lines of his face; and though, in addition, he must have been exhausted by long hours of uncongenial work (as a bank clerk) his air, to the contrary, was always lively, gay, even jaunty. His clothes, too — in London he usually wore check or 'sponge-bag' trousers and a short black coat — were elegant and he walked with a cheerful, easy movement.
Osbert Sitwell, LAUGHTER IN THE NEXT ROOM 1949

9 It was in the autumn of 1917 that we saw T. S. Eliot for the first time; a most striking being having peculiarly luminous, light yellow, more than tawny, eyes; the eyes, they might have been, of one of the greater cats, but tiger, puma, leopard, lynx, rather than those of a lion which, for some reason, display usually a more domesticated and placid expression. His face, too, possessed the width of bony structure of a tigrine face, albeit the nose was prominent, similar, I used to think, to that of a figure on an Aztec carving or a bas-relief.
Ibid.

10 Eliot's muscular conformation, and his carriage and the way he moved seem to explain the giant muscular control of rhythm he has acquired.
Ibid.

11 I once heard Eliot say that at the time of *The Waste Land* he seriously considered becoming a Buddhist.
Stephen Spender, T. S. ELIOT: THE MAN AND HIS WORK (*Edited by Allen Tate*) 1962

12 Without the tragedy of the failure of his first marriage Eliot would not have written the poetry that made him famous; *The Waste Land* was written out of a sensibility kept in a state of exasperated tension.
Stephen Spender, Observer 30 *Sep* 1984

13 Of the non-literary influences which most contributed to Eliot's poetic development his religion must be put first. The fastidiousness, the moral taste, and the intellectual severity, which were a legacy of his New England ancestry, merged with the Anglo-Catholic tradition to direct his poetry

ever farther in the exploration of spiritual awareness, the search for spiritual values.
The Times, Obituary 5 *Jan* 1965

1 His works in verse and prose have been translated into almost every European language except Russian, and have been the subject of more books and articles than have ever been published about an author in his lifetime.
Ibid.

2 The quality of his writing was inseparable, to those who knew him, from the integrity of his character. In public Eliot, a stooping, sombre-clad figure, appeared to be shy and retiring, formal in his manner, which was courtly and attentive, but detached. The impertinence of the curious, the sometimes intemperate attention of admirers, he kept alike at arm's length by a playful, evasive wit.
Ibid.

3 I feel a real apology is due to Mr Eliot, for whose work I profess a sincere and profound respect, though I fail to understand it.
Charles Williams, POETRY AT PRESENT

4 'Mr Eliot' was a fictional character and Tom himself helped to create him. Among the roles the poet deftly played were the Anglican Clergyman, The Formidable Professor, Dr Johnson and the Genteel Bostonian.
Edmund Wilson.

5 Tom's great yellow bronze mask all draped upon an iron framework. An inhibited, nerve-drawn, dropped face — as if hung on a scaffold of heavy private brooding; and thought. A very serious face, and broken by the flicker of relief, when other people interrupt.
Virginia Woolf, DIARY VOL 5 1936–41

ELIZABETH II

Born 1926. Daughter of George VI. Succeeded to the throne 1952.

6 On coronation day the Queen looked extremely minute under her robes and crown, her nose and hands chilled, her eyes tired. 'Yes', in reply to my question, 'the Crown does get rather heavy.' She had been wearing it now for three hours.
Cecil Beaton, THE STRENUOUS YEARS 1973

7 On this particular morning during which several matters of state had to be attended to, Her Majesty was a bit late for an audience with a new ambassador (who arrived in a horse-drawn coach) and had to be shown in by Anthony Eden. Suddenly Eden said, 'I think, ma'am, we must hurry this through as the Ambassador has been here some considerable time.' The Queen said, 'Oh yes, we can't keep the horses waiting.'
Cecil Beaton, DIARY 1951

8 The Queen came over and, as usual, as she talked to me her face relaxed into what can be her very charming smile. I can only conclude that she is naturally shy, or has inherited Queen Mary's glower without knowing it.
Barbara Castle, DIARY 3 *Apr* 1968

9 I do believe that a marriage may well be arranged one day between Princess Elizabeth and Prince Philip of Greece.
Sir Henry Channon, DIARY 16 *Feb* 1944

10 [At the age of two] she has an air of authority and reflectiveness astonishing in an infant.
Winston Churchill in a letter to his wife 1928

11 The aristocracy have their foibles. Eleven corgis would be considered mildly eccentric, if owned by anyone else.
Alan Hamilton, The Times 1 *Feb* 1982

12 If she is rich enough to give her daughter Gatcombe as a wedding present she ought to be able to afford a new runabout for the Windsor estate. But she prefers to hang on to her ancient green F-registered Vauxhall estate with lino on the floor to prevent the dogs from messing it.
Ibid.

13 Elizabeth II is a woman of great political astuteness, which in itself is her best ally against a changing climate beyond the gates of Buckingham Palace. She is on her eighth Prime Minister, and by her very position knows more than any of them.
Ibid.

14 Her experience is wider than any other head of state alive, and she has an excellent memory. Sir Harold Wilson, caught off guard at a Tuesday evening audience with a question about plans to build a new town at Milton Keynes, quickly learned the value of doing his homework.
Ibid.

15 She has been afflicted by a blend of shyness and severity and has cultivated the same devastating reaction as Queen Mary to observations by which she is not amused — totally ignoring the remark while looking its perpetrator full in the face.
Robert Lacey, MAJESTY 1977

1 In a magazine article in 1958 Lord Altrincham said the Queen's style of speaking (*not* her voice) was 'frankly a pain in the neck' and what she was given to say suggested a 'priggish school girl, captain of the hockey team, a prefect and a recent candidate for confirmation'. He was slapped in the face by a member of the League of Empire Loyalists for his pains.
Nigel Rees, SAYINGS OF THE YEAR 1984

2 I ran into the White House maid who'd been assigned to straighten the Queen's Room. Wide-eyed, she told me 'Queen Elizabeth sent *her* personal maids to bed early last night — she told them not to wait up for her because she'd be late.' Then in utter astonishment she described the morning scene in the Queen's Room. The fabulous diamond tiara, the heavy diamond necklace, the beribboned medals — all the precious jewels Elizabeth II had worn the night before — tossed casually on a dresser. Her gown and underthings were folded neatly on a chair. The Queen of England had undressed herself.
J. B. West, UPSTAIRS AT THE WHITE HOUSE 1974

DUKE (EDWARD KENNEDY) ELLINGTON

Born 1899 in America. Musician, composer, pianist. Although he is chiefly remembered for his work with his jazz orchestra he also composed a number of popular songs. Died 1974.

3 Such music is not only a new art form, but a new reason for living.
Blaise Cendrars, Observer 5 *Oct* 1958

4 Maybe it is 4000 or 5000 things he has written — no one knows. The chilling truth is that perhaps ninety per cent of it has not been preserved in manuscript. It is in the heads of his musicians, consciously or unconsciously, and already they are growing old.
Derek Jewell, DUKE — A PORTRAIT OF DUKE ELLINGTON 1977

5 I was more attracted by Duke Ellington personally than by the hour of his music I heard with Barney Seale, who wept from overpowering emotion; he said he had never been more moved by anything.
Reginald Pound, THEIR MOODS AND MINE 1937

6 He had already started studying the piano in 1906 and at school showed signs of being gifted both musically and artistically. It was while he was at school that he gained the nickname 'Duke' supposedly on account of his sartorial elegance.
The Times, Obituary 25 *May* 1974

7 He was one of American's better song-writers, having written such songs as *Mood Indigo*, *Caravan*, *Sophisticated Lady* and *Don't Get Around Much Any More*. They brought him enough royalties in later years to enable him to keep his beloved band on the road at a loss.
Ibid.

(HENRY) HAVELOCK ELLIS

Born 1859. English psychologist and author. His major work was *Studies in the Psychology of Sex*, which appeared in seven volumes from 1896 to 1928. Died 1939.

8 He had the air of a fake prophet, like a Santa Claus at Selfridges.
Graham Greene. Quoted Phyllis Gross Kurth, HAVELOCK ELLIS, A BIOGRAPHY

9 If the test of the personal culture of a man be the degree of freedom from the banal ideas and childish emotions which move the great masses of men, then Havelock Ellis is the most civilised Englishman of his generation.
H. L. Mencken, American Mercury

10 Mr Ellis, as he himself says of Swift, has a tendency to dwell upon excrement.
London Mercury. Quoted Lancelot Hogben, GREAT CONTEMPORARIES 1935

SIR JACOB EPSTEIN

Born 1880 in America of Russo-Polish descent. British sculptor whose work aroused violent controversy when first exhibited. Died 1959.

11 He seems to be obsessed by certain fundamental facts of life usually excluded from artistic representation, and we are not sure how far hieroglyphics based on the obvious physical aspects of these things can be considered to symbolise adequately their significance.
Athenaeum magazine

12 He spoke to me about his 'Oscar Wilde' in Paris. When he arrived he found the sexual organs had been covered over with plaster; later the Prefect of the Seine covered the

whole monument over with straw, as being altogether indecent. Epstein took off the straw, and then the plaster, and restored to his 'Wilde' his *couilles de taureau*, and through the petition of some artists was able to get the better of the civil authorities.
Gaudier Brzeska, Nov 1912

1 'Rima' is a bestial figure, horribly misshapen, with the face and head of a microcephalous idiot.
Hon. John Collier

2 My 'Genesis', with her fruitful womb, confronts our enfeebled generation. Within her man takes on new hope for the future.
Jacob Epstein. Quoted News Review 10 *Oct* 1946

3 In 1907 he began carving the figures on the Strand building of the British Medical Association, and chose to do first-hand carving on the stone, on the building itself. He tells with great gusto of the policeman who mounted the scaffolding on which he was carving, examined one figure, pulled out his notebook and wrote the word 'rude', then went on to another figure and wrote 'very rude', and departed to make his expert report to his superiors.
Louis Golding, GREAT CONTEMPORARIES 1935

4 Everything Epstein has ever done has shocked the great British public into fits. There were the nude figures on the British Medical building in the Strand some years ago. Respectable paterfamilias and mothers-of-ten went for rides on tops of buses for weeks especially to enjoy the sensation of being shocked.
Ethel Mannin, CONFESSIONS AND IMPRESSIONS 1930

5 His great figures on the new underground station have been assaulted by tar-and-feather bombs and subjected to the usual vapourings about modern ugliness — but Epstein goes on, magnificently heedless.
Ibid.

6 His manner is shy, retiring, diffident. In appearance he looks like the man who has come to see about the burst pipe. He is not concerned with outward appearances. He was paid a big sum for his work on the new St James's Park Underground station, but there is no sign of financial success in his home. If one did not know one would imagine that Epstein was still the struggling unknown artist.
Ibid.

7 When you meet Epstein's gentle dark eyes, kindly and yet penetrating and shrewd, you feel that he sees right through the outward trappings of civilisation to the living flesh and blood. He does not see women as they see themselves in their mirrors, with their lipstick, powder, rouge, their furs and their smart clothes; he sees them more naked than they ever see themselves.
Ibid.

8 Epstein is magnificently free of any ideas about his work. If you are unwise enough to say to him 'I take it you mean to express so-and-so', he will mutter, 'Yes, yes, that's it,' and then if you say quite the opposite thing he will say again, 'Yes, yes, that's it.' He simply does not care what you or anyone else reads into his work.
Ibid.

9 Epstein in his sculpture gets down to essentials. He does not ask to be understood. He asks nothing but to be allowed to get on with his work in his own way. He has the supreme lack of self-consciousness of the natural artist.
Ibid.

10 Journalists and people who conscientiously take an Intelligent Interest in his work are his *bêtes noires*.
Ibid.

11 I sit patiently to you, and you do exactly what you want to do, which is to strip me of the mask of my civilisation, to abolish the artificial refinements copied by Strobl and Rodin to show me in my crude humanity as you learnt it in Brooklyn. I became a Brooklyn navvy in your hands. My skin thickened, my hair coarsened, I put on five stone in weight, my physical strength trebled. The brilliant sketch became a thundering lie. When the bust went to the Leicester Galleries a workman, who was evidently a profound critic, completed the effect by putting his hat on it, and a press photographer snapped it in that condition. My wife saw the picture and immediately said that if that bust came into the house she would walk out of it.
G. B. Shaw, letter to Jacob Epstein

12 You have not learnt the first lesson of a fashionable sculptor which is; that no woman will look twice at a bust of her husband if its hair is not properly brushed.
Ibid.

DAME EDITH EVANS

Born 1888. English stage and film actress. Began her stage career in 1912, established herself as an actress of the first rank in the role of Millimant in *The Way of the World*, 1924. At the age of 60, in 1948, embarked on a film career in Pushkin's *Queen of Spades*, and in 1951 gave her unequalled performance as Lady Bracknell in Wilde's *The Importance of Being Earnest.* She continued to act in films almost until her death in 1976.

1 Talking about Hesione Hushabye (in *Heartbreak House*), Edith said she felt she was not well-mannered or bad-mannered but a complete 'original'. She saw her in flowing draperies but discarding their grandeur — screwing up her arms, and going to sleep in public lying back in a huddle with legs twisted. Edith shouted: 'She must gather up the sleeves of her lovely tea-gowns and wave!' It is by such touches that Edith brings her characters to life.
Cecil Beaton, DIARY 1943

2 Of her performance as Millimant she said that others too often have the wrong conception of the eighteenth century. 'It wasn't just finicking daintiness with little fingers raised, snuff-pinching and fluttering of fans. Why, the climate hasn't changed! Women nowadays are seldom hot enough to want to fan themselves! A fan should be used for poking the fire, or at best, making an aside behind. It should never be used for fanning. A parasol, too, was useful for poking people.'
Ibid.

3 At Gustave's, when Dolly the wig-maker fitted a *toile* on her head and she looked quite bald, Edith said 'This is how I'd like to appear sometimes, looking like a Flemish Madonna. When I went to the Dutch exhibition my friends said, "These are all you — bald — with gooseberry eyes."'
Ibid.

4 She had a faculty for endowing a stage character and its more striking passages of dialogue with such life that no other actress who subsequently attempted the part could escape unfavourable comparison.
W. A. Darlington, Daily Telegraph 15 *Oct* 1976

5 In private life she did not pretend to good looks. She was a plain woman who accepted her plainness and did not seek to disguise it. But on the stage she could put on beauty like a garment, and play the most glamorous of women with confidence and authority.
Ibid.

6 Edith Evans was no beauty in the ordinary sense. Her eyes, with their heavy lids, were set with one slightly lower than the other, giving her face an enigmatic originality. But it was a fascinating canvas on which she soon learned to paint any character she chose. I remember once saying as a young actor 'I would love to have a photograph of Edith Evans. I never know what she looks like: she always looks like the part.' It was probably the greatest compliment I could have paid her.
John Gielgud, AN ACTOR AND HIS TIME 1979

7 She was staying at my cottage in Essex one weekend just before the War when I suggested a possible revival of *The Importance of Being Earnest*. I took a copy from the bookshelf and we read the handbag scene together to the other guests. After the laughter had died down Edith handed back the book and remarked gravely 'I know those sort of women. They ring the bell and tell you to put a lump of coal on the fire.'
Ibid.

8 She grew to hate her success as Lady Bracknell though it was perhaps the most popular and famous of all her impersonations . . . she disliked the imitations of her trumpet tone in the famous line '*A handbag*' which many people seemed to think was the alpha and omega of her performance as Lady Bracknell. For me there was so much else to admire.
Ibid.

9 Edith Evans was the finest actress of our time and I am privileged to have known and worked with her so often. She was not always easy. She was not a cosy person. She was not gregarious and found it difficult to open out to people. She longed to be an ordinary woman, to have a home, a husband, perhaps children. She never had them.
Ibid.

10 At the Old Vic (in 1926) Edith Evans playing Rosalind woke me up to the instant power of poetry. Before this Shakespeare was a lesson to be endured, now it became an excitement, an immediate experience. I remember going home from the performance on top of a tram in the pouring rain. The lines glistened and the whole universe was translated into ideas.

Sixteen is late for this sort of awakening, but I was a late developer in lots of ways.
Joyce Grenfell, JOYCE GRENFELL REQUESTS THE PLEASURE 1976

1 Had Edith Evans died in her fifties she would probably be remembered as a comedienne; for — as James Agate called it — her smile of happy deliverance on uttering an author's wittiest conceits.
The Times, Obituary 15 *Oct* 1976

2 She always refused the part of Lady Macbeth because she found the character incredible.
Ibid.

3 Dame Edith Evans suggests a crested wave of Edwardian eccentricity vainly dashing itself on the rocks of contemporary life.
Kenneth Tynan, of Edith Evans in THE CHALK GARDEN

F

DOUGLAS (ELTON) FAIRBANKS

Born 1883 in America. Began his career as an actor in repertory theatre, but in 1915, realising the potential of silent films, moved to Hollywood and rapidly gained a world-wide reputation playing athletic, swashbuckling heroes in flamboyant costume dramas such as *The Mark of Zorro*, 1920, *The Three Musketeers*, 1921, *The Thief of Bagdad*, 1923. With the arrival of talking films his popularity declined. Died 1939.

1 He died at 56, his tanned body apparently untouched by age, but actually so muscle-bound that the blood could barely circulate. He had not so much died, some friends thought, as run down.
John Baxter, STUNT

2 For thousands of film fans he has meant a way of escape from a life where there is precious little room for scaling high walls, leaping on to high-powered horses and indulging in snappy sword play. 'Come with me', he said, 'and we'll play pirates.' You know it's absurd, but you play pirates.
Vere Denning, Pictorial Weekly 23 *Jul* 1932

3 Behind those acrobatic stunts and that schoolboy exuberance there was real genius. His leaps, and fights, and swift, violent trajectories were thrilling to watch, but they were inventive too; they had about them the quality of surprise. He was an unconscious harlequin.
C. A. Lejeune. Quoted David Shipman, THE GREAT MOVIE STARS

4 His *Black Pirate* is historic as being the first phenomenally successful film to be made in colour [in 1926].
Seton Margrave, DAILY MAIL 13 *Dec* 1939

5 Doug in his mid-fifties had the figure of a young athlete and he paid constant attention to keeping it that way. He took a sunbath daily in a small green canvas compartment in the garden, burning himself the colour of chewing tobacco. He was curiously coy in the presence of the friends he invited to join him there, always covering his private parts with his two cupped hands.
David Niven, BRING ON THE EMPTY HORSES 1975

6 Doug enjoyed hugely displaying his acrobatic talents and watching those half his age trying to catch up with him. I nearly killed myself jumping off his high diving board on to the low springboard alongside, which he had assured me would give 'a really tremendous bounce'. It did, I missed the water altogether and landed in some petunias below the drawing-room window.
Ibid.

7 His daring stunts, as a matter of pride, he did himself, scorning the use of doubles. In *The Black Pirate*, trapped in the highest cross-trees, he plunged his sword with both hands into the billowing mainsail, slid down it and arrived on deck leaving his adversaries in the rigging. He one day divulged that on the other side of the sail the sword had been bolted into a large board, but it was still a very dangerous descent.
Ibid.

8 Douglas has always faced a situation in the only way he knew how, by running away from it.
Mary Pickford, SUNSHINE AND SHADOW

9 Thomas Edison devoted his life to machines intended to make thinking unnecessary for the masses. Fairbanks is devoting his to pictures calculated to keep their minds off the fact that they are not thinking.
Terry Ramsaye. Quoted Lloyd Morris, NOT SO LONG AGO

KING FAROUK

Born 1920 in Egypt. Son of King Faud, succeeding him in 1936. Overthrown and exiled after a military coup by Naguib and Nasser, 1952. Died 1965.

10 Petticoat influence in childhood was the main factor in moulding his character. He grew up entirely surrounded by women — his dominating mother Queen Nazli, his four sisters, and his devoted English governess Ina Naylor, who strove in vain to neutralise the corrupting influences round him which ensured that Farouk was hopelessly spoiled before even reaching manhood.
Second Earl of Birkenhead, Daily Telegraph 28 *Dec* 1967

1 At the beginning of his reign Farouk was not, on occasion, without charm, but there was already in the king an appalling lack of discipline, application and sense of duty. He was a braggart and a liar, given over entirely to frivolity.
Ibid.

2 He sat the examination for the Royal Military Academy, Woolwich and waited expectantly for the answers to the questions to be supplied to him, as had always been done in Egypt. He was therefore unable to enter the Academy, but this did not prevent him afterwards boasting of his happy years spent at the dear old 'Shop'.
Ibid.

3 He collected objects of all kinds like an insane magpie, with a particular fondness for pornographic books and photographs. He was an ardent lover of practical jokes in every form, particularly those painful and humiliating for the victim. The jokes were further disfigured by the loud braying laugh that accompanied them.
Ibid.

4 King Farouk is a devout Moslem. He attends the mosque regularly. He always carries a miniature edition of the Koran and believes absolutely in its capacity to protect him. Not long ago he was in a house in Alexandria calling on a tutor when a lorry crashed into the motor-car he had left outside. 'What a good thing your Majesty was in here with us and not out there,' said a shocked courtier. 'Nothing would have happened to me' King Farouk answered serenely, 'I had my Koran in my breast pocket.'
Sefton Delmer, Sunday Express 29 *Nov* 1938

5 Psychoanalysts will say that it is the normal schoolboy collecting urge which makes young King Farouk spend hours in his library, cataloguing and arranging his books, oiling his guns, setting his collection of seventeenth- and eighteenth-century clocks working or washing and scraping at his Egyptian antiques in the laboratory he has set up. But there is nothing of the schoolboy in the pertinacity with which he hunts his treasures, or the prices he pays for them. At the moment three agents of his are scouring the world trying to find two missing agate drinking cups which he needs to complete a set.
Ibid.

6 Nothing could have been more fitting than that a nation reborn, as Egypt has been, and preparing to take its place among the young nations of the world, should have as its King a prince in whom, by reason of his age, its aspirations and its hopes stood thus symbolised. The people look to him for inspiration in their activities. Wherever he goes, the youth of the country acclaim him.
Arthur S. Merton, Daily Telegraph and Morning Post 12 *Dec* 1938

7 Until he came to England for the first time six months before his father died *he had never spent an hour alone in the company of a boy*. All his life his only playmates had been his four sisters.
Ina R. Naylor (governess to the Egyptian royal family), Sunday Express 29 *Aug* 1937

8 Within a few years he had not only ceased to be popular, but had become more unpopular than his father. He adopted the role of the 'pious king', visiting mosques on Fridays and posing as the champion of the Muslim faith. It soon got round that his private life was very different from his public profession.
The Times, Obituary 19 *Mar* 1965

WILLIAM FAULKNER

Born 1897. American novelist and short-story writer, created *The Imaginary Yoknapatawpha County*. Awarded Nobel Prize for Literature 1949. Died 1962.

9 The first fifty pages are always the hardest. Each time we must learn all over again *how* to read this strangely fluid and slippery and heavily mannered prose, and are even, like a kind of Laocoon, sometimes tempted to give it up.
Conrad Aitken, WILLIAM FAULKNER: FOUR DECADES OF CRITICISM (*Edited by L. W. Wagner*)

10 Every character who dies at 33 is a Christ-figure. Horses become symbols of destruction, and rain comes to signify death.
Cleanth Brooks, WILLIAM FAULKNER: THE YOKNAPATAWPHA COUNTY 1964

11 Mr Faulkner, of course, is interested in making your mind rather than your flesh creep.
Clifton Fadiman, New Yorker 21 *Apr* 1934

12 A great many people, I think, try to read too much into Bill's writings. It is simply not there, nor was it intended to be. If they would read him for the stories he was telling they would realise what a good story-teller Bill was.
John Faulkner, MY BROTHER BILL: AN AFFECTIONATE REMINISCENCE 1964

1 Poor Faulkner. Does he really think big emotions come from big words?
Ernest Hemingway. Quoted A. E. Hotchner, PAPA HEMINGWAY

2 Faulkner does not make things any easier for his readers. At their worst his sentences go on for pages piling up clauses and parentheses, and parentheses in parentheses, often without a comma to signpost the way.
David Holloway, Daily Telegraph 28 *May* 1964

3 He is the original of the story that crops up in almost every Hollywood novel of the writer who asks the producer's permission to work at home, is granted it and disappears. When, months later, he is needed, home is found to be not Beverley Hills, but Oxford, Mississippi.
Ibid.

4 He is inclined to lose his head. Laying on local colour is such fun that his brush goes slap, slap slap; purple passions and Southern nights, scarlet sins and dead yesterdays splash about so gloriously that there are times when the construction and significance of the whole scene is lost.
Robert Lynd, News Chronicle 2 *Mar* 1932

5 It happened, rather unfortunately perhaps, that the late Arnold Bennett once told Mr Faulkner that he writes like an angel. Since then Mr Faulkner has sometimes forgotten that his readers are only mortal, and cannot live for ever on angel's food.
Ibid.

6 He overdoes it. His tennis parties are as extravagant and passionate as his motor accidents.
Ibid.

7 It was because he ballasted his psychological exploration with immediacy of description and realism of dialogue that his work presents such rich — and at first bewildering — texture.
The Times, Obituary 7 *Jul* 1962

8 Faulkner's created world has the absolute authenticity of its creator's fanatical vision. We may detest his cracker-barrel philosophers, we make fun of his rustic idiots swooning over cows, we may abhor the whole society which Faulkner presents to us. But he has magically imposed his vision and it will certainly survive him.
Philip Toynbee, Observer 8 *Jul* 1962

9 Faulkner was shy. Faulkner was arrogant. Faulkner went barefoot on the streets of Mississippi. Faulkner tore up his driveway to discourage visitors.
James W. Webb and A. Wigfall Green, WILLIAM FAULKNER OF OXFORD

EDNA FERBER

Born 1887. American author. Began her career as a prolific writer of short stories for magazines. Her novel *So Big* won a Pulitzer Prize in 1924. Many of her novels were turned into films and plays, e.g. *Show Boat*, which Jerome Kern and Oscar Hammerstein II turned into a musical, 1929; *Cimarron*, 1930; *Saratoga Trunk*, 1941. Also wrote a number of successful plays in collaboration with George S. Kaufman. Died 1968.

10 Alexander Woollcott accompanied Edna Ferber to an auction one afternoon. Suddenly she spied her mother and made the mistake of hailing her by an uplifted hand. There was a crash of the auctioneer's hammer, and Miss Ferber discovered that she had become the owner of a particularly hideous grandfather clock. Every time Woollcott told the story the price of the clock went a little higher.
Bennett Cerf, TRY AND STOP ME 1947

11 Miss Ferber was fond of wearing tailored suits, and showed up at the Round Table one afternoon sporting a new suit similar to the one Noël Coward was wearing. 'You look almost like a man,' Coward said as he greeted her. 'So,' Miss Ferber replied, 'do you.'
Robert E. Drennan, WIT'S END

12 The idea for *Show Boat* was unwittingly suggested by Winthrop Ames, the theatrical producer. To cheer up the cast after a disappointing try-out of *Minick*, a play I had written with George Kaufman, Ames said that next time they would charter a show boat. 'What's a show boat?' I asked sourly. I had never heard of them. Winthrop explained, 'A show boat's a floating theatre. They used to play up and down the Southern rivers, expecially the Mississippi and the Missouri.'
Edna Ferber, A PECULIAR TREASURE 1939

13 Only amateurs say they write for their own amusement. Writing is not an amusing occupation. It is a combination of ditch-digging, mountain-climbing, treadmill and

childbirth. Writing may be interesting, absorbing, exhilarating, racking, relieving. But amusing? Never!
Ibid.

1 At one time her flat was picketed by the wives of the local dustmen after her complaints about the dirtiness of New York streets had made front-page news.
David Holloway, Daily Telegraph 17 *Apr* 1968

2 She squares off at her job in a workmanlike fashion and turns out a nationally advertised product that looks as sound as this year's model always does, until next year's model comes along.
T. S. Matthews, New Republic 6 *Mar* 1935

3 She writes a novel as a modern athletic girl might wear a crinoline and bustle. She manages the trick, but she is self-conscious and filled with secret amusement over the masquerade.
William McFee, New Republic 15 *Sep* 1926

4 When writing *Cimarron* she stayed in a house in the Basque country close to one taken by Louis Bromfield and his wife. Though the place was supposed to be inaccessible, they had a visit one black and moonless night from Noël Coward and Gladys Calthrop. When they pointed out to him that their retreat was difficult enough to find in the glare of noonday he retorted airily, 'Nonsense, not difficult at all. We merely got into a fiacre and I told the driver in my best French to drive us to where those crazy Americans were living. He came straight as a carrier pigeon.'
Campbell Nairne, John o' London's Weekly 5 *May* 1939

5 There are many explanations for the feud beween Alec Woollcott and Edna Ferber. None has the ring of truth . . . Miss Ferber referred to Woollcott as 'that New Jersey Nero who thinks his pinafore is a toga'. Aleck repaid his former friend with 'I don't see why anyone should call a dog a bitch when there's Edna Ferber around.' They never spoke after that.
Howard Teichmann, SMART ALECK 1976

6 Always-the-best-man-never-the-groom was a role that Alec Woollcott had been playing with increasing regularity. About the only one he didn't walk down the aisle was Edna Ferber, and Miss Ferber had a ready line for that. 'Being an old maid is like death by drowning, a really delightful sensation after you cease to struggle.'
Ibid.

GRACIE FIELDS

Stage name of Grace Stansfield, born 1898. English music-hall comedienne, singer, stage and film actress. Died 1979.

7 Even in far-off Tibet Gracie has at least one fan. Mr F. S. Smythe, a member of the Everest expedition, told of one aged and wrinkled Tibetan who would not listen to the bands on the camp gramophone at any price. He would hurry away as the first notes blared out. The only way to get him back was to put on a Gracie Fields record. He would rush back as soon as he heard her voice. There he would sit on his haunches till the record ended, looking for all the world as if he were mummified.
Bert Aza, Sunday Chronicle 20 *Aug* 1939

8 'Sally' was born through a chance meeting when we were making Gracie's first film *Sally in Our Alley*. We'd tried hundreds of tunes for a theme song and despaired of finding what we wanted when one evening I bumped into Will Haines, the music publisher, on the stage of the Holborn Empire. 'I've got a nice little song I'd like Miss Fields to hear,' he said. 'Hum it,' I said. He did. I liked it so much I took him straight to Gracie's dressing room. Will hummed the tune. 'Hum it again, lad,' Gracie said. He hummed it again. She hummed it with him. I hummed it with Gracie. We all hummed it. I saw Gracie's eyes light up. She turned to me and said, 'We've got it.' You know and I know how right she was.
Ibid. 30 *Jul* 1939

9 Once I saw her save a situation with a remark no one but Gracie would have dared to make. She had been giving a charity show at Alexandra Palace. Prince George, Duke of Kent had been at the show and afterwards came on the stage. Nobody seemed to know what to do. As the prince came up there was an embarrasssed hush and then: 'Ee, I can see it now, I'd never have believed it,' cried Gracie, advancing to meet him. 'Lots of people have told me. 'E's just like our Tommy.'
Cyril Harry Green, Sunday Express 18 *Jun* 1939

10 Her good temper is proof against anything. A baby squealed one night when she was in the middle of her burlesque of 'Toselli's Serenata'. Perhaps it was her top note that incited the baby high in the gallery. She stopped her performance and called out 'All

right luv, I'll be with you in a minute.' Looking down at me, conducting the orchestra, she asked 'Is that owt to do wi' you?' When I shook my head she went merrily on again.
Ibid.

1 During her clogs and shawl childhood at Rochdale — school unwillingly in the morning, cotton mill more unwillingly still in the afternoon — she wanted to become a second Adelina Patti. After a taste of the music halls she decided to become a second George Formby instead.
Observer, Profile 20 *Jul* 1947

2 She was the mill girl immensely enlarged and intensified by talent and art. She sang her head off, as they do or would like to do. She was independent, saucy, sharply humorous, bossy, maternal, blunt in manner but deeply feminine in her rapid alternations of sentiment and derisive laughter. She was the people in all the little back streets, now with full orchestra and the lid off.
J. B. Priestley, Radio Times 18 *Jul* 1947

3 She was a great artist precisely because she was a great clown. There were plenty who could sing as well as she could, and dance as well as she could but who else could achieve that amazing spontaneity of sheer downright damn nonsense that was at her fingertips and toetips and tongue-tip?
Howard Spring, Sunday Express 11 *Aug* 1940

W. C. (WILLIAM CLAUDE) FIELDS

Stage name of William Claude Dukinfield. Born 1886. American stage and film comedian. Began his career as a juggler. Appeared in his first silent film in 1915. Played Micawber in a film version of *David Copperfield*. Died 1946.

4 'When I was a tot,' confessed Fields, 'I swore that if ever I got in the chips, I'd help kids who were homeless waifs like I had been. For years I couldn't afford it. Then came Hollywood and riches.' 'Did you start a foundation as you had planned?' asked a girl interviewer eagerly. 'No' said Fields. 'I'm afraid I didn't. I said to myself, "To hell with 'em".'
Bennett Cerf, TRY AND STOP ME 1947

5 It is alleged that when co-starring with Baby le Roy he spiked the infant's milk with gin, and when Le Roy proved unfit for further work that day he stalked around yelling: 'The kid's no trouper'.
Leslie Halliwell, THE FILMGOER'S BOOK OF QUOTES 1978

6 His nasal delivery and orotund phrasing were imitated the world over, and they are essential to such oft-quoted lines as 'I must have a drink of breakfast' and 'somebody left the cork out of my lunch'.
Ibid.

7 Being of an irritable disposition he would often give vent to unprintable curses, which led him to invent his own set of swear words which, when uttered through gritted teeth, sounded infinitely more abusive than the originals. His favourite curse, 'Godfrey Daniel' became a kind of catch phrase, and so realistically foul did it sound that audiences marvelled at the censor's leniency in allowing such vulgarity.
Philip Jenkinson, Radio Times 28 *Oct* 1971

8 Because his early formative years left him dreadfully insecure his first act on reaching a strange town would be to open a bank account, usually in an assumed name. It is rumoured that dozens of these accounts still exist, scattered all over the United States and impossible to trace due to the many aliases Fields insisted on assuming.
Ibid.

9 His youthful experience as a juggler remanifested itself time and time again during his later, more successful years. Indeed George Cukor, the director of *David Copperfield*, had the greatest difficulty in restraining the persistent Fields who thought it might be nice to introduce some sleight-of-hand into Dickens's narrative.
Ibid.

10 Fields uses his humour to kick society in the groin and with a fervour gratifying to all mankind. When he snarls at little brats, punches obnoxious in-laws or out-foxes con men, he is rebelling against the impositions of an unreasonable society.
Michael M. Taylor, FIELDS FOR PRESIDENT

11 His main purpose seemed to be to break as many rules as possible and cause the maximum amount of trouble for everybody.
Robert Lewis Taylor, W. C. FIELDS

12 Actor Thomas Mitchell, to his amazement, found Fields thumbing through a Bible. When Mitchell asked what he was doing Fields answered 'Looking for loopholes.'
Nigel Rees, SAYINGS OF THE CENTURY 1984

JOHN ARBUTHNOT, FIRST BARON FISHER

Born 1841. British admiral. As First Sea Lord 1904–10, introduced the Dreadnought class of battleships. Was recalled to office at outbreak of World War I, but resigned in 1915 over Churchill's handling of the Dardanelles campaign. Died 1920.

1 Jackie Fisher made a deeper impression on the British Navy than any admiral since Nelson, his chosen hero.
Admiral Sir Reginald H. Bacon, THE LIFE OF LORD FISHER OF KILVERSTONE: ADMIRAL OF THE FLEET 1929

2 'I wish you would stop shaking your fist in my face,' said Edward VII, when being subjected to some of Fisher's forcible arguments.
Ibid.

3 Gertrude Bell pronounced Admiral Sir John Fisher to be 'rather an outsider', presumably because he talked too loudly.
Elizabeth Burgoyne, GERTRUDE BELL 1968

4 Fisher was a genius. Only a genius could have, in ten years, transformed the cast-iron-steam Victorian Navy into the Grand Fleet of ships of his own design.
Arthur J. Marder, FEAR GOD AND DREAD NOUGHT

5 In 1915, seated in a motor car outside the Admiralty, we talked for some half hour. Suddenly he said 'Do you understand war?' I replied 'No I don't.' He continued, 'If you read history you will find all successful wars have been waged by one man. It will not be Asquith. It will be Balfour or Lloyd-George.'
Lord Riddell, John o' London's Weekly 26 *Oct* 1929

6 His appearance was striking. His vitality, his inquiring, mystical eyes, his voice were fascinating. His square forehead, wide nostrils, straight-cut mouth and resolute chin gave him an air of bulldog tenacity. One felt that one was in the presence of a real man — a fighter and a biter.
Ibid.

7 Like many men of his type, he had a profound belief that he and his projects were objects of special care and approval by the Almighty. This belief no doubt accentuated his vanity — his chief defect. Notwithstanding his pleasant manner he was a ruthless, boastful fighter. He not only slew his opponents, but boasted he was going to slay them, and then dance on their graves.
Ibid.

8 He knew by instinct what to do and what his opponent was likely to do. In November 1911 he prophesied that the war would come in October 1914.
Ibid.

F. (FRANCIS) SCOTT (KEY) FITZGERALD

Born 1896. American author, prolific writer of novels, magazine serials, short stories and film scripts. His best work, e.g. *The Great Gatsby*, 1925, and *Tender is the Night*, 1934, is well regarded. Died 1940.

9 When Fitzgerald was at his commercial peak he was the only story writer who could always give the *Saturday Evening Post* precisely what it wanted; that is why the price was high.
Matthew J. Bruccoli, THE PRICE WAS HIGH 1979

10 The trouble with the life of Fitzgerald is that it is a potential novel in itself, and perhaps superior to any that Fitzgerald himself wrote.
Anthony Burgess, Observer 7 *Feb* 1982

11 Fitzgerald was an alcoholic, a spendthrift and a superstar playboy possessed of a beauty and a glamour that only a Byron could support without artistic ruination.
Ibid.

12 Fitzgerald was too writerly a writer ever to be really popular. He was not an Ernest Hemingway.
Ibid.

13 Fitzgerald incarnates the age of jazz, bootleg hooch, flappers doing the Black Bottom, and the nemesis of the Wall Street crash.
Ibid.

14 In 1924 F. Scott Fitzgerald suddenly lost confidence in himself despite the emphatic success of his first two novels *This Side of Paradise* and *The Beautiful and the Damned*. In a despondent note to Scribner's, his publishers, Fitzgerald concluded, 'I have decided to quit writing and become an ashman.' A few months later, however, he finished *The Great Gatsby* and was sufficiently restored in spirit to scribble on the top of the manuscript 'I think this is about the best American novel ever written.'
Bennett Cerf, SHAKE WELL BEFORE USING 1948

1 Fitzgerald's first notion for the title of *The Great Gatsby* was *Trimalchio in West Egg*, and when this was frowned upon by his publishers he suggested *The High-Bouncing Lover*. At the very last moment he cabled 'Crazy about title *Under the Red White and Blue*. What would delay be?' His publisher's one-word reply was 'Fatal'.
Ibid.

2 Lester Cowan, owner of the screen rights to F. Scott Fitzgerald's *Babylon Revisited* enlisted the service of a script writer. 'Fitzgerald did a script for this story,' Cowan told the writer. 'Since then at least a dozen top men have tinkered with it, but still I'm not satisfied with it. I want you to tackle it.' The writer read Fitzgerald's original script and came back to declare emphatically, 'This is the most perfect motion-picture script I ever read, I don't see why you want to revise it.' Cowan reflected a moment, and agreed. 'You're absolutely right. I'll pay you two thousand dollars a week to stay out here and stop me from changing one word of it.'
Ibid.

3 I am not a great man, but sometimes I think the impersonal and objective quality of my talent, and the sacrifices of it, in pieces, to preserve its essential value, has some sort of epic grandeur.
Fitzgerald in a letter to his daughter Scottie. Quoted Matthew J. Bruccoli, SOME SORT OF EPIC GRANDEUR 1962

4 When I met Fitzgerald in 1937 he was broke, drinking hard, and his wife Zelda was in an asylum. Who ruined who? I sometimes felt that a lot of their escapades were simply manufactured to put into the books.
Sheilah Graham, THE REAL F. SCOTT FITZGERALD 1976

5 'My material' as Fitzgerald called conversion of lived experience into literary production, resulted in some 160 short stories, a host of autobiographical essays, articles and self-interviews; numerous bad movie scripts (including some lines in *Gone With the Wind*) and five extraordinary novels of self-projection, of which perhaps three are modern classics — characteristically flawed or unfinished — yet unforgettable.
Richard Holmes, The Times 4 *Feb* 1982

6 He was better than he knew, for in fact and in the literary sense he invented a 'generation'.
New York Times, Obituary 1940

7 In Scott Fitzgerald, as in every writer of genius, there was something of the seer. He gave a name to an age — the Jazz Age — lived through that age, and saw it burn itself out.
Introduction to the Penguin edition of THE CRACK-UP 1965

8 I lunched with him in Hollywood in 1937. He was charming, an amusing talker, yet serious almost to the point of making one feel he might easily be shocked by some hastily expressed opinion. He drank milk, looked washed out, but somehow gave the appearance of inner vitality against the zombies of the movie world. A few weeks later he was to break out into a series of appalling drunken bouts. That was the other side of the absorbing split-man and pre-eminent novelist.
Anthony Powell, Daily Telegraph 2 *Nov* 1962

9 His reputation is far greater now than it was during his lifetime.
J. B. Priestley, LITERATURE AND WESTERN MAN 1960

10 You might become a very popular trashy novelist without much difficulty.
Edmund Wilson, letter to Fitzgerald. Quoted Andrew Turnbull, SCOTT FITZGERALD 1962

(HERMAN) JAMES ELROY FLECKER

Born 1884. British traveller and poet. *The Golden Road to Samarkand*, 1912, made him famous, but he died young, before he could fulfil his promise, in 1915.

11 His conversation was variegated, amusing, and enriched with booty from the by-ways of knowledge. He was always and restlessly driven by his mind down such paths. He sought beauty everywhere but preferred, for most of his life, to find her decoratively clad.
Rupert Brooke, The Times, Obituary 6 *Jan* 1915

12 There always seemed to be a worm slumbering at the root of his talent.
Edmund Gosse, letter to Edward Marsh Jan 1915

13 He preferred the exact word to the vague; he was always on his guard against the 'pot shot' and the complaisant epithet which will fit in anywhere. With passionate deliberation he clarified and crystallised his thoughts and intensified his pictures.
J. C. Squire, preface to Flecker's POEMS

1 The gentlest beings have often the fiercest imaginations and by all accounts Flecker was a very gentle being; which may partly account for the vigour and virility of much of his verse, and for the harsh, barbaric splendour of his great prose drama, *Hassan*.
Stephen Williams, Radio Times 19 *Jul* 1946

SIR ALEXANDER FLEMING

Born 1881. Scottish bacteriologist. Discovered penicillin. Awarded Nobel Prize for Medicine 1945. Died 1955.

2 When King George and Queen Mary visited the laboratories at St Mary's Fleming displayed some of his bench techniques, but suspecting that it might not interest them very much he also prepared one of his bacterial 'rock gardens' from all the microbes that produced growth of vivid colourings. The story goes that when the Queen saw this she whispered to the King 'What is the use of this?' It was no use — but it amused Fleming.
L. Colebrook, BIOGRAPHICAL MEMORIES OF FELLOWS OF THE ROYAL SOCIETY

3 I have been trying to point out that in our lives chance may have an astonishing influence and, if I may offer advice to the young laboratory worker, it would be this — never to neglect an extraordinary appearance or happening. It may be — usually is, in fact — a false alarm that leads to nothing, but it may on the other hand be the clue provided by fate to lead you to some important advance.
Alexander Fleming, lecture at Harvard

4 Fleming has not made a penny out of penicillin. 'That,' he says 'is the way it happened.' When somebody suggested in the House of Commons that he should at least be given a grant for his discovery Attlee replied: 'The Government policy is to support medical research work in progress, not to offer payments on the basis of results.'
William Hickey, Daily Express 18 *May* 1945

5 Fleming chain-smoking at his desk; amusing himself painting pictures with germ moulds in incubators — his first was called 'A Ship on Fire', had a violet ocean (bacillus violaceus) and a fine red glow (bacillus prodigiosis).
Ibid.

6 At yesterday's ceremony Fleming, with his bow tie, his silver hair and enormous brown eyes — he looks like Gerald du Maurier — had the scroll of the Freedom of the Borough of Paddington given him, took out his fountain pen and signed the roll to a flourish of trumpets. And said: 'I've lived long enough to know that flattering words spoken on these occasions are not to be taken at their face value.'
Ibid.

7 Yet had Fleming not possessed immense knowledge and an unremitting gift of observation he might not have observed the effect of the hyssop mould. 'Fortune,' remarked Pasteur, 'favours the prepared mind.'
André Maurois, LIFE OF ALEXANDER FLEMING 1959

8 Had Fleming not possessed a passion for water polo he might never have entered St Mary's Hospital. Had he not been an excellent rifle shot he might have become a surgeon and not been enrolled in the inoculation team. Had he not been an untidy man and apt to leave his cultures exposed on the laboratory table the spore of hyssop mould, the *penicillin notatum,* might never have floated in from Praed Street and settled on his dish of staphylococci.
Ibid.

9 He was an unworldly man and when asked by a journalist why he had not patented penicillin and thus made a fortune, he replied with crushing simplicity 'It never occurred to me.'
Ibid.

10 Fleming was fully aware, before he died, that his gift of observation and the spore drifting through the window from Praed Street had diminished human anxiety and saved millions of lives. It was a great reward.
Harold Nicolson, Observer 3 *May* 1959

11 No one, I think, ever saw him excited, and seldom, if ever, was there any suggestion that a judgement was being passed on any subject without the most serious and prolonged consideration.
Colonel Walter Parkes, Daily Telegraph 4 *May* 1959

12 There is, in St James's Church, Paddington, a window showing him at work in his laboratory, which was put there during his lifetime. When he was told that a visitor remarked. 'Isn't it most unusual for a window to be put in a church to a man still living?' Fleming replied, 'That can soon be put right.' He died soon afterwards.
Ibid.

IAN (LANCASTER) FLEMING

Born 1908. Novelist, created the secret agent character, James Bond. Died 1965.

1 Very poor lover. Always gets up and goes home for breakfast.
Cyril Connolly. Quoted Godfrey Smith, The Times (on the twentieth anniversary of his death)

2 Whenever I ate with Ian at Goldeneye the food was so abominable that I used to cross myself before I took a mouthful. Stewed guavas and coconut cream, salt fish and ackee fruit. I used to say 'Ian, it tastes like armpits.' And all the time there was old Ian smacking his lips for more while his guests remembered all those delicious meals he had put in his books.
Noël Coward. Quoted John Pearson, LIFE OF IAN FLEMING 1966

3 Fleming's squalid aspirations and dream fantasies happened to coincide with a whole generation's. He touched a nerve. The glorious appetite for speed at the touch of a foot on the accelerator, and for sex at the touch of a hand on the flesh, found expression in his books. We live in the Century of the Common Bond and Fleming created him.
Malcolm Muggeridge, Observer 30 *May* 1965

4 I was present with Fleming at an all-male dinner. His face, despite a good deal of carefully considered barber-treatment, looked rather flabby and rubicund and amiable. It was difficult to imagine him handling Pussy Galore in the Bond style. His clothes — in this case a dinner jacket — though chosen with elaborate consideration did not seem a particularly good fit or particularly elegant; and like so many athletes in middle age he had begun to put on weight; a condition he tries to correct from time to time by going on a starving cure.
Ibid.

5 The *oeuvre* comprises an interminable variation on the two themes of violence and lust at their most immature. It is in the vein of the *Boy's Own Paper* brought up to date with an admixture of public schoolboy fantasies of the kind entertained in dormitories after lights out about eroticism, torture, gambling and other such lurid subjects.
Ibid.

6 The truth is that Fleming had neither the inclination nor the staying power of the expert. He was something different; he was a born journalist, and true to the calling he knew how to mobilise and exploit the knowledge of others. Few men were ever more adroit with the knowing phrase, the exotic-sounding fact, the lightly brushed-on varnish of authority.
John Pearson, LIFE OF IAN FLEMING 1966

7 In later years whenever he was asked how he came to start writing novels Fleming would invariably say that it had been quite simply to take his mind off 'the shock of getting married at the age of forty-three'. It was the sort of flip, faintly cynical remark he enjoyed making. It embodied the Old Etonian myth of the effortless amateur able to turn his casual hand to anything with equally spectacular success.
Ibid.

8 Lord Beaverbrook used to call him the Chocolate Sailor, and perhaps there was something sugar-coated about his worldly façade.
Godfrey Smith, Sunday Times 26 *Aug* 1984

9 He took the name of his hero from a book in his house, *Birds of the West Indies* by James Bond.
Ibid.

10 His romance with Ann Rothermere was common knowledge — he was known in the office as Lady Rothermere's Fan — and he married her in 1952.
Ibid.

11 When his biographer, John Pearson, was researching his book he made an appointment to meet Ian's devoted secretary. He arrived to find her standing triumphantly over a pile of smouldering ashes. She had burnt Ian's papers, lest prying posterity should be privy to them.
Ibid.

ERROL FLYNN

Born 1909 in Australia, emigrated to Hollywood to act in films and created a reputation for himself as a swashbuckling hero both on and off the screen. Died 1959.

12 My problem lies in reconciling my gross habits with my net income.
Errol Flynn. Quoted Jane Mercer, GREAT LOVERS OF THE MOVIES

1 His life was a fifty-year trespass against good taste.
Leslie Mallory

2 Humility was a word unknown to Errol. He became a big star overnight with his first Hollywood production, *Captain Blood*, but it never crossed his mind that others — the producer, the director, the writers, the technicians, and above all the publicity department — might have had a hand in it. It all went straight to his head and by the time I joined him in his second super production, *The Charge of the Light Brigade*, he was cordially disliked by most of his fellow workers — particularly by the extras.
David Niven, BRING ON THE EMPTY HORSES 1975

3 The great thing about Errol was that you always knew where you were with him because he *always* let you down. He let himself down, too, from time to time, but that was his prerogative and he thoroughly enjoyed causing turmoil for himself and his friends.
Ibid.

4 To the Walter Mitty's of the world he was all the heroes in one magnificent, sexy package.
J. L. Warner, MY HUNDRED YEARS IN HOLLYWOOD

FERDINAND FOCH

Born 1851. French general, distinguished in battles of Marne and Ypres in World War I. Appointed Allied Supreme Commander, 1918. Died 1929.

5 A singular degree of integrity and harmony pervades the life of Marshal Foch. The drama of the conflict between France and Germany has fascinated the attention of the whole world, and ruined the prosperity of a large part of it. The life of Marshal Foch lies in the centre of this drama. He felt its passions and its pangs perhaps more intensely than any other human being, and he wielded the supreme executive power in its climax and decision.
Winston Churchill, GREAT CONTEMPORARIES 1937

6 The magnitude of events which Foch directed is of course beyond compare in the annals of war, but it will be found, I believe, as time passes, that the valour of his spirit and the shrewd sagacity of his judgment were of the highest order. Fortune lighted his crest . . . In 1914 he had saved the day by refusing to recognise defeat. In 1915 and 1916 he broke his teeth upon the Impossible. But 1918 was created for him and with the cry of '*Tout le monde à le bataille*' he heaved the mighty wave of allied armies, French, British, American and Belgian, forward in vast, united, irresistible attack.
Ibid.

7 Marshal Foch said to me: 'Do you know that I am not your subordinate?' 'No I don't,' I replied. 'I don't even want to know who put that notion into your head. You know that I am your friend. I strongly advise you not to act on this idea, for it would never do.'
Georges Clemenceau, GRANDEUR AND MISERY OF VICTORY 1930

8 At the time of his appointment to take charge on the Western Front, in a rush of agonised confusion and expediency, his name was almost unknown to the bewildered British public. 'Pronounce it Fosh' a London newspaper placard helpfully declared.
Sir John Eliot, Daily Telegraph 11 *May* 1972

9 During the First World War, Marshal Foch's chauffeur, Pierre, was constantly besieged by his comrades with 'Pierre, when is the war going to end? You ought to know.' Pierre tried to satisfy them. 'The moment I hear anything from the Marshal, I will tell you.' One day he came to them. 'The Marshal spoke today.' 'He did? What did he say?' 'He said, "Pierre, what do you think? When is this war going to end?"'
Lion Feuchtwanger, THE DEVIL IN FRANCE

10 My right gives way. My centre yields. Situation excellent, I shall attack.
Foch, message to Joffre at the battle of the Marne Sep 1914

11 When the German delegation came to Marshal Foch at the end of the war to ask for armistice terms the Frenchman picked up the paper from his desk and read a set of conditions. The leader of the delegation protested, 'These are terms which no civilised nation could impose on another.' 'I am glad to hear you say so,' replied Foch. 'These are not our terms. They are the terms imposed on Lille by the German commander when the city surrendered.'
Edmund Fuller, ANECDOTES 1946

12 When Marshal Foch visited the Grand Canyon, Colonel John R. White, who spoke French fluently, hung breathlessly on the Marshal's words as he turned to him after a

long scrutiny of the depths below. 'Now,' he thought, 'I shall hear something worthy to pass on to my children and grandchildren.' Observed the Marshal, 'What a beautiful place to drop one's mother-in-law.'
Ibid.

MICHAEL (MACKINTOSH) FOOT

Born 1913. English politician, author and journalist. Elected to Parliament as Labour member for Devonport 1948. Lost his seat 1955. Member for Ebbw Vale 1960. Elected leader of the Labour Party 1980. Resigned in favour of Neil Kinnock after defeat at the 1983 General Election.

1 He is like Shirley Williams, warm, sincere, but in the end lacking in ruthlessness.
James Callaghan

2 A good man fallen among politicians.
Daily Mirror, leader 20 *Feb* 1983

3 The job he was given, to unite a party determined to tear itself apart, was an impossible one. He could never be a strong leader — that is not his nature. Yet in a perfect world all our leaders would be like Michael Foot, people of compassion, honour and kindness.
Daily Mirror 28 *Jul* 1983

4 At 62 his popular image is all too well entrenched. It consists of the familiar figure rooted on some public stage — Aldermaston rally, Tribune meeting or miners' gala — coiled tensely over a microphone, white hair falling in strands across his face like some crazed Dr Who, the stare growing more and more fanatical as he winds up to an ear-shattering crescendo. And always, always on the attack.
Eric Jacobs, Sunday Times 28 *Mar* 1976

5 One of the Palace of Westminster's few remaining gents. Such figures are out of fashion now that the Conservative Party has gone resolutely down-market. Ironically it is now the Labour party that must try to persuade us that a fine old English gentleman with a taste for Byron might still make a humane and capable prime minister.
John Mortimer, IN CHARACTER 1983

6 Lord Beaverbrook, with whom he had a close and curious friendship, has been heard to call Foot the finest journalist in the world.
Observer, Profile 20 *Nov* 1960

7 He will of course popularise like mad and make demagogic speeches with the best of them — but only, one feels, to spread the Word, not to get his toes a couple of rungs up the ladder. He isn't much good at intriguing.
Ibid.

8 Whether Foot will ever influence the Left by any means other than simply being Michael Foot, by constantly demonstrating that radicalism survives, is another matter. To be visible, audible and honest has always seemed to him enough.
Ibid.

9 I love him because he speaks beautiful English.
Enoch Powell

10 The only man in the House of Commons to make his own shoes.
Jeremy Thorpe. Quoted Simon Hoggart, ON THE HOUSE 1981

11 He sounded like an affronted peke.
Honor Tracy, Daily Telegraph 12 *May* 1979

12 Foot is accepted by everybody because he is rarely wholly at ease with anybody. His private manner is diffident and can be positively awkward. But he has a kind of sweetness, even innocence.
Alan Watkins, Observer 16 *Nov* 1980

GERALD (RUDOLPH) FORD

Born 1913. Original name Leslie Lynch King. Became briefly American president almost by accident. Succeeded Agnew on his resignation as Vice-President 1973, and Nixon after his resignation, 1974. Defeated by Carter in the election of 1976.

13 A year ago Gerald Ford was unknown throughout America, now he is unknown throughout the world.
The Guardian, of Ford's appointment as Vice-President of America *Aug* 1974

14 Some people attain power through sheer ineptitude and ignorance. In one year alone, 1976, he FELL down aircraft steps on an official visit, BASHED his head on a helicopter door and SMACKED himself into the wall of a swimming pool. He wasn't all that hot on words, either. At a reception for President Sadat of Egypt he toasted the people and government of Israel.
TV Times 20 *Oct* 1984

HENRY FORD

Born 1863. American pioneer motor-car manufacturer. In 1915 set up the first factory exploiting mass-production techniques. Died 1947.

1 When he was thirteen he and his father were on the road from Dearborn to Detroit when they met a road-engine which had a chain connecting it with the rear wheels of the carriage on which it was mounted. Henry could not get this engine out of his mind. He began to attempt to make one. His first model was built entirely of wood except the boiler, which was improvised from a five-gallon oil can. With the experience thus gained he went further and built entirely from metal scraps an engine that really ran.
J. G. de Roulhac Hamilton, HENRY FORD 1928

2 His first flivver seemed such a joke that people said a squirrel was given with every car — to pick up the nuts.
The Leader 30 *Jul* 1938

3 His first car could not be driven in reverse and if you wanted to turn round in a narrow street you had to get out and lift the end round by sheer manpower.
Ibid.

4 At 52 Ford financed a Peace expedition, 'to take all the boys out of the trenches by Christmas 1915' (New York said Ford cars were stopping production because 'all the nuts were in Europe'). It failed.
Guy Ramsey, Daily Mail 9 *Apr* 1947

5 This man of unresting invention and experiment was content to turn out the ubiquitous black car and nothing else during the years of his sensational advance. Then, at 65, realising that the Model T had had its day, he closed his factories, scrapped the plant, and set out upon a new campaign of conquest in the most fiercely competitive of all markets.
S. K. Ratcliffe, Observer 9 *Jun* 1946

6 Every move he made was called crazy by the men of Detroit, when he decided to concentrate upon a single car, when he adopted the light alloy vanadium, when he buit the first mass-production factory, when he acted upon the principle that the price of a car for the people should be as low as possible (and upon his intuition that the profits would be stupendous) and above all, when in 1914, he sprang the standard five-dollar wage for eight hours upon an astonished world.
Ibid.

7 All his active life he opposed the trade union movement and insisted that his solution of 'a fair day's wage for a fair day's work' was all the working class needed or deserved.
S. L. Solon, News Chronicle 9 *Apr* 1947

8 Old Henry Ford had given his grandson a penny. The boy was not impressed and dropped it in the grass. The gaunt old billionaire bent his angular frame and started a methodical search for the coin. 'It's only a penny,' the little boy said politely. 'If you were alone on a desert island' the old man said, 'all the paper money in the world wouldn't do you any good. But a penny! There you have metal. Copper. You could hammer out a spearhead, sharpen it into a tool. That penny is important because it doesn't *represent* something. It *is* something. Now get down on the grass and find it.'
Ibid.

9 Henry Ford believed that a man with a tool in his hand represented the most meaningful achievement of civilisation.
Ibid.

10 The extraordinary reverence felt for him in the early 1920s, not only in his own country, probably reinforced his natural obstinacy in the belief that he was a major social prophet.
H. D. Ziman, Daily Telegraph 31 *Jan* 1958

11 One is amazed by the technical genius of this man who disdained any proper engineering research, set up no real administrative system, discarded his best assistants if they showed any independence of mind, and yet brought out within a few months a new model car with 5,500 new parts to be made, and got 200 major and 19,000 modifications applied to it in four years.
Ibid.

12 His first reaction to the slump has been to raise wages and cut prices.
Ibid.

E. M. (EDWARD MORGAN) FORSTER

Born 1879. English novelist and essayist. Made his reputation with *Howard's End*, 1910 and *Passage to India*, 1924. Died 1970.

13 Much of his art consists in the plainness of his writing, for he is certain of the truth of his convictions and the force of his emotions.
Cyril Connolly, ENEMIES OF PROMISE

14 *A Passage to India* as well as being his masterpiece is the strangest of all his novels.

It is thick with mystery, full of a sense that people are less than their feelings; that their feelings are more concrete than themselves, and have a destiny and a posterity of their own.
P. N. Furbank, LIFE OF E. M. FORSTER

1 His novels are fables for our times, concerned with problems of race, class, culture, sex, money, industry, and countryside, the struggling spirit. He sets out to create 'a more manageable world' than that one on this side of his looking glass, but although it has pattern, clarity and — usually — resolution, it is not a comfortable place. He may talk to us with candid charm, but he is never making cheerful conversation.
Barbara Hardy, Daily Telegraph 2 *Jan* 1959

2 As a person he had a genius for intimacy without being indiscreet. He never made a great *point* about friendship. He was just naturally concerned about his friends in the most natural way. He was wonderful, too, in the way he went into action if there were wrongs to be righted.
Christopher Isherwood. Quoted Michael Davie, Observer Magazine 12 *Aug* 1984

3 He has put English prose on a plane in many ways new. But he has found no school; his style has not, like Henry James's or Meredith's or Hemingway's, spawned; it is not mannered enough for that, and the mind behind it is too rare to be successfully aped. His influence is rather permeating like a dye, than an outside model that can be copied.
Rose Macaulay, THE WRITINGS OF E. M. FORSTER 1938

4 E. M. Forster made his his first flight in a glider on his ninetieth birthday. His comment on the experience afterwards, 'There is absolutely nothing to it. You go up, and you come down'.
Raymond Mortimer, TRY ANYTHING ONCE

5 In this, his ninetieth year, having got locked into the Cambridge Guildhall after a concert, he spent the whole night there alone without turning a hair.
Raymond Mortimer, Observer 29 *Jun* 1968

6 I don't think he is humble. 'I like being praised,' he said once with a smile. 'It is due to me.'
Ibid.

7 The face is triangular, more like a cat's than a bull's or a horse's, with clever eyes and a sensuous mouth, half hidden by a straggly moustache. His clothes would be a darkish indefinite grey and a touch old-fashioned, with a cloth cap, which has now become unconventional.
Ibid.

8 'Sometimes irritating is his refusal to be great' was Lionel Trilling's verdict — meaning that Forster had a habit of becoming playful in his writing when, considering the seriousness of his message, a more stentorian tone would have been more acceptable.
Roy Perrott, Observer 3 *Jan* 1969

9 A stranger might place him as a provincial gentleman of modest means and settled habits whose horizons were circumscribed by the parish boundary and his churchwarden duties.
Ibid.

ANATOLE FRANCE

Pen-name of Jacques Anatole François Thibault. Born 1844. French novelist and literary critic. Awarded Nobel Prize for Literature 1921. Died 1924.

10 The pockets of his cape are stuffed with little books, pious or licentious; the lives of saints, or salacious tales.
Jean Jacques Brousson, ANATOLE FRANCE ABROAD 1928

11 Under his eternal felt hat his eyes look out for ever mocking from a network of decorative wrinkles and crowsfeet.
Ibid.

12 In his day Anatole France was a towering figure. White-bearded, skull-capped, dressed with just the right amount of eccentricity, a member of the Académie and recipient of the Nobel Prize, with international sales and well-advertised love-affairs, he seems — and indeed was — a caricature of the successful French literary man.
Anthony Powell, Daily Telegraph 14 *Sep* 1967

13 As the Great War wound its slow length along M. France modified his views and he said bitterly that he looked back to the orations he had delivered to the soldiers — 'living or dead' — as 'the worst action I ever wrought in my life. Those who died knew not why they died.'
T.P.'s Weekly 3 *Sep* 1927

14 His life-long attachment was to Mme

Arman, who conducted a salon. 'On entering the drawing-room of Mme Arman,' wrote one of her guests, 'one had the impression of being in a railway-station of which Anatole France was the station-master.'
David Tylden-Wright, ANATOLE FRANCE 1967

GENERAL FRANCISCO FRANCO

Born 1892. Spanish political and military leader. Led Fascist forces in the Spanish Civil War 1936–9, and established a dictatorship. Restored the monarchy, 1947, and remained regent until his death in 1975, when he was succeeded by his nominee Juan Carlos.

1 One day while on a parapet in Morocco he picked up a Thermos bottle to drink some coffee. A Riff bullet fired with deadly accuracy tore the cork from between his fingers. The Captain did not change countenance; he drank the contents, and turning towards the enemy camp he cried 'Better luck next time.'
Don Joaquin Arraras, FRANCISCO FRANCO

2 In his main purpose — to improve the material conditions of all Spaniards — Franco believes implicitly in Order and Discipline as the essential pre-requisites of progress; and it is as the enemy of Order that he fears Communism — of which he began to make a careful study as early as 1928.
Brian Crozier, FRANCO 1967

3 We met General Franco. I think he is a very nice man. He is a keen golfer with a handicap of 2. He is received with great enthusiasm wherever he appears.
P. Dunne, MP for Stalybridge and Hyde, reported in Sunday Dispatch. Quoted Michael Bateman, THIS ENGLAND

4 Capable of inspiring the most intense loyalty and the bitterest hatred, he was ruthless to his enemies but, in contrast to Hitler and Stalin, lenient to his friends when they plotted against him.
Peter Kemp, Times Literary Supplement 28 *Dec* 1967

5 We may see him as the Cromwell of Spain; the soldier who, through civil war, has achieved undisputed charismatic power and exercises it in the form of a disguised regency for a non-existent monarch.
Hugh Trevor-Roper, Sunday Times 29 *Oct* 1967

SIR J. G. (JAMES GEORGE) FRAZER

Born 1845. Scottish author and anthropologist. Achieved fame with his *Golden Bough, 1890–1915*, an erudite study of primitive religion, superstition and magic. Died 1941.

6 He confessed to a modest pride in the fact that his descriptions of Israel, which he had never visited, were said to be as accurate as those of his familiar Greece and Rome.
R. Angus Downie, FRAZER AND THE GOLDEN BOUGH 1970

7 His worldwide fame is founded on what was originally a footnote to a passage in Virgil's *Aeneid*, finally swollen to 13 long volumes.
Ibid.

8 On May 11 1931 at a Literary Fund Dinner, as Frazer was reading his speech, his eyes filled with blood and all went dark. He held the paper in front of his face and finished the speech from memory before sitting down. He was never to see again.
Ibid.

9 As an undergraduate at Cambridge in 1924 I attended some of Frazer's lectures. With the possible exception of his oldest friend A. E. Housman he was the worst lecturer I ever sat under, reading his manuscript in a dull, expressionless voice.
Geoffrey Gorer, Observer 30 *Aug* 1970

10 It appears that Frazer is great at mechanical devices, among others a sliding door by which he can make his one drawing room into two. When not wanted, the door is made to fly up into the storey above, where it makes one bedroom into two. Once there were some celebrations at Cambridge and an influx of foreign visitors who were quartered on the Dons. Frazer sent up the door, put two married couples into the bedrooms and slept in the drawing room himself. In the middle of the night he felt cold and cheerless in the vast room, got out of bed, and pushed the knob which brought the door down — never realising the consequences till he sent up in the morning to ask why neither of the married couples had appeared at breakfast.
Edward Marsh, letter to Rupert Brooke 29 *Jun* 1913

11 His *Passages of the Bible* is one of the classic compilations. A deputation came from Iceland to study Bible matters at Cambridge with the object, mainly, of producing their own preface to an Icelandic version of the Bible. They came across Sir James's preface to his anthology in the University Library and at once stopped their researches,

translated his preface into Icelandic, and went home.
Reginald Pound, THEIR MOODS AND MINE 1937

1 Discussing her husband's work, Lady Frazer said that if I studied it carefully I should notice that he never expresses an opinion and that this is part of his code.
Ibid.

2 His gentleness is his cardinal characteristic. It is not only the humility of the great scholar, but a kind of world-grandfather glow of philosophic power.
Ibid.

3 At a luncheon at the Holborn Restaurant I was put next to old Sir James Frazer and his wife, and wondered how I could live up to this unexpected privilege. We talked about travel. I supposed him to have pottered intellectually round Polynesia, New Guinea, the Great Barrier Reef and a few other places where our aboriginal brothers and sisters reside. When he told me he had never been farther than Greece I probably seemed naïvely surprised.
Ibid.

4 The word 'tabu', now required in almost every newspaper article, was quite unknown before Frazer put it on the map.
Anthony Powell, Daily Telegraph 1 *Jul* 1970

5 Frazer apart from the study of anthropology was a complete innocent, brought up in a world almost of drawing the blinds on Sunday, and to a large extent he remained in that moral condition all his life.
Ibid.

6 Frazer's Gibbonian style, together with a certain disregard for continuity in the immense amount of factual material he provides, does not make for exactly easy reading, but he is one of the great openers-up of a new world of both fact and imagination.
Ibid.

JOHN (DENTON PINKSTONE) FRENCH, EARL OF YPRES

Born 1852. British soldier. Commanded the British Expeditionary Force, 1915. Lord-lieutenant of Ireland, 1918–21. Died 1925.

7 Douglas Haig unburdened himself today. He thinks French quite unfit for high command in time of crisis. He says French's military ideas are not sound; that he has never studied war; that he is obstinate and will not keep with him men who point out obvious errors.
General J. Charteris, FIELD MARSHAL LORD HAIG 1929

8 Although I was with French's column in many a march and skirmish, and although I was intimate with several of his staff, French completely ignored my existence, and showed me no sign of courtesy or goodwill.
Winston Churchill, GREAT CONTEMPORARIES 1937

9 French was a natural leader. Although he had not the intellectual capacity of Haig, nor perhaps his underlying endurance, he had a deeper military insight. He was not equal in precision of detail; but he had more imagination and he would never have run the British Army into the same long drawn-out slaughters.
Ibid.

10 His recurrent desire to retreat was overborne by the greater will-power, and perhaps the more consistent self-delusion, of Foch, who by flattering deference, as well as forceful personality, gained a strong influence over French.
B. H. Liddell Hart, HISTORY OF THE WORLD WAR 1934

11 French was a cavalry man who made his name in the Boer War. The campaign brought out his best qualities although it was rather like a chess match played on a large floor with no board.
A. J. P. Taylor, Observer 8 *Nov* 1981

12 He enjoyed life, running through a succession of well-to-do mistresses and neglecting his family. His idea of relaxation was to spend his leave in the London Ritz or the Paris Crillon.
Ibid.

13 French's small force found itself resisting the whole force of the German army. French decided that the only strategy was to withdraw from the battle altogether. Kitchener hastened over and more or less ordered French to stay in line.
Ibid.

14 He had one final achievement which is in its way unique. He wrote an account of his command in 1914 which contained some inaccuracies and some telling strokes against other generals, particularly Sir Douglas Haig. For this he was officially rebuked by

King George V. The old boy, it seems, went blustering to his grave.
Ibid.

SIGMUND FREUD

Born 1856. Austrian psychiatrist, founder of psychoanalysis. Experimented in dream interpretation, and in investigation of the effects of the repression of childhood experiences. Died 1939.

1 Freud simply didn't understand religion.
W. H. Auden. Quoted Roy Perrott, Observer 18 *Jun* 1970

2 Tranquillity comes with years, and that horrid thing which Freud calls sex is expunged.
E. F. Benson, MAPP AND LUCIA 1935

3 A clever, favoured boy — his sisters had candles in their room, he had the oil lamp.
Ronald W. Clark, FREUD: THE MAN AND THE CAUSE 1980

4 Hunting for rare mushrooms was a particularly favourite pastime. His son Martin recalled how 'he would pounce dramatically on a new specimen and throw his hat over it before giving a shrill signal on the flat silver whistle he carried in his waistcoat pocket to summon his platoon. We would all rush towards the sound of the whistle, and only when the concentration was complete would father remove the hat and allow us to inspect and admire the spoil.'
Ibid.

5 He formulated his ideas in extravagant and exclusive forms, which have since got quietly modified — I doubt whether psychoanalysts would now maintain that dreams of overcoats, staircases, ships, rooms, tables, children, landscapes, machinery, airships, and hats commonly represent the genitals.
Rosemary Dinnage, Observer 20 *Jul* 1980

6 . . . a vindictive hater and a powerful autocrat; what is least likeable about him is that the discoverer of the therapy of honesty concealed these qualities under an effective screen of courteous denials.
Ibid.

7 I am actually not at all a man of science, not an observer, not an experimenter, not a thinker. I am by temperament nothing but a *conquistador*, an adventurer — with all the inquisitiveness, daring, and tenacity characteristic of such a man.
Freud. Quoted Ronald Clark, FREUD: THE MAN AND THE CAUSE 1980

8 Freud's foibles tell us a lot about the great man (he himself taught us to notice such things). One was resolutely smoking long, and surely suggestive, cigars, even when he was dying of jaw cancer.
Richard Holmes, The Times 7 *Aug* 1980

9 'What *have* you been reading, Cary?' 'Well — a book about dreams.' 'Dreams? Who by?' 'A man called Frood.' 'Frood? — Oh I see. But it's a pretty nasty book, Freud on dreams — There's nothing horrid really about how babies come, or about marriage or anything; only he'd make anything sound filthy. He's got that kind of mind.'
Rose Macaulay KEEPING UP APPEARANCES

10 Many humanitarians have little affection for humanity, and Freud was no exception. He once wrote in a letter: 'I have found little that is "good" about human beings on the whole. In my experience most of them are trash.'
Anthony Storr, Sunday Times 26 *Apr* 1981

11 'Why are you looking like that?' asked Kyril. 'I was wondering why people put ferrets in their trousers,' said Aunt Irene.
'*Thanatos*,' said Kyril. 'An illustration of the death wish.'
'What I wish,' said Aunt Irene, 'is that you'd never read Freud. It's had a very leaden effect on your conversation.'
Alice Thomas Ellis, THE 27TH KINGDOM 1982

12 He has shown us all how awful we really are, for ever nursing grudges we felt in childhood.
Rebecca West. Quoted Jill Craigie, The Times 6 *Dec* 1982

ROBERT (LEE) FROST

Born 1874. American lyric poet, his favourite subject New England rural life. Died 1963.

13 I'd just as soon play tennis with the net down as write free verse.
Robert Frost, Newsweek 30 *Jan* 1956

14 I have never started a poem yet whose end I knew. Writing a poem is discovering.
Robert Frost, New York Times 7 *Nov* 1955

15 Ordinary readers think him the greatest poet alive, and love some of his best poems almost as much as they love some of his worst ones . . . there's something reassuring about his poetry, they feel — almost like prose.
Randall Jarrell

ROBERT FROST

1 The hiding places of his power asked darkly to be kept hidden. 'I always hold that we get forward as much by hating as by loving.' His highest commandment was 'And thou shalt hate they neighbour as thyself'. 'All puffed out with self-hate that would have curdled the ink in my pen.' He was not loth to loathe.
Christopher Ricks, Sunday Times 7 *Mar* 1971

2 His family life and its wanderings were grimly restless and repetitious. His sister went mad. The marriages of two of his daughters were rocky and were to crash. His wife had discovered that if there was one thing worse than being married to a ruthless unsuccessful poet it was being married to a ruthless successful poet.
Ibid.

3 He once tried to score over T. S. Eliot by persuading him to read one of his minor poems and then pretending to improvise a better one — in fact one he had written weeks before.
Lawrence Thompson, ROBERT FROST: THE YEARS OF TRIUMPH 1915–1938 1971

G

(WILLIAM) CLARK GABLE

Born 1901. American film actor. Made his debut in a silent film with Pola Negri in 1924. His last appearance was with Marilyn Monroe in Arthur Miller's *The Misfits*, 1960, the year in which he died.

1 He was the King of an empire called Hollywood. The empire is not what it was — but the King has not been dethroned, even after death.
Joan Crawford

2 Clark is the sort of guy, if you say 'Hiya Clark, how are ya?' — he's stuck for an answer.
Ava Gardner. Quoted Donald Sinden, A TOUCH OF THE MEMOIRS 1982

3 Clark was happiest when on hunting trips but, like most overtly male Americans, he felt obliged to have a large quota of affairs . . . As a rule they were not outdoor types. Clark's third and fourth wives, Carole Lombard and Sylvia Fairbanks (widow of Douglas) were indoor girls, from both of whom I heard complaints about that sleeping bag of Clark's.
Anita Loos, KISS HOLLYWOOD GOOD-BYE

4 I most admired Clark for his lack of vanity. He was equipped with a premature set of false teeth for which he felt no embarrassment. One day I happened on him at an outdoor faucet where he had stopped to wash off his denture. Clark grinned, pointed to his caved-in mouth and said with an exaggerated lisp 'Look, America'th thweetheart.'
Ibid.

5 In Hollywood people occasionally nudged each other and said 'Gable only likes older women.' It was the understatement of the century. Gable loved *all* women — older, younger, blondes, brunettes and redheads — he loved the lot.
David Niven, BRING ON THE EMPTY HORSES 1975

6 During the war, in which Gable served with distinction as an air gunner, he was also considered a prize catch by the Luftwaffe. In a special bulletin Goering promised the flier who downed Gable, dead or alive, a bounty of 5000 dollars, a promotion and a furlough.
Charles Samuels, THE KING OF HOLLYWOOD 1962

7 Gable's chest was completely bald, so he insisted that all actors appearing with him should have their chests shaved once a week.
Donald Sinden, A TOUCH OF THE MEMOIRS 1982

YURI (ALEKSEYEVITCH) GAGARIN

Born 1934. Russian cosmonaut. First man to orbit the earth, April 1961. Killed in an air crash 1968.

8 Yuri Gagarin's smile alone must have earned his country more goodwill than all the speeches of Soviet leaders since.
Michael Binyon, The Times, The Immortal Spaceman 11 *Apr* 1981

9 We watch an interview with Gagarin on TV. He certainly possesses great propaganda charm, and will personify Holy Russia for many millions. How can a country be a menace when it has as its hero a man with so entrancing a smile.
Harold Nicolson, DIARY 14 *Jul* 1961

10 Yuri Gagarin's flight was a triumph of socialism, a brilliant confirmation of Lenin's prediction about the stormy growth of the socialist state; about the flourishing of the inexhaustible talents of our people.
Official USSR government announcement

HUGH (TODD NAYLOR) GAITSKELL

Born 1906. British Labour politician. Chancellor of the Exchequer 1950–1. Leader of the Parliamentary Labour Party 1955–63. Died 1963.

11 Gaitskell, rather nattily if unsuitably dressed and wearing a red carnation, began to address the crowded and attentive benches . . . He has a Wykehamistical voice and manner and a 13th-century face; he was lucid, clear and coherent and there was a commendable absence of Daltonian sneers

JOHN GALSWORTHY

or bleak Crippsian platitudes. A breath of fresh air.
Sir Henry Channon, DIARY 10 *Apr* 1951

1 An intellectual highbrow who is naturally anxious to impress British labour with the fact that he learnt Latin at Winchester.
Winston Churchill

2 He incorporated into a radio speech an appeal to the Tories with doubts on the Government's policy on Suez to throw over Sir Anthony Eden. At best it was a clumsy gesture. In the long run it was perhaps a costly mistake. A Leader of the Opposition can get along well enough without any affection from the ranks opposite. But he should, if he can, command their respect. His opponents judged him to be ungenerous. Magnanimity did not come to him easily.
Daily Telegraph, Obituary 19 *Jan* 1963

3 Hugh Gaitskell dreaded a Communist takeover of the Labour movement, and wildly exaggerated the extent of Communist Party influence. He genuinely believed that most of those in the party associated with Nye were either undercover Communists or fellow-travellers.
Jennie Lee, MY LIFE WITH NYE 1980

4 Gaitskell led every attempt to expel Nye from the party and not just Nye. Let Stafford Cripps go, George Strauss, John Freeman, Harold Wilson, Charles Trevelyan. Off with their heads was his motto.
Ibid.

5 In the House of Commons one could tell when he was making a case in which he did not have confidence, his whole style became uneasy, like a pullet left out in a thunderstorm.
William Rees-Mogg, The Times 19 *Jan* 1964

6 He reached the top through none of the obvious stratagems which seem to be a necessary passport to success . . . He took the cynicism out of politics.
W. T. Rodgers, HUGH GAITSKELL 1906–63 1964

JOHN GALSWORTHY

Born 1867. English novelist and playwright. Most popular work *Forsyte Saga*, a series of novels about an Edwardian family, 1906–22. Awarded Nobel Prize for Literature 1932. Died 1933.

7 Among literary reputations Galsworthy is a corpse that will not lie down.
Cyril Connolly, Sunday Times 27 *Jan* 1963

8 The tortures of composition which his friend Conrad endured he knew nothing of. He created with the effortless ease of Sir Walter. Just a writing pad and an inkpot with a J. pen and a sunny room or a garden chair, which at intervals he would move further into the sun as the shadows crept over the grass — and he wanted no more.
H. V. Marrot, LIFE AND LETTERS OF JOHN GALSWORTHY 1935

9 Even before the war Galsworthy had made it his regular rule to live on less than half his income, giving all the rest away. During the war his personal and domestic expenditure was still further reduced, so that it was perhaps three-quarters of his income that was given away. After the war the pre-war rule was observed to the end.
Ibid.

10 Photographs show him with the frozen young old-boy look of Boat Race veterans in their caps, or of Freemasons out on the spree.
Malcolm Muggeridge, Observer 18 *Jun* 1967

11 When he sets out to depict what he conceives as the desirable type of human it turns out to be simply a cultivated, humanitarian version of the upper-middle-class *rentier*, the sort of person who in those days used to haunt picture galleries in Italy and subscribe heavily to the Society for the Prevention of Cruelty to Animals.
George Orwell, THE REDISCOVERY OF EUROPE

12 Galsworthy began as a critic of the Edwardian upper middle classes. He endures as their chronicler.
Robert Pitman, Sunday Express 27 *Jan* 1963

13 He was a sound and sympathetic craftsman in both fiction and drama, but was on the whole inferior to several contemporary English writers who did not, as he did in 1932, receive the Nobel Prize.
J. B. Priestley, LITERATURE AND WESTERN MAN 1966

14 J.G. and I were always on cordial terms; but there were no incidents. The elegance and economy of his style were pleasant to me — so unlike my own Italian-operatic manner.
G. B. Shaw. Quoted Hesketh Pearson, BERNARD SHAW 1942

15 The most difficult writer I have worked for is Galsworthy, and I have heard other actors say the same. For a distinguished author he always struck me as being singularly wanting

in imagination or sympathy, but perhaps it was something in me which failed to penetrate his Olympian aloofness.
Ernest Thesiger, PRACTICALLY TRUE 1927

1 I played Ferrand in a revival of *The Pigeon*, and it is certainly one of my favourite parts. I might have said 'one of my best parts' had not the author shown me so clearly that he disliked everything I did with it. At rehearsals he nearly broke my heart, but one critic wrote 'Mr Thesiger's vision of the part was much greater than that of the author' which did a great deal to heal my wounds.
Ibid.

2 I first read *The Forsyte Saga* at the age of fifteen with great respect and pleasure. I re-read it in my late twenties with less respect but still great pleasure. I re-read it last week with no respect and precious little pleasure.
Angus Wilson, DIVERSITY AND DEPTH IN FICTION 1983

3 The author of *The Forsyte Saga* must be the most widely read Harrovian since Byron.
David Williams, Daily Telegraph 24 *Oct* 1968

INDIRA GANDHI

Born 1917. Daughter of Jawaharlal Nehru, first Prime Minister of independent India. Became leader of the Congress Party, and Prime Minister in 1966. In 1978 was expelled from parliament on charges of misuse of her official position. Re-elected and again Prime Minister 1980. Assassinated 1984.

4 Her weapon is the snub, a regal, chilling silence. Her silences, as could be testified by ex-President Nixon, whom she disliked, can be disconcerting.
Trevor Fishlock, The Times, Empress Indira 22 *Mar* 1982

5 After the portrayal of her as a ruthless natural autocrat it was stunning to meet her; to see with what composure and courtesy she managed her entourage and her Cabinet colleagues.
Michael Foot, Observer 4 *Nov* 1984

6 She has few peers in the cold-blooded calculation of the elements of power.
Henry Kissinger. Quoted Trevor Fishlock, The Times, Empress Indira 22 *Mar* 1982

7 A woman who has mastered the art of adapting her demeanour to the occasion, but whose true self is rigorously concealed, and whose look, if you happen to catch her unawares, is often one of cold disdain.
Observer, Profile, The Last Empress of India 21 *Mar* 1982

8 It was a very lonely life for her as a child, as her father and mother were often in jail . . . It was during these years that she would model her life on that of Joan of Arc and could be observed practising poses suitable to that famous and feminine opponent of the British.
The Times, Obituary 1 *Nov* 1984

MAHATMA (MOHANDAS KARAMCHAND) GANDHI

Born 1869. Indian religious and political leader. Conducted a civil disobedience campaign for Indian independence. Imprisoned 1930. Released and participated in independence negotiations, but opposed the partition of India and Pakistan. Assassinated 1948.

9 Toothless, and dressed in his habitual *khaddar* he talked rapidly, in a low voice and at inordinate length; but his utterance was impressive.
Lord Butler, THE ART OF THE POSSIBLE 1971

10 I had brought some photos of my sculpture. Gandhi looked at them intently and said, 'I see you make heroes out of mud.' And I retorted 'and sometimes vice versa'.
Jo Davidson, BETWEEN SITTINGS

11 It costs a great deal of money to keep Gandhi in poverty.
Arojini Naida, Indian poetess. Quoted Woodrow Wyatt, Sunday Times 27 *Nov* 1977

12 The greatest Indian since Buddha.
Edward Thompson, News Chronicle, Obituary 31 *Jan* 1948

GRETA GARBO

Born 1905. Swedish actress. Original name Greta Gustafsson. Went to America, and became most famous film star of her era.

13 There is no doubt she can act, if by acting is meant the power to suggest that she is feeling emotion and giving it out again in terms of her own personality.
James Agate, AROUND CINEMAS

1 No shadow of the conventional New York woman of fashion hovered near her; the hat could have belonged to a tinker engraved by Callot; and her skirt was that of a highwayman. In her all-greys she looked like a Mantegna. Although she exuded no impression of luxury one knew her to be a person of the most sifted quality.
Cecil Beaton, DIARY 15 *Mar* 1946

2 She had changed in appearance since our first meeting. Then she had been like a large apricot in the fullness of its perfection; she was rounded, of a smooth surface. Now the apricot quality had given place to vellum. Her eyes were still like an eagle's — blue-mauve and brilliant, the lids the colour of a mushroom — but there were a few delicate lines at the corners.
Ibid.

3 I am not a versatile actress.
Greta Garbo

4 Garbo's temperament reflected the rain and gloom of the long, dark Swedish winters.
Lillian Gish, THE MOVIES, MR GRIFFITH AND ME 1969

5 I heard one day that she had lost her only sister, and I sent her flowers and a note. Garbo came to thank me but she could not speak English. Tears came to her eyes. I couldn't speak Swedish so I put my arms around her and we both cried.
Ibid.

6 A great actress? Oh, undoubtedly, one wearily assents, but what dull, pompous films they make for her, hardly movies at all, so retarded are they by her haggard equine renunciations, the slow consummation of her noble adulteries.
Graham Greene, COLLECTED ESSAYS

7 Boiled down to essentials she is a plain mortal girl with large feet.
Herbert Kretzmer

8 She is the dream princess of eternity, the knockout of the ages.
Life magazine 1928

9 A deer in the body of a woman, living resentfully in the Hollywood zoo.
Clare Boothe Luce

10 Garbo had an icy look in her eyes when anyone sought to impose on her as Groucho Marx discovered one day. He saw a well-known figure approaching in slacks and floppy hat, waylaid her, bent down in his famous crouch and peered up under the brim. Two prisms of pure Baltic blue stared down at him and he backed away muttering 'Pardon me, ma'am. I thought you were a guy I knew in Pittsburgh.'
David Niven, BRING ON THE EMPTY HORSES 1975

11 'Why did you give up the movies?' I asked. She considered her answer so carefully that I wondered if she had decided to ignore my personal question. At last, almost to herself, she said: 'I had made enough faces.'
Ibid.

12 I can't make up my mind whether Garbo was a remarkable actress or simply a person so extraordinary that she made everything she did, including acting, seem remarkable.
Isobel Quigley

13 Garbo was the only one we could kill off. The Shearer and Crawford pictures had to end in church, but the public seemed to enjoy watching Garbo die.
J. Robert Rubin

GEORGE V

Born 1865. Succeeded his father, Edward VIII as King of Great Britain, 1910. Died 1936.

14 He was a pious man, rather in the way that Queen Victoria was pious. He once said, sadly: 'I am afraid the young people among my subjects do not say their prayers.'
Hector Bolitho. Quoted Reginald Pound, THEIR MOODS AND MINE 1937

15 He had a racy mind and liked a vulgar joke, so long as the point was obvious.
Sir Henry Channon, DIARY 8 *Feb* 1938

16 When broadcasting George V somehow stirred one; after hearing him one wanted to shout, sing patriotic songs; and those wonderful blue eyes, can one ever forget them?
Ibid.

17 Born in the ranks of the working class, the new king's most likely fate would have been that of a street-corner loafer.
Keir Hardie, of George V's accession 1910

18 With his spare, upright frame, the merest hint of a stoop, kindly eyes, cherry-red cheeks and a grizzled beard and moustache reminiscent of the Sealyham terriers he loved so much, George V provided Princess Elizabeth with the very archetype of a grandfather; and to his peoples he was the model of a national patriarch.
Robert Lacey, MAJESTY 1977

1 King George passing slowly in a closed car, looking like a rather worn *penny* in the window.
Geoffrey Madan, NOTEBOOKS 1981

2 The 700 pages [of Eden's memoirs] contain only one joke — by King George V apropos Sir Samuel Hoare's resignation. 'No more coals to Newcastle; no more Hoares to Paris.' In any compendium of Royal humour it deserves a place.
Malcolm Muggeridge, TREAD SOFTLY FOR YOU TREAD ON MY JOKES

3 I feel that I am getting a down on George V just now. He is all right as a gay young midshipman. He may be all right as a wise Old King. But the intervening period when he was Duke of York, just shooting at Sandringham, is hard to manage or swallow. For seventeen years he did nothing at all but kill animals and stick in stamps.
Harold Nicolson, while writing LIFE OF GEORGE V, *in a letter to Vita Sackville-West* 17 *Aug* 1949

4 He was a man who preferred continuity to variation, the familiar to the surprising, the accustomed to the unexpected. His love of orderliness expressed itself in the extreme neatness of his personal habits, as in his insistence on punctuality and exactitude on the part of his Ministers and the members of his household. He believed that, with a little forethought, time itself could be made to conform to a pattern; he loved the symmetry of anniversaries, statistics, repetitions, coincidences and recurrences.
Harold Nicolson, LIFE OF GEORGE V

5 George V was distinguished by no exercise of social gifts, by no personal magnetism, by no intellectual powers. He was neither a wit nor a brilliant raconteur, neither well read nor well educated, and he made no great contribution to enlightened social converse. He lacked intellectual curiosity and only late in life acquired some measure of artistic taste.
Ibid.

6 His planned education ended just where and when it should seriously have begun. He was (until he had painfully taken his own education in hand late in life) below the educational and perhaps intellectual standards of the ordinary public-school-educated country squire.
Ibid.

7 With so many crowned heads in abeyance, the Monarch himself smiled seldom, but his gruff maritime sense of duty endeared him to the nation.
John Raymond, History Today, The Baldwin age Sep 1960

8 King George V approached by a friend who hoped that a word from His Majesty in the right quarter would solve a difficulty said, 'My dear fellow, I can't help you. You'd better write to *The Times*.'
Helen Reid, letter to The Times 4 *Feb* 1970

9 His trousers were creased at the sides, not front and back.
A. J. P. Taylor, ENGLISH HISTORY 1914–1945 1965

10 In 1932 King George V took to broadcasting a message on Christmas afternoon to families replete with turkey and plum pudding. Amateur Freudians were not slow to remark that the king had become a father figure; with his old-fashioned beard and guttural pronunciation, grandfather figure would have been nearer the mark.
Ibid.

GEORGE VI

Born 1895. Succeeded to the throne on the abdication of his brother Edward VIII, 1936. Died 1952.

11 Constant tact from others had the effect of making him far too modest and he had quite lost sight of his own merits, if he ever knew them. He was, in fact, ideally suited for the British throne.
Ronald Blythe, THE AGE OF ILLUSION

12 I watched the television, and saw the King, bare-headed, almost mad-looking, waving farewell to the Edinburghs, who have flown to Kenya en route to Australia. He is reported to be going out duck-shooting next week. Suicidal.
Sir Henry Channon, DIARY 2 *Feb* 1952

13 The late King, whom I knew fairly well at different times, was uninteresting, unintellectual, but doubtless well-meaning. He improved with the years. His natural shyness and inferiority complex towards his eldest brother made him on the defensive. He had no wit, no learning, no humour except of a rather schoolboy brand. He was nervous, ill-at-ease though slightly better after some champagne. He had no vices and few interests other than shooting. He had few friends and was almost entirely dependent on the Queen whom he worshipped; she was his will-power, his all.
Ibid.

1 The new King's agonised reaction [to Edward VIII's abdication], stemmed from a double mistake made in all humility: underestimation of himself, and over-estimation of his brother.
Elizabeth Longford, THE QUEEN MOTHER 1981

2 The present King was devoted to his brother and the whole abdication crisis made him miserable. He sobbed on my shoulder for a whole hour — there upon that sofa. But he has made good. And now he is so ill, poor boy, so ill.
Queen Mary. Quoted Harold Nicolson, DIARY 21 *Mar* 1949

3 George VI in the conventional parlance was a Good King who sacrificed his life to his sense of duty. If we are to have monarchs it would be hard to find a better one.
A. J. P. Taylor, Observer, A dutiful monarch 24 *Oct* 1982

GEORGE GERSHWIN

Born 1898 in America. Original name Jacob Gershwin, son of Russian Jewish emigrants. Found employment as pianist to a music publisher at the age of 15 and began composing songs. Composed a great deal for films, including Fred Astaire–Ginger Rogers musicals. Established his reputation with *Rhapsody in Blue*, 1924. Died 1937.

4 If Gershwin had not died so young I think he might have lived to become one of the greatest composers of this century.
Lord Boothby, RECOLLECTIONS OF A REBEL 1978

5 George Gershwin played the complete score of *Porgy and Bess* for the first time in public for the edification of Getrude Stein. She sat beside him at the piano in a straight-backed chair, her arms folded, and said not a single word until he had finished. Then she rose and threw her arms around him. 'George, it's wonderful!' she cried. 'Now I know it's all right,' said George.
Bennett Cerf, TRY AND STOP ME 1947

6 One day I happened to mention that the score of one of his infrequent failures *Pardon My English* was below par. George demurred. All of us were sun-bathing in the nude. George insisted that we all go inside while he proved his point by going through the score from opening chorus to finale. I can still see him sitting at the piano, stark naked; playing the songs and singing them, too, at the top of his voice. George belonged at a piano. I have never seen a man happier, more bursting with the joy of living, than George when he was playing his songs. He would improvise and introduce subtle variations, and chuckle with childlike delight when his audience exclaimed over them.
Ibid.

7 He reserved one unpublished little waltz tune for affairs of the heart. 'You're the kind of girl who makes me feel like composing a song,' he would tell the enraptured lady of the moment and lead her off to his suite. We would follow on tiptoe to hear him compose the familiar tune for her. 'It will be dedicated to you,' he would conclude soulfully.
Ibid.

8 In Havana George reached his greatest height of indignation. A lovely Cuban miss failed to keep a luncheon date with him. Later that afternoon he spied her on the Yacht Club terrace, and exclaimed 'Hey, do you know that you stood me up?' 'Oh, I meant to phone and tell you I couldn't meet you,' said the contrite maiden, 'but do you know something? I couldn't remember your name.' George didn't recover for days.
Ibid.

9 While George Gershwin was at work on *Rhapsody in Blue* his father thrust his head into the room. 'Make it good, George,' he counselled, 'it might be important.' So indeed it proved as Pa Gershwin was able to demonstrate irrefutably to a Doubting Thomas. 'Of course it's a great piece! Doesn't it take fifteen minutes to play?'
Edmund Fuller, ANECDOTES 1942

10 Oscar Levant is said to have once asked George Gershwin 'Tell me, George, if you had to do it all over would you fall in love with yourself again?'
Ibid.

11 He was on the train journey to Boston for the première of *Sweet Little Devil* when the concerto for the first time came into focus. The train whistles, the rattle of the wheels, the strange symphonic sounds which even the unmusical can hear in the confused roar of a train when it moves rapidly — all these things excited him until by the time he reached Boston the complete construction of the rhapsody was in his mind. *Rhapsody in Blue* is many things but it includes the description of a train journey as its central element.
Robert Payne, GERSHWIN

(JEAN) PAUL GETTY

Born 1892. American financier, reputed the richest man in the world. Died 1976.

1 As late as 1960 he was painstakingly checking the number of coats of paint on the bulkheads of his tankers.
H. F. D. Green, Daily Telegraph 14 *May* 1964

2 The question posed by his book *My Life and Fortunes* is not how to become a millionaire, but whether to.
Ibid.

3 He bought his first oil lot by bluff. He hired a local bank executive to bid for him at the auction. This unnerved the other bidders who assumed the executive was acting for a big oil company. They decided it was futile to bid at all. The lot was knocked down to Getty at the bargain price of £180. Four months later he sold it for £14,000. By 23 Paul Getty was a millionaire and had retired. At 25 he came out of retirement.
Pete Grosvenor, Daily Express 14 *May* 1964

4 He has been married five times, mainly, it seems, because he cannot spare the time to keep a wife happy.
Ralph Hewins, J. PAUL GETTY 1961

5 (He) had always been vastly, immeasurably wealthy, and yet went about looking like a man who cannot quite remember whether he remembered to turn the gas off before leaving home.
Bernard Levin, THE PENDULUM YEARS 1981

6 In 1957 *Fortune* magazine made a list of the richest men in America. The name of Paul Getty, until then comparatively unknown, was at the top. After that the stream of begging letters became a torrent. In one record mail delivery came requests for 15 million dollars.
Russell Lewis, Daily Telegraph 5 *Sep* 1960

7 No conscience-stricken billionaire he, who seeks deliverance from the guilt of riches by setting up charitable trusts in the Rockefeller or Carnegie style. He is rather in the old Victorian tradition of the rich man conscious of being chosen by God for good and sufficient reasons of His own to be trusted with great possessions.
Malcolm Muggeridge, Observer 18 *Sep* 1966

ANDRÉ GIDE

Born 1869. French author. Awarded Nobel Prize for Literature 1947. Died 1951.

8 So André Gide is dead. He once scandalised an earlier generation though he became foolish and venerable with time. I used to see him fairly often in 1918 when I was in the literary as well as social swim in Paris. He was a friend of Madeline La Chevrel's and of Proust's, though Proust never did like him and never thought him 'smart'.
Sir Henry Channon, DIARY 22 *Feb* 1951

9 The *concierge* of the Marseilles hotel said to the French critic Edmond Jaloux 'M. Gide does nothing but come in and go out'. How well she summed up an entire existence — Gide's literary career.
Jean Hytier, ANDRÉ GIDE 1963

10 André Gide, French Nobel winner, moved to a new house in Normandy with a study containing every possible convenience. His cousin visiting him there found Gide working at a folding table in the hall. He explained 'The new study is much too comfortable. I simply can't work there.'
News Review 30 *Dec* 1948

11 He is boyishly demure, demurely boyish. And he is almost eighty years of age!
Harold Nicolson, DIARY 3 *Jun* 1947

12 Whatever French criticism may say, he is not a major creative writer.
J. B. Priestley, LITERATURE AND WESTERN MAN 1960

13 Gide was a liberator, like D. H. Lawrence; he fought a single-handed battle against French Victorianism on behalf of sensual enjoyment and self-expression, and in so far as nineteenth-century inhibitions were wrong, he had a salutary effect.
John Weightman, Observer 3 Mar 1968

14 No other man wrote so much about himself, and he belonged to one of those cultured, middle-class families whose members, in spite of being stiff with inhibitions, were for ever corresponding with each other or debating with their consciences in private diaries, and never threw away a single scrap of paper. When Gide was over 21 his mother was still sending him 16-page letters.
Ibid.

SIR (ARTHUR) JOHN GIELGUD

Born 1904. English stage and film actor and producer.

1 Gielgud has managed to remain naïve about money. When he appeared on television in *Stars on Sunday* he said with surprise and gratitude 'They are paying me the most enormous amount of money just for reading the Bible' as if he had been expecting to do it for free.
Mark Amory, Sunday Times Magazine 14 Apr 1974

2 His largest role was as the heavy father in *The Barretts of Wimpole Street*. 'I was awful in that. When I saw the film there was a woman in the row behind me and whenever the camera came back to me she said "Here comes old beastly again."'
Ibid.

3 A gentleman in the old-fashioned sense of the word. He's like a — he's a sort of Russian character. He's saintly but it requires no effort. He was born good. There's been no struggle to get there.
Alan Bennett. Quoted ibid.

4 I have three besetting sins, both on and off the stage; impetuosity, self-consciousness, and a lack of interest in anything not immediately concerned with myself or with the theatre.
Sir John Gielgud, EARLY STAGES

5 Gielgud once had lunch with a writer called Edward Knoblock. 'Do you see that man just coming in?' Gielgud said to Knoblock, in one of those glorious, unmalicious boobs when the rushing stream of his thought breaks its banks. 'He's the biggest bore in London, second only to Edward Knoblock,' and then a terrible attempt to put matters right, he added hopelessly, 'Not *you* of course, I mean the *other* Edward Knoblock.'
John Mortimer, IN CHARACTER 1983

6 During Alan Bennett's play, *Forty Years On* in which he played a headmaster, he would leave the stage each night with a line ad-libbed to one of the schoolboys, such as, 'So glad Green House did so well in the swimming cup, Jenkins' or, 'Got to beat Swain in the cross-country haven't we, Jenkins?' One night he went off saying sadly, 'Jenkins, I've got the most terrible trouble with my income tax.'
Ibid.

7 His first professional engagement came at the age of seventeen when he walked on to the stage at the Old Vic as the herald in *Henry V*, whose only line is, 'Here is the number of slaughtered French.' It seems that the delivery of that somewhat lugubrious statement was so poor that for the rest of the season, although he walked on in *King Lear* and *Peer Gynt*, he was given no line at all.
Ibid.

8 His back is straight, his head cocked, the nose is like an eager beak cleaving the air, the eyes are hooded as if prepared to wince in fastidious disapproval at what the over-inquisitive nose might sniff. He has the bald head of a priest, the pink health of a retired admiral, the elegant suiting of what was once known as a 'man about town' and the competent hands of an artist. After playing most of the great tragic roles in his youth, John Gielgud has developed, in his seventies, into the world's subtlest comic actor.
Ibid.

9 His eyes are still hooded or turned to gaze around the room as though, through modesty, not yet taking part in the conversation. His hands move rhythmically. 'Tynan said I had only two gestures, the left hand up, the right hand up — what did he want me to do, bring out my . . . ?' The word is swallowed. The talk sweeps on.
Ibid.

LILLIAN GISH

Born 1896. Original name Lillian de Guiche. American film actress who, with her sister Dorothy (1898–1968), entered silent films in 1912 under the direction of D. W. Griffith. Achieved international fame with *Orphans of the Storm*, 1922.

10 The seriousness with which Lillian Gish undertook her work was undermined at MGM in 1928 when it was suggested that a scandal might improve her performance at the box office. 'You are way up there on a pedestal and nobody cares,' said her producers. 'If you're knocked off the pedestal everyone *would* care.' Lillian Gish realised that her days at MGM were numbered. She returned to her first love, the theatre, and the cinema lost her for a decade.
Kevin Brownlow, Sunday Times Magazine 27 *Nov* 1983

11 Lillian Gish may be a charming person, but she's not Ophelia. She comes on stage as if

she'd been sent for to sew rings on the new curtains.
Mrs Pat Campbell. Quoted Cecil Beaton, DIARY 1938

1 I never married — somehow it seemed like a full-time job and I never had that kind of time, what with the movies, and then looking after my mother for 20 years after her stroke and then Dorothy when she got ill. I had a lot of good men friends but I thought, why ruin their lives by marrying them.
Lillian Gish, THE MOVIES, MR GRIFFITH AND ME 1969

2 The Gish sisters, Lillian and Dorothy, went to work in 1912 at the Biograph studios where the up-and-coming director D. W. Griffith tied different coloured ribbons round them to tell them apart.
David Robinson, The Times 2 *Dec* 1983

3 No actress in silent films, except perhaps Garbo, could so immediately intimate raw feeling. In Gish's case we are often shocked by the disparity beween her small, frail frame and the enormity of her emotions.
Ibid.

4 By the 1920s she was the greatest diva of the silent screen . . . whom James Agate likened to the young Bernhardt, while Nemirovitch Danchenko of the Moscow Art Theatre placed her 'in the small circle of the first tragediennes of the world'.
Ibid.

5 The movies have never known a more dedicated artist.
King Vidor, when making La Bohème in 1926

ELINOR GLYN

Born 1864. English romantic novelist whose work, beginning with *Three Weeks*, 1907, was considered by her contemporaries to be extremely daring, even scandalous. Died 1943.

6 She is of medium height, but so graceful that you first get the impression that she is tall. Her hair is a delicate red, her skin snow white and smooth. Her eyes are green, a deep shade, eyes that can be truthfully described as enigmatic, Oriental in their fascinating depths.
Douglas Brent, Picture Goer

7 Her favourite subject is re-incarnation. She is convinced she has been born before, has lived for at least two hundred years. Gravely she will inform you that once she was a powerful queen, in some past century, that she has been born and born again to repent for past sins. She also has a theory that there has been a time when she was upon this earth in the form of a tigress, an animal that has always fascinated her oddly.
Ibid.

8 The Reaper has bagged Elinor Glyn; she was an extraordinay woman; feline, theatrical, a 'poseuse' and a vulgarian, but a personality. She was a little in love with me in 1918, though I always, perhaps unkindly, called her 'Grandma'. I once saw her every day for months in Paris; her long red hair was famous, as were her tiny green eyes that used, all too often, to light up amorously. But she was a brave old girl, tough, upright, and unexpectedly religious. She tried hard to marry Lord Curzon; and, indeed, redecorated Montacute in her own appalling taste, with tiger skins and mauve carpets. But it was Lord Alistair Innes-Ker who was (as she often told me) the love of her life, and he is the hero of the period piece, the once fashionable and so daring book *Three Weeks* which made her famous.
Sir Henry Channon, DIARY 23 *Sep* 1943

9 I wrote *Three Weeks* as an escape from the deprivations of my married life. My imagination was roused to the worship of Love not by the possession of its joys but by a longing for them.
Elinor Glyn, ROMANTIC ADVENTURE 1936

10 My passion for tiger-skins dates from a visit to the Jardin des Plantes in company with an attractive young man who kept whispering '*belle tigresse*' and I was very thrilled.
Ibid.

11 On looking back at my life I see that the dominant interest, in fact the fundamental impulse behind every action, has been the desire for *romance*. I have sought it continually. It is the only thing worth having.
Ibid.

12 I discovered that my husband had spent the whole of his capital. The years from the summer of 1908 to the winter of 1913 stay in my memory as one long nightmare of recurring financial crises as fresh debts of Clayton's came to light, of hastily written novels, the advance payments on which were already mortgaged to some pressing creditor or urgently required to pay the household bills or school fees for the children.
Ibid.

1 I have read but little of Madame Glyn. I did not know that things like *It* were going on. I have misspent my days.
Dorothy Parker, New Yorker 26 *Nov* 1927

2 Elinor Glyn telephoned, speaking practically in a whisper and very rapidly . . . as if it is a special style she has evolved for herself. Everyone assumes that 'It', she said, is her definition of sex appeal. No such thing. 'I mean by "It" a special quality of the spirit.' She spoke resentfully of the attacks made on her by the critics, and ended; 'But I don't really mind them. A higher power looks after me.'
Reginald Pound, THEIR MOODS AND MINE 1937

(PAUL) JOSEPH GOEBBELS

Born 1897. German politician. Hitler's minister of propaganda. Committed suicide on fall of Berlin 1945.

3 He is supposed to be as ruthless as any other German leader. An undersized, dark little man with a club foot could hardly be otherwise in a movement which boasts so much about blond and beefy Aryans. Gifted — or cursed — with such intense nationalism the physical disability which prevented him from serving in the war must have warped his mind. But he has a charm which the others lack. Not only a charm but also a great sense of humour and a considerable courage.
Vernon Bartlett, THIS IS MY LIFE 1937

4 During his one and only visit to Geneva he received the world's press, which included almost every newspaper that was hostile to his regime. The hotel authorities had made a sort of reading-desk for him out of packing cases covered with a hotel table-cloth. The result was that he looked very much like a small priest standing in front of a large lectern, and he made his declaration and answered his questions with the fire and fury of a great religious reformer.
Ibid.

5 Joseph Goebbels was neither the first nor the last practitioner in the art of political propaganda, though perhaps the most brilliant and malignant this century has seen so far.
Ernest K. Bramstead, GOEBBELS AND NATIONAL SOCIALIST PROPAGANDA 1965

6 I had expected to dislike him intensely, but am ashamed to say I did not.
Lord Halifax, AUTOBIOGRAPHY 1951

7 The Goebbels children, who were not consulted, might reasonably have been left alive in charge of their relatives, if Goebbels had not decided that their sacrifice would serve his dramatic purpose.
Roger Manvell and Heinrich Fraenkel, DOCTOR GOEBBELS: HIS LIFE AND DEATH 1960

8 In the 24 hours after Hitler's death when Goebbels himself held the title of Reich Chancellor, he staged what seemed to him the appropriate exit, for which he had already written his chosen lines. His suicide, in which he took his wife and family with him, was to provide the German people with an example of loyalty to the Fuehrer, a lesson for posterity.
Ibid.

9 Apart from Speer (who lacked his vanity) he was the only intellectual among the Nazi leaders. It is the cold, deliberate misuse of his intellect which makes him so unattractive a figure, even in that calculated death scene.
H. D. Ziman, Daily Telegraph 11 *Mar* 1960

HERMANN (WILHELM) GOERING

Born 1893. German politician, took part in the Munich putsch of 1923, became Hitler's air minister, 1933. Committed suicide during the Nuremberg trials.

10 The bullying and blustering General Goering I have only met once and then I disliked him so cordially that I find it difficult to believe he is among the Nazi leaders one of the most reasonable and most open to discussion. But even he seems to have become more moderate with the years.
Vernon Bartlett, THIS IS MY LIFE 1937

11 Goering, in full uniform and covered in decorations, waddled into the restaurant, accompanied by several staff officers. He bowed and smiled to all of us and sat down at the table next to mine. Gradually my indignation gave way to interest. I don't think I've ever seen anyone eat and drink so much. He had three or four courses, and drank two bottles of hock. At frequent intervals he took a pill. When he left the restaurant he gave me a cheerful wave of the hand.
Lord Boothby, RECOLLECTIONS OF A REBEL 1978

12 I found him bloated and over-bearing.
Count Ciano. Quoted Roger Manvell and Heinrich Fraenkel, HERMANN GOERING 1962

1 I am able to reveal that Hermann Goering was detained in a Swedish mental hospital as a raving drug fiend. He was put into a padded cell. Special watch was put over him because of his violent fits of rage. He threatened women nurses with a dagger. He tried to strangle a woman nurse with his bare hands. An affidavit by his own physician reads 'It is hereby certified that Captain Goering is a victim of morphine, for which reason his home must be considered inappropriate for his (step)son Thomas Kantzow. Karl A. R. Lundberg, Stockholm 16 April 1926.'
Leonard Clairmont, Sunday Chronicle 7 *Apr* 1940

2 A big, fat, good-humoured man who loves display above everything.
William Dodd (US Ambassador), DIARY

3 Hermann Goering accompanied the Fuehrer on one of his visits to Rome. On the crowded railway platform filled with dignitaries and troops the massive Marshal jostled roughly past an Italian gentleman of aristocratic bearing who turned and haughtily demanded an apology. Fiercely the Marshal turned upon him and snapped, 'I am Hermann Goering.' The Italian bowed and said, 'As an excuse that is not enough, but as an explanation it is ample.'
Edmund Fuller, ANECDOTES 1942

4 I was immensely entertained at meeting the man. I remembered all the time that he had been concerned with the 'clean-up' in Berlin on June 30, 1934, and I wondered how many people he had been responsible for killing. Like a great schoolboy full of life and pride in all he was doing, showing it all off, and talking high politics out of the setting of green jerkin and red dagger.
Lord Halifax

5 He loved children and animals and had a fondness for playing with toy trains, and toy aeroplanes that dropped bombs.
Sir Nevile Henderson. Quoted Roger Manville and Heinrich Fruenkel, HERMAN GOERING 1962

6 Hermann Goering started the concentration camps, founded the Gestapo, launched the bombing attacks on Guernica, Rotterdam and Coventry which added a new dimension of horror to modern war, planned the systematic starvation of millions in Eastern Europe and alone among the defendants at the Nuremberg Trials, confronted his judges with an unrepentant apologia for National Socialism.
James Joll, Daily Telegraph 15 *Dec* 1962

7 He was able to supply the relaxed affability that Hitler totally lacked, and his easy and jovial manner gave him a deceptive appearance of moderation.
Ibid.

8 He marched with Hitler on the Munich *putsch* of 1923 and received wounds which drove him to morphine to relieve his pain — an addiction which may well account for much of his strange behaviour.
Ibid.

9 Very soon after I entered Goering's service I realised the labyrinth of intrigue and brutal egotism surrounding the marshal. Goering himself was responsible. He determined the character of his house, his staff and his entire surroundings. He lived in the twilight of his own ill-defined and unstable character. He lusted for luxury and comfort and it was of no consequence for him how it was provided.
Eitel Lange, THE FANTASTIC GOERING 1951

10 When Germany attacked Russia it was decided something must be done about Goering. Nobody was capable of getting him to the front, and the method of dealing with the difficulty was cheap and pathetic. I was made to look through my photographs and found one I had taken on a country road in France of him standing deep in thought, his left hand holding a pipe. Eight days later, on the front page of the newspapers, was my French country road photo headed 'The Reichmarshall on the Eastern Front'. Though it became the most talked-of picture of my career it caused a frightful row. When Hitler saw it he flew into a royal rage. We had broken the strict rule that no leader should be pictured smoking — a bad example for German youth.
Ibid.

11 He loved the pompous, the exaggerated, especially in boots. With his uniforms he would wear long red hunting boots of Russian leather, and with them silver spurs, even though one could see, if one examined him carefully, that he belonged to the air force. Naturally he never went on horseback. (Stripped, he weighed 18 stone.)
Ibid.

12 An aviator of some distinction, embittered by defeat, mentally unbalanced, reckless, defiant, self indulgent, his whole being is pervaded by potions of hate and revenge.
Harold Laski, Daily Herald 15 *Jul* 1933

13 By 1916 he is already an 'ace' with a large number of destroyed enemy machines to his

credit. After Richthofen's death he is the natural choice for the leader of the famous Death Squadron. He is a national hero. The highest orders adorn his breast. His photograph is cherished by every flapper.
R. H. Bruce Lockhart, Evening Standard 30 *Mar* 1933

1 My first impression was of meeting a dissolute Roman emperor, game to the last. I caught the full menace of his narrow, bright eyes. His wide lips suggested nameless appetites.
Airey Neave, NUREMBERG 1978

2 Goering is the dominant figure. Clad in a loose-fitting light uniform without badges of rank, he leans his pasty face upon a fat pasty hand, and at times he will place his fist against his chin in the attitude of Rodin's Penseur. For so vast a man, although he is now shrunken, his movements are alert, rapid, nervous, impulsive.
Harold Nicolson, NUREMBERG TRIAL DIARIES 30 *Apr* 1946

SAM GOLDWYN

Born 1881. Original name Samuel Goldfish. Emigrated from Poland to become a pioneer in the film industry, an early silent success being *The Squaw Man*, 1913. With Louis B. Mayer, formed Metro-Goldwyn-Mayer in 1924. Died 1974.

3 There are lucky ones whose great hearts, shallow and commonplace as bedpans, beat in instinctive tune with the great heart of the public, who laugh as it likes to laugh, weep the sweet and easy tears it likes to weep — Goldwyn is blessed with that divine confidence in the rightness (moral, aesthetic, commercial) of his own intuition — and that I suppose is the chief reason for his success.
Lindsay Anderson 1974

4 It must be said that though Sam recognised and paid for talent he was always afraid to use it. In the war between art and showmanship, art lost.
Daily Telegraph, Obituary 1 *Feb* 1974

5 You always knew where you were with Goldwyn — nowhere.
F. Scott Fitzgerald. Quoted Matthew J. Bruccoli, SOME SORT OF EPIC GRANDEUR

6 He disdained subtlety. When a harassed publicist devised a campaign that began 'The directing skill of Rouben Mamoulian, the radiance of Anna Sten and the genius of Samuel Goldwyn have combined to bring you the world's greatest entertainment.' Goldwyn nodded approval. 'That's the kind of advertising I like. Just the facts. No exaggeration.'
Leslie Halliwell, FILMGOER'S BOOK OF QUOTES 1978

7 When he meditates, he thinks that everyone should, by some telepathic process, be listening in. He awakened an assistant at midnight once and started the telephone conversation by saying 'The woman must die in the end.' 'What woman?' the man asked. Goldwyn had been thinking out the plot of a picture: the employee was expected to know by thought transference all that had gone before. Sam was as annoyed as if the man had gone to sleep at a conference.
Alva Johnston, THE GREAT GOLDWYN 1937

8 Sam's mind is so concentrated on pictures that much of the time he is practically in a trance. One day he registered at the Hotel Blackstone in Chicago, went directly to his room, seized the telephone and said 'Get my office.' He expected the operator, without even knowing his name, to connect him with his studio in Hollywood.
Ibid.

9 He told a composer that his music would not do. 'What's the matter with it?' he was asked. 'There's not enough sarcasm in it', he replied.
Ibid.

10 A director who was asked his opinion of a script said 'It's too caustic.' Mr Goldwyn replied. 'To hell with the cost. It's a good picture. We'll make it.'
Ibid.

11 Quaint utterances ascribed to Mr Goldwyn have become as apocryphal — and perhaps as valuable from the publicity angle — as jokes about Ford cars. Among the genuine Goldwynisms are 'My horse was in the lead — and then the caddie had to fall off' . . . 'We can get all the Indians we need at the reservoir.' 'Directors are always biting the hand that lays the golden egg.'
Ibid.

12 He waxed very enthusiastic about the song *Night and Day*. 'We must have something like *Night and Day* for our new show,' he declared. A friend heard him rave all the afternoon about it, then dined at the Goldwyn house. After dinner someone put a record of the song on the gramophone. 'What tune is that?' asked Goldwyn.
Ibid.

1 His publicity man showed him a batch of reviews damning one of his pictures. 'It runs off my back like a duck,' was his comment.
Ibid.

2 Sam made his first dent in the wall of prejudice against the movies in October 1913. On Columbus Day he telephoned Arthur Friend to meet him at the Hoffman House. 'I've found a backer,' said Sam. 'He wants us to meet him with a prospectus. What's a prospectus?'
Ibid.

MAXIM GORKY

Born 1868. Pen-name of Aleksei Maksimovich Peshkov. Russian novelist and short story writer. Died 1936.

3 Maxim Gorky is an example of the type of writers who live first and write afterwards, in contra-distinction to the type that, like the late George Gissing, wrote first and hoped to live some day or other.
Stephen Graham, T.P.'s Weekly 4 *Apr* 1928

4 The balance between sincere belief and conscious propaganda is left as obscure as the dispute over his death. Stalin was soon to announce that he had been poisoned by Trotskyists — a charge which few believed at the time and fewer do now. Beyond all doubt there was a genuine sense of bereavement in Russia on his death. I remember the red flags, edged with black, hanging in the streets; the crowds at the funeral; and the whispered regrets among ordinary people that a fine old gentleman from the past had gone.
Iverach McDonald, The Times 2 *Mar* 1968

5 Successively dock-worker, baker, night-watchman, tramp, clerk and keeper of military stores, Gorky meets and mixes with all sorts and conditions of men; officials who abuse their office, professors, students, peasants, thieves, lunatics and wastrels. Every one is individualised. Distinct figures, sometimes drawn with repulsive detail, often with touching tenderness, live and move before our eyes.
Beatrice Marshall, T.P.'s Weekly 9 *Apr* 1927

6 He was responsible for the adoption of 'socialist-realism' which was accepted in 1934 throughout the whole of Soviet literature. It is probably by the wonderful reminiscences of his early life and by his portraits of his fellow authors, that he will be best remembered.
J. B. Priestley, LITERATURE AND WESTERN MAN 1960

7 He looks about him like one of the spies that has come from Canaan. He feels himself a stranger, notices everything, and reports to a God of his own.
Leo Tolstoy. Quoted Iverach McDonald, The Times 2 *Mar* 1968

PERCY (ALDRIDGE) GRAINGER

Born 1882 in Australia. Pianist and composer, made his reputation as a collector and arranger of folk music. Died 1961.

8 Percy certainly was a most lovable creature, so full of enthusiasm and strange Australian slang. His letters were almost unintelligibly original in their phrasing, and he carried this trait into his composition. Instead of the usual *molto crescendo* Percy would put 'Louden lots' and such expressions as 'Breathe when blown' and 'Louder hugely' enliven his MSS.
Ernest Thesiger, PRACTICALLY TRUE 1927

9 He was not above employing banjos and combs in his orchestra, and if any of the performers were too unskilled to strike a needed chord on banjo or guitar, their untutored hands were guided by pieces of stamp-paper pasted on the fingerboard.
Ibid.

CARY GRANT

Born 1904, original name Archibald Leach. British actor who moved to Hollywood to make films, e.g. *Bringing Up Baby*, 1938, *Arsenic and Old Lace*, 1944, *Charade*, 1963.

10 When Cary Grant married Barbara Hutton, the couple did not depart for a wedding trip because it was necessary for Grant to report on the lot for the filming of *Once Upon a Honeymoon*.
Edmund Fuller, ANECDOTES 1942

11 He cured himself of smoking by saying over and over again for weeks, 'Your fingers are yellow, your breath smells, and you only smoke because you are insecure.'
David Niven, BRING ON THE EMPTY HORSES 1975

12 The accent is hard to locate; not precisely mid-Atlantic but a long way from Bristol.

And his delivery is just as mysterious. For custom-car buffs it might bring to mind a vintage Morgan with a wilful clutch. There are always a few throat-clearings before the power surge pins you back in your seat.
Philip Oakes, The Times 18 *Jan* 1984

1 At some time in his fifties, while Cary Grant still looked as if he were in his forties — happily combining an elegant and easeful maturity with an undiminished capacity for playfulness — he simply ceased to age. 'Everyone grows older,' his friend and co-star Grace Kelly once said wearily, 'except Cary Grant.'
Richard Schickel, Observer Magazine 16 *Oct* 1983

ROBERT (RANKE) GRAVES

Born 1895. English novelist and poet. Among his best-known works is his novel of classical Rome, *I Claudius*, 1934, and his autobiography *Goodbye to All That*, 1929. Died 1985.

2 He was not an ordinary boy; he was very early interested in poetry, for which his school-fellows pilloried him. His housemaster rated him for writing what he chose to describe as 'filthy poems'; and his head's laconic farewell was, 'Well, good-bye Graves, and remember this, that your best friend is the waste-paper basket.'
John o' London's Weekly 7 *Dec* 1929

3 On the Somme he was so badly wounded in the lung that he was left for dead and officially listed as 'died of wounds'.
Observer, Profile 26 *Feb* 1961

4 Graves talked about the First World War. 'Unlike the angry young men of today, I had something to be angry about. I decided to write it (*Good-bye to All That*) quickly and get out of England. I didn't care what people thought of me any longer. It broke my friendship with Siegfried Sassoon. He said he would break my neck if he saw me. Edmund Blunden was furious, too, but we are friends again now.'
Robert Pitman, Sunday Express 24 *Nov* 1957

5 I had always found Graves's character to be exactly divided, half and half, between schoolboy and schoolmaster — to me, not a very attractive combination.
Osbert Sitwell, LAUGHTER IN THE NEXT ROOM 1949

(HENRY) GRAHAM GREENE

Born 1904. English novelist, whose work exploits the theme of individuals faced with moral dilemmas in dramatic situations. His *Third Man*, 1950, was turned into a highly successful film.

6 His life and work have been grounded on faith, and on its opposites and counterparts; loyalty and betrayal, stoicism and doubt.
Martin Amis, Observer, Graham Greene at eighty 25 *Sep* 1984

7 Graham Greene, of whom it was said, he had to be obscene to be believed.
Basil Cottle, NAMES 1983

8 His passion for strange countries and difficult beliefs seems to come from the boyhood terror of boredom which led him to play Russian roulette with an old service revolver. At seventy-five Mr Greene still sounded like a boy, speaking of the risks he had enjoyed.
John Mortimer, IN CHARACTER 1983

9 What has always fascinated me is his Catholicism, which, despite heresies and irregularities, has continued to occupy his mind, and perhaps also his soul. I cherish the memory of walking up and down with him beside the Sea of Galilee and talking about the Incarnation as expounded in the New Testament. His favourite text is also mine; 'Lord, I believe; help thou mine unbelief.'
Malcolm Muggeridge, The Times 6 *Sep* 1984

10 Graham's novels may well have been coloured by his incredible imagination, but when one knows of his endless urge to swan over the world and sample every person and every experience, they are not more than spicy autobiographies.
Duke of Norfolk, The Times 7 *Sep* 1984

11 Mr Greene has the most sensitive nose of all contemporary writers for the odour of spiritual decay. He smells it wherever he goes, whether in the jungle of English bed-sitting-rooms or in the streets of Africa and Mexico.
Observer, Profile 27 *Nov* 1949

12 One day in 1930, Grahame Greene, a young man whose first novel had been a great success, sat down to write for a newspaper what he hoped and desired from life. He inserted one odd item, 'to become thoroughly acquainted with such strange and slightly sinister suburbs as Brixton and Streatham Hill'.
Ibid.

1 His characters, particularly his heroes, are usually without glamour. They are seedy, down-at-heel, weak, rather stupid individuals, and essentially failures. Seldom able to control the external world, they are buffeted about by it and caught up in events like plaintive puppets; all they have to rescue themselves with is a soul and a sense of its purpose.
Ibid.

2 Greeneland, the famously seedy world of terrace houses, dingy offices, inept private detectives with ulcers, oppressed teachers of absurd international languages, Harrovians gone to the bad, tarts and bookies in Brighton, communists caught up in a bus strike, mediums in benighted suburbs, forlorn, maltreated chambermaids in frightful hotels.
Anthony Quinton, The Times 7 *Sep* 1984

3 I was struggling over a half-cooked novel when I read that someone had turned up a 60,000-word manuscript that Graham Greene had written years ago and *forgotten about*. I thought briefly about doing away with myself. To me, forgetting having written a book is like forgetting having had heart surgery.
Keith Waterhouse, The Times 6 *Sep* 1984

4 He has created a climate of crackbrained confusion between vices and virtues — a climate in which the traitor flourishes.
Rebecca West. Quoted J. W. Lambert, Sunday Times, The Private World of Graham Greene 5 *Mar* 1978

EDWARD GREY, FIRST VISCOUNT GREY OF FALLODON

Born 1862. British politician. Foreign Secretary 1905–16. Died 1933.

5 A curious combination of the old-fashioned Whig and the Socialist.
A. J. Balfour

6 One day in Downing Street during the war someone asked Grey what he would do if the Germans won and said to him 'Unless you salute our flag you shall die'. But Lloyd George said 'The Germans would put a stiffer one to him than that, they would say, "Unless you salute our flag we shall shoot your squirrels!"'
J. M. Barrie. Speech at Grey's seventieth birthday luncheon

7 Europe and the other civilised countries were *prima facie* disposed to accept as true anything Grey said. His great asset was his character.
Lord Robert Cecil

8 A friend came to see me on one of the evenings of last week — he thinks it was on Monday, August 3 (1914). We were standing at a window of my room in the Foreign Office. It was getting dark, and the lamps were being lit in the space on which we were looking. My friend recalls that I remarked on this with these words: 'The lamps are going out all over Europe; we shall not see them lit again in our lifetime.'
Viscount Grey of Fallodon, TWENTY-FIVE YEARS 1925

9 A well-meaning, peace-loving nobleman, but a man with a kink in his soul.
Hermann Lutz, LORD GREY UND DE WELTKRIEG

10 Edward Grey disliked holding office, and was apt to regard all foreigners as ill-behaved.
Harold Nicolson, Observer 12 *Oct* 1958

11 He was not an orthodox Christian. He shared his wife's view that 'one might be able to be kind about the Church of England if one didn't belong to it'. He was 'nearer to Quakerism than anything else'. But he clung to the faith that 'God rules in the Universe and evil cannot prevail'.
G. M. Trevelyan, GREY OF FALLODON 1937

H

DOUGLAS HAIG, FIRST EARL HAIG OF BEMERSYDE

Born 1861 in Scotland. British Field Marshal. Commanded First Army Corps in France, 1914. Commander-in-Chief of British forces 1915–17. The slaughter resulting from his policy of prolonged trench warfare has evoked much criticism. Died 1928.

1 A man whose power of expression was so disorganised that in congratulating a successful regimental athletics team he confided to them that he hoped they would 'run as well in the presence of the enemy'.
Daily Telegraph 2 *May* 1963

2 Right at the end, when even Foch had lost his vision, it was Haig, in September 1918, only six weeks before the Germans collapsed, who answered Winston Churchill's plea to 'conserve our forces for 1920' with a blunt 'What rubbish! If we act with vigour now a decision can be obtained in the very near future.'
Sir John Eliot, Daily Telegraph 25 *Apr* 1963

3 I feel that every step in my plan has been taken with the Divine help.
Haig, DIARY 30 *Jun* 1916, *on the eve of the Battle of the Somme, in which the British sustained* 57,000 *casualties in one day*

4 He seemed to be the most highly equipped thinker in the British Army.
Lord Haldane

5 A man who avowed without shame a simple belief in God and the Empire, a figure straight from the pages of Kipling and Newbolt, can expect little mercy at the hands of sophisticated *literati*.
Michael Howard, Sunday Times 21 *Apr* 1963

6 A commander not unworthy to be ranked with those sombre masters of mass-warfare von Moltke and Ulysses S. Grant, both of whom made mistakes and were equally prepared to accept huge casualties in their search for victory.
Ibid.

7 He was as able a staff officer as any in the British army, unrivalled in his mastery of railway timetables. He was confident that he could win the war, though he did not know how. Like most British generals of the time he disliked politicians, especially Liberals, and got on badly with them. All the same, he was more adroit and supple than he seemed, and this hidden skill enabled him to outmanoeuvre even Lloyd George, though only just.
A. J. P. Taylor, ENGLISH HISTORY 1914–1945 1965

HAILE SELASSIE

Born 1891, originally called Tafari Makonnen, Emperor of Ethiopia 1930–74. Led resistance to Italian invasion 1935, took refuge in England 1936, returned 1941. Deposed 1974. Died 1974.

8 This afternoon the Emperor Haile Selassie came to Belgrave Square to tea; it was a very secret meeting, arranged for him to meet Rab. The Emperor entered gravely, wearing a bowler hat and the famous cape. He has dignity, but he has aged since that night I dined at Boni de Castellane's to meet him in 1925.
Sir Henry Channon, DIARY 11 *Jun* 1940

9 This diminutive Christian monarch, the Chosen One of God and successor to King Solomon, was widely respected for his plucky resistance to Mussolini (before sitting it out in Bath) and devotion to caged lions he fed every morning.
David Cute, reviewing Ryszard Kapuscinski's THE EMPEROR: DOWNFALL OF AN AUTOCRAT, *The Times* 4 *Dec* 1983

10 Finally the old man was left entirely alone in his palace with a single servant. Revolutionary officers demanded that he return his loot, reckoned in millions, to the nation. He feigned innocence. The vast Persian carpet was lifted and there were the rolls of dollar bills.
Ibid.

11 Like the Tsar of Russia before him, he was

regarded with mystical reverence by his own people: himself above the law, he held power of life and death over his subjects.
Ibid.

1 The last days of Haile Selassie were not unlike the last days of Nixon; the paranoia, the entourage not knowing which way to jump. Haile Selassie, on the whole, did not care what his Ministers did, provided they were totally and utterly loyal.
Michael Davie, Observer 19 *Aug* 1984

2 'It was a small dog.' The speaker was a man whose job it was for 10 years to attend the Emperor's receptions and when the dog (which was allowed to sleep on the Emperor's bed) peed on the shoes of visiting dignitaries, to go round wiping off the urine with a satin cloth.
Ibid.

QUINTIN HOGG, LORD HAILSHAM

Born 1907. English politician and lawyer. First elected to parliament in 1938. Held various ministerial posts under Harold Macmillan. After succeeding to the peerage in 1951 he temporarily relinquished it in order to take his seat as member for Marylebone. Appointed Lord Chancellor 1970.

3 He is a kind man with a large heart and what used to be called nobility of soul. Yet in a fit of anger he will tear or rend anybody. His family, to whom he is devoted, shout back or go into another room until the storm is passed. But some others find it hard to believe that anyone could be so vitriolic one moment and forget it the next. 'Perhaps that's the way they used to treat the peasants,' it is said in resentment.
Susan Barnes, Sunday Times Magazine 12 *Mar* 1972

4 He once broke his walking stick over a portrait of Harold Wilson.
Ibid.

5 Quinton Hogg was born into a decidedly superior family. At a revivalist meeting led by his grandfather a small Hogg was approached by a simple-minded penitent and asked 'Are you saved?' 'All the Hoggs are saved,' the child replied.
Ibid.

6 His boredom threshold is unusually low, and when you see him balancing an ashtray on his head or squinting at you through a glass prism, you know he's very bored indeed.
Ibid.

7 When Mr Khrushchev heard that Lord Hailsham had been made responsible for the British answer to the Russian scientific challenge a chill went through the Kremlin . . . this man of detached judgement, with his emotions under control all the time . . .
Aneurin Bevan, sarcastic comment in House of Commons on Hailsham being sent by Macmillan to Moscow to negotiate a Test-Ban Treaty, Jul 1963

8 In court dress he looked as weird as a square grape.
Clive James, POEM OF THE YEAR 1983

9 When self indulgence has reduced a man to the shape of Lord Hailsham, sexual continence involves no more than a sense of the ridiculous.
Reginald Paget MP, House of Commons 16 *Jun* 1963

10 He is able at the same time as he is shouting, to run his hands through his hair and make it stand on end, higher and higher. Immediately after one of these rages he would suddenly decide he's been rather funny, and stand there, his face wreathed in smiles, quite unconscious that by now everyone else was in a rage. As far as Quintin was concerned, if it was all right with him, it was all right with everybody.
A. J. P. Taylor

J. B. S. (JOHN BURDON SANDERSON) HALDANE

Born 1892. British scientist specialising in genetic research. Wrote essays popularising scientific subjects. Died 1964.

11 Professor Haldane of London University thrilled the *Thetis* Tribunal yesterday by telling them how he locked himself for fourteen and a half hours in an airtight steel cylinder filled with poisoned air like the Davis escape chamber in the doomed submarine, breathing a mixture probably corresponding to the air in the *Thetis* at about 10 p.m. the day she sank.
Daily Mirror 21 *Jul* 1939 (*His wife said afterwards: 'He was very weak when he came out but he recovered by ten o'clock in the evening when we went to a party. He stayed up enjoying himself until five in the morning.'*)

12 The British Navy was so frightened of diving that the authorities said that before a man

could go down 40 feet he must have months of training. My father thought that anyone could go down 40 feet at once and to prove it he said 'Here is my son. He's only thirteen. Throw him overboard.' I went down all right but the diving suit was too big for me and when I was hauled up it was full of water up to the neck. That is the way I found things out.
J. B. S. Haldane, Daily Mirror 15 *Nov* 1937

1 The second world war saw him, though now a Communist, engaged in those scarifying Admiralty experiments — in compression chambers, in tanks of melting ice, convulsing to unconsciousness from oxygen poisoning — which first made him familiar to the public in a way that Haldane's Law or the Mathematical Theory had never done. If he had not been restrained by naval colleagues he might indeed, out of sheer bravado, have destroyed himself.
Margaret Lane, Daily Telegraph 29 *Oct* 1968

2 As a boy of 14 he tested fire-damp by standing with his head in it reciting 'Friends, Romans, countrymen . . .' till he collapsed.
News Chronicle 25 *Feb* 1932

3 Haldane's strange, unweaned ways fascinated me; if he reverted to thumb sucking I shouldn't be in the least surprised. His intellect is powerful, his logic a cold shower in an age of tepid thinking. He always strikes me as having been terrifically highly developed in some lobe of his brain, and in some hardly at all. This makes him both attractive and irritating to know.
Reginald Pound, THEIR MOODS AND MINE 1937

4 One has the impression that Haldane is rarely present at any casual conversation. He will burble a commonplace remark now and then, but one is quite sure, all the time, that his inner mind is ceaselessly occupied with some problem of biology or genetics.
Ibid.

5 Recently, when trying to find a cure for diabetes, he allowed himself to be 'acidised' to produce an artificial diabetic condition, and was then operated on — without anaesthetic — in order that his colleagues might take tests during the operation of his spinal fluid and the blood in his arteries.
Radio Times 29 *Jan* 1932

RICHARD BURDON HALDANE

RICHARD BURDON HALDANE, VISCOUNT HALDANE OF CLOAN

Born 1856 in Scotland. British politician. As Secretary for War 1905–12 he remodelled the Army and formed the Territorials. In 1915 was the victim of violent and totally unfounded accusations, in Northcliffe's newspapers, of being pro-German, and resigned from the Cabinet. Died 1928.

6 Haldane's mind is full of black sludge.
Augustine Birrell. Quoted Duff Cooper, OLD MEN FORGET 1953

7 He was an old friend of my father. When I was three I greeted him with 'I have seen you before, Mr Haldane' and went on to explain that I had recognised him from my Nonsense Book. His spheroid figure, his twinkling benignity and pneumatic bulk reminded irresistably of those familiar and dearly loved figures, the Old Men of Edward Lear.
Lady Violet Bonham Carter. Quoted Dudley Sommer, HALDANE OF CLOAN 1960

8 He had the hallmark of nobility. Those who knew him trusted him. Lord Rothschild once said to him: 'I do not know what you have come for, but I have said to myself that if you ask me to write a cheque for £25,000 and to ask no questions I will do it on the spot.' Sir Ernest Cassel gave him half a million for education on the one condition that Lord Haldane took control of it.
Children's Newspaper 30 *Mar* 1929

9 That oily old Jesuit who sits on the Woolsack.
Lord Fisher. Quoted Dudley Sommer, HALDANE OF CLOAN 1960

10 Haldane looked very magnificent, pacing up and down his room with his heavy legs thrown alternately in front of him with his odd elephant — or tapir-like — movement.
Edmund Gosse, UNPUBLISHED DIARY. *Quoted ibid.*

11 The accusation that Haldane was pro-German is now treated as beneath contempt and needs no further refutation.
Jo Grimond, Daily Telegraph 12 *May* 1960

12 Much as I disliked Haldane personally, I was conscious that no man could be as epicene as he appeared if he could acquire the devotion of Edward Grey. When I was told later of all that Haldane had done for the reorganisation of our Army and for adult education I came to regard him with respect and gratitude.
Harold Nicolson, Observer 15 *May* 1960

1 Haldane invented what I call the oil-and-feather method. He gently sprayed his adversaries for hours at a time with feathers and oil — feathers in the shape of facts and argument, and oil in the shape of compliments and pious aspirations for the success of his scheme. When he concluded, most of his opponents, who had entered the House breathing fire and slaughter, staggered out gasping for air.
Lord Riddell, John o' London's Weekly 8 *Sep* 1928

2 Lord James of Hereford commented on Haldane's definition of predestination: 'I never knew how incapable I was of understanding these things until I heard your argument.'
Dudley Sommer, HALDANE OF CLOAN 1960

3 Haldane's urbane voice carried his words, as it were, on a salver.
H. G. Wells

EDWARD FREDERICK LINDLEY WOOD, FIRST EARL OF HALIFAX

Born 1881. British politician. Viceroy of India 1926–31. As Foreign Secretary 1938–40 supported Chamberlain's appeasement policy. Died 1959.

4 When Halifax went to see the Nazi leaders in Germany, Lloyd George said it was like sending a curate to visit a tiger; he wouldn't know whether it was growling in anger or fun; and in either case he wouldn't know how to reply. So it proved.
Lord Boothby, RECOLLECTIONS OF A REBEL 1978

5 Anne Wood brought her father, Lord Halifax, to lunch; his charm is proverbial. He was born with one hand, and he looks like a dashing Cecil, if one can imagine that priest-like race ever looking dashing.
Sir Henry Channon, DIARY 27 *Feb* 1934

6 Lord Halifax recently heard the word 'pansy' and had to send for one of his secretaries to ask the meaning of the word.
Ibid. 18 *Jun* 1935

7 Lord Halifax carried the Sword of State, indeed he held it throughout the ceremony (Opening of Parliament); quite an ordeal for a man with only one hand.
Ibid. 26 *Oct* 1937

8 Whether in Doncaster or Delhi he saw himself as a Yorkshire gentleman with sporting tastes and deep religious beliefs. He believed that his life in Vice-Regal House should be as close as possible to the way in which he lived in the Wolds of the East Riding. 'How characteristic', his biographer has written, 'that his Christmas gathering was just like a dinner-party at Garrowby with Edward's presence merely encouraging the young, and Harry Stavordale leaping over chairs on all fours, and the Viceroy blowing his hunting horn.'
Roy Jenkins, The Times 28 *May* 1973

9 He showed no special strength in the 48 hours of bewildering delay which followed the German invasion of Poland on September 1. After making a holding statement in the Lords on the Saturday evening he went home to Eaton Square, and changed for dinner, unaware of any great problem until he was hurriedly summoned to Downing Street by an agitated Prime Minister who said he could no longer hold the House of Commons.
Ibid.

10 He never really understood the American political system. He regarded much of it as a mixture of the squalid and the incomprehensible. Walter Lippmann recorded that 'every time an election took place he had to have the whole thing explained to him over again'.
Ibid.

(MARGUERITE) RADCLYFFE HALL

Born 1886. English author. Her novel *The Well of Loneliness* provoked an uproar when it was published in 1928 because it had a lesbian theme. It was the subject of an obscenity trial and for a time banned in both Britain and America. Died 1943.

11 The book (*The Well of Loneliness*) is insipidly inoffensive, in language, in description. All was a matter of subject. 'A person who chose an obscene theme could not but write an obscene book' said prosecuting counsel.
Vera Brittain, RADCLYFFE HALL: A CASE OF OBSCENITY 1968

12 Sam Goldwyn, impressed by the wide sale of Radclyffe Hall's *The Well of Loneliness*, expressed a desire to purchase the film rights. 'You can't film that,' he was advised. 'It's about Lesbians.' 'So all right,' replied Goldwyn 'where they got Lesbians we'll use Austrians.'
Edmund Fuller, ANECDOTES 1946

1 The one thing now easily discernible about *The Well of Loneliness* is its lack of any literary merit.
Geoffrey Grigson, The Times 8 *Sep* 1968

2 Radclyffe Hall is a Roman Catholic and a socialist. Her outlook on life is essentially humanitarian. When a rich man offered to pay the expenses of litigation over *The Well of Loneliness*, she refused because she could not accept so great a sum of money while thousands of miners were starving. She sold her house to meet the expenses of the case herself.
Ethel Mannin, CONFESSIONS AND IMPRESSIONS 1930

3 Radclyffe Hall isn't that distressing thing 'a lady novelist'; she is a woman writer.
Ibid.

4 *The Well of Loneliness* is a ladylike book in all senses; not only in being perfectly gentlemanly, for whatever Radclyffe Hall's own inclinations towards bohemianism, it belongs inside the traditional British world of thoroughly nice, wealthy and landed families where all rode straight to hounds, the women sidesaddle till Stephen Gordon, our Lesbian hero, showed them differently, and where you couldn't hear an aitch drop outside the stables which she haunted.
Kathleen Nott, Observer 15 *Sep* 1968

WARREN (GAMALIEL) HARDING

Born 1865. President of the United States 1921–3. During his term the Teapot Dome scandal produced charges of government corruption. Died 1923.

5 Few deaths are unmingled tragedies. Harding's was not, he died in time.
Samuel Hopkins Adams, THE AMERICAN HERITAGE

6 He was grey at 30, a poker-playing, virile, foot-on-the-brass-rail man, easy-going and gregarious, with a voice that enthralled audiences. He had few other talents.
Michael Davie, Observer 31 *Aug* 1969

7 As President, Harding may have been the worst in American history. At first he thought it was 'an easy job'. Later he found it 'hell'.
Ibid.

8 He grasped little of what was going on; he admitted he 'didn't know anything about this European stuff', and he was wholly bewildered by economics, once telling an astonished journalist that he was in favour of United States tariffs because they helped the Europeans to build up their industries.
Ibid.

9 Harding married a woman of formidable unattractiveness, who chewed gum, nagged him unmercifully and was known as 'the Duchess'. He could never bring himself to get rid of her.
Ibid.

10 Harding was not a bad man. He was just a slob.
Alice Roosevelt Longworth. Quoted Isabel Ross, GRACE COOLIDGE AND HER ERA

11 His speeches leave the impression of an army of pompous phrases moving over the landscape in search of an idea. Sometimes these meandering words would actually capture a straggling thought and bear it triumphantly a prisoner in their midst until it died of servitude and overwork.
Senator William McAdoo

12 He writes the worst English that I have ever encountered. It reminds me of a string of wet sponges; it reminds me of tattered washing on the line; it reminds me of stale bean soup, of college yells, of dogs barking idiotically through endless nights. It is so bad that a sort of grandeur creeps into it.
H. L. Mencken

13 He became President chiefly because of his superb image; his hair was frosted, his profile imposing, and his mind empty. His career illustrated the fallacy of image-worship in politics. He was a superbly packaged void.
Karl E. Meyer, Sunday Times 7 *Sep* 1969

14 He was more pathetic than evil. Power never corrupted Harding because he never learned how to wield it.
Ibid.

15 His friends were his undoing. Trusting and naïve, he allowed them to accept bribes to sell public lands in the province of Wyoming at a place called Teapot Dome. In 1923, when the crimes of his colleagues threatened to be exposed, he died while on a trip after eating a midnight meal of crab meat.
Ibid.

16 Of the Twelve American Caesars from Theodore Roosevelt to Richard Nixon, 'Wurr'n' as his wife called him, was the buffoon, the Nero who played poker while the Capitoline was stripped of Gold.
Ibid.

1 Keep Warren at home. Don't let him make any speeches. If he goes out on tour somebody is bound to ask him questions, and Warren's just the sort of damned fool that will try to answer them.
B. Penrose

2 If ever there was a he-harlot it was this same Warren G. Harding.
William Allen White. Quoted Francis Russell, PRESIDENT HARDING: HIS LIFE AND TIMES 1969

3 He has a bungalow mind.
Woodrow Wilson. Quoted C. W. Thompson, PRESIDENTS I HAVE KNOWN

JEAN HARLOW

Born 1911. Original name Harlean Carpentier. American film actress. Known as the Blonde Bombshell. Died 1937.

4 There is no sign that her acting would ever have progressed beyond the scope of the restless shoulders and the protuberant breasts; her technique was the gangster's technique — she toted a breast like a man totes a gun.
Graham Greene of Saratoga, her last film, released a month after her death

5 Harlow's hipswinging, gum-chewing, slangy, wise-cracking characterisations were a delight. She perfectly understood the roles she was playing, even to the point of asking her agent, when he phoned with a new part, 'What kind of whore am I this time?'
Clyde Jeavons and Jeremy Pascall, A PICTORIAL HISTORY OF SEX IN THE MOVIES

6 Jean Harlow kept calling Margot Asquith by her first name, pronouncing it Mar*got*. Finally Margot set her right: 'No, no, Jean, the "t" is silent, as in Harlow.'
T. S. Matthews, GREAT TOM

7 Despite her obvious lack of dramatic ability Miss Harlow became, virtually overnight, one of Hollywood's top box-office attractions. Her wardrobe, her enticing languor, and her platinum hair were all, with varying degrees of success, widely copied.
Charles Van Doren, WEBSTER'S AMERICAN BIOGRAPHIES 1974

WILLIAM RANDOLPH HEARST

Born 1863. American journalist, and newspaper proprietor. Became notorious for his eccentric and extravagant lifestyle at his castle at San Simeon, California. Died 1951.

8 The car shot through a gate and we were in the grounds of the Hearst estate. A sign warned 'Danger! This road is dangerous to pedestrians on account of wild animals.' Soon we passed herds of buffalo, zebra, deer and antelope. In the distance, at the top of a tree-spotted mountain was a sparkling white castle. It was right out of a fairy tale. The sun poured down with theatrical brilliance on tons of white marble, white stone. There seemed to be thousands of marble statues, pedestals, urns. Hearst stood smiling at the top of one of the many flights of garden steps.
Cecil Beaton, DIARY 2 *Jan* 1931

9 George Oppenheimer was once invited for a weekend to the fabulous Hearst ranch in San Simeon, and his mother made him render a prompt and detailed report of the goings on. The morning after his arrival she received the following wire: 'Two things have happened to me already that never happened to me before. My car was stopped by a camel, and I fell downstairs in my own bedroom.'
Bennett Cerf, TRY AND STOP ME 1947

10 'I cannot understand,' said Bernard Shaw, 'why so many Americans shudder at the thought of Hearst. Doesn't he represent everything you worship most: success, power, fortune? Why don't you make him President?'
Ibid.

11 A visit to William Randolph Hearst's fabulous ranch at San Simeon, California usually provided the dazzled guests with dinner-table conversation for weeks. One important novelist tarried there recently and, searching for some writing paper, came across a document in Mr Hearst's own handwriting that had evidently been left in the desk by mistake. It was headed 'Shopping List', and the items on it ran as follows: 1 pair shoelaces, 1 croup kettle, 2 hippopotami.
Bennett Cerf, SHAKE WELL BEFORE USING 1948

12 Guests at San Simeon are supplied with a toxin against snake bite in case one of the

many reptiles that slither about the remoter parts of the ranch should bite them.
Prince Franz Joseph Hohenlohe, Sunday Express

1 The Hearst estate at San Simeon covers an area as large as Bedfordshire.
Ibid.

2 At the age of seventy-five he was bankrupt. Like other equally undeserving characters his financial position was restored by the war, and when he died in 1951 he left a fortune of many tens of millions of dollars.
Cecil Harmsworth King, Observer 29 *Apr* 1962

3 For 50 years he was the most powerful, and the most feared, man outside the White House.
David Sanders, Sunday Express 29 *Apr* 1962

4 In his eighties he became obsessively depressed over the passage of time. He tinkered with the idea of monkey-gland transplantation. He was furious when a slow lift wasted precious seconds of his life.
Ibid.

5 In a single hour he does everything from buying a Venetian palazzo to scrapping a dozen printing presses and remodelling the fashion pages of *Harper's Bazaar*.
World's Press News 18 *May* 1933

EDWARD (RICHARD GEORGE) HEATH

Born 1916. Conservative politician. Became leader of the party, 1965. Prime Minister 1970–4. Negotiated Britain's entry into EEC, 1974. Replaced as leader by Margaret Thatcher 1975.

6 Edward Heath is a very unusual man. He reminds me in some ways of those Olympic athletes who develop certain qualities of performance to a very high degree at the cost of a complete sacrifice of other qualities which other men possess. For instance he has clearly sublimated the normal man's sex drive to the point of being uninterested in women without any suggestion of its having been diverted into any improper or irregular direction.
John Boyd-Carpenter, WAY OF LIFE 1980

7 Heath came from a stratum close to hardship, where nevertheless good management as well as luck managed to fend off disaster. He was therefore less sympathetic to its victims.
Margaret Laing, EDWARD HEATH 1972

8 For all his professional *bonhomie* he does not make friends easily and some have been struck by his apparent awkwardness in company. He sometimes startles people by laughing unexpectedly and loudly at a trivial joke that amuses no one else.
Observer, Profile 18 *Oct* 1959

9 Part of Edward Heath's success is that he belongs to the middle class who have, slowly but steadily, taken over a party once exclusively controlled by the rich, the landed gentry and the aristocracy.
Ibid.

10 He has developed the worst case of sulks since Achilles refused to leave his tent to fight the Trojans.
The Sun 16 *Jan* 1985

ERNEST (MILLER) HEMINGWAY

Born 1899. American novelist. Among his best-known works are *Farewell to Arms*, 1929, *For Whom the Bell Tolls*, 1940 *The Old Man and the Sea*, 1952. Awarded Nobel Prize for Literature 1954. Died 1961.

11 He became a sort of crapulous Peter Pan. Arguments were settled, not in the normal manner, but with the fists, and it is pitiable to read of two renowned middle-aged men, Hemingway and Knapp, the publisher of Colliers, slugging it out on the deck of his yacht off Cuba.
Second Earl of Birkenhead, Daily Telegraph 25 *May* 1962

12 Surely no one since the days of the late Lord Desborough can have wrought such havoc in the animal world. He was mainly interested in the killing sports and would speak of the 'privilege' of death.
Ibid.

13 Hemingway saw life as a cruel but glorious game which you must win decently or lose with becoming courage — this was the era of prohibition, prosperity, rackets and gangsterdom in the United States.
Lord Boothby, RECOLLECTIONS OF A REBEL 1978

14 He is the bully of the Left Bank, always ready to twist the milksop's arm.
Cyril Connolly, Observer 24 *May* 1964

15 He is a literate who can't stand the company of other literates.
Martha Gellhorn. Quoted Joyce Grenfell, JOYCE GRENFELL REQUESTS THE PLEASURE 1976

1 Once Ernest had taken a dislike to a person he treated that person as a nurse might treat a fly that had accidentally entered a hospital room.
Leicester Hemingway, MY BROTHER, ERNEST HEMINGWAY 1962

2 His stories have the effect of the lifting of a stone — queer, ugly things revealed for a moment, scuttling away; managers of bullfights, negro cooks, American dilettantes, engaged in self-preservation, self-gratification, self-advantage.
Sylvia Lynd, reviewing MEN WITHOUT WOMEN, *John o' London's Weekly* 1927

3 The great exponent of physical courage as the supreme human quality had lacked the courage to go on living: the great believer in action as the supreme human fulfilment had taken the one action which puts an end to action for ever. The connoisseur of guns had chosen a gun for a special purpose of his own — to put a bullet through his own head; the amateur of the bull-ring had made a killing — of himself.
Malcolm Muggeridge, Observer 25 *Feb* 1968

4 In the Hotel Scribe, after the liberation of Paris in 1944, I caught a glimpse of Hemingway surrounded by admirers, and with several hand grenades tied absurdly to his person; rather drunk, as we all were, more or less. He made me think at once of Falstaff, but afterwards on reflection I realised this was unfair both to Falstaff and to him. He was an emanation, I decided, not so much of Falstaff as of Walt Whitman.
Ibid.

5 His novels are unlikely, in my opinion, to engage the attention of posterity, but his journalism — essays like 'The Prevention of Literature' and 'Politics vs Literature' — will surely always be read.
Ibid.

6 Hemingway, as I see it, destroyed himself, as our world is destroying itself, by excessive indulgence in fantasy and self-delusion by coming to believe in the ravings of his own ego as it strove with increasing hysteria and desperation to sustain itself against the ravages of flagging appetites and tired vanity.
Ibid.

7 His only good qualities seem to have been generosity with money and a rather meaningless kind of physical courage — courage for its own sake, or for the sake of admiration, rather than for the sake of others.
Philip Toynbee, Observer 28 *May* 1962

8 Hemingway's heroes are wounded because his view of life is a tragic stoical pessimism. It is the losing fight, or the fight carried on under some cruel disadvantage, that interests him. He sees life essentially as a losing battle.
John Wain, Observer 9 *Jul* 1961

KATHERINE HEPBURN

Born 1907. American stage and film actress.

9 She has a face that belongs to the sea and the wind, with large rocking-horse nostrils and teeth that you just know bite an apple every day.
Cecil Beaton, DIARIES

10 The famous Dorothy Parker critique of the young Hepburn — 'she runs the gamut of emotions from A to B' — suggests not only limited range but a nervy intensity that critics and colleagues might have found exhausting. Miss Hepburn says the remark was 'extremely accurate and funny'.
Mary Blume, The Times 28 *Apr* 1969

11 A passion for life, that is the thing about Katherine Hepburn. She adores every moment. She is always amazed.
Anthony Harvey director of The Lion in Winter, 1968

12 You see before you the result of a lifetime of chocolate.
Katherine Hepburn, of her addiction to chocolate

13 You could throw a hat at her, and wherever it hit, it would stick.
Robert Hopkins. Quoted Leslie Halliwell. A FILMGOER'S BOOK OF QUOTES 1976

14 She makes dialogue sound better than it is by a matchless clarity and beauty of diction, and by a fineness of intelligence and sensibility that illuminates every shade of meaning in every line she speaks.
Tennessee Williams

SIR A. P. (ALAN PATRICK) HERBERT

Born 1890. English author, novelist, journalist. As an MP campaigned for a reform of the divorce laws. Died 1971.

15 A. P. Herbert's maiden speech was a brazen hussy of a speech.
Winston Churchill. Quoted Geoffrey Madan, NOTEBOOKS 1981

1 A campaigner for diverse causes — including the reinstatement of Greenwich Mean Time, the provision of a barrage to make the Thames non-tidal above Woolwich; the retention of the gallon, the ton, and the Fahrenheit scale, the nautical mile, the fathom and Greek and Latin education; author's rights in lending libraries, the removal of literary censorship; and divorce law reform — to begin with.
John Hall, Radio Times 17 *Sep* 1970

2 In 1934 he swam the Thames from Waterloo to Westminster Bridge. Nearing Hungerford Bridge he heard the loud-hailer of a pleasure steamer inform the passengers: 'On the left is the Savoy Hotel and Cleopatra's Needle. The gentleman swimming in the water is Mr A. P. Herbert, the well-known novelist'. He waved his acknowledgement and almost sank.
Philip Oakes, Sunday Times 6 *Sep* 1970

3 He wrote the words to 'A Nice Cup of Tea' first sung by Binnie Hale and subsequently chosen for the Tea Council as its anthem for TV commercials.
Ibid.

RUDOLF HESS

Born 1894 in Egypt. German Nazi leader, appointed Hitler's deputy 1933. Flew to Scotland on a peace mission 1941. Imprisoned until the end of the war, and subsequently, at the Nuremberg trials, sentenced to imprisonment for life.

4 The flight to Scotland was about the most infantile as well as the most fantastic operation of the whole war. Hess and his adviser, Prof. Haushofer, picked the Duke of Hamilton on the strength of a chance pre-war meeting and in the belief that he would be 'dining every night with the King'.
Gordon Brook-Shepherd, Daily Telegraph 4 *May* 1962

5 He came to us of his own free will, and though without authority, had something of the quality of an envoy. He was a medical and not a criminal case, and should be so regarded.
Winston Churchill

6 As Churchill heard the duke's news that Hess had apparently landed in Scotland, incredulity showed for an instant on his round pink face. Then, almost thinking aloud, he said slowly, 'The worm is in the bud.'
James Leasor, RUDOLF HESS: THE UNINVITED ENVOY 1962

7 It is officially announced by the National Socialist Party that Party Member Rudolf Hess who, as he was suffering from an illness of some years, standing, had been strictly forbidden to embark on any further flying activity, was able, contrary to the command, again to come into possession of an aeroplane. On Saturday May 10 Rudolf Hess set out on a flight from Augsburg from which he has not so far returned.
Munich radio station 22 *May* 1941

SIR EDMUND HILLARY

Born 1919 in New Zealand. Mountaineer and explorer. With Tensing Norkay was the first to reach the summit of Everest, 1953. Made an overland expedition to the South Pole 1958.

8 George Lowe met us with a mug of soup just above the camp, and seeing his stalwart frame and cheerful face reminded me how fond of him I was. My comment was not specifically prepared for public consumption, but for George. 'Well, we knocked the bastard off' I told him and he nodded with pleasure. 'Thought you must have.'
Sir Edmund Hillary, NOTHING VENTURE, NOTHING WIN 1975

HEINRICH HIMMLER

Born 1900 in Germany. Joined Nazi party. Appointed head of the SS by Hitler in 1929, and of the Gestapo in 1936. Minister of the Interior 1943. Responsible for enforcing Hitler's extermination policies in concentration camps. Committed suicide, 1945.

9 It is his utter commonplaceness which is so staggering. Hitler could be off his head, Goering a half-crazy buccaneer, Goebbels nasty beyond anything. Himmler was dim, suffocatingly ordinary. He would have found it hard to keep his place as a junior master in a run-down school in a remote province.
Roger Manvell and Heinrich Fraenkel, HEINRICH HIMMLER 1965

10 Thirteen years ago Gregor Stresser sized up Himmler, wrongly. He said 'Our gentle Heinrich' was too shy to come to any good — by which he meant prominence in Tyranny. Yet Himmler rose to sinister

supremacy, and incidentally took part in the liquidation of his benefactor.
Lord Vansittart, Evening News 25 *May* 1945

1 Himmler looked more like a ferret than a wholesale *massacreur*.
Ibid.

2 He kept dossiers about everybody and everything. He was as pains-taking as pains-giving. His SS formations were well selected (so were their wives); his executions, or 'head-days' as he called them, were well organised; his stimulation of illegitimate breeding was methodical.
Ibid.

PAUL LUDWIG HANS ANTON VON BENECKENDORFF UND VON HINDENBURG

Born 1847 in Germany. Supreme commander of German Central Forces, 1916. Elected president of the German Reich 1925, re-elected 1932. Appointed chancellor by Hitler 1933. Died 1934.

3 It is a measure of Hindenburg's extraordinary career that at eighty-five there is not a responsible politician in Germany who can think without dismay of the prospect of his successor.
Robert Bernays, News Chronicle 1 *Oct* 1932

4 He dislikes Hitler and can hardly bear to be in the same room with him. When asked his opinion of Hitler after his first meeting with him Hindenburg replied: 'I know the type. They are like the Austrian rifles in the war; they do not shoot straight.' All his life he has viewed the world in the simple terms of the battlefield.
Ibid.

5 In 1916 the Germans made a wooden image of him, colossal, towering above mankind; and faithful admirers, by scores of thousands, paid their coins to the War Loan for the privilege of hammering a nail into the giant who stood for Germany against the world. In the agony of defeat the image was broken up for firewood. But the effect remained — a giant; slow-thinking, slow-moving, but sure, steady, faithful, warlike yet benignant, larger than the ordinary run of men.
Winston Churchill, GREAT CONTEMPORARIES 1937

6 In the last phase we see the aged President, having betrayed all the Germans who had re-elected him to power, joining reluctant and indeed contemptuous hands with the Nazi leader. There is a defence for all this and it must be made on behalf of President von Hindenburg. He had become senile. He did not understand what he was doing. He could not be held physically, mentally or morally responsible for the opening of the floodgates of evil upon German, and perhaps European, civilisation. We may be sure that the renowned veteran had no motive but love of his country, and that he did his best with declining mental strength to cope with problems never before presented to a ruler.
Ibid.

7 'The Captains and the Kings depart.' They did — in a great hurry. The Kaiser, the Kings, Princes, Grand Dukes, all the Generals ran away. All save one. Hindenburg did not run away. It was not his custom.
Daily Express, Obituary 3 *Aug* 1934

8 In 1925 they asked him to stand for President. He was, they said, the one man who could by his presence give the German people confidence when everything was collapsing round them. He addressed no meetings. But he was triumphantly elected. 'As God wills. Let me sleep another two hours' he said when they brought him the news.
Ibid.

9 He personifies Teuton tradition. Huge broad shoulders. Hanging arms. Ponderous features. Granite. Old soldier's moustache. A man sternly sculpt. Snowy hair. Snow on the grim Rhine castle. Legendary giant from the old Teutonic epics.
Passing Show 2 *Apr* 1932

ALFRED (JOSEPH) HITCHCOCK

Born 1899. British film director. Became famous for suspense thrillers, beginning with *Blackmail*, 1929. Others include *The Thirty-Nine Steps*, 1935, *The Lady Vanishes*, 1938, *Psycho*, 1960. Died 1980.

10 He had little reason for complaint: 'Even my failures make money and become classics a year after I make them.'
Leslie Halliwell, A FILMGOER'S BOOK OF QUOTES 1978

11 His little epigrams include, 'Drama is life with the dull bits left out', 'Always make the audience suffer as much as possible', 'There

is no terror in a bang, only in the anticipation of it', and 'Terror is a matter of surprise; suspense of forewarning'.
Ibid.

1 The suspense-master has obliged the press with a variety of *bon mots* about himself and his work. Personally I like best his story of how he caused consternation in a crowded elevator by muttering very audibly to a friend: 'I didn't think the old man would bleed so much.'
Ibid.

2 If I made *Cinderella* the audience would be looking out for a body in the coach.
Hitchcock

3 He did not go in for fancy cars, racehorses, yachts, or any of the other Hollywood accoutrements. He was very, very conservative and used to say, 'I never want to risk anything.'
His daughter Patricia. Quoted Peter Weymark, The Times 15 *Nov* 1983

4 The London Jesuits (by whom he was educated) probably helped to develop his fine sense of exquisite suspenseful torture of an audience. As a boy he used to have to write his name down in the book for punishment and wait around all day for the blows to fall.
Peter Lennon, Sunday Times 1 *Aug* 1971

5 He emerges as an innocent in politics. When he took out American citizenship he gave as a reason that he wanted to have 'the constitutional right to sound off acidly on all the ludicrousness around me in America'. It was just a schoolboy raspberry.
Ibid.

6 He is innocent in his jokes, God knows. He says ponderously to a new actress 'Genuine chopper.' 'Genuine chopper?' she repeats, bewildered. 'Real axe,' he says. 'Real axe?' she repeats. 'Say it quick.' 'Relax.' 'That's it dear,' he says, and stomps off (while you go around thumping your skull with your fists).
Ibid.

ADOLF HITLER

Born 1889, in Austria. German dictator, founded National Socialist Party, 1921. Became German Chancellor, January 1933, established dictatorship March 1933, created Third Reich, with himself as Führer, 1934. Committed suicide in his Berlin bunker, April 1945.

7 As I was wondering how it was possible that so great a country should be ruled by a man who uttered such platitudes as those with which he began our talk he suddenly started shouting. It was almost as though, like Joan of Arc, he heard voices coming out of the air. I imagine that a man in a trance might behave in much the same way, and while he was shouting I am convinced that I could have walked out of the room and he would not have noticed my departure.
Vernon Bartlett, THIS IS MY LIFE 1937

8 One can so easily understand how the millions of German unemployed or barely employed listen to the National-Socialist speeches. Hitler was going to defend the weak against the strong. He was going to destroy the capitalists who had replaced the worker by machinery in order to increase their own profit. He was going to put an end to the 'Kultur-Bolshevism' which had played hell with the nation's morals. There was, too, a genuine simplicity about the man which attracted thousands of people who were tired of the pompous display of wealth during the boom years.
Ibid.

9 Young Adolf was almost penniless in a great city. If that city had not been Vienna the present ruler of Germany would have been a very different man. In the first place there was in Vienna a tremendous contingent of Jews, and he made friends who lent him books — not always the most authoritative ones — about the Jewish race. It was in Vienna that he decided that 'by fighting against the Jews I am doing God's work'. And in the second place, he discovered the Austro-Hungarian Empire.
Ibid.

10 He had no sense of humour. He asked me how I would feel if Germany had won the last war, and driven a corridor between England and Scotland. 'You forget, Herr Hitler, I come from Scotland. We should have been delighted.' He did not smile. Instead he brought his fist down with a crash on the table, and said: 'So! I had no idea the hatred between the two peoples was so great.' Perhaps this was one of the reasons why he sent Hess to Scotland in 1940, for I am sure that he did; and why he never bombed Edinburgh.
Lord Boothby, RECOLLECTIONS OF A REBEL 1978

11 The way in which Hitler managed to impart his own hysteria to the vast audiences he addressed was not only miraculous but

terrifying. No wonder he had often to be carried out prostrate from his meetings.
Ibid.

1 I thank heaven for a man like Adolf Hitler, who built a front line of defence against the anti-Christ of Communism.
Frank Buchman, New York World, Telegram 25 *Aug* 1936

2 Speech was the essential medium of his power, not only over his audiences but over his own temperament. Hitler talked incessantly, often using words less to communicate his thoughts than to release the hidden spring of his own and others, emotions, whipping himself and his audience into anger or exaltation by the sound of his voice.
Alan Bullock, HITLER: A STUDY IN TYRANNY

3 The Pogroms in Germany and the persecutions there have roused much indignation everywhere. I must say Hitler never helps, and always makes Chamberlain's task more difficult.
Sir Henry Channon, DIARY 15 *Nov* 1938

4 It is said that Hitler is dead, but nobody now cares.
Ibid. 1 *May* 1945

5 The German dictator, instead of snatching the victuals from the table, has been content to have them served to him course by course.
Winston Churchill, House of Commons speech after Munich 5 *Oct* 1938

6 This wicked man Hitler, the repository and embodiment of many forms of soul-destroying hatred. This monstrous product of former wrongs and shame.
Winston Churchill, BBC broadcast 11 *Sep* 1940

7 His dark complexion had a fungoid quality and the famous hypnotic eyes that met mine seemed without life — dead colourless eyes. The silly mèche of hair I was prepared for. The smallness of his occiput was unexpected. His physique on the whole was ignoble.
Diana Cooper, AUTOBIOGRAPHY 1963

8 Our Constitution is the will of the Führer.
Hans Frank. Quoted Allan Bullock, HITLER

9 When Lord Boothby met Hitler in Berlin in 1932 the Nazi dictator suddenly leapt up, shot out his arm in the Fascist salute, and shouted 'Hitler'. Boothby clicked his heels together, smartly raised his own arm and yelled 'Boothby'.
Graham Lord, Sunday Express 15 *Oct* 1978

10 Hitler, a bilious ascetic, drank next to nothing and picked at his food like an anxious raccoon.
Robert Lewis Taylor, THE AMAZING MR CHURCHILL

SIR SAMUEL (JOHN GURNEY) HOARE, VISCOUNT TEMPLEWOOD

Born 1880. British politician. Secretary of State for Air 1922-9. Secretary of State for India 1931. As Foreign Secretary his pact with Laval proposing the dismemberment of Abyssinia created an uproar which led to his resignation. First Lord of the Admiralty, 1936. Appointed Home Secretary 1937. Died 1959.

11 He was stationed in Petrograd. On New year's Eve 1916 he heard the news that Rasputin had been murdered. His wife, Lady Maude Hoare, helped him code an urgent wire to London giving the news. It was the first news of the murder to reach western Europe. Actually, he was the first man apart from the murderers to know of the slaying.
Owen Blake, Sunday Referee 5 *Mar* 1939

12 As Secretary for India he piloted the India Bill through the House. It was an immense task. When he gave evidence before the Joint Select Committee on Indian Reforms he was in the witness chair for nineteen days and answered 15,000 questions.
Ibid.

13 He won a tango competition at a continental casino. It was during the Commons recess. He told Lord Baldwin about it who said: 'Thank God one member of the Cabinet has done something in the recess.'
Ibid.

14 He skates — to the delight of cartoonists and foreign critics who can talk glibly about thin ice. Every morning at 8.30 he leaves his home in Cadogan Square for half an hour on the ice, usually at the Queen's Ice Skating Club. He wears black tights and jacket with yellow gloves. Skating, he says 'has helped me throw off my arthritis'.
Ibid.

15 On 10 March 1939 Sir Samuel Hoare denounced those of us who were still clamouring for rearmament as 'jitterbugs'. 'These timid panic-mongers are doing the greatest harm,' he said. Of all the political pygmies, he was the pygmiest. The only things I remember him saying were 'Yees,

yees, yees' or 'Quaite quaite, quaite'. Four days after his speech the German tanks thundered into Prague.
Lord Boothby, RECOLLECTIONS OF A REBEL 1978

1 Sam Hoare is back at the Admiralty as First Lord. Six months ago he was ignominiously turned out. The Government simply bowed to public opinion and chucked him overboard. Events have now proved him a hundred times right, but he was discredited, humiliated and let down.
Sir Henry Channon, DIARY 1 *Jun* 1936

HERBERT (CLARK) HOOVER

Born 1874. American President, 1929–33. His period of office coincided with the Wall Street stock market collapse and the Great Depression. Died 1964.

2 It might be said that wherever and whenever Hoover has mystified people or been misunderstood by them nearly always it has been because he is an extremely plain man living in an extremely fancy age.
James B. Cox, Springfield Sun 10 *Aug* 1949

3 The phenomenal memory and the 'card-index' mind, these one would expect to find in him; but what of the pitiable picture of embarrassment that he presents when making one of his infrequent and ineffectual speeches? I believe him to be a bundle of nerves that are held in subjection by one of the strongest wills possessed by a living man.
Philip Hewitt-Myring, Daily News and Westminster Gazette 8 *Nov* 1928

4 During his six months in office he has only made three speeches and written three State papers of any length. Psychologists explain that the President is a visual thinker — that is to say he thinks not in words and phrases, as do most people, but in mental images. His brain has therefore an extra process to go through before his thoughts can be put on paper.
Morning Post 12 *Sep* 1929

5 I predict high things from Herbert Hoover's White House term; unexampled prosperity at home, and a policy of co-operation with Europe which may make the Fathers turn in their graves.
Ignatius Phayre, Morning Post 8 *Nov* 1928
(*Within months came the Wall Street Crash*)

6 In recent years Hoover had enjoyed something of a return to esteem and affection at home — though never again to real influence. He is remembered not only as the President of the Depression but for the magnificent relief work he did during and after the First World War and for his many years of public service. Then there was the brilliance of his earlier life as an engineer. This is the correct perspective. His career was more than the story of one great failure.
The Times, Obituary 31 *Oct* 1964

7 His habit of trying to restore confidence by statements of facile optimism did not help. To a good number of his compatriots at the time it seemed that he neither coped nor cared.
Ibid.

J. (JOHN) EDGAR HOOVER

Born 1895 in America, trained as a lawyer and became a clerk in the US Department of Justice. Became director of the department's Bureau of Investigation, 1924. Dedicated himself to reorganising it. In 1935 it was renamed the Federal Bureau of Investigation, and he remained its director until his death in 1972.

8 His only excesses flowed from his preoccupation with communism. A former agent once said that the party was so heavily infiltrated by FBI undercovermen that they outnumbered the actual communists. There was a strong suspicion that unwittingly the party dues of undercover men were a subsidy without which the party would have collapsed.
Louis Heren, The Times 3 *May* 1972

9 He has piercing black eyebrows, the brow of a scholar, the face of a prize-fighter and the build of a revolver barrel. He cleaned up America's scarlet carpet of crime so well that he ousted men like Al Capone and John Dillinger from being schoolboys' no. 1 heroes.
Percy Hoskins, Daily Express 5 *May* 1964

10 He has become a household word, a hero to millions of citizens and anathema to evil men.
President Lyndon Johnson 1964

11 Anything or anyone — likely to interrupt his pursuit of the 'Red menace' is in Hoover's eyes potentially subversive. For that reason Senator Joseph McCarthy had, during those tragic witch-hunting fifties, the ear of the FBI Director. The Bureau was deeply

involved in the worst of McCarthy's excesses, and the Senator could never have created the havoc he did without the eager assistance of the director.
Cal McCrystal, Sunday Times 12 *Jan* 1969

1 Hoover's voice comes rasping and staccato and without cadence — a sort of dalek voice. And when he speaks the unwavering brown eyes are the hardest points of all in what could otherwise be a rather cherubic face.
Ibid.

2 He has strict ideas of what the public image of an FBI agent should be. Agents remember this and nervously wipe their right hand on their trouser leg before being ushered in to see the director since he is known to have a horror of sticky palms.
Ian McDonald, The Times 18 *Jan* 1971

3 Every morning when Mr J. Edgar Hoover is driven down to his office he carefully props his hat in the car window opposite his seat. The idea, a former agent explains, is that if any would-be assassin should lurk behind one of the Department of Justice's marble columns he would aim at the familiar grey hat instead of its owner.
Ibid.

4 The need for information has dominated Mr Hoover's career and he counts it as one of his most lasting achievements that he has collected the fingerprints of more than 80 million Americans.
Ibid.

A. E. (ALFRED EDWARD) HOUSMAN

Born 1859. English poet. Established his reputation with *A Shropshire Lad*, 1898. Died 1936.

5 Housman is a common little soul, who thinks that the don-epicure is a gentlemanly thing — it is not; it's the worst development of snobbish greediness.
A. C. Benson, DIARIES

6 A prim, old-maidish, rather second-rate, rather tired, rather querulous person.
Ibid.

7 Housman's cap, like a damp bun or pad of waste which engine-drivers clean their hands on.
A. C. Benson. Quoted Geoffrey Madan, NOTEBOOKS 1981

8 To read both volumes of Mr A. E. Housman's verse (*A Shropshire Lad* and *Last Poems*) would take but an hour or so. But it is a walk through the world — and beyond.
Ivor Brown

9 That sad, compassionate, romantic, loving man.
Richard Perceval Graves, A. E. HOUSMAN: THE SCHOLAR POET 1979

10 On occasions, after drinking a pint of beer at luncheon there would be a flow into my mind, with sudden and unaccountable emotion, sometimes a line or two of verse, sometimes a whole stanza at once, accompanied, not preceded, by a vague notion of the poem which they were destined to form a part of. Then there would usually be a lull of an hour or so, then perhaps the spring would bubble up again. I say bubble up because, so far as I could make out, the source of the suggestions thus proffered to the brain was the pit of the stomach.
A. E. Housman, lecture at Cambridge 1933

11 Of the reputation which his poems won for him he wrote recently to an American correspondent, 'Though it gives me no lively pleasure, it is something like a mattress interposed between me and the hard ground.' Those words were written when life was ceasing to have any comfort for him.
Laurence Housman, MEMORIES OF A. E. HOUSMAN 1936

12 At some Cambridge Feast where speeches were not expected, but where the fare and wine had been good, Alfred was seen to rise slowly to his feet, and to the astonished delight of his audience spoke as follows: 'There were two things which it was difficult to find in Cambridge a hundred and twenty years ago; the one was Wordsworth drunk, the other was Porson sober. I am a better scholar than Wordsworth; I am a better poet than Porson; here I stand half-way between Wordsworth and Porson.' And he sat down again.
Ibid.

13 Visit to Max Beerbohm at Rapallo. A. E. Housman like an absconding cashier. We certainly wished he would abscond. Sitting silent, then saying only, 'There's a bit of a nip in the air tonight, don't you think?'
Geoffrey Madan, NOTEBOOKS 21 *Jan* 1929

14 He was difficult to engage in conversation. 'Can you get him to talk?' Robert Bridges

once asked me in despair. 'I can't.' Housman was not taciturn because he had nothing to say but because his first and last characteristic was inscrutability — a buried life that he was determined to keep buried.
Percy Withers, A BURIED LIFE 1940

1 He scorned limited editions, having no feeling for printing or book production as a fine art. All he asked of a book was that the type should be easy to read, and the price as low as possible.
Ibid.

2 Housman cared nothing for pictorial art. Year after year he spent a holiday in Italy but he ignored its artistic treasures. I never once heard him mention Florence, its paintings or its sculptures, though I believe he did pay it one visit.
Ibid.

SIR GEOFFREY HOWE

Born 1926 in Wales. British politician. Elected Conservative MP for Bebington 1964. Lost the seat 1966, and was subsequently returned for Reigate. Appointed Chancellor of the Exchequer in Margaret Thatcher's Cabinet 1979. Foreign Secretary 1984.

3 Being attacked by him is like being savaged by a dead sheep.
Denis Healey Dec 1978

4 I enjoyed the famous incident when he lost his trousers on the train. I thought that one of the funniest remarks came from a colleague who said 'I am thrilled about the loss of your trousers because it revealed your human face.'
Elspeth Howe. Quoted Observer 12 *Jan* 1984

5 He lacks only two qualities; a wider political vision to inspire people, and the remotest ability to judge the House of Commons.
Observer, Profile 12 *Feb* 1984

6 Richard Crossman dealt with him and was impressed; 'He is an elegant young man, good looking, sharp and keen, an enormously ambitious Tory lawyer.' (He has put on much weight since; his Treasury nickname was Fat Geoff.)
Ibid.

7 The patient Fabian of Thatcherism.
Peter Riddell, THE THATCHER GOVERNMENT 1984

HOWARD (ROBARD) HUGHES

Born 1905. American industrialist, film-maker, aviator, inventor, property and casino owner. In later life became a highly eccentric recluse, breaking his seclusion only once (in 1972) to denounce, and prevent the publication of, a hoax autobiography. Died 1976.

8 Right after Mr Hughes appeared in Las Vegas I began getting calls that he'd like the station to stay open a little longer because he liked to watch television between midnight and six o'clock in the morning and we went off the air at one o'clock. Then they wanted to know if we'd put on Westerns, or airplane pictures. I'd get calls from Hughes aides to change the format so that Hughes could watch it all night long. Finally I said in exasperation, 'Why doesn't he buy the damn thing and run it the way he pleases?' He did, without a quibble, for 3.65 million dollars.
Hank Greenspun, proprietor of TV station KLAS–TV. Quoted Elain Davenport and Paul Eddy, THE HUGHES PAPERS 1977

9 Hughes was the only man I ever knew who had to die to prove he had been alive.
Walter Kane. Quoted J. Phelan, HOWARD HUGHES: THE HIDDEN YEARS

10 As a Hollywood film producer early in his career he had introduced Jean Harlow in *Hell's Angels* and designed the brassière that made Jane Russell's bust famous.
Michael Knipe, The Times 12 *Dec* 1970

11 Irving Thalberg asked Jean Harlow, 'How did you make out with Howard Hughes?' 'Well, one day he was eating a cookie and he offered me a bite.' When we all laughed Jean interrupted 'Don't underestimate that. The poor guy's so frightened of germs it could darned near have been a proposal.'
Anita Loos, KISS HOLLYWOOD GOODBYE

12 When Howard Hughes sold his 77 per cent holding in Trans-World Airline in May 1966 for 546,594,771 dollars the question was, what was he going to do with all that money? One Wall Street financier said 'I hope he changes it into pennies and drops it on his foot.'
Raymond Palmer, Observer 10 *Mar* 1968

13 He has been successively, and sometimes simultaneously, a record-breaking pilot, movie producer and tycoon, playboy, aircraft designer, inventor, business man, airline operator, escort to some of the most desirable women in the world, and once, for two months under an assumed name, an air-line co-pilot.
Ibid. 17 *Mar* 1968

ALDOUS (LEONARD) HUXLEY

Born 1894, son of the biologist T. E. Huxley. English novelist and essayist. His works include *Point Counter Point*, 1928, *Brave New World*, 1932, *Eyeless in Gaza*, 1936. Died 1963.

1 From the beginning of his career he had been haunted and oppressed by his sense of the world as being, in MacNeice's phrase, 'incorrigibly plural'. The contrast, the irreconcilable conflict, between the idealisations of art and religion and human aspirations on the one hand, and the animal physiological actualities of human existence on the other was the theme of Huxley's work from start to finish.
Walter Allen, Daily Telegraph 17 *Jul* 1969

2 I met Aldous Huxley slinking out of a bank, as if he was afraid to be seen emerging from a capitalist institution, from where he had doubtless drawn large sums.
Sir Henry Channon, DIARY 16 *Dec* 1935

3 Along with many scientists he considered the discovery of psychedelics one of the three major scientific break-throughs of the twentieth century, the other two being the splitting of the atom and the manipulation of gentic structures.
Laura Huxley, THE TIMELESS MOMENT 1969

4 Fastidiousness was a handicap. Not only did the human race still appear stupid to him, but now mean and dirty as well. He found himself becoming a sort of Nietzsche upside-down standing on the dignity of the perpetual outsider, and he liked it less and less.
Observer, Profile 27 *Feb* 1949

5 He decided that he could teach the world how to put its house in order, but at the same time he found he could not support the spectacle of Europe falling again into ruins and moved to California in the spirit of the prophet withdrawing into the wilderness.
Ibid.

6 Like a piece of litmus paper he has always been quick to take the colour of his times.
Ibid.

7 As a young man, although he was always friendly, his silences seemed to stretch for miles, extinguishing life, when they occurred, as a snuffer extinguishes a candle.
Edith Sitwell, TAKEN CARE OF

8 His interests are multifarious. He is the only man I ever heard of (my informant was his brother Julian so I assume the story to be well founded) who, on setting out to go round the world, caused a special packing case to be made for his *Encyclopedia Britannica*.
Frank Swinnerton, THE GEORGIAN LITERARY SCENE 1935

9 He can tell a story when he wishes to do so (it is usually a short story); but he is a man who uses the fiction form as a vehicle for his ideas, and not a man who writes novels because he must do so or remain sterile.
Ibid.

10 His great height has given some of those who encountered him the impression that he lives remote from the world, wrapped in distant hauteur. This is not the case. He uses long words because he thinks in long words; and not because he is aware they are long words.
Ibid.

11 Aldous Huxley, if anyone, might have been expected to go with the times. Combining literary sophistication and scientific descent of the greatest distinction, he was a walking reconciliation between art and science. Somehow the reconciliation failed to work, or Huxley failed to provide it. He turned against both and retired to a life of contemplation in California.
A. J. P. Taylor, ENGLISH HISTORY 1914–1945 1956

I

IBN SAUD

Born 1880 in exile. Full name Abdul Aziz ibn Abdul Rahman ibn Feisal ibn Saud. Grandson of the deposed sultan of Nejd. By defeating his rival Husein ibn Ali and annexing Hejaz in 1924 he united the two territories to form the kingdom of Saudi Arabia. Died 1953.

1 Ibn Saud expressed surprise to Belhaven, a member of the British Mission, that in enlightened England adultery should go unpunished, whereas in the desert the punishment was death by stoning. Belhaven, piqued, retaliated, 'How many women have you had?' 'I have four wives, as the prophet allows,' replied Ibn Saud. 'But how many have you had and how many have you divorced?' 'I have married and divorced a hundred, and if God wills I shall marry and divorce many more.'
H. G. Armstrong, LORD OF ARABIA 1934

2 The American destroyer *Murphy* was sent to Jidda to pick up Ibn Saud. The king found it hard to imagine travelling with fewer than 200 people in attendance and the Americans had the greatest difficulty persuading his advisers that a harem would be an inconvenience aboard a destroyer . . . At the last minute a dhow came alongside to deliver eighty-six live sheep; the King was so used to feeding everybody that he assumed he would feed the crew.
David Howarth, THE DESERT KING 1964

3 With the exception of a railway from the Persian Gulf to Riyadh and a good many water wells Ibn Saud spent hardly any money on anything that might be classified as public works. It seemed never to occur to him that his overflowing wealth laid any duty on him to give his people the amenities they lacked, a medical service, schools, sanitation, roads and public transport, or any kind of insurance less whimsical than his personal bounty.
Ibid.

4 When oil was found in Saudi Arabia King Ibn Saud became the richest man in the world, with the possible exception of the Sheik of Kuwait. By the end of his life he was receiving well over a million pounds a week, and every week the payments grew bigger.
Ibid.

5 When Churchill heard Roosevelt promise Ibn Saud the gift of an aircraft Churchill promised him 'the best car ever made'. A suitable vehicle was found — no easy task in 1945 when luxury cars were not being manufactured in Britain. The King was delighted until he saw that the car had a right-hand drive. This would have meant him sitting on the left of his driver when he went out hunting in it; an intolerable lowering of prestige. He gave the car to his brother.
Ibid.

6 American oil men, when they reported thefts, were horrified to see their employees returning without hands.
Ibid.

W. R. (WILLIAM RALPH) INGE

Born 1860. English churchman and writer on religious and social topics. Dean of St Paul's Cathedral 1911–34. His writing earned him the nickname 'The Gloomy Dean'. Died 1954.

7 After his retirement from the Deanery he became a regular contributor to a London journal and told us, with a chuckle, of the critical comment that he had ceased to be a pillar of the Church and had become two columns in the *Evening Standard*.
Alfred Noyes, TWO WORLDS FOR MEMORY 1953

8 Dean Inge was delighted by an angry letter he received from a lady who disagreed with one of his articles. 'I am praying nightly for your death,' she wrote. 'It may interest you to know that in two other cases I have had great success.'
Ibid.

9 A luncheon at the Holborn Restaurant, given by Willie Foyle and his pretty daughter, Christina, as an aid to getting his bookshop talked about. Dean Inge made a dull, catarrhal speech, standing with a piece

of paper cupped in his hand, held before him, lectern-wise.
Reginald Pound, THEIR MOODS AND MINE 1937

EUGENE IONESCO

Born 1912 in Romania. French playwright, an exponent of the Theatre of the Absurd in works such as *Rhinoceros*, 1969.

1 'Thank you so much for watching my film. The English are so polite. In Paris they walked out after ten minutes,' said Ionesco after his first film *La Vase* had been shown at Oxford . . . After a series of close-ups of rotting substances it was a relief to see Ionesco himself, covered in white paint, lying dead in a river, a latter-day Orpheus, his dismembered limbs decomposing . . . the audience of dons, émigré Frenchmen and undergraduates trickled out of the cinema, some bemused, some smiling.
Melinda Camber, The Times 12 *Feb* 1974

2 I am in the position of someone who hopes to win first prize in a lottery without having bought a ticket.
Eugene Ionesco, FRAGMENTS OF A JOURNAL 1968

3 Apart from the oblivion achieved through alcohol, he seems to have known only two forms of happiness, the bliss he experienced during childhood in the French countryside and very rare moments in adult life in the waking state or in dreams, when the world appears to be flooded with light and, for no reason at all, a fleeting sensation of delight occurs.
John Weightman, Observer 24 *Mar* 1968

4 I think he is an extreme example of that common modern type, the religious temperament divorced from any religious conviction.
Ibid.

5 He is someone with a permanently exposed metaphysical nerve, which can be seen to throb during the most casual conversation. He is the sort of funny man who cannot be other than deadly serious.
Ibid.

CHRISTOPHER (WILLIAM BRADSHAW) ISHERWOOD

Born 1904. English novelist and, in collaboration with W. H. Auden, playwright. Novels include *Mr Norris Changes Trains*, 1935 and *Goodbye to Berlin*, 1939. Died 1986.

6 That photograph of 1931 is unforgettable . . . little Christopher Isherwood, neat features, well-brushed hair, the smile of a dirty-minded cherub.
Anon., Observer 26 *Feb* 1984

7 In many ways Isherwood is an ordinary person who does not try to be extraordinary. As a writer 'he never goes butterfly-hunting for a fine phrase' as Evelyn Waugh (who sometimes did) pointed out.
Michael Davie, Observer Magazine 12 *Aug* 1984

J

JOHN RUSHWORTH JELLICOE, FIRST EARL JELLICOE

Born 1859. British admiral. Commanded the Grand Fleet, 1914–16, notably at the Battle of Jutland 1916. First Sea Lord 1916–17. Governor-general of New Zealand 1920–4. Died 1935.

1 Jellicoe has a nutcracker mouth. He will crunch the German Fleet.
Admiral Fisher. Quoted Lord Riddell, John o' London's Weekly 26 *Oct* 1929

2 I once heard Lord Jellicoe say that people who saw him in mufti for the first time wondered whether he was a lawyer or a parson.
Edward Marsh, A NUMBER OF PEOPLE 1939

ROY (HARRIS) JENKINS

Born 1921 in Wales. British politician. Elected Labour MP for Central Southwark 1948. Chancellor of the Exchequer 1967–70. Home Secretary 1974–6. Resigned to become President of the European Commission 1977–81. Joined the Social Democratic Party 1981. Elected member for Hillhead 1982.

3 My private tête-à-tête with Roy took place over lunch at No. 11. Why do I always feel constrained at these private talks? Perhaps because Roy is always so deferential and friendly and I fear the snare is a silken one.
Barbara Castle, DIARY 1964–70 1984

4 When George Blake escaped from prison Harold Wilson said 'That will do our Home Secretary a great deal of good. He was getting too complacent and he needs taking down a peg'.
Richard Crossman, DIARY 1966

5 As a debater he was devastating, one of the best of the post-war era, even though over-given to taking his glasses on and off for rhetorical effect . . . He consistently annihilated Iain Macleod at the dispatch box and Macleod never forgave him.
Alan Watkins, Observer 15 *Jun* 1980

6 All that was required of Jenkins was a few trips round the tea room; a discreet word here, a small joke there, a kindly enquiry somewhere else. If he had followed this course instead of remaining aloof (so the theory goes) he would be Leader of the Labour Party today. According to this view Jenkins was like a Conservative who resolutely refused to wear either his Old Etonian or his Brigade tie. He wantonly threw away his greatest natural assets.
Ibid.

C. E. M. (CYRIL EDWIN MITCHINSON) JOAD

Born 1891. English philosopher, author and broadcaster. Founder member of the BBC's Brains Trust. Died 1953.

7 Joad was not above coining a catch-phrase. His expression 'It all depends on what you mean' became a popular by-word. *Punch* published a cartoon showing him saying to a waiter wanting to serve him some soup 'It all depends on what you mean by (a) thick and (b) clear.'
Fenton Bresler, Sunday Express 19 *Sep* 1971

8 'My religion,' he declares, 'was a very drastic kind. I held, you must take the Bible literally or not at all. I took it literally, insisted on the reality of Hell and preached terrifying sermons about unbaptised babies frying in their own blood.' Most people will agree that it was a lucky day for Christianity in England when Mr Joad gave it up.
Robert Lynd, News Chronicle 20 *May* 1932

9 He has acquired notoriety instead of fame; he knows that he is popular, and as such a slightly comic figure. He wishes he had acquired either the cloistered dignity of a scholar and philosopher or the arena victories of the politician. He has no domestic background. He has quarrelled with his son; his daughters have married; his wife has left him. He is famous and alone.
Harold Nicolson, DIARY 9 *May* 1947

AUGUSTUS (EDWIN) JOHN

Born 1878. Welsh artist, painter of portraits of notable people of the day, among them Bernard Shaw and Thomas Hardy. Died 1961.

1 Augustus is great and grand, like a figure in the Old Testament. He has completely the manner of an artist. He can be lustful and he can drink to excess, but he never uses bad language. He is a gipsy but he is also a great gentleman.
Cecil Beaton, DIARY *Jun* 1960

2 Went to 33 Tite Street and sat for Augustus John. The drunken old Druid was gracious; he is like some great force of nature, so powerful, immense and energetic. We made friends at once, and he drew me, or rather, my head.
Sir Henry Channon, DIARY 8 *Mar* 1944

3 Augustus still looks like a major prophet and his eyes sparkle with amusement and intelligence until he becomes be-fuddled, as he eventually always does, by drink.
Ibid.

4 Early in life Augustus turned his back on respectability. He started as an anarchist but ended as a supporter of Mr Harold Wilson.
Romilly John, SEVENTH CHILD 1975

5 I often passed him in the King's Road without receiving a flicker of recognition. Looking neither to right nor left he would stride on towards the Six Bells in his wide-brimmed hat.
Ibid.

6 Not all his sitters have liked their portraits. Lord Leverhulme was so discontented with his that he decided to hide it in a steel safe. To get it in the safe he cut out the head. The rest of the picture was sent back. John publicly protested against this murder of a work of art. Leverhulme retorted that he'd paid for the picture and could do what he liked with it. He sent John a postcard. 'Yah! Beaver! Leverhulme.' Far from resenting the gibe at his tawny-red beard John was so tickled that he invited the Soap King to a dinner of reconciliation.
Sunday Referee 2 *Apr* 1939

7 Romilly John is the seventh child of Augustus John, although no one can guarantee absolute precision when it comes to the number of children the famous painter actually fathered.
Sunday Times, John's relative values 29 *Jul* 1984

8 There was one student at the Slade who didn't care for me very much (he objected to my wearing a top hat, which I did on occasions) but I didn't care much for him either, because of his pose of Bohemianism. Also, I thought him conceited. He undoubtedly drew well, but I did not think that any excuse for his writing at the top of one of his most successful drawings: 'There was a man sent from God whose name was John'. *His* name was John: Augustus John.
Ernest Thesiger, PRACTICALLY TRUE 1927

POPE JOHN XXIII

Born 1881. Italian cardinal, Angelo Giuseppe Roncalli. Elected Pope 1958. Advocate of reform and reconciliation. Promoted the Second Vatican Council 1962. Died 1963.

9 He outraged his domestic staff by asking his gardener to lunch with him. Popes are supposed to eat alone — but when this one did he lost his appetite.
Geoffrey Ashe, Sunday Express 2 *Jun* 1963

10 He was not a great scholar or diplomat. He was just a loving shepherd.
Cardinal John Heenan, Sunday Times 2 *Jun* 1963

POPE JOHN PAUL II

Born 1920 in Poland. Karol Wojtyla. Elected Pope 1978.

11 The young Wojtyla seems to have left an indelible impression on the minds of his schoolfellows. Most of all are they proud of his skill as actor. They recall the time when a visiting director told him 'One day you will be a great actor.' There was no school production in which he did not take part, and it was usually the leading part.
Mary Craig, Sunday Telegraph 7 *Jan* 1979

12 He was, and still is, inclined to see Western Europe as too permissive, too much engrossed in materialism and the consumer society. There can be no doubt that he looks on Communist societies, with all their glaring faults, which he experienced at first hand, as better societies for the spiritual well-being of their people.
Peter Nichols, The Times 28 *May* 1982

13 Karol Wojtyla is a philosopher, a disciple of the personalist Max Scholer; he is a mystic and a solitary, a student of St John of the Cross; he is a moral theologian and that most

unpapal thing, a poet who has actually published his verse.
Norman St John Stevas, Observer 6 *May* 1979

1 Nuns in Rome are a notoriously fierce breed, but this must be the first time a tribe of them have pulled every button off the papal cassock, and one is said to have tried to bite his ear.
Ibid.

2 A pop Pope for our time.
Ibid.

LYNDON (BAINES) JOHNSON

Born 1908. American politician. Became president of the United States on the assassination of Kennedy in 1963. Re-elected for a further term, his administration encountered the difficulties and unpopularities of the Vietnam War, and he was defeated by Richard Nixon in 1969. Died 1973.

3 Mr Johnson's ebullience sometimes got him into trouble. Dog lovers protested when he appeared in a photograph lifting up his pet beagles by their ears. He claimed the dogs enjoyed it. 'My mother used to pull my ears,' he said, 'and it never did get that much attention.'
Daily Telegraph, Obituary 24 *Jan* 1973

4 Face-saving, the President observed, was not his major purpose in life. 'While you're trying to save your face,' he declared, 'you're losing your ass.'
Philip L. Geyelin, LYNDON B. JOHNSON AND THE WORLD

5 He is, as someone has said, 'a back-slapper, a shoulder-hugger, a knee-squeezer', and he himself confesses he likes to be in the closest possible physical contact with a man when he talks to him. When this proximity is established Johnson is apt to straighten his visitor's tie for him if this seems necessary.
Observer, Profile 24 *Nov* 1963

6 At times he could be the epitome of earthy Americanism, slapping backs, squeezing elbows, pumping hands and uttering the corniest social platitudes with devastating sincerity. In this mood he could seem very much the country boy grown rich. In the upper reaches of diplomatic and international life he could be out of his depth and often embarrassing.
The Times, Obituary 24 *Jan* 1973

7 Johnson was never comfortable with intellectuals, and used to delight in making fellow politicians swim 'bare-assed' naked in his pool.
TV Times 20 *Oct* 1984

8 Lyndon Johnson fortifies the proposition that many men without brilliant gifts would be satisfactory as presidents or prime ministers, and that the spectacular are no more fitted for the rôle than the humdrum.
Woodrow Wyatt, Observer 23 *Jan* 1972

AL JOLSON

Born 1886 in Russia. Stage name of Asa Yoelson. American singer and film actor. Famous for having appeared in the first sound film, *The Jazz Singer*, 1927. Died 1950.

9 Al Jolson was known to bound on to the stage when his show was half way over and say 'Well, I'll tell you how the story comes out: The fellow gets the girl. Now shall we go on with it or do you want to hear me sing?' And he wouldn't go on with it, he would just sing for the rest of the night.
Joe Adamson, GROUCHO, HARPO, CHICO AND SOMETIMES ZEPPO 1973

10 Born in Russia, he sang of Dixie and a Swanee River he never saw until he was 40. He once said 'I've got so much dough that fourteen guys couldn't spend it in their lifetimes. But I'd rather die than quit this business.'
Michael Freedland, JOLSON

11 There were six spoken words in *The Jazz Singer* (1927) which found their way on to the sound track by the sheerest chance. Jolson had not been expected to speak, but before going into his song he said: 'Come on Ma, listen to this'. When the words were heard on the play-back it was decided to leave them in.
Geoffrey Lake, Evening News 4 *Oct* 1950

SIR KEITH JOSEPH

Born 1918. British politician. Elected Conservative MP for Leeds North-East 1966. Appointed Secretary of State for Education and Science, 1981.

12 Keith Joseph? A mixture of Rasputin and Tommy Cooper.
Denis Healey. Quoted John Mortimer, IN CHARACTER 1983

13 Joseph has little truck with the classless society. He once remarked privately 'We

liberated the proletariat, but they've let us down.' By this he meant that they continued to watch TV and read *The Sun* instead of going to the opera.
Observer, Profile 9 *Dec* 1984

JAMES JOYCE

Born 1882. Irish novelist poet and critic who wrote in his own eccentric and surrealist style and language. His most famous work, *Ulysses*, began serial publication in the American *Little Review* in 1918, but had to be suspended when the magazine was prosecuted. Died 1941.

1 It would be silly to pretend that *Ulysses* is not a difficult book, but over the years a web of criticism, exegesis and explication has been woven around it that can have the effect of making it appear more inaccessible than it really is. At times it seems like one of those cathedrals that cannot be properly viewed because of the network of scaffolding that seems permanently to surround them.
Walter Allen, Daily Telegraph

2 I was both disqualified and castigated when, in a school essay competition, I declared that James Joyce's *Ulysses* was my favourite book. Disqualified because the book, being banned, did not officially exist; castigated for dirty mindedness.
Anthony Burgess, Observer Magazine 20 *May* 1974

3 When Joyce produced *Ulysses* it was promptly banned except in Paris. This, to the bourgeoisie, confirmed the equation of art and dirt.
Anthony Burgess, Observer 31 *Jan* 1982

4 To underscore the pervasive recognition of physical life in his book each chapter was allotted an organ of the body. The episodes also have their own colours, arts and symbols.
Richard Ellmann, Preface to Penguin edition of ULYSSES 1969

5 I've put in so many enigmas and puzzles that it will keep the professors busy for centuries over what I mean, and that's the only way of ensuring one's immortality.
James Joyce. Quoted Robert H. Denning, JAMES JOYCE: THE CRITICAL HERITAGE

6 Joyce's ultimate works are like a man who is too shy to write a love-letter except in the form of a crossword puzzle.
Constant Lambert, MUSIC HO!

7 The fact is that Joyce cannot be regarded as a very nice man. He was egotistical, envious, disloyal, untrustworthy, quarrelsome and a great physical coward (moral courage he possessed in a high degree). His drunkenness and lack of scruple about money somehow never lent him the charm those characteristics sometimes bring; just as his obscenity lacks all Rabelaisian joy in life.
Anthony Powell, Daily Telegraph 30 *Oct* 1959

8 *Ulysses* is written by a man with a diseased mind and a soul so black that he would even obscure the darkness of hell.
Senator Reed Smoot

9 I put the manuscript of *Ulysses* in the drawer of an inlaid cabinet. One day Katherine Mansfield came and I had it out. She began to read, ridiculing; then suddenly said, 'But there's something in this'; a scene that should figure, I suppose, in the history of literature.
Virginia Woolf, DIARY (*Ulysses was rejected by the Woolfs' Hogarth Press*)

K

FRANZ KAFKA

Born 1883 in Prague. German author whose works include *The Trial*, 1925 and *The Castle*, 1926. The bulk of his work was not published until after his early death from tuberculosis in 1924.

1 The world at large does not have to know about Franz. He is nobody else's business because, well, because nobody could possibly understand him.
Dora Diamant. Quoted Ernst Pawel, THE NIGHTMARE OF REASON 1984

2 Kafka was a tough, neurasthenic unetiolated visionary who lived from the inside out, spinning his writing out of his guts.
D. J. Enright, Observer, The Man Within 5 *Aug* 1984

3 I've often thought that the best way of life for me would be to have writing materials and a lamp in the innermost room of a spacious locked cellar. Food would be brought and put down a long way from my room. My only exercise would be a walk wearing my dressing gown, through the vaulted cellar — But what I'd write! What depths I'd tear it up from.
Kafka, letter to Felice Bauer Jan 1913

4 One day he wrote in his diary 'Hysteria making me surprisingly and unaccountably happy'. He was often like that in his life.
Derwent May, Radio Times 27 *Nov* 1982

5 Kafka seems to have written for no one but himself; the desire for fame, or even recognition, or even minimal communication, appears to have played little part in his obsession.
Philip Toynbee, Observer 25 *Jan* 1981

KENNETH (DAVID) KAUNDA

Born 1924. Zambian politician. Founded the United National Independence Party, which opposed the inclusion of Northern Rhodesia in a federation with Southern Rhodesia and Nyasaland. With the granting of independence to Northern Rhodesia, renamed Zambia, in 1964, he was elected president.

6 Music has always ranked high with Kaunda. He has used it as a method of spreading his message ever since he was a young teacher in what was then called Northern Rhodesia. In his spare time he would bicycle around the villages with a guitar slung over his back, stopping to sing political songs — often his own compositions — interspersed with hymns.
Observer, Profile 20 *Mar* 1983

7 One of the memorable social moments at the 1979 Commonwealth Conference in Lusaka came when Kaunda, in a white dinner jacket, took Mrs Thatcher on to the dance floor for a foxtrot. She allowed herself to be led around in a most demure fashion.
Ibid.

SIR GERALD (FESTUS) KELLY

Born 1879. British portrait painter. Elected President of the Royal Academy 1949. Died 1972.

8 He made a last desperate coup to persuade the world that he was an artist by marrying a model. But this device deceived nobody. The evidence of his pictures was too glaring.
Aleister Crowley (Kelly's brother-in-law), CONFESSIONS

9 He is described in the telephone book as an artist; and the statement might have passed unchallenged indefinitely had not the Royal Academy recently elected him an associate. He is hardly to be blamed for this disgrace. He struggles manfully.
Ibid.

JOHN F. (FITZGERALD) KENNEDY

Born 1917. American politician. Elected president 1961. Confronted Soviet Union over the attempted siting of nuclear

weapons in Cuba. Assassinated in Dallas 1963.

1 His speaking style is pseudo-Roman: 'Ask not what your country can do for you . . .' Why not say 'Don't ask'? 'Ask not' is the style of a man playing at the role of being President, not of a man being President.
Herb Gold, New York Post 1 *Jun* 1962

2 Mrs Kennedy could never quite get over the feeling that most of her husband's associates (including, initially, her in-laws) were uncouth to the point of being coarse.
Anthony Howard, Observer, The glittering prize 28 *Jan* 1979

3 He was the first president since F.D.R. with anything to say to the young.
Arthur Schlesinger Jr, Observer, The Kennedy legend 20 *Nov* 1983

4 In some ways John Fizgerald Kennedy died just in time. He died in time to be remembered as he would like to be remembered, as ever young, still victorious, struck down undefeated. For somehow one feels that in the tangled dramaturgy of events this sudden assassination was the only way out. The Kennedy Administration was approaching an impasse, certainly at home, quite possibly abroad, from which there seemed no escape.
I. F. Stone, THE BEST OF I. F. STONE

JEROME (DAVID) KERN

Born 1885. American composer of about fifty musical-comedy scores. His first hit was *They Didn't Believe Me*. His *Last Time I Saw Paris* won an Academy Award in 1940. Died 1945.

5 Genius takes many shapes and colours. You have genius of one sort in Jerome Kern. Why deny it?
John Barbirolli, Observer 8 *Jul* 1947

6 He was filled with melody, and kept a bust of Wagner on his piano; 'When it smiles,' he said, 'I know the melody is right.'
Lord Boothby, RECOLLECTIONS OF A REBEL 1978

7 A small, amicable, quiet man, with tremendous stores of nervous energy, Kern wore horn-rimmed glasses, smoked constantly, poured forth hundreds of facile tunes with a radio blaring in his ears, and modestly called himself a dull fellow with little talent and lots of luck.
Wesley Towner. Quoted Max Wilk, THEY'RE PLAYING OUR TUNE

JOHN MAYNARD KEYNES, FIRST BARON KEYNES

Born 1883. English economist, who predicted the economic errors of the Versailles Treaty with *The Economic Consequences of the Peace*, 1919. In 1936 he published *The General Theory of Employment, Interest and Money*, advocating planned government spending to cure unemployment. Died 1946.

8 He possessed limpid, Satanic fluency.
Cyril Asquith. Quoted Geoffrey Madan, NOTEBOOKS 1981

9 He was the first Englishman since Horace Walpole to tell the Long Run to go jump into a lake. 'In the long run', said Maynard Keynes, 'we are all dead.'
Claud Cockburn, ASPECTS OF ENGLISH HISTORY

10 He is a wonderful fellow, but has passed his life in a cloister and has had no experience in handling men or in assessing their temperaments.
Lord Crawford, DIARY 9 *Apr* 1919

11 He had been a parent of the Bretton Woods agreement and he had negotiated the American Loan which enabled Britain to enter the post-war world in a position of relatively stable austerity rather than of economic collapse.
Roy Jenkins, The Times 18 *Mar* 1972

12 I work for a Government that I despise for ends which I think criminal.
Keynes, letter to Duncan Grant *Dec* 1917

13 Obviously a nice man, but I did not enjoy his company. He made me feel a fool.
Bertrand Russell. Quoted Harold Nicolson, DIARY 22 *Jan* 1951

14 He had no feeling for industry except as figures in a book. Lloyd George had denounced 'the penguins of the city'. Keynes

was a heretical penguin, not a bird of a different species.
A. J. P. Taylor, ENGLISH HISTORY 1914–1945 1965

NIKITA (SERGEYEVITCH) KHRUSHCHEV

Born 1894. Soviet politician, became First Secretary of the Communist Party on Stalin's death in 1953. In 1956 began a policy of denigrating Stalin. Became Prime Minister 1958. Was involved in a confrontation with President Kennedy over the siting of Soviet missiles in Cuba 1962. Deposed in favour of Brezhnev 1964. Died 1971.

1 Nikki was no egg-head, but he was always a load of laughs.
Sir Alec Douglas-Home. Quoted Michael Bateman, Sunday Times 26 *Sep* 1971

2 Khrushchev could claim to be the man who released more than anyone else from prison. He caused more than 20 million people to be 'rehabilitated' — many of them posthumously, alas.
David Floyd, Daily Telegraph 30 *Dec* 1982

3 I sat in Albany, listening to Khrushchev howling in the Palais Chaillot (at the Paris Summit Conference, after the U-2 spy plane incident). I heard the boos with pleasure. He sounded just a little mad and Miss Macmillan [Nicolson's housekeeper] says he was 'like a schoolboy searching for rude words', which was true.
Harold Nicolson, letter to Vita Sackville-West 19 *May* 1960

4 When Khrushchev was guest of honour at 20th Century Fox his party was herded on to a sound stage where Shirley MacLaine and a troupe of dancers were about to shoot a take of *Can-Can*. The visitors were seated in a specially built box and looked down with undisguised horror as Shirley and Co., complete with garter-belts and fishnet stockings, kicked their legs, swirled their petticoats, waggled their knees, and ended up with their skirts over their heads and their bottoms pointing directly at the Guest of Honour and his family. As the publicity department gathered round for Khrushchev's eagerly awaited 'quote' he gave it to them in one word — DISGUSTING.
David Niven, BRING ON THE EMPTY HORSES 1975

MARTIN LUTHER KING JR

Born 1929. American Negro clergyman and civil rights leader. Awarded Nobel Peace Prize 1964. Assassinated in Memphis 1968.

5 From a historical viewpoint King's role was that of a primer to help start a revolution, which, in its speed and magnitude, was to leave him, ironically, behind.
Dilip Hiro, The Times 24 *Jan* 1978

6 He was the last one in the world who should ever have received the Nobel Prize. I held him in complete contempt because of the things he said and because of his conduct.
J. Edgar Hoover. Quoted Ramsey Clark, CRIME IN AMERICA 1971

7 A Baptist preacher whose extraordinary rhetorical abilities were not quite matched by practical intelligence and political radicalism.
David L. Lewis, MARTIN LUTHER KING 1970

8 He got the peace prize; we got the problem. If I'm following a general, and the enemy gives him rewards, I tend to get suspicious. Especially if he gets a peace award before the war is over.
Malcolm X. Quoted Peter Goldman, THE DEATH AND LIFE OF MALCOLM X

NEIL KINNOCK

Born 1942 in Wales. Labour politician. Elected MP for Bedwellty 1970. Succeeded Michael Foot as leader of the Labour Party after its defeat in the 1983 election.

9 He has given a good imitation of a political eunuch during a calamitous period in which working people and their families have been shamefully betrayed.
Frank Chapple, SPARKS FLY 1984

10 The Welsh blatherskit.
Bernard Levin, The Times, Labour's joke 26 *Jul* 1983

11 Neil Kinnock is no doubt extremely likeable. He is everyone's favourite best man. The best at organising the guests, the maker of the funniest speech. The first to kiss the bride. But will he ever win the hand of the Great British Public?
John Mortimer, Sunday Times 27 *May* 1984

12 He has a furious temper which he does not often display, and even then it is as likely to

be over bad football refereeing as about politics.
Observer, Profile 26 *Sep* 1982

1 There is not much brain, but there are alert political instincts, torrents of attractive words, and a personality that women like to mother.
Woodrow Wyatt, The Times 18 *Oct* 1984

(JOSEPH) RUDYARD KIPLING

Born 1865, in India. English novelist and poet. Awarded Nobel Prize for Literature 1907. Died 1936.

2 He was the voice of every soldier who stoically fulfilled his duties under the Indian sun and the keen moralist of the burdens of empire. Neither quality in itself is worth a literary candle, but remember Eliot. On the best authority, this star could write.
Bryan Appleyard, The Times, Reviewing KIPLING: INTERVIEWS AND RECOLLECTIONS (*edited by Harold Orel*) 16 *Aug* 1984

3 His coffin was borne by the Prime Minister, the Admiral of the Fleet, one field marshal, one classical scholar, the editor of the *Morning Post* and, of course, his agent A. P. Watt, probably the saddest of them all.
Ibid.

4 Over the port I found myself next to this little man and was immediately struck by the long hairs protruding from his ears. Somehow the conversation got on to bullfights, and he recounted in vivid language one he had witnessed. A few moments later I discovered he was Kipling.
Sir Henry Channon, DIARY 18 *Jan* 1936

5 In the days of Kipling's most popular vogue his literary works yielded him great sums. An American wit once wrote to him, 'I hear that you are retailing literature for a dollar a word. I enclose a dollar for which please send me a sample.' Keeping the dollar, Kipling wrote, 'Thanks'. Shortly afterwards he received another letter 'Sold the "Thanks" anecdote for two dollars. Enclosed please find forty-five cents in stamps, being half the profits on the transaction, less postage.'
Edmund Fuller, ANECDOTES 1942

6 If he had never come under imperial influences, and if he had developed, as he might well have done, into a writer of music-hall songs, he would have been a better and more loveable writer. In the role he actually chose one was bound to think of him, after one had grown up, as a kind of enemy, a man of alien and perverted genius.
George Orwell, New English Weekly 23 *Jan* 1936

7 Some friends came from town and wanted to see the Kipling country. I drove them up to Burwash and, as we were passing The Sugar Loaf — a folly at Brightling — one remarked 'Perhaps we shall meet Kipling out walking', and he very obligingly came round the next bend, a wire-haired terrier at his heels. 'There he is!' I exclaimed, struck by the coincidence. Hearing my voice Kipling stopped, looked at us, then panicked up a bank and into some fields, behaving to our distress as if he thought we were going to pull up and have a good stare at him. But I think he might have been a trifle amused at the comment he evoked from our boy Plum when we were discussing the incident afterwards. 'Oh, you mean the man with the three moustaches.'
Reginald Pound, THEIR MOODS AND MINE 1937

8 Kipling has done more than any other since Disraeli to show the world that the British race is sound to the core and that rust and dry rot are strangers to it.
Cecil Rhodes. Quoted J. G. MacDonald, RHODES: A LIFE

HENRY (ALFRED) KISSINGER

Born 1923 in Germany. American Secretary of State 1973–7. Awarded Nobel Peace Prize 1973.

9 There cannot be a crisis next week, my schedule is full.
Kissinger, Time magazine 24 *Jan* 1977

10 President Ford did not bother himself with minor details. He let me use his swimming pool. He only got upset when I tried to walk across the water.
Kissinger, WHITE HOUSE YEARS 1979

11 President Nixon hated people bursting into his office without knocking. Henry Kissinger had a habit of doing this, and did it once when Nixon was talking to Chuck Colson. Nixon pretended not to notice and said, 'I think you are right, Chuck. It's time for nuclear weapons in Vietnam.' Kissinger reputedly went ashen white and then grey. This would mean World War Three! Nixon smiled and said to Kissinger, 'Sit down, relax.'
TV Times 20 *Oct* 1984

HORATIO HERBERT KITCHENER, FIRST EARL KITCHENER

Born 1859 in Ireland. British field marshal. Secretary of State for War 1914. Drowned aboard HMS *Hampshire*, torpedoed when taking him to Russia, 1916.

1 He had cheeks like a map of the Polish railway system.
Cyril Asquith. Quoted Geoffrey Madan, NOTEBOOKS 1981

2 Yes, I liked him. But he had a mania for secrecy and intrigue. And that will never make a man popular.
Margot Asquith. Quoted Reginald Pound, THEIR MOODS AND MINE 1937

3 Kitchener came into Downing Street with the text of the Guildhall speech in his hand which had been prepared for him by the War Office very well, with short, stabbing, soldierly sentences into which he most unexpectedly wanted to introduce journalese like 'shell-torn'.
Lady Violet Bonham Carter

4 Emerald Cunard said she had found Kitchener 'alarmingly dull'. Once, in desperation, she had asked him who was his favourite author, and after long hesitation he replied 'Stanley Weyman'.
Sir Henry Channon, DIARY 18 *Sep* 1939

5 It was a case of dislike before first sight.
Winston Churchill

6 Kitchener looked like an officer who had got mixed up with a lot of strolling players and is trying to pretend he doesn't know them.
Duff Cooper, DIARY *Mar* 1916

7 The Prime Minister said he had only once seen Kitchener really rattled and that was when it had been settled to evacuate Gallipoli. Kitchener came to him one morning and said that he hadn't slept for two nights, thinking of the terrible casualties we were bound to suffer. He estimated them at 50,000 while other military experts put it at twice that figure. The PM likes quoting these instances of the miscalculations of military experts.
Ibid. 10 *Jul* 1916

8 He abominates our files and methods of working. In fact he is just like a caged lion stalking to and fro and dashing his bruised and lacerated head against the bars.
Lord Curzon. Quoted Lord Ronaldshay, LIFE OF LORD CURZON, VOL 2 1928

9 He is fearfully wrong-headed sometimes, but he is always *homme serieux*, practising himself, and enforcing on others, the highest standard of workmanlike strenuousness, indefatigable industry and iron perseverance. Great qualities these in a wishy-washy world.
Lord Milner, letter to Lady Edward Cecil, Jan 1902

10 There were occasional rumours that he had not been drowned but secretly landed somewhere to reappear at the appropriate moment as his country's saviour. It was Claud Cockburn who floated a story that the whole affair was a brilliant Secret Service manoeuvre whereby Stalin was spirited away and replaced by Kitchener. Their features, it must be admitted, were not dissimilar and certainly Stalin's subsequent policy was very much in Kitchener's vein.
Malcolm Muggeridge, Observer 18 *Jan* 1970

11 The famous drawing by artist Alfred Leete appeared in an advertisement on the cover of *London Opinion*, 5 September 1914 and was taken up by the Parliamentary Recruiting Committee for a poster issued 14 September. Kitchener was shown with staring eyes and pointing finger and the slogan 'Your Country Needs You'.
Nigel Rees, SAYINGS OF THE CENTURY 1984

12 On 5 June 1916 the *Hampshire* with Kitchener on board struck a mine within two hours of leaving Scapa Flow. Kitchener and most of the crew were drowned. So perished the only British military idol of the First World War. The next morning Northcliffe burst into his sister's drawing-room with the words 'Providence is on the side of the British Empire after all.' This reflected a common view that the secretary for war still held the key to victory, and that Kitchener had been incapable of turning it.
A. J. P. Taylor, ENGLISH HISTORY 1914–1945 1965

OTTO KLEMPERER

Born 1885 in Germany, which he left in 1933 to settle in America, where he became conductor of the Los Angeles Symphony Orchestra. Established a particular reputation for his interpretation of Beethoven. Died 1974.

13 In depression, he tore up his works and disappeared into sanatoria for weeks or months on end, restoring his calm and studying scores.
Peter Heyworth, OTTO KLEMPERER: HIS LIFE AND TIMES 1983

1 Klemperer was a manic-depressive Jew of abnormal height who turned Catholic not like Mahler, for professional reasons, but because he found Christianity intellectually attractive.
Ibid.

2 The leader of the old Philharmonia told me that when he was leaving the orchestra he went to see Klemperer. He'd done so much with the old man, even played his trio, and he felt some kind of relationship with Klemperer. After his last concert he felt he should go and say something. He said 'Dr Klemperer, after all these years this is my last concert with you.' And Klemperer replied, 'What you want me to do, cry?'
Robin Ray, WORDS ON MUSIC 1984

RONALD (ARBUTHNOT) KNOX

Born 1888. British author, whose literary output was divided into serious religious works, popular essays, and detective stories. Died 1957.

3 It is alleged by a friend of my family that I used to suffer from insomnia at the age of four, and that when she asked me how I managed to occupy my time at night I answered 'I lie awake and think about the past.'
Ronald Knox, LITERARY DISTRACTIONS 1941

4 Father Knox, dispensing port and bananas to his Oxford undergraduates, smiled wanly.
John Raymond, History Today, The Baldwin age Sep 1960

SIR ALEXANDER KORDA

Born 1893 in Hungary. British film producer. One of his earliest successes was *The Private Life of Henry VIII*, 1932. Died 1956.

5 Mr Korda, a publicity man of genius, who has not as yet revealed a talent for the films, casts his pictures with little regard for anything but the gossip paragraphs.
Graham Greene, reviewing The Man Who Could Work Miracles

6 Born in poverty, he was irresistibly attracted to titles, wealth, glamour, the opulent, extravagant and exotic. He had a streak of ruthless ambition, and although warm, genial, with vivid eyes flashing through horn-rimmed glasses, and a captivating smile, he exemplified the old cliché, 'A Hungarian and a Rumanian will both sell you their grandmother — the difference is, a Rumanian will deliver.'
Charles Higham and Roy Moseley, MERLE 1983

7 In appearance he is a scholarly figure; and those who know him well speak of his almost hypnotic charm, his beautiful manners, his fastidious tastes, his humour, generosity and erudition. Only in this adulation he inspires among his entourage, and his passion for cigars, does he fit the usual conception of a film tycoon.
Observer, Profile 22 Apr 1951

FRITZ KREISLER

Born 1875 in Austria. Violinist and composer. Died 1962.

8 Walking along a Dublin street in very bad weather he was vexed to hear a talented young lady (Lilian McEvoy) playing the violin in the gutter. He stood for a few minutes listening as she played in the rain, and then told her he would find her a job. Of course he had no idea how to start this undertaking, but he did not rest until he had secured her a permanent post in a theatre orchestra.
Donald Brook, VIOLINISTS OF TODAY

9 On one occasion a fabulously wealthy lady demanded his services and would not be deterred even when he quoted a fee of 3000 dollars for playing just a few little pieces. So he accepted the engagement. The lady then told him that she did not wish him to mix with the guests, many of whom would be very prominent people. He replied immediately: 'In that case, madam, my fee will be only two thousand dollars.'
Ibid.

10 His playing was characterised by a sweetness of tone and a charm of interpretation that can only have been an expression of his own personality.
The Times, Obituary 20 Jan 1962

11 In later years Kreisler was apt to take the easy course marked out for him by his great popularity, choosing his programme from attractive, but musically trivial, pieces which delighted the vast audience, and playing them with an ease that became almost mechanical. But there was always another Kreisler, more rarely to be heard, who could play great music in great style.
Ibid.

L

GEORGE LANSBURY

Born 1859. English Labour politician. Played an influential part in the launching of the *Daily Herald*. Leader of the parliamentary Labour Party 1931–5. Died 1940.

1 Lansbury has been going about dressed in saint's clothes for years, waiting for martyrdom. I set fire to the faggots.
Ernest Bevin, Labour party conference 1935 *of his demolition of Lansbury's pacifist speech on the Abyssinian crisis*

2 He was no political innocent. Why, even on the night that he was speaking at the conference [in 1935] he was trying to manipulate the time so that nobody could reply to him that night. I have known him for years and have worked with him: he is not a guileless old gentleman.
Ernest Bevin. Quoted Alan Bullock, THE LIFE AND TIMES OF ERNEST BEVIN 1960

3 He is the Compleat Socialist – the sort of honest-to-God-down-with-the-rich-and-up-with-the-poor sort of socialism that one had imagined had gone out with the war.
Ethel Mannin, CONFESSIONS AND IMPRESSIONS 1930

4 The most loveable figure in modern politics.
A. J. P. Taylor, ENGLISH HISTORY 1914–1945 1965

5 George Lansbury, first commissioner of works [1929], took Wheatley's place as spokeman of the Left. He got on surprisingly well with George V. The two men happily exchanged anecdotes about their respective illnesses.
Ibid.

CHARLES LAUGHTON

Born 1899. British film actor. Best known roles include those of Henry VIII in *The Private Life of Henry VIII*, 1933 and of Captain Bligh in *Mutiny on the Bounty*, 1935. Died 1962

6 Alvin Johnson called him 'A great man who only accidentally became an actor'. It's a pity he wasn't happy in the part.
Leslie Halliwell, FILMGOER'S BOOK OF QUOTES

7 This great actor, the tyrannical Captain Bligh of *Mutiny on the Bounty*, was at heart a soft, gentle and miserable homosexual who hated himself because of his ugliness, his weight and was an easy victim of ruthless young hustlers who stripped him financially and reduced him to grovelling servitude.
Charles Higham and Roy Moseley, MERLE 1983

8 You can't direct a Laughton picture. The best you can hope for is to referee.
Alfred Hitchcock

9 With him acting was an act of childbirth. What he needed was not so much a director as a midwife.
Alexander Korda

10 A conversation with him is tremendously entertaining but a little exhausting: he does not stay still for five minutes at a time; mere mention of a foreign railway porter will cause him to leap to his feet to give an impersonation — being with him is rather like being all the time in an engine room with all the engines running.
Ethel Mannin, CONFESSIONS AND IMPRESSIONS 1930

11 Charles Laughton has a disgusting handshake. I was lunching with Cedric Hardwicke at Quaglino's. Laughton came up and talked with extraordinary speed for a few minutes. He offered me a hand that had as much life in it, let alone cordiality, as a filleted Grimsby cod.
Reginald Pound, THEIR MOODS AND MINE 1937

12 The Beerbohm Tree of Tomorrow. A few years ago he was a waiter at Claridges. He is not a pretty boy.
Hannen Swaffer, SWAFFER'S WHO'S WHO FOR 1930

13 He had a face that faintly resembled a large wad of cotton wool.
Josef von Sternberg, of Charles Laughton

PIERRE LAVAL

Born 1883. French politician. Premier and foreign minister 1931–2, 1935–6, and after the Nazi occupation, 1942. After the liberation, tried for treason and executed 1945.

1 A silly little man whose love for his country was deep and passionate in its way, but who grossly exaggerated his capacity to counter Hitler's plans for destroying France.
Herbert Cole, LAVAL 1963

2 In this country his help during the 1931 gold crisis [when he authorised a £120 million loan] is forgotten, whereas his part in the Hoare–Laval plan for buying off Mussolini and halting the Abyssinian war is painfully recollected.
H. D. Ziman, Daily Telegraph 3 *May* 1963

3 No Frenchman in my lifetime has ever incurred such intense detestation from this side of the Channel as Pierre Laval. Here was a man who had publicly declared on three successive occasions 'I wish for the victory of Germany'.
Ibid.

ANDREW BONAR LAW

Born 1858 in Canada. British politician. Elected leader of the Conservative Party, 1911. Served in Lloyd George's wartime coalition 1915–21. Became Prime Minister 1922. Died 1923.

4 Bonar Law had never led his party. He was always looking back over his shoulder to see if he was being followed.
Lady Violet Bonham Carter, The Times 2 *Nov* 1964

5 Bonar Law had his prejudices. He could not stand or trust or believe a man with a narrow head.
Lord Castlerosse, Sunday Express 19 *May* 1940

6 The Scots-Canadian statesman, one of the most respected political figures of his day, ought never to have assumed the responsibilities of the Premiership. The burden of office and his personal anxieties concerning Baldwin's debt settlement hastened the end. His health broke down completely. He went on a sea voyage. He took a cure at Aix-les-Bains. But he grew steadily worse and on May 20 asked the King to accept his resignation. He had been Prime Minister for just about six months.
Norman Hillson, Leader 6 *Mar* 1937

7 Bonar Law was playing golf at St Andrews. On one green his caddie placed the toe of his boot to one side of the hole and said; 'Aim at ma foot.' 'No, I'm sure it's straight' Bonar Law replied, aimed for the hole and missed it by some inches. As the party moved off to the next tee the caddie was heard to remark to his colleague, 'What a bloody fool to hae for Prime Minister.'
Peterborough, Daily Telegraph

D. H. (DAVID HERBERT) LAWRENCE

Born 1885. English novelist and poet. His novel *Lady Chatterley's Lover*, written in 1928, gained notoriety as a result of the prosecution of Penguin books in 1960, following the publication in paperback. Died 1930.

8 Lawrence thought every women should/Be shown that her desires are good,/That *amour naturale*'s error/ Lies in obeying Ego's terror./Lawrence, too, contrived to train us/ In the importance of the anus./NOT *Sade*-like as a matter of course/But to return us to the Source/Which, with some conscientious plumbing/Could liberate the Second Coming.
John Fuller, THE ART OF LOVE

9 Lunched with Pinker to meet D. H. Lawrence, that provincial genius. Interesting, but a type I could not get on with. Obsessed with self. Dead eyes, and a red beard, long pale narrow face. A strange bird.
John Galsworthy. Quoted H. V. Marrot, LIFE AND LETTERS OF JOHN GALSWORTHY 1935

10 I finished a novel *Women in Love*, which I know is a masterpiece — but it seems it will not find a publisher. It is no good, I cannot get a single thing I write published in England. There is no sale of the books that *are* published. So I am dished.
D. H. Lawrence, letter to Edward Marsh

11 *Lady Chatterley's Lover* has made short work of a prosecution by the Crown. It still has to face more formidable judges. Nine of them, and all goddesses.
C. S. Lewis, SELECTED LITERARY ESSAYS: *Four-Letter Words* 1969

12 I ask you, is anything in life or literature, past or present, in earth, heaven or hell, anything more devastatingly tedious than D.H.L's interest in the human genitalia.
G. W. Lyttelton, THE LYTTELTON HART-DAVIS LETTERS 29 *Mar* 1956

1 The 'dear man' in him whom we all loved is hidden away, absorbed, completely lost, like a little gold ring in that immense German Christmas pudding which is Frieda. And with all the appetite in the world one cannot eat one's way through Frieda to find him.
Katherine Mansfield, COLLECTED LETTERS VOL. 1 1903–1917

2 Capable of an occasional joke in his letters, he is consistently without humour in his books, a failing rarely, if ever, to be found in novelists of the highest class, from Petronius to Proust.
Anthony Powell, THE STRANGERS ARE ALL GONE VOL. 4, THE MEMOIRS

3 His were the ideas of a sensitive would-be despot who got angry with the world because it would not obey. When he realised that other people existed, he hated them. But most of the time he lived in a solitary world of his own imaginings, peopled by phantoms as fierce as he wished them to be.
Bertrand Russell, AUTOBIOGRAPHY 1967

T. E. (THOMAS EDWARD) LAWRENCE

Born 1888. British soldier who, under Allenby in 1916, assisted the Arabs in their revolt against the Turks, and recounted his alleged experiences in *The Seven Pillars of Wisdom*, 1926. Richard Aldington, in his biography of Lawrence, denounced the work as largely fictional. Died 1935.

4 I once asked Bernard Shaw whether Lawrence was genuine or phoney; and he said 'Both'. The discovery that he was a fraud has, I am afraid, only deepened my admiration for him. To have done what he said he did would have been amazing. To have invented it all, and then got away with it, seems to me an even more remarkable achievement. Churchill was completely taken in by him. So was John Buchan who once said to me that Lawrence was the only man he would have followed to the end of the earth.
Lord Boothby, RECOLLECTIONS OF A REBEL 1978

5 It has now transpired that the whole grim story in the *Seven Pillars of Wisdom* of his capture by the Turks in Deraa where he was beaten and tortured and raped is a myth. Perhaps some part of his subconscious wished it had happened. In fact he never went to Deraa, nor did most of his alleged exploits ever take place. He was liaison officer between Feisal and Allenby, and little more.
Ibid.

6 In those days I owned an open two-seater 6½ litre Bentley. One day I left it outside Port Lympne when Philip Sassoon was giving a party. When I came out I found that the bonnet had been opened by a grubby little Air Force mechanic in uniform, who was peering into the engine. 'I do apologise' he said, 'but I can never resist looking at a beautiful piece of engineering when I see one.' I said that I was delighted and that I loved it myself; and we talked for a little while about this and that. Then, to my surprise, he said 'I think we will go in.' We did, and Philip introduced him. It was Lawrence of Arabia.
Ibid.

7 [He was] a bore, a bounder and a prig. He was intoxicated with his own youth and loathed any milieu which he couldn't dominate. Certainly he had none of the gentleman's instincts, strutting about Peace Conferences in Arab dress.
Henry Channon, DIARY 25 *May* 1935

8 T. E. Lawrence is one of those great men for whom one feels intensely sorry because he was nothing but a great man.
Aldous Huxley, letter to V. Ocampo 1946

9 On one of his spells in the ranks he was assigned as batman to an officer of the class who used to be known in the War as 'temporary gentleman'. Lawrence hated him at sight, and on the first evening, when he was unpacking his kit, looked round and said 'I beg your pardon, sir, but I can only find one of your razors!' 'I've only got one razor.' 'Indeed sir? I thought most gentlemen had a razor for every day in the week.' After a moment he looked around again. 'Sir, I can't find your left-handed nail-scissors.' The poor man rushed out of the tent and applied for a less exacting batman.
Edward Marsh, A NUMBER OF PEOPLE 1939

10 I had bought for I think three guineas a copy of the limited edition of D. H. Lawrence's *Lady Chatterley's Lover*, but found myself quite unable to get through it, so when T.E. told me he had read it twice in borrowed copies I felt that 'his need was greater than mine' and made him a present of the volumes. He rewarded me with the loan of his book on the R.A.F., *The Mint*, in manuscript.
Ibid.

11 He was retiring and yet craved to be seen, he

was sincerely shy and naively exhibitionist. He had to rise above others and then humble himself and in self-inflicted humiliation demonstrate his superiority.
Lewis B. Namier. Quoted A. W. Lawrence, T. E. LAWRENCE BY HIS FRIENDS

1 His eyes riveted my attention. They were the bluest I had ever seen. They seemed to be looking right through me to distant horizons. Despite his modest bearing there was a dignity about Lawrence that compelled respect.
Sir Evelyn Wrench, STRUGGLE 1935

LAURIE LEE

Born 1914. English author. Has written poetry and documentary film scripts, but is best known for his autobiography *Cider With Rosie*, 1959.

2 Laurie Lee wrote his original manuscript of *Cider with Rosie* on the back of old Archers scripts. Lee, then impoverished and unknown, was a friend of the poet Louis MacNeice, a BBC employee who passed on the discarded typescripts to help the struggling author. Tomorrow the BBC is presenting Lee with a framed Archers title page bearing the message, 'With grateful thanks for writing behind our backs'.
Daily Telegraph 5 *Nov* 1984

3 Louis MacNeice gave me a whole cupboard full of old BBC scripts. I like writing on the backs of them because the sheets are huge and it satisfies my sense of peasant economy. And when you can't get going you can always turn the page and read the script. You can waste hours that way.
Laurie Lee. Quoted Philip Oakes, Sunday Times 1 *Jun* 1969

4 People were upset if they were in the book [*Cider with Rosie*]. But they were a damned sight more upset if I'd left them out.
Ibid.

5 He is amiably secretive, a born burrower. His cottage has no telephone. He spends half the week in London. To make contact you send a telegram and await his answering call . . . His cottage is his bolt hole. Books to be autographed are passed over the garden wall.
Philip Oakes, Sunday Times 1 *Jun* 1969

6 He is notorious among his friends for his secretiveness. This may date from his bachelor days when he maintained a number of affairs at the same time. 'Only when I was in bed once with a temperature of 103 did they discover about each other. They all came round to look after me. God what a dreadful day that was.'
Henry Porter, Sunday Times 9 *Oct* 1983

VIVIEN LEIGH

Born 1913 in India. Original name Vivien Mary Hartley. British film actress, famous roles include Scarlett O'Hara in *Gone With the Wind*, 1939. Died 1967.

7 She was often underrated because she was so beautiful.
George Cukor, of Vivien Leigh. Quoted Gavin Lambert, ON CUKOR

8 Slim and dainty, with a small oval face and grey-green eyes set wide apart which seemed for ever to be contemplating something far away, she possessed a piquant charm which was not the least of her attractions.
Daily Telegraph, Obituary 10 *Jul* 1967

9 The utterly delicious and kitten-like Vivien Leigh.
David Niven, BRING ON THE EMPTY HORSES 1979

VLADIMIR ILYICH LENIN

Born 1870. Original name Ulyanov. Russian revolutionary leader. Brought back from exile by the Germans. Overthrew the Kerensky government, November 1917, to establish the Council of People's Commissars. After a period of Civil War, established the Union of Soviet Socialist Republics, 1920. Died 1924.

10 I think Lenin was an admirable man, possessed by a terribly wrong idea. It was terribly wrong because it was only partly right. And it was so absolutely punitive that it needed to be absolutely right.
Robert Bolt, STATE OF REVOLUTION

11 A man of Tartar features, with high cheekbones, a small beard and short hair came towards me. It was Lenin. We exchanged greetings. He lisped slightly.
Feodor Chaliapin, MAN AND MASK: FORTY YEARS IN THE LIFE OF A SINGER 1934

12 He alone could have led Russia into the enchanted quagmire; he alone could have found the way back to the causeway. He saw, he turned, he perished. The Russian people were left floundering in the bog.
Winston Churchill, THE WORLD CRISIS

1 It is not an overstatement to say that he was an unknown person in the public life of the world until October 1917. From that date his personality penetrates the most remote corners of the globe. This fact must remain as one of the wonders of history.
James Maxton, LENIN 1932

2 When I met Lenin I had much less impression of a great man than I had expected; my most vivid impressions were of bigotry and Mongolian cruelty. When I put to him a question about socialism in agriculture, he explained with glee how he had incited the poorer peasants against the richer ones — 'And they soon hanged them from the nearest tree. Ha! Ha! Ha!' His guffaw at the thought of those massacred made my blood run cold.
Bertrand Russell, UNPOPULAR ESSAYS, EMINENT MEN I HAVE MET 1950

3 Lenin considered himself to be an atheist, but in this he was mistaken. He thought that the world was governed by a dialectic, whose instrument he was; he conceived of himself as a human agent of a Superhuman power.
Ibid.

4 He was rather strange — short, bald, of striking appearance, not bad looking, with a dark reddish bead, an alert manner and broken English. He seemed highly educated. He liked the rooms and took them.
Leonard Yeo, whose mother was Lenin's landlady at 30 *Holford Square, Finsbury, in* 1902. *Quoted Harold Atkins, Daily Telegraph* 5 *Nov* 1984

JOHN (WINSTON) LENNON

Born 1940. English musician, composer, writer. Dominant member of The Beatles pop group until it broke up in 1971, when he retreated into seclusion with his second wife Yoko Ono. Murdered in New York 1980.

5 John, being too witty, never conformed to the received image of a pop star.
Lewis Duder, The Times 27 *Jun* 1984

6 Whenever John walked out of the front door he was walking into a truly crazy world.
Cynthia Lennon (John's first wife), The Times 27 *Jun* 1984

7 When the distancing from, and then the alienation of, the Beatles fans began with the retreat into kaftans, joss-sticks and drugs it bore the hallmarks of Lennon's cast of mind and intellectual preoccupations.
Ibid.

OSCAR LEVANT

Born 1906. American author, actor, musician. Died 1972.

8 A character who, if he did not exist, could not be imagined.
S. N. Behrman, A SMATTERING OF IGNORANCE

9 Levant played background music for a Parisian picture under the guidance of a brilliant producer. 'It's good.' said the connoisseur, 'but it isn't Frenchy enough.' He thought for a moment and then added, 'I've got it, Oscar. Put in more French horns.'
Bennett Cerf, TRY AND STOP ME 1947

10 Oscar Levant once played with an orchestra whose conductor he detested. The conductor reciprocated the feeling and delighted in pointing out errors in his playing. Levant finally lost his temper and convulsed the other members of the orchestra — and also terminated his own association therewith — by shouting 'If you bawl me out any more I'll follow your beat.'
Ibid.

11 Mr Rufus Lemaire was host at a buffet supper. The servants had forgotten to pass napkins. 'It is on account of the war shortages,' Oscar Levant explained. 'Instead of napkins, from time to time a woolly dog will pass among you.'
Ibid.

12 For one year and one month Oscar Levant declared my house his house. For one year and one month he ate my food, played my piano, ran up my phone bills, burned cigarette holes in my landlady's furniture, monopolised my record player and my coffee pot, gave his guests the run of the joint, insulted my guests, and never stopped complaining. He was an egomaniac. He was a leech and a lunatic — but I loved the guy.
Harpo Marx, HARPO SPEAKS

13 Scheduled to play a short piece by Brahms on the Cream of Wheat show, Levant arrived at the studio and was asked if he might shorten the work by thirty seconds as the programme was running long. Shortly thereafter he was asked by Woollcott if he could cut it by another twenty seconds. Always willing to oblige, Oscar made the second cut. It was only when Woollcott

asked him if he terribly minded making another cut that Levant answered 'I don't mind, but you'll hear from Brahms in the morning.'
Howard Teichmann, SMART ALECK 1975

C. S. (CLIVE STAPLES) LEWIS

Born in Belfast 1898. Was elected Fellow and Tutor at Magdalene College in 1925 where he remained until 1954. Novelist, essayist, poet. Among his best-known works are *The Screwtape Letters*, 1942, *Out of the Silent Planet*, 1938 and his series of children's books based on the mythical land Narnia. He died in 1963.

1 Objectively our Common Room/Is like a small Athenian State — /Except for Lewis; he's all right/ — But do you think he's *quite* first rate?
John Betjeman, A HIKE ON THE DOWNS 1937

2 Lewis, you see, could not see *any* humour in religion. He would look at me as though ducking away from barbed attacks. I loathed him and he thought me a ne'er-do-well aesthete.
John Betjeman, BBC 2, Time with Betjeman 13 *Feb* 1983

3 John Betjeman was sent down from Magdalene after only a few terms for failing the obligatory University examination in Divinity. He sought out Lewis 'in his arid room' but was told bluntly, 'You have only got a third.' Some years later Betjeman turned the tables on his tutor. In the volume of poems *Continual Dew* (1937) he wrote in the preface that he was 'indebted to Mr C. S. Lewis for the fact on page 250'. The book consisted of only forty-five pages.
Humphrey Carpenter, THE INKLINGS 1978

4 Many women found Lewis as unbearable as he found them. If they had no 'real conversation' he had no small talk whatever, and they often felt that he was blundering, brusque, or downright rude.
Ibid.

5 Coming out of church at Headington Quay on a summer Sunday morning Lewis was 'struck by an idea for a book which I think might be both useful and entertaining. It would be called *As One Devil to Another* and would consist of letters from one elderly retired devil to a young devil who has just started work on his first "Patient". The idea would be to give all the psychology of temptation from the *other* point of view.' *The Screwtape Letters* were finished in a few months.
Ibid.

6 A graduate of St John's College, Bruce Montgomery, published one of his first detective stories under the name of Edmund Crispin. He set one scene in the Bird and Baby (Eagle and Child) and made the professor-detective Gervase Fen remark: 'There goes C. S. Lewis. It must be Tuesday.'
Ibid.

7 Lewis's taste in *light* literature was that of a Victorian schoolboy. His *serious* literary taste was also nineteenth century, but that of a mid-nineteenth-century scholar and man of letters. He liked the grand, the noble, or the Romantic. Virgil, Homer, Milton, also Spenser, Malory etc. — though he also did get a great deal of pleasure from writers as different as Lamb and Jane Austen. But his taste did stop about 1890.
David Cecil, letter to Humphrey Carpenter Jan 1978

8 In 1943 I came across *Screwtape Letters*. I was a junior in college then and trying to find myself intellectually and spiritually. I resolved on that Sunday evening to live a positive life for Christ, rather than one just out of reach of evil.
Edward T. Dell, letter to C. S. Lewis 1 *Feb* 1949

9 Friendship with Lewis compensates for much.
J. R. R. Tolkien, DIARY 1929

10 *Peterborough*, usually fairly reasonable, did him the doubtful honour of a peculiarly misrepresentative and asinine paragraph in the *Daily Telegraph* of Tuesday last. It began 'Ascetic Mr Lewis — !!!' I ask you! He put away three pints in a very short session this morning and said he was 'going short for Lent'.
J. R. R. Tolkien, letter to his son Christopher 1 *Mar* 1944

11 He was keen-witted rather than clear-sighted, logical within some given position, but in ranging argument neither lucid nor coherent. On the fallacies, verbal subterfuges and false deductions of his opponents (and of his friends) he could dart like a hawk; yet he was himself often confused, failing to make essential distinctions or seeming unaware that the immediate contention had already been

damaged by some 'point' he had already made elsewhere.
J. R. R. Tolkien, THE ULTERIOR MOTIVE, *written 1969, unpublished. Quoted Humphrey Carpenter*, THE INKLINGS 1978

1 The book that brought Lewis to fame *The Allegory of Love* is one of the most original works of scholarship in the twentieth century.
Rachel Trickett, Daily Telegraph, A warfaring Christian 19 *Nov* 1983

2 I regard your *Allegorical Love Poems* as practically the only book I have ever come across, since Dante, that shows the slightest understanding of what this very peculiar identity of love and religion means.
Charles Williams, letter to C. S. Lewis 12 *Mar* 1936

PERCY WYNDHAM LEWIS

Born 1884, in America. English painter and novelist. Collaborated with Ezra Pound in producing the periodical *Blast*. As a painter was the leading exponent of the Vorticist movement. His most successful novel was *The Apes of God*, 1930. Died 1957.

3 Wyndham Lewis wore a wide black hat, like a character in the quarter, and was dressed like someone out of *La Bohème*. He had a face that reminded me of a frog, not a bullfrog but just any frog, and Paris was too big a puddle for him.
Ernest Hemingway, A MOVEABLE FEAST 1964

4 I do not think I had ever seen a nastier-looking man. Some people show evil as a racehorse shows breeding. Lewis did not show evil; he just looked nasty.
Ibid.

5 Anyone who has read him will know that hard slap in the face that his sentences administer to the reader, the brief, challenging laugh that follows the slap, and the sudden note of deadly, and of often pessimistic seriousness that follows the laugh.
E. Newton. Quoted C. Handley-Read, THE ART OF WYNDHAM LEWIS

6 It would be a very heavy labour to read *Tarr* right through. Some indefinable quality, a sort of literary vitamin, is absent from it.
George Orwell, Tribune 2 *Nov* 1945

7 It was his interest in politics that bedevilled Lewis's life. There can rarely have existed an amateur in politics who so consistently guessed wrong on every important political issue that arose during his lifetime.
Anthony Powell, Daily Telegraph 5 *Apr* 1963

8 There existed in Wyndham Lewis a streak of real silliness. Although he was never tired of announcing himself as a terrifying dominating, intensely masculine figure — 'I belch, I bawl, I drink' — it is clear that he suffered intensely from a persecution mania, ill-health, and almost complete ignorance of much that makes up the practical affairs of life.
Ibid.

9 Part of Lewis's trouble was a superfluity of gifts. In addition to creating in Vorticism, largely if not entirely by his own efforts, a respectable school of 'modern' English painters, and writing prose of real originality, he was also preoccupied with political theory.
Ibid.

10 Like a medieval tyrant, he was said to fear poisoning and carried a small pearl-handled revolver to fashionable luncheon parties, where he placed it on the table beside his plate.
Peter Quennell, Observer 7 *Apr* 1965

11 One night in the summer of 1919 when he and my brother and sister and I were dining at Verrey's he made a celebrated pronouncement. At the end of the dinner, in the quietness, he first made a calculation with a pencil on a matchbox and then, with the usual yellowing cigarette-stub clamped to his upper lip when he spoke, its smoke drifting across his left eye which, in accordance, he had partially to close, thus imparting to his face a more than customarily knowing look, said firmly but in a carefully lowered voice, 'Remember! I'm thirty-seven until I pass the word around.' The seriousness with which he laid this injunction upon us so intimidated my sister that she has told me that, until many years later, if a doctor came to see her and in the course of examining her chest commanded 'Say 99' she would instinctively and invariably say '37'.
Osbert Sitwell, LAUGHTER IN THE NEXT ROOM 1949

12 Wyndham Lewis, tall and thin, looked rather like a young Frenchman on the rise, perhaps because his feet were very French, or at least his shoes.
Gertrude Stein, AUTOBIOGRAPHY OF ALICE B. TOKLAS 1933

1 Percy Wyndham Lewis was another student [at the Slade] who made a cult of the unkempt. He has given up drawing now, I believe, and become a Futurist, or a Cubist, or some other of the *ists*, who think they can paint without bothering to draw, but in other respects his habits are unchanged.
Ernest Thesiger, PRACTICALLY TRUE 1927

SINCLAIR LEWIS

Born 1885. American novelist, his most successful works *Main Street*, 1920; *Babbitt*, 1922; *Elmer Gantry*, 1927. Awarded Nobel Prize for Literature 1930. Died 1951.

2 He was the first American to be measured and weighed and certified as an international giant of letters.
Malcolm Cowley, AFTER THE GENTEEL CONDITION 1937

3 Sinclair Lewis began his literary career in the publicity department of Frederick L. Stokes and Company, publishers. At the end of his second year he was making 23 dollars a week and had the temerity to demand a two-dollar raise. Old Mr Stokes gave it to him, with the comment, 'You're a bright young fellow, Lewis, but you want raises too often. This is the top salary for the job you're doing. I'll never pay you any more.' Less than fifteen years later the same gentleman offered Lewis a 75,000 dollar advance on a new novel, sight unseen!
Bennett Cerf, SHAKE WELL BEFORE USING 1948

4 Sinclair Lewis was a particularly unpleasant man, even for an author. He wrote himself out and drank himself to death, slowly and laboriously, and savaged all his contacts, both male and female.
Cyril Connolly, Sunday Times 14 *Apr* 1963

5 Sinclair Lewis, a rangy ranting ego-maniac, liberated nothing but aggression from his drinking; he talked incessantly, went in for compulsive imitations, and insulted the guests until he fell asleep.
Ibid.

6 Lewis never got over the shock of discovering that the ideal American world of Thoreau, Twain and Whitman was an imaginary one. He was inspired by anger and sheer terror, split open by disgust; and like other men of similar temperament was at heart mawkishly sentimental.
John Davenport, Observer 31 *Mar* 1963

7 He was a writer who drank, not, as so many have believed, a drunk who wrote.
James Lundquist, SINCLAIR LEWIS

CHARLES (AUGUSTUS) LINDBERGH

Born 1902. American aviator who made the first non-stop Transatlantic flight. His son died after being kidnapped 1932. His heroic image was severely damaged when he took up an isolationist and pro-Nazi attitude. Died 1974.

8 I was in a theatre listening to a funny tuneful musical comedy. On a sudden the grotesquely painted comedian came on, turned to the audience and said 'Captain Lindbergh landed in Paris half an hour ago.' There was almost a sob in the theatre, a second's pause, then a storm of applause broke out.
E.B., T.P.'s Weekly 16 *Jul* 1927

9 Lindbergh is a religious man and a devoted son. He is a teetotaller, of course.
Children's Newspaper 4 *Feb* 1928

10 He suffered atrociously from the publicity of which he became the victim. He could never enter a train, or theatre, and if he walked up Fifth Avenue he was forced to adopt the disguise of a garage hand in dark glasses. 'Smile', the photographers would say when they managed to encircle him. 'At what?' Lindbergh would glumly reply.
Kenneth C. Davis, THE HERO 1960

11 Like that other folk-hero of the twenties, with whom he seemed to have many points of resemblance, Edward VIII, he got involved with the Nazis. Convinced that Germany must win the war, he became a crusading isolationist.
E. C. Hodgkin, The Times 2 *Sep* 1976

12 He was almost too good to be true. Not only had he proved himself an incomparable flier and insuperably brave, but he was young, handsome, polite and, it seemed, instinctively modest.
Leonard Moseley, LINDBERGH 1976

13 Lindbergh's achievement came to the Americans as a symbol of pioneer skill and courage revealed to the world in most dramatic form. Their hearts throbbed at the thought of 'a young American boy with a sandwich in his pocket' flying across the Atlantic. They forgot that almost eight years previously Alcock and Brown had made it non-stop across the ocean.
Harold Nicolson, Observer 18 *Sep* 1960

1 Villagers tell the story that as a boy he would hoist his bicycle into some tree-top near his father's house, climb aboard it, and sit there dreaming that he was flying.
Dale Van Every and Morris de Haven Tracy, CHARLES LINDBERGH: HIS LIFE 1927

ERIC (ROBERT RUSSELL) LINKLATER

Born 1899. Scottish novelist and short-story writer. His earliest successes were *Juan in America*, 1931, and *Ripeness is All*, 1935. Died 1974.

2 A very quiet fellow with an egg-shaped head and a critical eye, brought to the flat by Lesley Storm, who introduced him as an old Aberdeen University flame of hers — Eric Linklater. He sat like a mandarin in a corner, but I think he wanted to be sociable. I gather he has lived mostly in the Shetlands, and is more used to the cries of the seabirds and the music of the wind than to London talk.
Reginald Pound, THEIR MOODS AND MINE 1937

3 He has Viking blood. He lives in the Orkneys when not roaming the world. In literature he is a he-man, but never a tough. People say of him that he looks like a severe schoolmaster.
John Pudney, News Chronicle 30 *Oct* 1947

KEN LIVINGSTONE

Born 1945. Labour politician. Elected leader of the Greater London Council 1981.

4 A nondescript, instantly forgettable little fellow with a nasal voice.
Frederick Forsyth, THE FOURTH PROTOCOL 1984

5 He is a man who has virtually no life outside politics. He lives on his GLC salary of £2500 a year plus expenses, travelling to work on the Tube, having returned the leader's official car to the car-pool on taking office.
John Mortimer, IN CHARACTER 1983

6 His manner is open, courteous, direct and extraordinarily unshadowed by any trace of anxiety. He seldom expresses any emotion stronger than gentle amusement. This consistency mystifies reporters who are accustomed to politicians voicing sardonic opinions in unbuttoned moments.
Ibid.

DAVID LLOYD GEORGE, FIRST EARL LLOYD-GEORGE OF DWYFOR

Born 1865 in Wales. British Liberal politician. Chancellor of the Exchequer 1908–15, Prime Minister 1916–22. Continued to be a member of parliament until 1944. Died 1945.

7 He spent his whole life in plastering together the true and the false and therefrom extracting the plausible.
Stanley Baldwin. Quoted Leon Harris, THE FINE ART OF POLITICAL WIT

8 Many a time England has had a Chancellor who knew nothing of finance, but never before has she had one who thought there was nothing to know.
Stanley Baldwin, House of Commons, Budget debate 1914

9 He did not care in which direction the car was travelling, so long as he remained in the driver's seat.
Lord Beaverbrook. Quoted New Statesman 14 *Jun* 1963

10 Lady Astor once said to Lloyd George 'If Waldorf and I had known that you were living with Frances Stevenson we would never have lent you our villa in Deauville during the Peace Conference.' Lloyd George said, 'What were you doing with my secretary Philip Kerr?' 'Absolutely nothing,' blazed back Lady Astor. 'Then,' said Lloyd George, 'you ought to be ashamed of yourself.'
Lord Boothby, RECOLLECTIONS OF A REBEL 1978

11 Once in the 1920s, when I was staying in a country house in a party which included several distinguished statesmen, somebody asked the rhetorical question 'Can you point to any permanent constructive achievement of Lloyd George?' Lord Butler, who had appeared to be asleep in a corner, stirred in his armchair, gazed meditatively at the ceiling, and remarked, 'He won the greatest war in history. That really was something of an achievement.' Pressed for an explanation he went on to say that, in his considered opinion, we should never have inflicted the defeat that we did on Germany in 1918 without Lloyd George. 'That', he added, 'can be said of no other man.'
Ibid.

12 Lloyd George's private life was, to say the least of it, remarkable. He had two wives, two homes, and two families; and in the

words of his private secretary, A. J. Sylvester, 'he got away with it'.
Ibid.

1 When, before the outbreak of the First World War, Frances Stevenson became Megan's governess, they fell in love with each other. He then gave her a choice. She could become his personal private secretary and his mistress, or go; but she could not become his wife. She accepted. The consequences were pretty rough for all concerned.
Ibid.

2 No loyalty—therefore no rancour.
Violet Bonham Carter. Quoted Geoffrey Madan
NOTEBOOKS 1981

3 The Happy Warrior of Squandermania.
Winston Churchill

4 Lloyd George looked untidy, ordinary and common.
Duff Cooper, DIARY *Mar* 1916

5 Ireland saved Lloyd George's life. He and Kitchener had projected a visit to Russia in order to inspirit their flagging ally. At the last minute Lloyd George called off because of the negotiations over Ireland. Kitchener went alone. On 5 June 1916 the *Hampshire* with Kitchener on board struck a mine. Kitchener and most of the crew were drowned.
Sir Almeric Fitzroy, MEMOIRS

6 My one ardent desire is that after the war he should be publicly castrated in front of Nurse Cavell's statue.
Lytton Strachey to Francis Birrell. Quoted Michael Holroyd, The Times 15 *Jan* 1972

7 At a meeting at the Carlton Club, Baldwin attacked Lloyd George as 'a great dynamic force — a very terrible thing'. Lloyd George resigned the same afternoon, never to hold office again. He was the first prime minister since Lord North to resign because of a private meeting of MPs and not as a result of an adverse vote in parliament or at a general election. Thus he maintained to the end his disregard for the established constitutional machinery. He was the most inspired and creative British statesman of the twentieth century, but he had fatal flaws. He was devious and unscrupulous in his methods. He aroused every feeling except trust. In all his greatest acts there was an element of self-seeking. Above all, he lacked stability. He tied himself to no men, to no party, to no single cause.
A. J. P. Taylor, ENGLISH HISTORY 1914–1945 1965

ANITA LOOS

Born 1897 in America. Novelist, playwright and film script writer. Began her career writing scripts for silent films for D. W. Griffith. Achieved fame with her novel *Gentlemen Prefer Blondes*, 1925.

8 I'm furious about the Women's Liberationists. They keep getting up on soap boxes and proclaiming that women are brighter than men. That's true, but it should be kept very quiet or it ruins the whole racket.
Anita Loos, Observer, Sayings of the week 30 *Dec* 1973

JOE LOUIS

Born 1914 in America. Original name Joseph Louis Barrow. World heavyweight boxing champion. Won the title from J. J. Braddock, 1937. Retired undefeated 1949. Died 1981.

9 The innate good nature and high sense of responsibility of Louis made him the most respected of all champions, as well as the greatest.
The Times, Obituary 14 *Apr* 1981

10 After his boxing days were over he went into professional wrestling for a time. For Louis it seemed particularly sad because he was scuffling to make ends meet. He was asked how it felt to be in that line of work and replied in his pithy manner 'It beats stealin'.'
The Times 6 *Sep* 1984

SIR EDWIN (LANDSEER) LUTYENS

Born 1869. English architect, designed Hampstead Garden Suburb 1908, the Cenotaph in Whitehall, the lay-out of New Delhi, Liverpool Anglican Cathedral. Died 1944.

11 Sir Edwin Lutyens came to the hotel. He was working on the plans for New Delhi and had just returned from Buckingham Palace after an interview with King George V. He had taken with him a workable miniature toilet; it was about six inches high with a cistern that held about half a wineglass full of water, and when the chain was pulled it flushed like a regular toilet. Both the King and Queen had been so charmed by it that Lutyens had suggested building a doll's house round it. Later he arranged for various important artists to paint miniature pictures for the principal rooms. Every domestic installation

was made in miniature. When it was finished the Queen permitted it to be exhibited in public, and collected large sums for charity.
Charles Chaplin, MY AUTOBIOGRAPHY 1964

1 He had been commissioned by Lloyd George only two weeks before it was needed, to design a 'catafalque' past which the troops could march during the victory parade of 1919. He quickly sketched the design for his temporary monument. It was built in wood and plaster and was an instant success. Next day *The Times* in a leading article demanded that it be rebuilt in stone and by November 11 1920 the body of the Unknown Warrior was carried past Lutyens's new stone cenotaph.
Roderick Gradidge, The Times, The human face of genius 14 *Nov* 1981

2 At a banquet at the Café Royal I was with George Stampa when Lutyens came up, grinning like a schoolboy out for a lark and said he was so sorry to have to say goodnight, but it was getting late for him. George took his outstretched hand, and with it a squashed chocolate eclair, a horrible mess. Lutyens laughed so much I thought he would fall over. Some time later he came up again, and, seeming very apologetic, said to George, 'You're not angry with me, are you?' and caressed the top of George's head, this time with a handful of green jelly.
Reginald Pound, THEIR MOODS AND MINE 1937

M

GENERAL DOUGLAS MACARTHUR

Born 1880. American soldier. Conducted operations against the Japanese in World War II. Relieved of his command in Korea by President Truman because of disagreements over policy. Died 1964.

1 MacArthur was uniquely American, and like all great men liked no one else so much as himself.
D. Clayton James and Leo Cooper, THE YEARS OF MACARTHUR 1971

2 MacArthur was typical enough of one America, with his arrogance, his eloquence, his paranoia and his bombast; though not the America which is best known, and best loved in Europe.
Gavin Long, MACARTHUR AS MILITARY COMMANDER 1969

3 Even the placid Eisenhower found life difficult on MacArthur's staff. 'Not only have I met him, madam,' he replied to one of the General's admirers 'but I studied dramatics under him for five years.'
Ibid.

4 He gave himself such a mysterious and exalted eminence in Japan that he is known as the White Mikado.
Observer, Profile 9 *Jul* 1950

5 I fired him because he wouldn't respect the authority of the president. I didn't fire him because he was the dumb son of a bitch, although he was, but that's not against the law for generals. If it was, three quarters of them would be in jail.
Harry S. Truman. Quoted Merle Miller, PLAIN SPEAKING: AN ORAL BIOGRAPHY OF HARRY S. TRUMAN

SIR DESMOND MACCARTHY

Born 1878. English essayist, literary and dramatic critic. Much of his best work was done for newspapers and magazines and does not survive in more permanent form. Died 1952.

6 It was as if he were a full jug without a handle, full of precious liquid but with no means of pouring it out.
His wife. Quoted David Cecil, DESMOND MACCARTHY 1984

7 When writing about a play or a book he knew that the reader's first question would be 'Shall I enjoy it?' and sought to provide the answer. 'The first step to culture is always to learn what to enjoy, not what is best.'
Raymond Mortimer, The Times 12 *Sep* 1963

8 The range of his sympathies induced a various public to welcome his guidance. A Liberal himself, he made Conservatives read the *New Statesman* and Socialists the *Sunday Times*.
Ibid.

9 His easy-seeming style was the fruit of exceptional care. Though he always set to work at the last moment, he wrote slowly, struggling to find the exact word and to give every sentence the proper shape. Had he been engaged upon a book, and not an ephemeral review, he could hardly have taken more trouble to make his language limpid, euphonious and telling.
Ibid.

JAMES RAMSAY MACDONALD

Born 1866 in Scotland. British politician. First Labour Prime Minister 1924. Led a coalition National government 1931. Died 1937.

10 I remember interviews with Ramsay MacDonald because of the incredible woolliness with which he expressed his thought.
Vernon Bartlett, THIS IS MY LIFE 1937

11 I am glad Ramsay has gone. I have always disliked his shifty face and his inability to give a direct answer. What a career. A life-long Socialist, then for 4 years a Conservative Prime Minister. What an incredible volte-face. He ends up distrusted by Conservatives and hated by Socialists.
Sir Henry Channon, DIARY 8 *Jun* 1935

12 MacDonald was not the sort of man one could like. Many years ago he belonged to the Fabian Society; but he was also a member of the Independent Labour Party, all the Fabians thought him an ILP spy and the ILP folk thought him a Fabian spy. It

struck me that he was doing himself no good, so I wrote to tell him quite frankly what the situation was. Now I think you'll agree that most people would have received my letter with a scream of indignation, and I certainly expected MacDonald to sever our relationship and thenceforth to cut me dead. But not a bit of it! He took no offence at being called a spy. His reply was shrewd, tactful, conciliatory and diplomatic. So I knew that he would make a first-rate politician.
G. B. Shaw. Quoted Hesketh Pearson, BERNARD SHAW 1942

1 There are no professions he ever made, no pledges he ever gave to the country, and no humiliation to which he would not submit if they would only allow him still to be called Prime Minister.
Viscount Snowden, House of Lords 3 *Jul* 1934

2 MacDonald preferred high society, and in particular the society of Lady Londonderry, to that of his proletarian followers.
A. J. P. Taylor, ENGLISH HISTORY 1914–1945 1965

3 MacDonald owes his pre-eminence largely to the fact that he is the only artist, the only aristocrat by temperament and talent in a Party of plebeians and plain men.
Beatrice Webb DIARY *May* 1950

SIR COMPTON MACKENZIE

Born 1883. English writer of novels, essays, memoirs. Gained fame with *Sinister Street*, 1913. Was involved in a somewhat farcical prosecution for allegedly revealing state secrets in his *Gallipoli Memories*, 1929. Wrote *My Life and Times*, his autobiography, in ten volumes 1963–71. Died 1972.

4 Lunched at the Saintsbury Club and was next to Compton MacKenzie whom I had never met before. He looked like a Velasquez with his pointed beard, and wore a green velvet tie and diamond links.
Sir Henry Channon, DIARY 23 *Oct* 1944

5 His work has somewhat the appearance in places of the waste-paper basket of a man who has been tidying a long-neglected desk.
Norman Collins, News Chronicle 27 *Oct* 1932

6 His writings are an eternal Punch and Judy show; the harlequin kiosk set up on beach after beach, the same crocodiles beaten over the head, the same babies thrown out of the window.
Bevis Hillier

7 All his life he has written steadily. He may look like a latter-day Cunningham Grahame; but he sticks to his desk like another Trollope.
Observer, Profile 31 *Jul* 1949

8 *Gallipoli Memories* got him into trouble with the War Office. Though he extricated himself from this trouble with the official penalty of no more than a £50 fine the episode cost him a great deal more than that sum and a considerable distress of mind.
Ibid.

9 He retained a practically continuous recollection of his life from before he was two, and not merely of incidents, but of what he thought about them at the time. He taught himself to read at 22 months.
The Times, Obituary 1 *Dec* 1972

10 He began as an infant prodigy and ended as an octogenarian with the energy and undimmed zest for life of a teenager.
Ibid.

(MAURICE) HAROLD MACMILLAN

Born 1894. British politician. Foreign Secretary 1955. Chancellor of the Exchequer 1955–7. Prime Minister 1957–63. His period of office was marked by many former colonies achieving independence. Created Earl of Stockton, 1984.

11 Harold Macmillan, the unprepossessing, bookish, eccentric member for Stockton-on-Tees (and incidentally the Duke of Devonshire's son-in-law) has now repudiated the Government Whip, and has received a frigid note from Mr Baldwin.
Sir Henry Channon, DIARY 8 *May* 1936

12 It was impossible to believe that he was anything but a down-at-heel actor resting between engagements at the decrepit theatres of minor provincial towns.
Bernard Levin, THE PENDULUM YEARS 1976

13 If ever I am forced out of public life I shall certainly put up for mayor of Tunis.
Macmillan, Speech, Tunis 1943

14 Harold Macmillan was the first person to recognise that in the modern world of media exposure a Prime Minister has to be

something of a showman, equally at home in the theatre spotlight or the sawdust of the circus ring. He was an actor-manager with an instinct for productions with appeal for all.
James Margach, THE ABUSE OF POWER 1981

1 What a pity it is that now we have the most intelligent Prime Minister of the century, he has to conceal his intelligence from the public for fear they will suspect it.
Harold Nicolson, DIARY 9 *Feb* 1957

2 Macmillan's role as a poseur was itself a pose.
Harold Wilson, A PRIME MINISTER ON PRIME MINISTERS 1977

3 He was a Disraelian, perhaps the last Disraelian Prime Minister Britain will see . . . He had what Disraeli had, a profound sense of history. It is not impossible, but it is difficult for a Prime Minister to fulfil his duties without that sense. This was Macmillan's strength, even if it became perverted over Suez.
Ibid

4 Macmillan, off to Moscow in his fur hat, evinced a positive lust to embrace the bear.
Hugo Young, Sunday Times 3 *Oct* 1971

GEORGE LEIGH MALLORY

Born 1887. British mountaineer. Disappeared with Andrew Irvine while attempting to reach the summit of Everest 1924.

5 He was one of those figures of the early 1900s, like Rupert Brooke, around whom a fervent, but somehow impotent, cult seems to have accumulated. Everyone said how marvellous he was.
James Morris, The Times 1 *Mar* 1969

6 Mountaineering was his lust. Contemporaries say his style was uniquely graceful, and he himself seems to have regarded the sport as some kind of art — akin to ballet, perhaps with metaphysical elements of nature-worship and self-knowledge thrown in.
Ibid.

7 In 1911 at Cambridge A. C. Benson had urged Mallory to read Carlyle's Life of John Sterling — a book that achieved high quality simply by being *there*. In 1923 during a lecture tour of the US he was frequently asked why he wanted to climb Everest. He replied 'Because it is there'.
Nigel Rees, SAYINGS OF THE CENTURY 1984

8 George Mallory! My hand trembles, my heart palpitates, my whole being swoons away at the words — oh heavens! heavens!
Lytton Strachey. Quoted David Robertson, GEORGE MALLORY 1969

KATHERINE MANSFIELD

Born 1888 in New Zealand. Pen-name of Katherine Mansfield Beauchamp. First attracted attention with short stories based on her childhood experiences in New Zealand. Was married to John Middleton Murry. Died 1923.

9 Comfortable, if masterful adult men are to be found (convincingly) in her stories. None played a part in her life. She had a predilection for 'boyish' lovers'. Middleton Murry was the climax of her mistakes.
Elizabeth Bowen, Sunday Times 4 *Jul* 1971

10 What was unusual about Katherine Mansfield — genius apart — was the persistence within her of the schoolgirl; theatrical, passionate in her wishes, surgically inquisitive, ruthlessly self-regarding in her decisions. As against which, reckon her generosities, her tenderness to the weak, and her doughty courage.
Ibid.

11 Katherine Mansfield's life is so fascinating because it presents a very simple symbolic pattern. This is a variant of the Garden of Eden theme. An apple of knowledge is eaten, with bitter consequences. And then, under the curse and blessing of that knowledge, comes the attempt to regain paradise. It is a deeply moving story but not really a tragic one, for it ends in sight of success.
Christopher Isherwood, EXHUMATIONS 1966

12 During her college days Katherine was often preoccupied with the question of degrees of friendship. One day she suddenly asked me what I would do if I found out she had done something really awful, like killing somebody with a hatpin.
Katherine Mansfield, THE MEMORIES OF L.M. 1971

13 Her talk was marvellous, much better than her writing, especially when she was telling of things she was going to write but when she spoke about people she was dark, envious and full of alarming penetration in discovering what they least wished known

and whatever was bad in their characteristics.
Bertrand Russell, AUTOBIOGRAPHY 1967

1 The beautiful idol-like quietness of Katherine Mansfield made her absolutely enchanting.
Frank Swinnerton, THE GEORGIAN LITERARY SCENE 1935

2 Katherine Mansfield was a very fastidious person, a literary person, enamoured of her art. She was herself a simple person. But she tried hard, at one time or another, to be something a little more grandiose . . . I think she was a little too literary and perhaps even a little insincere — both accidents inevitable in one who was quickly moved by her own writings and by kindness from others, and one who was still, as far as I can see, seeking some aesthetic touchstone.
Ibid.

3 The later New Zealand stories, when her artistic powers were more assured, are clouded by that horrible sense of irrevocable ever nearer death that advanced consumptives of the early Twenties knew all the time.
Angus Wilson. Reviewing Anthony Alpers, THE LIFE OF KATHERINE MANSFIELD, *Observer* 11 *May* 1980

MAO TSE-TUNG

Born 1893, in China. Organised and led the Chinese Red Army in the civil war against Chiang Kai-Shek's Nationalists. Became Chairman of People's Republic of China, 1949. Died 1976.

4 The *Thoughts of Mao Tse-Tung* have become to his own people in his own age what the Sayings of Confucius were to the Chinese people for the past 2000 years; the source of inspiration and guidance in matters social, political and moral. Whether they will continue to exercise this tremendous influence in the ages to come cannot be known, but it is now clear that no Chinese thinker in the period since Confucius has attained the degree of acceptance and authority which Mao has acquired.
C. P. Fitzgerald, MAO TSE-TUNG AND CHINA 1976

5 He dominated the room as I have neve seen any person do except Charles de Gaulle.
Henry Kissinger, MEMOIRS 1982

GUGLIELMO MARCONI

Born 1874 in Italy. Physicist and inventor, developed wireless telegraphy. Transmitted the first transatlantic signals 1901. Awarded Nobel Prize for Physics 1909. Died 1937.

6 One day Marconi said he was going to send a wireless message across the Channel. We went over near Boulogne and sent a message and then awaited an answer. None came and Marconi was terribly upset. He was nearly crying with disappointment. Suddenly we heard a sound, and the answer came. 'Why ever did you not answer before?' demanded Marconi. 'Well, we went away to supper,' replied the England end.
Agnes Baden-Powell, News Chronicle 18 *May* 1938

7 When he came to England and his baggage was examined by customs officials something like panic ensued over the discovery of his apparatus. The pale, slenderly-built young man who had brought it was suspected of carrying an infernal machine and notwithstanding all his protests it was promptly dropped into a bucket of water.
Daily Telegraph, Obituary 21 *Jul* 1937

8 Marconi's most cherished possession was a gold tablet presented to him by 600 survivors of the *Titanic* who had been saved by the fact that the ship's wireless transmitter had been able to call ships from hundreds of miles away to pick up survivors.
Douglas Walters, Daily Herald 21 *Jul* 1937

QUEEN MARY

Born 1867 at Kensington Palace. Daughter of the Duke of Teck. Christened Victoria Mary Augusta Louise Olga Pauline Claudine Agnes. Consort of George V. Died 1953.

9 That undivided bust popularised by Queen Mary.
Nancy Banks-Smith, Guardian 8 *Jan* 1977

10 Lady Astor once escorted Queen Mary round some nursery schools. Afterwards she remarked: 'Queen Mary is magnificent and kindness itself. I felt like a small tug towing the *Queen Mary*.'
John Beevers, Sunday Referee 10 *Feb* 1939

11 Queen Mary, it seems, drinks a half-bottle of hock every night with her dinner, and has done so all her life; sometimes at luncheon, too. And the stock of hock is running low in

this country. I hear she still keeps up some state at Badminton where her tireless energy quite exhausts her long-suffering but devoted entourage.
Sir Henry Channon, DIARY 4 *Feb* 1942

1 She was magnificent, humorous, worldly, in fact nearly sublime, though cold and hard. Her appearance was formidable, her manner — well it was like talking to St Paul's Cathedral.
Ibid. 25 *Mar* 1953

2 She was never much liked by the Edwardian smart set who used to giggle at the fringe of artificial hair she wore on her forehead like a thick sponge.
Robert Lacey, MAJESTY 1977

3 She made me feel the meaning of the phrase *grande dame*.
Harold Nicolson DIARY 21 *Mar* 1949

4 Baldwin told his daughter of a meeting he had had with Queen Mary as the abdication storm grew. I had a tremendous shock. For instead of standing immobile in the middle distance, silent and majestic, she came trotting across the room exactly like a puppy dog, and before I had time to bow she took hold of my hand in both hers and held it tight. 'Well, Prime Minister,' she said, 'here's a pretty kettle of fish!'
Nigel Rees, SAYINGS OF THE CENTURY 1984

5 When next I met the Queen I had to shake hands with my left hand, as my right hand was in a sling. There was nothing very extraordinary about that — in 1915 most men who were in London had a bandage of some description — but what did surprise me was that meeting her again, four years later, she came up to me and said without a moment's hesitation, 'I hope your hand is quite well again'. When one thinks of how many wounded men Her Majesty had seen during that space of time, it is a wonderful example of the royal memory that she should have remembered the exact place where I had been hit.
Ernest Thesiger, PRACTICALLY TRUE 1927

JOHN (EDWARD) MASEFIELD

Born 1878. English poet, playwright, novelist. Poet Laureate 1930–67. Died 1967.

6 The ceremonial effusions expected of a Laureate proved an embarrassment to Masefield, whose dutiful compositions were submitted to *The Times* with a stamped envelope for their return if they were unsuitable.
Alan Bell, The Times 20 *Sep* 1982

7 John Masefield visited the studio; he was a tall, handsome, gentle man, kindly and understanding. But for some reason these qualities made me extremely shy. Fortunately I had just read *The Widow in the Bye Street*, which I admired, so I was not entirely mum and quoted some of my favourite lines from it.
Charles Chaplin, MY AUTOBIOGRAPHY 1964

8 *The Everlasting Mercy* (1911) was shocking as the first poem to use the adjective 'bloody'.
Gavin Ewart, Observer 18 *Nov* 1984

9 Masefield was a first-class narrative poet, the last full-blown one we have had, and *Reynard the Fox* is rightly praised as the height of his achievement.
Ibid.

10 There is no strain in being Poet Laureate, one wants to do it. It is a happy duty. It is a delight to try to show your skill by overcoming a problem. A crossword seems impossible at first, and then you think of something. It's the same with verse, By George, that's it, you say. It lights up something else and you are encouraged.
John Masefield. Quoted Hunter Davies, Sunday Times 26 *May* 1963

JAMES MASON

Born 1909. English film actor. Began his cinema career in 1935, and appeared in over 100 films. Among his notable successes were *Odd Man Out, The Seventh Veil, Wicked Lady*, and *The Desert Fox*. Died 1984.

11 Mason is for women who have knocked about a bit.
Leslie Arless, author of THE WICKED LADY

12 When I see a film of my own on the screen I am pleased when I see myself but bored with the rest of it.
James Mason. Quoted Ernest Betts, Daily Express 4 *Jan* 1946

13 His handsomeness was of a type not regarded as acceptable for the celluloid hero of the day. He seemed too smooth, not only in his usually well-groomed appearance, but above all in his way of speaking.
Rupert Morris, The Times 28 *Jul* 1984

14 He cannot have much interest in clothes. A typical Mason ensemble is a brown suit, a

white shirt with stiff cuffs that looks like a hangover from Gerry, Lord Manderstoke, a floppy collar, a blinding tie, socks that almost fall over cheap shoes, and cuff-links as large as half-crowns — but more theatrical. 'I looted them in Germany' he says.
Roland Wild, Illustrated 16 *Feb* 1946

HENRI MATISSE

Born 1869 in France. Painter and sculptor, leader of a group known as *Les Fauves*. Died 1954.

1 One day Matisse wanted to do a lithograph. I offered him all my chalk and stones, but he would have none of them. He got some lithographic paper, broke one of my lithographic chalks in half, and left himself with only about an inch and a quarter of grease to draw with. When I protested and pressed him to take the box, he assured me it was unnecessary, and much too expensive a gift, a comment on the wonderful French economy and the appalling poverty he must have suffered in his early days.
C. R. W. Nevinson. Quoted Edmund Fuller, ANECDOTES 1946

2 In the years immediately before his death whilst sick and bedridden Matisse continued to produce his art. By tearing and cutting brightly coloured paper into large shapes he was able to form large compositions by giving the pieces to assistants to assemble under his instruction. When attached to walls these shapes seem to float reflectively or energetically in space, reanimating the themes of former years when Matisse painted the murals for the Barnes Foundation at Merion in the USA.
Pat Turner, MAKERS OF MODERN CULTURE (*Edited by Justin Wintle*) 1981

SIR STANLEY MATTHEWS

Born 1915. English footballer. Most successful player of his era. Played 54 times for England, and continued in first-class football until he was 50 years of age.

3 He came from that England which had no reason to know that the Twenties were naughty and that the Thirties had style.
Arthur Hopcroft, THE FOOTBALL MAN 1968

4 Matthews will be remembered for his sportsmanship. Not one caution did he receive during his 33 years as a player; not once did he demur at the referee's decision. So it was fitting that he should be soccer's first player knight.
Mary Raine, Sunday Times, 1000 Makers of the Twentieth Century

W. (WILLIAM) SOMERSET MAUGHAM

Born 1874 in France. English novelist, playwright and short-story writer. A favourite theme was the effect on white people of living in the Tropics. Died 1965.

5 Somerset Maugham was attending a dinner party. The Chinese butler remarked pleasantly, 'Good evening Mr Maugham. I think it only fair to tell you I didn't much care for your last book.' An hour later Mr Maugham was missing from among the assembled guests. A scouting party discovered him in the kitchen, hotly defending his literary style to the butler.
Bennett Cerf, SHAKE WELL BEFORE USING 1948

6 Mr Maugham, in reminiscent mood, told of his elation when Sir Edmund Gosse, dean of English critics, wrote an enthusiastic review of Maugham's first novel *Eliza of Lambeth*, in 1897. Until he died in 1928, however, Sir Edmund never saw Maugham without patting him on the shoulder and murmuring, 'Capital piece of work, that *Eliza of Lambeth*. How smart you were never to have written anything else.'
Ibid.

7 We lunched with Emerald Cunard. Somerset Maugham was also there with his shrewd brain and Chinese face. Though he is a brilliant writer he is not, of course, a gentleman.
Sir Henry Channon, DIARY 4 *May* 1935

8 Many reminiscences of every kind from Willie, who has had a long, amorous career, and now at 75 is still lusty. He has been everywhere, met everybody, tasted everything. His interest in the world and in society and food and drink, is acute, though he occasionally has flashes of amnesia.
Ibid. 29 *Apr* 1949

9 He inclines towards the exotic. His very presence somehow suggests black marble bathrooms and the last word in bathsalts. He reminds one of something out of a Wilde play. He dresses immaculately upon all occasions. When he gives someone a gift it is invariably something rare — such as a white malacca cane which has belonged to an

Eastern prince. Anyone can buy a malacca cane, but it takes Somerset Maugham to find a white malacca.
Ethel Mannin, CONFESSIONS AND IMPRESSIONS 1930

1 He is a disciple of the exquisite, and he has the material means with which to indulge his taste for the exquisite in all directions. His famous Villa Mauresque at Cap Ferat is as exquisite as the utmost resources of civilisation drawn upon by an epicurean taste can make it.
Ibid.

2 My world popularity is the most interesting thing about me.
W. Somerset Maugham. Quoted Ted Morgan, SOMERSET MAUGHAM 1980

LOUIS B. (BURT) MAYER

Born 1885 in Russia. Emigrated to Canada and then to the United States to set up in business as a motion picture distributor. Laid the foundation of his fortune by purchasing the New England rights of D. W. Griffith's *Birth of a Nation*, 1915. With Samuel Goldwyn and Marcus Lowe, founded the Metro-Goldwyn-Mayer Corporation in 1924. Died 1957.

3 His arguments were often irritatingly unanswerable. If a writer complained of his work being changed Mayer always said: 'The number one book of the ages was written by a committee, and it is called *The Bible*.'
Arthur Freed. Quoted Leslie Halliwell, THE FILMGOER'S BOOK OF QUOTES 1978

4 This Hollywood rajah was perhaps the archetypal movie mogul: sentimental, commonsensical, businesslike, unaesthetic, arrogant, illogical, naïve, amoral, tasteless and physically unappealing. For twenty years he ran MGM splendidly in his own image, and became a legend of autocracy.
Leslie Halliwell, THE FILMGOER'S BOOK OF QUOTES 1978

5 As early as 1922 his credo was fully formed: 'I will only make pictures that I won't be ashamed to have my children see.' His cry in later years, when permissiveness was creeping in, was: 'Don't show the natural functions!'
Ibid.

6 In argument Mayer was a great and exhausting opponent, violent, wheedling and pleading by turns. Robert Taylor remembered going in for more money. When he emerged a friend asked him: 'Did you get the rise?' 'No, but I gained a father.'
Ibid.

7 Czar of all the rushers.
B. P. Schulberg

GOLDA MEIR

Born 1898 in Russia. Emigrated to United States then, in 1921, settled in Palestine. Worked for the formation of the republic of Israel and became its Prime Minister, 1969. Resigned 1974.

8 When Golda Meir took over the Israeli cabinet she ran it like a drill sergeant. Inattentive ministers had been inclined to read newspapers under the table when bored. 'There will be no newspapers read at government meetings,' she announced firmly. And instead of sitting at the head of the table she took a chair bang in the middle, hawk-eyed and alert — 'So that I can see you all.'
Meriel McCooey, Radio Times

9 When President Nixon suggested that she might send some of her generals to Vietnam to help with the war she replied 'Certainly, if we can have a couple of yours in exchange.' When asked which two she replied 'General Motors and General Electric.'
Ibid.

10 She has an electrifying warmth which irradiates her strong face with its prominent nose, weary eyes and fine bold brow. She has not changed her hairstyle for as long as anybody can remember; and her habits of dress are — not to put too fine a point on it — rather plain.
Observer, Profile 9 *Mar* 1969

11 Ask her what it is like to be a woman Foreign Minister and she will reply with a puckish smile that she does not know what it is like to be a man Foreign Minister.
The Times 6 *Feb* 1981

DAME NELLIE MELBA

Born 1859 in Australia. Original name Helen Porter Mitchell. Achieved world-wide fame as a soprano. Died 1931.

12 She remarked on hearing the famous record of Ernest Lough singing *Hear My Prayer*, 'I could murder that infant; he has all the qualities I worked for years to acquire;

phrasing, breath control, diction, everything.'
Percy Colson, MELBA 1932

1 It is a nice question whether the pleasure Melba gave with her own singing was not outweighed by the pleasure she deprived London of by blocking the careers of so many other singers.
Ronald Hastings, Daily Telegraph 21 *Sep* 1967

2 The charm of her voice was its notable purity. It extended over a compass of two and a half octaves. Her shake was one of the most perfect examples of the voice trill ever heard. She had an extraordinary command of pathos, which made her Desdemona ever memorable, and in her Mimi there was a personality and grace which stamped her as a great artist.
Morning Post, Obituary 24 *Feb* 1931

3 She retained a keen sense of her own fiscal value. When she was invited to dinner by a rich hostess who suggested that after the meal she might 'sing a little song' Melba declined. It was no trouble, she agreed, to sing a little song. But it was even less arduous to sign a little cheque.
Joseph Wechsberg, RED PLUSH AND BLACK VELVET 1962

4 She was in the great tradition of prima donnas. Commanded to sing at Windsor Castle with Mary Garden, the reigning diva of the Opera Comique, she confided to the Lord Chamberlain in a penetrating whisper 'What a dreadful concert this would have been if I hadn't come.'
Ibid.

YEHUDI MENUHIN

Born 1916 in America of Jewish parentage. Violin virtuoso who made his debut at the age of seven, and first appeared in London with the San Francisco Orchestra in 1929.

5 When two years old he asked for, and was given, his first violin and immediately smashed it because it was a toy one and would not 'sing'; his grandmother gave him a proper one, small size, and at four and a half he started taking violin lessons.
Donald Hodson, News Chronicle 6 *May* 1938

6 Most star players have a handful of pieces which they play wherever they go. Not so Yehudi who hardly ever repeats a programme. There is so much undiscovered music that it is ridiculous, he thinks, to go on playing only the outstanding ones.
Ibid.

HENRY MILLER

Born 1891. American novelist. Lived in France 1930–9, during which time his *Tropic of Cancer* was published in Paris, 1936, but banned in America until 1961. On his return to America he expressed his reactions to his native country in *The Air Conditioned Nightmare*, 1945.

7 It is relatively rare to discover a novel whose obvious intention is to debauch as many readers as possible, mentally, morally, phsyically and politically.
Anonymous review of BARBARY SHORE 1951

8 No one has tried harder to write pornographically or more signally failed.
Cyril Connolly, Observer 31 *Mar* 1963

9 A gay, fierce, shocking, profound, sometimes brilliant, sometimes madly irritating first novel by the American Céline.
Cyril Connolly, Introduction to TROPIC OF CANCER

10 I never liked the language of Henry Miller. I don't think pornography has added to our sensual life.
Anaïs Nin. Quoted Harriet Chare, The Times 1 *Jun* 1970

11 I first met Miller in a Montparnasse café, trying to get drunk enough to tell the waiter he had no money. His private economy system was then a simple one. On the assumption that he needed two meals a day and could count on a friend to provide one a week he set out to find 14 friends. He found he had more than he needed, among them Lawrence Durrell and George Orwell.
Alfred Perles, MY FRIEND, HENRY MILLER 1956

12 At last, an unprintable book that is readable.
Ezra Pound of Henry Miller's TROPIC OF CANCER

A. A. (ALAN ALEXANDER) MILNE

Born 1882. English author, and journalist, now mainly remembered for his children's books *When We Were Very Young*, 1924 and *Winnie the Pooh*, 1926. Died 1956.

13 *When We Were Very Young* is not the work

of a poet becoming playful; it is the work of a light-verse writer taking his job seriously even though he is taking it into the nursery. It seems that the nursery, more than any other room in the house, likes to be approached seriously.
A. A. Milne, IT'S TOO LATE NOW 1939

1 I am not inordinately fond of, or interested in, children; their appeal to me is the physical appeal such as other young animals make. I have never felt the least bit sentimental about them, or no more sentimental than one becomes for a moment over a puppy or a kitten.
Ibid.

2 At the end of his first year of free-lancing Mr Milne discovered that he had spent the whole of his capital, £300, and earned £20.
Campbell Nairne, John o' London's Weekly 6 *Oct* 1939

3 Tonstant Weader fwowed up.
Dorothy Parker (Constant Reader) reviewing WINNIE THE POOH *for the New Yorker* 1926

NANCY (FREEMAN) MITFORD

Born 1904. English novelist, author of *The Pursuit of Love*. In collaboration with Professor Alan Ross, produced *Noblesse Oblige*, which coined the term 'U and non-U'. Died 1973.

4 Her English is beautifully uncontemporary. The best thing she can say about a person, a place, a holiday, a book, a country is that it was terribly amusing.
Atticus, Sunday Times 28 *Aug* 1966

5 Nancy Mitford has lived for twenty years in Paris, yet when anyone bumps into her in the street they always look at her and say Sorry, in English.
Ibid.

6 Nancy, researching for a book, still had to ask as late as the sixties, 'What are jeans?'
Jonathan and Catherine Guinness, THE HOUSE OF MITFORD 1984

7 I recall *Highland Fling* being written in an exercise book. It was the debut of our father, Lord Redesdale. The, larger than life-size, felicitously named 'General Murgatroyd', was Farve.
Jessica Mitford, HONS AND REBELS 1960

8 Some reviewers do get a bit sarky. One once said that I was like an ormolu clock, chiming away on the mantelpiece. He was probably being awfully rude, but I rather liked it. If you're an honest little clock, and tell the time properly, isn't that rather nice?
Nancy Mitford, Sunday Times 28 *Aug* 1966

9 She had no formal education. She never learnt to spell or to punctuate; she spoke French fluently but with an aggressive English accent and knew no other foreign language. Her style with its paucity of clauses has been called a schoolgirl burble. By pertinacity and tireless re-writing she made it, however, finely economical and easy to read.
The Times, Obituary 2 *Jul* 1973

10 Some of her remarks about 'U' and 'non-U' are questionable. Her talk of such distinctions must not be taken seriously; it was part of her love for teasing; and she was enchanted when her friends teased her in return.
Ibid.

11 Nice cheap girl to take out for the evening. Costs you only eighteen and six for an orangeade in a night club.
Evelyn Waugh, of Nancy Mitford. Quoted Maurice Bowra, MEMORIES

VYACHESLAV MIKHAILOVITCH MOLOTOV

Born 1890. Russian politician, his original surname Skriabin. Foreign Minister, 1939–49 and 1953–6. Negotiated the non-aggression pact with Germany 1939. Expelled from Communist Party 1964.

12 I have never seen a human being who more perfectly resembled the modern conception of a robot.
Winston Churchill, THE GATHERING STORM

13 Molotov was actively involved in dealing out death to his comrades and colleagues. He had a particularly repellant habit of adding obscene abuse as well as his signature, against the names on Stalin's death list. Here, at least, the abominable No-man became the enthusiastic Yes-man.
Roy Medvedev, ALL STALIN'S MEN

14 Molotov has a nickname, invented by the brilliant journalist and publicist Karl Radek: Stone Bottom. It stuck because the supreme quality of Mr Molotov was, as it is today, his capacity for sitting at an office desk.
Observer, Profile 7 *Dec* 1957

15 While Lenin, immensely his senior, saw him as a highly competent junior party official, and once called him 'the best filing-clerk in

Russia' Stalin had already fixed on him as his born chief-of-staff.
Observer, Profile 7 *Dec* 1947

1 His record in Stalin's purges makes him one of the most wretched remnants of an appalling regime.
George Walden, The Times, Cocktail with a bitter aftertaste 17 *Jul* 1984

2 Improbably Molotov — real name Skryabin — was related to the composer, though he seems to have been born with a dirge rather than with music in his soul.
Ibid.

MARILYN MONROE

Born 1926. Original name Norma Jean Baker. Film actress, starred in many Hollywood comedies, including *Gentlemen Prefer Blondes*, 1953, *The Seven Year Itch*, 1955. Died in 1962, allegedly suicide, although the circumstances were never fully explained.

3 Kissing her is like kissing Hitler.
Tony Curtis

4 You don't have to hold an inquest to find out who killed Marilyn Monroe. Those bastards in the big executive chairs killed her.
Henry Hathaway. Quoted Leslie Halliwell, THE FILMGOER'S BOOK OF QUOTES 1978

5 Anyone who holds to the opinion that Marilyn Monroe was a great natural comic identifies himself immediately as a dunce. She was good at being inarticulately abstracted for the same reason that midgets are good at being short.
Clive James, AT THE PILLARS OF HERCULES

6 EGGHEAD WEDS HOURGLASS
Newspaper headline when Arthur Miller married Marilyn Monroe

7 A professional amateur.
Laurence Olivier

8 Directing her was like directing Lassie. You needed fourteen takes to get each one of them right.
Otto Preminger. Quoted Leslie Halliwell, THE FILMGOER'S BOOK OF QUOTES 1978

9 Of course, as a sex symbol she was stunning, but, sadly, she must be one of the silliest women I have ever met.
Donald Sinden, A TOUCH OF THE MEMOIRS 1982

10 She knows the world, but this knowledge has not lowered her great and benevolent dignity; its darkness has not dimmed her goodness.
Edith Sitwell

11 Anyone can remember lines, but it takes an artist to come on the set and not know her lines and give the performance she did.
Billy Wilder

C. E. (CHARLES EDWARD) MONTAGUE

Born 1867. English writer who spent most of his life as a leader writer, critic and essayist on the *Manchester Guardian*. On retirement turned to writing novels which won acclaim: *Disenchantment*, 1922, *Rough Justice*, 1926 and *Right Off the Map*, 1927. Died 1928.

12 Inside his *Manchester Guardian* office he spent nearly the whole evening till midnight, reading first his material, then writing with astonishing rapidity, then pausing over the proof, until he reached the very severe criterion he had laid down to himself for correct writing. Then going home; and the same thing the next evening and every evening until he had done nearly forty years of work in the office.
T. P. O'Connor, T.P.'s Weekly 19 *Oct* 1929

BERNARD LAW MONTGOMERY, FIRST VISCOUNT MONTGOMERY OF ALAMEIN

Born 1887. British field marshal. Commanded the British 8th Army in 1942 at the Battle of Alamein. Commanded the land forces in Normandy 1944. Died 1976.

13 When I asked him what made him the great field commander which was his undisputed claim to fame he said: 'During the First World War I hardly ever saw my Army Commander, and never my Commander-in-Chief. I then made up my mind that if ever I reached high command my troops should know me and understand quite clearly what I was trying to do.'
Lord Boothby, RECOLLECTIONS OF A REBEL 1978

14 The result Monty achieved could not have been produced by an officer who was concerned to behave as a gentleman.
Field Marshal Lord Carver, The Times, Monty: the toughest battle 8 *Jun* 1981

1 He was almost insanely jealous. Nobody must share the credit and the glory. He and he alone had gained it, and, although the sun of his glory could shine downwards on those who had served under him, there must be no other source of light.
Ibid.

2 He got so damn personal to make sure that the Americans and me, in particular, had no credit, had nothing to do with the war, that I eventually just stopped communicating with him. I was just not intersted in keeping up communications with a man that just can't tell the truth.
General Eisenhower. Quoted Cornelius Ryan, A BRIDGE TOO FAR 1974

3 General Jacob says that Montgomery was assuredly a very great general. Not for certain as great as Wellington, since he never had to cope with the same shortages of supply and support from home. But nonetheless a very great general 'who could always impose his own battle on the enemy'.
Harold Nicolson, DIARY 9 *Jan* 1947

4 In 1946 Montgomery appeared in California and Sam Goldwyn gave a dinner for him . . . Goldwyn rose at the other end of the table and beat a knife against a wineglass. The clatter was cut to a minimum and we braced ourselves to hear the inevitable words of welcome to the distinguished guest. Goldwyn cleared his throat 'It gives me great pleasure tonight to welcome to Hollywood a very distinguished soldier — ladies and gentlemen I propose a toast to Marshall Field Montgomery.' There was a stunned silence, during which Frances Goldwyn sat very still looking as though she had been hit by a halibut, finally broken by Jack Warner who cracked 'Montgomery Ward, you mean'. Marshall Field and Montgomery Ward, it should perhaps be explained, are two of the biggest US department stores.
David Niven, BRING ON THE EMPTY HORSES 1975

5 The Wolfenden report recognised the facts of homosexuality and tried to deal with them. Field Marshal Montgomery was utterly opposed to what he told me was the 'Buggers' Charter'. He could not understand bishops who wanted to change the law. He was appalled that the Primate, Michael Ramsey, had supported the charter. At the committee stage he tried to render the Bill harmless by suggesting that the age of consent should be raised from the age of twenty-one to the age of eighty, adding with a disarming smile that he himself would achieve four-score years at his next birthday.
Mervyn Stockwood, CHANCTONBURY RING 1982

GEORGE MOORE

Born 1852. Irish novelist, playwright, art critic. His *Hail and Farewell,* 1911–14, is an autobiographical triology. Died 1933.

6 His work to me is always more like music than prose, and indeed when I once asked him if he was rewriting Ulick and Soracha he replied, 'My dear young man, I have re-orchestrated it.'
Sir Henry Channon, DIARY 8 *Apr* 1935

7 He had blue eyes, pink face, white moustache and white hair, and looked like a walrus; and was as pleased as a child with attentions from the Prince of Wales, when he was over eighty.
Ibid.

8 George Moore was licentious in mind and collected photographs of his women adorers, and told racey little anecdotes with the idea of appearing more of a rake than he was. I think he was really an old monk, living in the wrong century, and it pleased him to play the rake.
Ibid.

9 His smile is like sunshine on putty.
Michael Field, Journals

10 I never quite took to Moore, or got accustomed to his large tallowy (or on his good days apple-blossom-waxy) face and pale eyes ('I'm glad he's found someone to paint his blobby eyes for him' said an inimical lady at sight of Walter Sickert's famous portrait).
Edward Marsh, A NUMBER OF PEOPLE 1939

11 Oliver Gogarty and George Moore were travelling in a train out Dundalk way. Moore was holding forth about the beauties of nature, and suddenly cried out 'Look quick, Gogarty! Isn't that view superb now? I would give pounds to be able to see it for just a few minutes.' 'Right,' said Oliver, 'you'll have your wish.' He pulled the communication cord and the train stopped. I've often wondered since if Moore paid the five pounds fine.
Sir William Orpen, STORIES OF OLD IRELAND AND MYSELF 1931

1 Sir John Lavery's wife Hazel, talking of George Moore, said he had the reputation at one time of visiting the graves of his dead Irish loves and telling whoever was with him exactly how each behaved in his company. But a great friend of hers, a Dublin doctor, hearing this repeated, exclaimed: 'What nonsense! The old fool's been impotent since he was four!'
Reginald Pound, THEIR MOODS AND MINE 1937

HENRY MOORE

Born 1898. British sculptor and artist. Worked in bronze, wood and stone, and was particularly attracted to producing large pieces for open-air exhibition. As an official artist during World War II, produced a particularly evocative series of studies of underground air raid shelters.

2 Henry considered carving to be soothing work, not too strenuous either physically or mentally. Much of the time the work was automatic, he could work for eight or twelve hours a day. But drawing, or inventing new shapes in small model form, was creative and took a greater toll.
Cecil Beaton, DIARY 1956

3 The biggest influence in my work is the human figure and how much it matters to me. I don't mean faces and lips and the expression on people's faces. I mean the human figure in the sense that the human figure mattered to Michelangelo and Rodin.
Henry Moore. Quoted John Gale, Observer 28 *Jul* 1968

4 Sculptor Henry Moore has been asked not to leave any holes in which boys could trap their heads when he carves 'Family Group' for Harlow New Town.
News Chronicle. Quoted Michael Bateman, THIS ENGLAND

J. P. (JOHN PIERPONT) MORGAN

Born 1837. American financier, inherited large fortune from his father, which he greatly enlarged by his operations in railroads and steel. Died 1913.

5 Morgan succeeded in bringing a measure of order into capitalist chaos. But because he never set up a deal or a trust without taking his cut, he also became unimaginably rich in the process. But deeming the order which he imposed to be in the public interest, he was thus able to maintain that he served both God and Mammon, to the edification of both.
John Naughton, Observer 12 *Jun* 1981

6 By the end of the nineteenth century he effectively controlled the entire US railway industry. Later he did something similar with steel, creating single-handed the 1400 million dollar steel corporation.
Ibid.

7 The prolonged period of living under his parents' shadow had the same repressive effect on Morgan as it had on his friend Edward VII. It certainly gave both men an inexhaustible appetite for young actresses (some of whom they exchanged) a *penchant* for eight-course breakfasts, a colossal weight problem, and an aversion to physical exercise that bordered on paranoia.
Ibid.

8 He was two things to all men: admirable to the few people who knew him, dreadful to the masses who did not. Solitaire was his usual card game and his silences explained nothing.
Andrew Sinclair, CORSAIR 1981

HERBERT (STANLEY) MORRISON, BARON MORRISON OF LAMBETH

Born 1888. British politician. Leader of the London County Council 1934–40. Home Secretary in Churchill's war-time government 1940–5. On retirement of Attlee as leader of the Labour Party, was defeated by Gaitskell in contest for the succession. Died 1965.

9 I am worried about Morrison. Dick Law tells me that his speech on Foreign Affairs on Monday was absolutely deplorable. Everyone squirmed in agony. He pronounced the first syllable of 'Tigris' to rhyme with 'pig', and called the Euphrates the 'You Frates', in two separate words. Now, I do not mind people pronouncing foreign names incorrectly, but to pronounce the Tigris and Euphrates in that way indicates not only a lack of education, but also that one has not heard the Middle East discussed by men of experience. It is that which is so terrifying.
Harold Nicolson, DIARY 1 *Aug* 1951

10 The Labour government did not live up to expectations and the position worsened when Attlee became ill. Herbert Morrison was supposed, rightly or wrongly, to have had dreams of a ride to the Palace to kiss

hands. I remember walking up the stairs at Downing Street as members of the Government were assembling for a meeting. Cripps was in front of me, and Morrison was in front of him. As both men paused on the landing I heard Cripps say; 'My dear Herbert, the idea that you could be Prime Minister is ridiculous.' Morrison moved silently to the next flight of stairs.
Mervyn Stockwood, CHANCTONBURY RING 1982

1 When he saw a beautiful waterfall he wondered only how many watts it would generate.
Colin Welch, Daily Telegraph 4 *Oct* 1973

J. B. (JOHN CAMERON ANDRIEU BINGHAM) MORTON

Born 1893. English author who became most widely known for his contributions to the *Daily Express*, which he joined in 1924, and for which he wrote a daily column under the pen name Beachcomber.

2 Funny chap. Yelling the glass out of the windows in his rage and, in the middle of it, stopping to do a dance he has seen in Andorra. At invective he is superb. Working in a room next to him is not my idea of a planned life. It is like being in the wings of a music-hall crazy week.
Reginald Pound, THEIR MOODS AND MINE 1937

3 Some weeks back he and I were in a London–Eastbourne train. He was in one of his raves about the absurdity of working for a newspaper that paid him for being humorous and then cut out all the humour. The only other traveller in the compartment was a spinsterish person who sat upright in a corner disliking us and our talk very much. Observing this, Johnny began making horrible hyena noises and then hauled himself up into the luggage rack, and lay there scratching and chattering like a chimp — an abominably funny exhibition. I was sorry for the prude in the corner. At Three Bridges she gathered herself together, leaped out and ran along the platform to another carriage like a gazelle.
Ibid.

4 His laugh is like the crackling and popping and roaring of a gorse bush on fire.
Ibid.

5 The contradictions in his nature are curious. He loves the mud of England and is contemptuous of her people. He is Harrow and Oxford and often behaves like Borstal and Parkhurst.
Ibid.

SIR OSWALD MOSLEY

Born 1896. British politician, who became a Labour MP in 1929, but by 1932 no longer supported socialist policy and resigned to form the British Union of Fascists. Imprisoned in 1940. Released in 1943. Died 1980.

6 Mosley won't come to any good, and we need not bother about him.
Stanley Baldwin to Tom Jones 1934

7 I know Mosley intimately, or rather I did. He is an unscrupulous but not unattractive fellow, dominated by an urge for power and publicity.
Sir Henry Channon, DIARY 23 *Nov* 1943

8 Sir Philip Sassoon took me to Consuelo Vanderbilt Balsan's house for lunch. One guest stands out, a tall lean man, dark haired with cropped moustache, pleasant and engaging, to whom I found myself addressing my conversation. I must have said something that particularly appealed to the tall gentleman, for his face lit up and his eyes opened so wide that I could see the whites of them. He seemed to be endorsing everything I said until I reached the climax of my thesis, which must have veered in direct contrary to his own, for he looked disappointed. I had been talking to Sir Oswald Mosley, little realising that this man was to be the future head of the blackshirts of England.
Charles Chaplin, MY AUTOBIOGRAPHY 1964

9 Those eyes with the whites showing over the pupils and the broad grinning mouth stand out in my memory vividly as an expression most peculiar — if not a little frightening.
Ibid.

10 My father, it seemed, never much liked Hitler. In old age he used to refer to him as 'a terrible little man'. One of the sayings he liked to bring out over the dinner table was that Italy, being a feminine country, had fallen in love with Mussolini, a man; whereas Germany, being a masculine country, had fallen in love with Hitler, a woman. At the other end of the table my stepmother Diana would smile patiently with closed eyes.
Nicholas Mosley, BEYOND THE PALE 1983

11 His fatal step was the formation of the New Party in February 1931, surely the most

bizarre episode in modern politics. The money for this extraordinary venture came from Sir William Morris, later Lord Nuffield, who stumped up £50,000 — the most disastrous piece of generosity which Mosley ever received.
Robert Skidelsky, OSWALD MOSLEY 1975

1 He was an ardent European and a powerful propagandist. He had facts and figures at his finger-tips and he transmitted his enthusiasm. I sought his advice when I spoke in the Lords on our entry into the Common Market and some of my speeches were drafted by him. On one occasion I was warmly congratulated by members of all parties, but I thought it wise to conceal the source of my inspiration.
Mervyn Stockwood, CHANCTONBURY RING 1982

2 My guess is that he was so impressed by the achievements of Mussolini that he thought similar autocratic methods rather than the bumblings of a MacDonald or a Baldwin were necessary to overcome the ghastly unemployment of the 30s and to save Britain from war. Had he lived earlier, he might have been accepted. But it was too late.
Ibid.

LOUIS (FRANCIS ALBERT VICTOR NICHOLAS) MOUNTBATTEN, FIRST EARL MOUNTBATTEN

Born 1900. Supreme Allied Commander in South-East Asia 1943–6. Last viceroy of India 1947. Admiral of the Fleet 1958–9, Chief of Defence Staff 1959–65. Assassinated by the IRA 1979.

3 When he finally retired as Chief of Defence Staff in 1965 there was a sigh of relief among the professionals. One can see why and understand, but his departure was the eclipse of a genius — maddening, unveracious, and arrogant, but a genius nevertheless.
Lord Blake, The Times 14 *Mar* 1985

4 In August 1943 Churchill made him Supreme Commander in South East Asia. He was the fourth choice, but it was an amazing promotion nevertheless, and very successful.
Ibid.

5 When Churchill offered him his Asian command Mountbatten asked for 24 hours to ponder the offer. 'Why?' snarled Churchill. 'Don't you think you can do it?' 'Sir,' replied Mountbatten, 'I suffer from the congenital weakness of believing I can do anything.'
Larry Collins and Dominique Lapierre, FREEDOM AT MIDNIGHT

6 When the job's hopeless, they call in Dickie.
Noël Coward. Quoted Leonard Mosley, LAST DAYS OF THE BRITISH RAJ

7 Not everyone liked him. He was too successful, too rich, too vain, and not quite clever enough to compensate for his faults, but surely no one would deny that he was a hero.
David Holloway, Daily Telegraph 20 *Aug* 1980

8 In the public eye Lord Mountbatten was a dashing hero, but in some quarters at the Admiralty he was considered a bit too intrepid. When his friend Noël Coward made a film of the *Kelly* epic called *In Which We Serve*, Lord Mountbatten's critics dubbed it *In Which We Sink*.
Albin Krebs, New York Times 28 *Aug* 1979

9 Actually I vote Labour, but my butler's a Tory.
Lord Mountbatten, to a Tory canvasser during the 1945 election

10 A certain admiral coined a phrase about me: 'I know of nobody I'd sooner be with in a tight corner than Dicky Mountbatten, and I know of nobody who could get me into one quicker.'
Mountbatten. Quoted John Terraine, LIFE AND TIMES OF LORD MOUNTBATTEN

11 I am sure that Dickie has done marvellously. But it is curious that we should regard as a hero the man who liquidated the Empire which other heroes such as Clive, Warren Hastings, and Napier won for us. Very odd indeed.
Harold Nicolson, DIARY 3 *Jun* 1947

12 He seldom read any books for pleasure except works of genealogy. Mountbatten would relax over the tapestry of his ancestry, enumerating the generations which separated him from the Emperor Charlemagne and marvelling at the intricate web of cousinship which bound him many times over to the Wittlesbachs, the Romanoffs, the Habsburgs and Hohenzollerns.
Philip Ziegler, MOUNTBATTEN 1985

MALCOLM MUGGERIDGE

Born 1903. English author, journalist, TV personality. Edited *Punch* 1953–7. Publications include *Tread Softly for You Tread on My Jokes*, 1966, *Chronicles of Wasted Time*, 1972–3.

1 His fame increased the more he went on television to denounce the way television makes people famous.
Julian Barnes, Observer, Well, Why Not? 11 *Jul* 1982

2 He combined the roles of the voice crying in the wilderness and the voice full of the most worldly relish.
Bernard Levin, THE PENDULUM YEARS 1981

3 On the telly (which he affects to despise but so clearly loves) he is a superb, acidulated comic, with his magnificent gargoyle's face and his extraordinary voice pulling and kneading the words as he mocks the world.
Observer, Profile 28 *Nov* 1982

4 He once played a clergyman in a Peter Sellers movie, and he was even more memorable as the Gryphon in Dr Jonathan Miller's television *Alice*. He could have been a great character actor. Come to think of it he *is* one.
Ibid.

5 Muggeridge found himself in the dire situation of a thief crucified between two Christs.
Anthony Powell, THE STRANGERS ARE ALL GONE, VOL. 4, *The Memoirs*

ALFRED (JAMES) MUNNINGS

Born 1878. British painter, known particularly for his pictures of horses. President of the Royal Academy, 1944–9. Died 1959.

6 Often I would dine with him, John, McEvoy, Orpen and others at the Garrick Club. He was a bit of a Jarvey, a sporting looking fellow. Up he used to hop to declaim his ballads with much vehemence and gesticulation usually to a round of applause. Masefield praised his hunting ballads and Asquith noted in his diary 'he delivered them with marvellous brio'. So he did; everything about A.J. was explosive. His moods veered sharply between exultation, nostalgic sadness and almost incoherent scorn.
Sir Alec Martin, Daily Telegraph 20 *Oct* 1962

7 He reminds me of the sort of boy at school who keeps newts and beetles and things in his pocket. Over the port he recited a ballad of his own, composed with no obvious attempt at style or metre except that it rhymed when he wanted it to; good homespun stuff.
Reginald Pound, THEIR MOODS AND MINE 1937

8 He loved parties, was a born master of ceremonies and once boasted that he had organised more parties, picnics, outings and Christmas festivities than anyone else in the country.
Frank Ruhrmund. Western Morning News 3 *Nov* 1965

9 Some of his parties gained him notoriety; a Christmas Party which he organised at Stanhope Forbes' house lasted for several days and nights, and at a punch party that he gave in a studio at Chywoone Grove four of his guests became stretcher cases.
Ibid.

10 His deep regard for horses could not be denied. It has been said that when one of his mares foaled he behaved as if it was a 'blessed event'. He toured the neighbourhood announcing it and his loud, graphic recital of the obstetric details in the Lamorna Inn had to be restrained 'on account of the ladies'.
Ibid.

BENITO MUSSOLINI

Born 1883. Italian dictator. Organised Fascists as a political party in 1921 and assumed dictatorial powers in 1926. Resigned after the Allied invasion of Sicily. Executed by partisans 1945.

11 Few people at the time he came to power can have realised that Signor Mussolini was going to stay for years and years, and to influence civilisation almost as much as Lenin had done. I am ashamed to say that I once was proud of coining a contemptuous description of him in *The Times* as 'this cinema Napoleon' and that I fully believed all the reports about his imminent death from one of half a dozen fatal maladies from which he was said to be suffering.
Vernon Bartlett, THIS IS MY LIFE 1937

12 Signor Mussolini is fond of explaining Fascism by declaring that it was a reaction against a brutal Communism. Actually it was nothing of the sort. There had been a period when engine-drivers would refuse to drive

BENITO MUSSOLINI

trains carrying an officer in uniform and when Italians who had fought for their country were subjected to every possible humiliation. But that period was over long before Mussolini became a really important figure in Italy. There was no Communist danger in Italy by the time I arrived there in December 1920, and Mussolini was still the relatively inconspicuous editor of a newspaper in Milan.
Ibid.

1 Just before the famous march on Rome in October 1922 The Duce was to speak at the San Carlo Opera House in Naples. From my point of vantage I could see in the wings opposite The Duce talking and laughing like any normal human being. At least, he talked and laughed until someone suggested to him that the time had come to address the crowd. The change was instantaneous and miraculous. Preceded by two young men blowing trumpets of tremendous length Mussolini came out of the wings and paced down the middle of the stage to the footlights. His hand was thrust in his black shirt as Napoleon's would have been had black shirts been fashionable then. His chin was thrust out as far as it would go. There was no sign of a smile, no sign of friendliness, hardly any sign of humanity on his face. For what seemed five minutes, and was probably at least thirty seconds, he stared at the crowd, and never in any theatre have I ever known such complete silence. The whole business was stupendous, magnificent, absurd.
Ibid.

2 The only occasions I have seen Mussolini alone I have been completely captivated by his charm and intelligence. The only occasions on which I have heard him speak in public I have been shocked by the bombastic nonsense he talked and at the same time filled with admiration for his power of dramatisation.
Ibid.

3 At Easter 1934 we paid a visit to Rome where I had an interview with the Duce. I was favourably impressed. There were no histrionics, nor was I obliged, as I had been told would happen, to walk the length of a long room from the door to his desk. He met me at the door and accompanied me to it when I left. We agreed on the importance of re-armament and he laughed when I said that the idea that armaments produced wars was as foolish as to think that umbrellas produced rain. Because he laughed at my joke I thought that he had a sense of humour, and was quite prepared to imagine he had other good qualities. It is too early to pronounce a final verdict on Mussolini . . . It may be that he began well and meant well, like so many of the Caesars before him, but that he ended ill as they did, because of the corruption of power.
Duff Cooper, OLD MEN FORGET 1953

4 Look at that man's eyes. You will hear more of him later.
Andrew Bonar Law 1926

5 He was alert and nervous. I noticed that he would glance suddenly round, and he caught my eye, twenty yards off, three or four times. Then he recovered himself and looked every inch a Dictator. This is of course exactly what a born ruler never does. King George would have been entirely oblivious to his surroundings, while Asquith would have mistaken the occasion and worn grey flannel trousers.
Geoffrey Madan, NOTEBOOKS 26 *Jan* 1928

N

V. S. (VIDIADHAR SURAJPRASSAD) NAIPAUL

Born 1932 in Trinidad. Author of comic novels with a Caribbean setting, including *The Mystic Masseur*, 1957 and *A House for Mr Biswas*, 1961.

1 In all his work Naipaul writes about civilisation by writing about its absence. His great theme is that of the exile, the emigrant, the man without a society. We accept this as a central twentieth-century experience, but we probably under-estimate its harshness.
Martin Amis, Observer 6 *Jul* 1984

2 Naipaul practised magic — superstitious, propitiatory. He always used stolen 'non-rustle' BBC paper ('it seemed less likely to attract failure'). He never numbered his pages ('for fear of not getting to the end'). And on the typescript of his first four books, he never wrote his own name.
Ibid.

3 I'm the kind of writer that people think other people are reading.
V. S. Naipaul, Radio Times 24 *Mar* 1979

JAWAHARLAL NEHRU

Born 1889. Indian politician, first Prime Minister of India. Died 1964.

4 Like Gandhi he was an anti-imperialist, but he had a far greater regard for the teaching of Lenin than had his mentor. The future of India, according to Nehru, lay in a multiplicity of hydro-electric dynamos rather than spinning wheels.
Daily Telegraph, Obituary 28 *May* 1964

5 Nehru's outlook was that of Western industrial Socialism. While declaring that he was 'not a Communist in the accepted sense' he confessed himself strongly attracted towards Marxism as 'the only reasonable and scientific explanation of history'.
Martin Moore, Daily Telegraph 28 *May* 1964

6 Nine times imprisoned by the British for political agitation, he clapped Communists into gaol when they attempted the same methods against his own Government.
Ibid.

NICHOLAS II

Born 1868. Tsar of Russia 1894–1917. His autocratic rule, combined with the defeats Russia sustained against Japan in 1905 and the Germans in World War One, forced his abdication. With his family he was arrested and taken to Ekaterinburg, where all are believed to have been murdered by revolutionaries although details of their fate remain a mystery.

7 It was his misfortune that he was married to a dangerous, stupid and designing woman with a far stronger will than his own, and with a reckless ignorant conceit which led him into fatal interference in matters he did not understand.
Second Earl of Birkenhead, Daily Telegraph 11 *Nov* 1960

8 He was not unteachable. He had a good memory. 'He learned very well,' complained one of his tutors 'but he never could understand what it was he was learning.'
Princess Catherine Radziwill, NICHOLAS II: LAST OF THE TSARS 1931

9 He was thoroughly weak, stupid and unimaginative.
Ibid.

10 The Tsar is not treacherous, but he is weak. Weakness is not treachery, but it fulfils all its functions.
Wilhelm II. Comment on diplomatic despatch from his ambassador in St Petersburg 16 *Mar* 1907

BEVERLEY NICHOLS

Born 1898. English writer, novelist, playwright. He first gained acclaim by publishing his autobiography *Twenty Five* when he was that age: 'the very latest age at which one should write an autobiography'. Died 1983.

11 I can tell you one of his accomplishments — he can play 'The Church's One Foundation' so that it sounds like a new funeral march by Chopin. He knows more idiotic games — the kind which are played round a table without pencil or paper — than anyone I know. A

really nice man, and a man with more intellect than he ever allows you to believe when you first meeet him.
Naomi Jacob, ME — A CHRONICLE ABOUT OTHER PEOPLE 1933

1 When he dislikes anyone he can behave very badly and be as tiresome as an obstreperous small boy.
Ethel Mannin, CONFESSIONS AND IMPRESSIONS 1930

2 He has a lot of the charm that has been tediously attributed to him, much of it in his voice, which is pleasant.
Reginald Pound, THEIR MOODS AND MINE 1937

3 He and I walked round Holborn discussing how he could be decently seduced from his *Daily Mail* writing contract, which he found irksome soon after signing it. There is an exacting and no doubt necessary censorship in the *Daily Mail* office. But it does seem to be going a little too carefully when they won't let a writer liken the petals of some flower or other to the debutante's lingerie.
Ibid.

4 I don't suppose Beverley Nichols's complexion owes anything to beer and yet it looks as if it has come out of several tankards. This was what I noticed immediately when I first saw him some time ago; unimportant, but it sticks as my incongruous first impression.
Ibid.

VASLAV NIJINSKY

Born 1890. Russian ballet dancer. Career ended prematurely by mental breakdown. Died 1950.

5 Off the stage he struck most observers as rather ugly, more like a pasty-face, thick-set shop assistant than a hero of romance. He seemed to assume another personality while engaged upon his make-up, in which he looked stunning.
Richard Buckle, NIJINSKY 1972

6 He was a serious man, beautiful-looking, with high cheekbones and sad eyes, who gave the impression of a monk dressed in civilian clothes.
Charles Chaplin, MY AUTOBIOGRAPHY 1964

7 We were shooting *The Cure*. Nijinsky sat behind the camera watching me at work. Although the other onlookers laughed Nijinsky sat looking sadder and sadder. For two more days he sat lugubriously watching me. On the last day I told the cameraman not to put film in the camera, knowing Nijinsky's doleful presence would ruin my attempts to be funny. Nevertheless at the end of each day he would compliment me 'Your comedy is balletique, you are a dancer,' he said.
Ibid.

8 No one has equalled Nijinsky in *L'Après-midi d'Un Faune*. The mystic world he created, the tragic unseen lurking in the shadows of pastoral loveliness as he moved through its mystery, a god of passionate sadness — all this he conveyed in a few simple gestures without apparent effort. Six months later he went insane.
Ibid.

9 Nijinsky's height was below average. His soul and body were one single professional deformation. His face, with its Mongol features, was linked to his body by a very long very thick neck. His fingers were stubby. In short, no one could have thought that this little ape was the idol of the public.
Jean Cocteau

10 He first danced in London in 1911. Later, when he was about to start a season that would have brought him in £1000 a week he had a nervous breakdown. His mind became unbalanced in 1917. Now his hands folded he sits quietly in his room at the Sacher Hotel, Vienna. He did not speak for 22 years, says his wife, not because he could not, but because he did not want to.
Daily Express 3 *Aug* 1945

11 They say he is very patient and gentle in his affliction. Sometimes he knows he is mad. Sometimes he knows he is Nijinsky.
George Edinger, News Chronicle 28 *Jul* 1936

12 At his last dance recital Nijinsky announced 'Now I will show you the war, with its suffering, its destruction, its death. The war you did not prevent and so are responsible for' . . . He seemed to fill the room with horror-stricken suffering humanity. It was tragic; his gestures were all monumental, and he entranced us so that we saw him floating over corpses. The public sat horrified and so strangely fascinated. We felt that Vaslav was like one of those overpowering creatures, full of dominating strength, a tiger let out from the jungle who in any moment could destroy us. Whirling through space, taking his audience away with him to war, to destruction.
Romola Nijinsky, NIJINSKY 1934

1 At tea on the terrace of the House of Commons he compared a famous hostess to a giraffe. He meant it as a compliment.
Ibid.

ANAÏS NIN

Born 1914 in France of mixed French, Spanish, Danish and Cuban descent. Emigrated to America. Novelist, diarist, dancer and psychologist. Biographer of D. H. Lawrence. Until 1946, when Doubleday published *Ladders to Fire*, she printed, on her own printing press, and published, all her works herself.

2 Self-abnegation, excessive good looks, a real willingness to put her hand in her pocket for almost anybody (where the money came from is never clear) and a certain lack of levity seem to have elevated her to the status of a Muse, a circumstance which all right-thinking women will envy.
Harriet Chare, The Times 1 *Jun* 1970

3 In 1939 she went to New York from Paris and the war to find herself penniless in an alien setting. She started writing erotic literature — called dirty books now — for an anonymous millionaire, beavering away for months at stuff which, these days, reads pretty tame.
Ibid.

4 She has obsessively maintained a diary since the age of 11. Amounting now to more than 150 invaluable volumes it is locked carefully away in a Brooklyn bank.
Ibid.

5 A polite, sweet black sheep, that is what I would like to be.
Anaïs Nin, JOURNAL OF A WIFE 1984

RICHARD (MILHOUS) NIXON

Born 1913. American politician. Republican vice-president under Eisenhower. Elected president 1969, extricated America from the Vietnam War, but on being threatened with impeachment on grounds of involvement in government corruption, resigned in 1974.

6 Nixon is a purposeless man, but I have great faith in his cowardice.
J. Breslin, Observer 16 *Nov* 1969

7 It wasn't Watergate that did for Nixon. It was the cover-up. He had it all on *tape*.
Billy Graham. Quoted John Mortimer, Sunday Times 29 *July* 1984

8 The Soviets regarded him as our most formidable president. Gromyko said he had a great respect for Nixon. He opened dialogue with Russia and China.
Ibid.

9 Do you realise the responsibility I carry? I am the only person standing between Nixon and the White House.
J. F. Kennedy. Quoted Arthur M. Schlesinger Jr, A THOUSAND DAYS *Oct* 1960

10 He attracts distrust. When he wept at an emotional moment after being greeted by Eisenhower during the 1952 campaign there was somebody to recall that he had been taught to weep in his days of amateur theatricals.
Earl Mazo and Stephen Hess, PRESIDENT NIXON: A POLITICAL PORTRAIT 1968

11 President Nixon's eyes twice flickered away from his questioners as if checking which camera he was on. The involuntary sliding away of the eyes sharpened the feeling that the performance was a performance, calculated and self-monitored, carefully designed to create a certain impression.
Ibid.

12 The study of Richard Nixon requires a steadfast clinging to the fact that he is human. This is not easy.
John Osborne, THE NIXON WATCH 1970

13 Nixon is the kind of politician who would cut down a redwood tree, then mount the stump for a conservation speech.
Adlai Stevenson. Quoted Leon Harris, THE FINE ART OF POLITICAL WIT

14 We know a great deal about him but we don't know him. He is one of the most unusual and most compelling public figures ever to walk the American political stage.
Bob Woodward, Washington Post. Quoted Christopher Thomas, The Times 9 *Aug* 1984

MONTAGU NORMAN, LORD NORMAN

Born 1871. English banker. Became Governor of the Bank of England in 1920 and held the position for the next twenty-four years from which he was able to exert a crucial, and not always beneficial influence on the financial policies of successive governments. Died 1950.

15 Montagu Norman was described by

1 McKenna as an intellectual without any intellect.
Geoffrey Madan, NOTEBOOKS 1981

2 He looks like a romantic poet. Or a retired sea captain who has done a bit of gun-running in his day. Trim, pointed beard. Dark piercing eyes. Long, nervous fingers that tap on the table when he is impatient. An old-fashioned tie threaded through a gold ring. An air of restless interest.
Passing Show 9 *Apr* 1932

3 They have gone on electing him Governor year after year because they can think of no one to replace him. Sometimes they don't know why he decides as he does. Sometimes he doesn't know himself. He works by inspiration. Like an artist. It is a bit dangerous. A banking experiment affects more people than does an experiment with paint that doesn't come off.
Ibid.

4 When a government committee on Finance and Industry called him as a witness before them he parried their questions with answers like 'it all depends on the circumstances' and 'I really cannot remember'. When the questioning was over the committee knew very little more about the Bank of England, or Montagu Norman's views, than they had done before.
Pictorial Weekly 1933

5 He believed that banking, like the heart, has its reasons which reason does not know. He told the MacMillan Commission: 'I don't have reasons; I have instincts.' Lord MacMillan said, 'We understand that, of course, Mr Governor, but nevertheless you must have *some* reasons.' Norman replied tartly, 'Well, if I had, I've forgotten them.'
A. J. P. Taylor, Observer 12 *Nov* 1967

6 He regarded his calling as a religious mystery and delighted to enhance the secret romance of it. He travelled under the name of his secretary, until the world press made the name of Professor Skinner more famous than that of Montagu Norman.
Ibid.

7 In 1913 he consulted the famous psychiatrist Jung, and Jung concluded that he had general paralysis of the insane. The diagnosis was wrong. Jung himself was next door to mad at this time, a prey to deep neurotic anxieties and should have been under treatment himself, instead of attempting to treat others.
Ibid.

8 He tried to set his stamp on history and for a time succeeded. Great Britain of the nineteen-twenties was Norman's work. The general strike, the permanent mass-unemployment, and ultimately the crisis of 1931 were all his doing, however unwittingly, and he largely shaped Central Europe, down to the arrival of Hitler, as well.
Ibid.

ALFRED CHARLES WILLIAM HARMSWORTH, VISCOUNT NORTHCLIFFE

Born 1865. British magazine publisher and newspaper proprietor. Built up the Amalgamated Press to be the largest periodical enterprise of its day, founded the *Daily Mail*, 1896 and the *Daily Mirror*, 1903. Acquired *The Times*, 1908. Died 1922.

9 Once when he felt the advertisement department was unresponsive to his wishes he electrified it by appointing Mr Glover, the office door-keeper, to be Censor of Advertisements. The gigantic Irishman spent some days, perhaps weeks, in this rôle. Some of the staff shook their heads over what they feared was a portent of his coming breakdown, but it was just his humour.
Tom Clarke, MY NORTHCLIFFE DIARY 1931

10 Lloyd George, when invited by Beaverbrook to meet Northcliffe, grimly replied: 'I would rather go out walking with a grasshopper.'
A. J. Cummings, News Chronicle 11 *May* 1932

11 'How much money do you get?' he asked a reporter. 'Eight pounds a week' was the reply. 'Are you satisfied?' 'Quite.' 'Then you'd better go. Nobody who thinks he is earning enough is any good here.'
Hannen Swaffer, World's Press News 18 *Jun* 1933

12 On February 25, 1917 he was staying at his house at Broadstairs when, in the middle of the night, a German destroyer started to shell his mansion. The building was struck and a secretary rushed into his room shouting 'Chief, the German are shelling us. We will die in our beds.' He said, 'You go and die in yours.' And he turned over and went to sleep.
Ibid. 25 *Jun* 1931

1 He seems to think he is the only person who can run the country.
Sir Evelyn Wrench, DIARY 8 *Nov* 1917

IVOR NOVELLO

Born 1893 in Wales. Full name Ivor Novello Davies. Composer, playwright and actor. Died 1951.

2 He can wade through tosh with the straightest face; the tongue never visibly approaches the cheek. As an actor and as an author he can pursue preposterous adventures with that solemn fixity of purpose which romantic melodrama inexorably demands.
Ivor Brown, Observer

3 Ivor was gentle, good, kindly, affectionate, lovable and loyal; and he gave pleasure to millions. His dark good looks were famous, and he might have been Neapolitan; actually he was Welsh, and his hair, long since white, was carefully dyed. His little court of adorers kept him wrapped in cotton wool.
Sir Henry Channon, DIARY 6 *Mar* 1951

4 One day in December 1915 Viola Tree was taking me to His Majesty's for *Mavourneen*, in which Lily Elsie played Nell Gwynn; but in the morning she sent me my ticket 'as we shouldn't be sitting together'. I meekly went to the theatre and from my lonely stall beheld my hostess with a remarkably good-looking young man in the stage box, to which after the first act she beckoned me. 'Do you know Ivor Novello?' she said. 'He wrote *Keep the Home Fires Burning*.' I looked blank. 'You know,' she said 'Tum-ty-tum-tum-tum-tum.' At this light dawned, for it was the only tune I had heard for months, but I had never learnt its name. The young man had looked a little taken aback, as well he might.
Edward Marsh, A NUMBER OF PEOPLE 1939

5 In those days [1915] Ivor was then very much what he is now, but there was one difference which may be of interest to students of Career — he was infernally lazy, and never did a hand's turn till the day or two before a number had to be sent in, when he would shut himself up with his piano and work round the clock with feverish nerve-wracked, white-lipped energy till it was done. Nowadays he hardly knows how to take a holiday.
Ibid.

WILLIAM RICHARD MORRIS, LORD NUFFIELD

Born 1877. Motor car manufacturer and philanthropist. Began his business on a capital of £4 as a bicycle repairer. Set up his factory at Cowley in 1912 to manufacture motor cars. His bequests, during his lifetime, amounted to £25,000,000, which included £10,000,000 for the endowment of the Nuffield Foundation. Died 1963.

6 A pleasant, wrinkled little man, with no 'aitches' and a weak handshake.
Sir Henry Channon, DIARY 12 *May* 1938

7 His love of doing things with his hands stayed with him all his life, even to the point of his having a work-bench, lathe, and a complete kit of small tools in an alcove in his bedroom. When obsessed with some problem he would find release from tension and relief from insomnia by doing some delicate metal work.
Sir Miles Thomas, Sunday Times 25 *Aug* 1963

8 'The idea that it is easy to give money away is the biggest fallacy in the world,' said Morris. The statement throws a strong light on his quality and method as a philanthropist. His larger benefactions were not mere sporadic gestures of impulsive generosity. They were the implementation of great schemes which he had worked out in intimate detail. He accompanied his gifts with well-considered prescriptions as to their administration and use.
The Times, Obituary 23 *Aug* 1963

9 He is said to have wandered into the office of the National Council for Social Service one day, wearing a creased old raincoat, and asking to see the secetary, an official who was not unfamiliar with cranks yet was patient by nature. They got round to a project at that time languishing for lack of means, to assist old people. The courteous official humoured what he thought was a mildly inquisitive engineer with time on his hands. Finally Morris said 'All right, I'll give you £50,000 for the pilot project' and went on his way.
Sir William Emrys Williams, Observer 25 *Aug* 1963

RUDOLF NUREYEV

Born 1939 in Russia. Ballet dancer. Moved to the West in 1961 and with the encouragement of Margot Fonteyn rapidly established an international reputation.

1 When I was introduced to the young fawn at Margot's cocktail party I kissed him on the cheek and forehead in gratitude.
Cecil Beaton, DIARY *Nov* 1961

2 Diana Cooper, next to me, whispered 'He's better than Nijinsky!' This boy — a peasant until seventeen when he won a scholarship to be trained as a dancer — looks like all the young Beatniks of today. What we were now seeing was the culmination of the development of dancing since it began.
Ibid.

3 The torso was broad-shouldered, and rather narrow at the waist; the arms were strong and long, and swayed with an ineffable grace and strength. The hands, too, did everything that a sculptor in mobility would choose if he happened to be a master of the ultimate taste and refinement.
Ibid.

4 The curtain went up to the music of Scriabin. The huge stage was empty except for the scarlet-shrouded object standing centre. A crack of applause broke from the audience. Here was the exile of the Soviet Union, subdued no longer. Suddenly the cloak moved more swiftly than the eye could follow, to reveal a savage young creature, half-naked, with wild eyes in an ecstatic, gaunt face and a long mop of flying, silk hair, rushing towards the footlights. The force and dynamic power of this unexpected figure was shocking and compelling.
Ibid.

5 Rudolf brought me a second career, like an Indian Summer.
Margot Fonteyn, AUTOBIOGRAPHY 1975

6 As he stepped out of the taxi that brought him from the airport he seemed smaller than I had expected. He had a pinched little face with a curious pallor. His face reflected every thought, changing like lightning. Once or twice a cold light flashed through his eyes. Now I realise it was a manifestation of fear that was always just below the surface, ready to show itself at the slightest suspicion of attack.
Ibid.

O

SEAN O'CASEY

Born 1880. Irish playwright. His works include *Juno and the Paycock*, 1924, *The Plough and the Stars*, 1926, and *The Silver Tassie*, 1929. Died 1962.

1 His was a truly Christian nature, one of the kindest and most genuine men I have ever known — a saintly man.
Harold Macmillan. Quoted Eileen O'Casey, SEAN 1971

2 Sean O'Casey is all right now that his shift from Dublin slums to Hyde Park has shown that his genius is not limited by frontiers. His plays are wonderfully impressive and *reproachful* without being irritating like mine. People fall crying into one another's arms saying God forgive us all! instead of refusing to speak and going to their solicitors for a divorce.
G. B. Shaw, letter to Lady Astor 9 *Feb* 1934

LAURENCE (KEIR) OLIVIER, BARON OLIVIER OF BRIGHTON

Born 1907. British film and stage actor and director. Knighted in 1947. Director of the National Theatre 1962–73. Created a life peer 1974.

3 He was a comedian by instinct, a tragedian by art.
James Agate. Quoted Alan Hamilton, The Times 17 *May* 1982

4 Olivier's was, to my mind, the definitive Macbeth. Olivier had murder in his heart from the moment he came on the stage.
John Gielgud, AN ACTOR AND HIS TIME 1979

5 When we alternated as Romeo and Mercutio in a pre-war London production I had the voice: Larry had the legs.
Ibid.

6 The American actor Dustin Hoffman, playing a victim of imprisonment and torture in the film *The Marathon Man*, prepared himself for the role by keeping himself awake for two days and nights. He arrived at the studio dishevelled and drawn to be met by his co-star, Laurence Olivier. 'Dear boy, you look absolutely awful,' exclaimed the First Lord of the Theatre: 'Why don't you try acting? It's so much easier.'
Alan Hamilton, The Times 17 *May* 1982

7 Minute attention to detail has always been the hallmark of Olivier's acting. When he played Othello at the National he trained his voice down two octaves, spent months in physical training to adopt his frame to the lope of an African, and took two hours every night to apply his shiny black body make-up.
Ibid.

EUGENE (GLADSTONE) O'NEILL

Born 1888. American playwright. Works include *Mourning Becomes Electra*, 1931; *The Iceman Cometh*, 1946. Awarded Nobel Prize for Literature, 1936. Died 1956.

8 For thirteen years, except when writing, he hardly drew a sober breath. He preferred to keep company with those companionable or (even when most horrible) intensely dramatic phantoms and obsessions which 'with caressing claws in my heart and brain, used to lead me for weeks at a time, otherwise lonely, down the everchanging vistas of that No Man's Land lying between the DT's and Reality as we suppose it'.
Arthur and Barbara Gelb, O'NEILL 1962

9 Late in 1953 a fever seized him, raged in his wasted frame for three days. Once he struggled for a moment back from oblivion. Clenching his shaking fists he gasped out a belated bitter joke, a line far more reverberant than any he had ever written, the sardonic epitaph of the dispossessed; 'Born in a hotel room and God damn it, died in a hotel room.'
Ibid.

10 His daughter's [Oona's] successful marriage to Charlie Chaplin he seemed to take as a personal insult.
J. W. Lambert, Observer 4 *Nov* 1962

SIR WILLIAM ORPEN

Born 1878 in Ireland. British portrait painter. During World War I was commissioned by the government to paint battle scenes on the Western Front. Died 1931.

1 'He loved money,' said his friend Beatrice Glenavy, 'it's born in some people.' He kept a china bowl full of money in his studio for friends and hangers-on to help themselves.
Bruce Arnold, ORPEN: MIRROR OF AN AGE 1981

2 Orpen was commissioned to paint the scene of the signing of the Versailles Treaty. He made the sketches. He worked for nine months puting in the portraits of over forty statesmen and generals. Then he rubbed them all out. His soul revolted. He must tell the truth. And in his picture the body of the Unknown Soldier lies in the Salle des Miroirs, guarded by two gaunt wraiths from the trenches. He said 'The pleasure this completed picture gives me, however critics may rage, is worth the £2000 it cost me'.
Sidney Dark and P. G. Konody, SIR WILLIAM ORPEN: ARTIST AND MAN 1932

3 Orpen's last pictures do not mark a final step in his artistic evolution. They are the work of a man no longer in full possession of his faculties. He had already taken up his quarters in a nursing home from which he escaped occasionally in defiance of doctor's orders to spend an hour at his easel. No one will know what happened in those hours at his studio; but one can imagine that the realisation of failing powers must have caused him mental anguish far more terrible than all his physical suffering.
Ibid.

4 As he approached his sitter he would take a cigarette from a box on the platform, light it, pull it for four or five pulls, and as he returned to his canvas the cigarette, of which not one quarter of an inch had been smoked, was ejected on to the floor. And there it lay with thirty, forty, fifty of its kind until, the sitting over, Mrs Smyth, Orpen's wonderful old housekeeper, would sweep up the rubbish.
Robin H. Legge, Daily Telegraph 9 *Nov* 1932

5 I once asked Orpen if a successful portrait painter must be a good judge of character. His reply provided a revealing criticism of his work. 'No. The skilful painter, with his keen powers of observation, selects a characteristic aspect of the sitter. He sees him from the outside. He depicts what could be seen by all, if they had the eyes to see it.'
Lord Riddell, introduction to Sidney Dark and P. G. Konody's SIR WILLIAM ORPEN: ARTIST AND MAN 1932

GEORGE ORWELL

Born 1903 in India. Pen-name of Eric Arthur Blair. English novelist and essayist. His most famous works are *Animal Farm*, 1946, a satirical allegory on revolution, and *Nineteen Eighty-four*, 1949, an ironical view of a future Utopia. Died 1950.

6 One story about him says something of his real feelings towards the poor. A journalist who worked with him on *Tribune* described how he caught Orwell, with a guilty look on his face, stuffing something into a packet. It turned out that the packet was full of unusable verses which Orwell was returning to an unlucky contributor. He was looking guilty because he had added a bonus to the packet—a ten shilling note.
Ian Cotton, TV Times 11 *Oct* 1973

7 His uncompromising intellectual honesty made him appear almost inhuman at times. There was an emanation of austere harshness around him which diminished in proportion to distance; he was merciless towards himself, severe upon his friends, unresponsive to admirers but full of understanding for those on the periphery, the 'crowds in the big towns with their knobbly faces, their bad teeth and gentle manners'. Thus, the greater the distance from intimacy the more warming became the radiations of this lonely man's great power of love.
Arthur Koestler, Observer, Obituary Jan 1950

8 It would be true to say that he had, as it were, resigned from the world in which he was brought up, or anything like it, while never really contriving to join any other.
Anthony Powell, The Times 14 *Oct* 1967

9 Nothing could have been more English than his consciously old tweed coat and corduroy trousers which always maintained exactly the same degree of shabbiness, no worse, no better. 'Does it matter my coming in these old clothes?' he once asked, before entering the room at a party we were giving.
Ibid.

P

VLADIMIR DE PACHMANN

Born 1848 in Russia. Pianist, internationally famous, particularly for his interpretation of Chopin. Died 1933.

1 On the evening of May 19, 1928 Pachmann made his farewell to the London public at the Mayfair Hotel. The audience was insatiable. Only when the firemen unscrewed the legs of the piano stool, closed the lid of the piano and placed the stool on top of it did they realise that Pachmann had really said goodbye.
Daily Telegraph, Obituary 8 *Jan* 1933

2 On one occasion he refused to begin until two men (his 'keepers', my father told me) were brought on to the platform to readjust his piano stool. They were even required to slip two pieces of writing paper under one leg of the piano which Pachmann maintained was not correctly balanced.
John Gielgud, AN ACTOR AND HIS TIME 1979

3 Vladimir de Pachmann was exquisite as an interpreter of Chopin, though his antics on the platform were somewhat grotesque. He would grimace and mutter to himself and sometimes to the audience. 'Chopin crying' he would exclaim during a sad nocturne for the benefit of the people sitting in the three front rows.
Ibid.

4 By his strange pranks he made himself more popular than men who were greater musicians. His favourite trick was to put a visiting card under the leg of his piano stool to make it higher. He would play a few bars, then break off and take the card out again. I asked him once why he did these weird things. He laughed and said 'I play to English public on Sunday afternoons. On Sunday English people eat splendid luncheon. They are like lions, they like sleep when they are full. I don't like to play to people who fall asleep. So I invent my own technique. I play foolish tricks. I make them laugh at Crazy Old Pachmann until I am sure they are awake. Then I begin my concert.'
Patrick Murphy, Daily Express 8 *Jan* 1933

5 If anyone young came to his house he insisted on them kissing the parlourmaid, because she was young too.
Ibid.

6 He insisted on taking his beautiful piano about with him, both because of its tone, and because he had fitted to it pedals as large as saucepan lids so that he could reach them easily with his tiny legs.
Ibid.

7 His interpretations of the most familiar things in the whole range of Chopin's piano music, such as the Berceuse, or the C sharp minor waltz, had a spontaneity that made them seem the result of sudden inspiration. He might have just been discovering their beauties for the first time — and his nods and smiles and delighted asides to the front rows of the stalls all took their place in the picture.
H. E. Wortham, Daily Telegraph 8 *Jan* 1933

IGNACY JAN PADEREWSKI

Born 1860. Polish pianist, who became prime minister for ten months in 1919. Died 1941.

8 Paderewski became Prime Minister of Poland but I felt like Clemençeau who said to him during a conference at the ill-fated Versailles Treaty: 'How is it that an artist like you can stoop so low as to become a politician?'
Charles Chaplin, MY AUTOBIOGRAPHY 1964

9 Paderewski had charm, but there was something bourgeois about him, an over-emphasis of dignity. He was impressive, with his long hair, severe slanting moustache, and the small tuft of hair under his lower lip, which I thought revealed some form of mystic vanity. At his recitals, with the house lights lowered and the atmosphere sombre and awesome when he was about to sit on the piano stool, I always felt someone should pull it from under him.
Ibid.

10 An American girl visited Beethoven's home, saw the piano at which he wrote the Ninth Symphony, flung herself at it and banged out a few notes. 'I suppose you get a lot of

famous people here', she said to the guide. 'Ja, Fraulein. Paderewski was here a few days ago.' 'Say, did he play too?' 'Nein, Fraulein. He thought he was not worthy.'
Bruce Clavering, Sunday Referee 9 *Aug* 1936

DAME CHRISTABEL PANKHURST

Born 1880. English suffragette, daughter of Emmeline Pankhurst, founder of the Women's Social and Political Union. Died 1958.

1 I heard Christabel Pankhurst the other day. She was very able, very clever, and very unpleasant. Her idea of progress is that females should meet together in masses and orate. But I agreed with most of her remarks, and her tone did not unconvert me.
E. M. Forster, LETTERS, VOL 1

2 Crowds that now scream for film stars used to shout 'We want Chrissie'; she was newsworthy from the moment when she spat at a policeman, in order to be the first of her movement to be arrested.
Felicia Lamb, Daily Telegraph 15 *Jun* 1959

3 Christabel's militant group lived in an artificial world of their own creating, where danger followed quick upon danger, and excitement always ran high. To them their work seemed supremely important, and if they faltered or held back they believed all would be lost. But it was not so.
Ray Strachey, THE CAUSE 1928

DOROTHY PARKER

Born 1893, née Dorothy Rothschild. American journalist, essayist, poet, short-story writer, script writer and playwright. Prolific contributor to *New Yorker*. Died 1967.

4 When Dorothy Parker was first assigned to her own little cubicle in a writer's studio her fame was not yet universal, and not a soul dropped in to see her for days on end. Panting for company, Miss Parker took steps one evening after the other hired help had left. First she scratched the 'Dorothy Parker' off her door. Then she replaced it with the legend 'Gents' Room,' the next day her problem was solved.
Bennett Cerf, TRY AND STOP ME 1947

5 She was for a while rich, famous and powerful. She had two husbands, four lovers, a mansion in Beverley Hills, a country estate in Pennsylvania, and a series of apartments in New York. She was a central figure of the celebrated Algonquin Hotel Round Table; newspaper columnists quoted her: practically every bright remark of the day was attributed to her — she was the most talked-about woman of her time.
John Keats, YOU MIGHT AS WELL LIVE: *The Life and Times of Dorothy Parker* 1971

6 Dorothy Parker's apartment on West 57th Street was hardly pretentious. She said that all she needed was 'space to lay a hat — and a few friends'. The only things that belonged to her were a portable typewriter and a canary she called Onan because he spilled his seed upon the ground.
Ibid.

7 In best-selling verse and prose, as well as in witticism, she spared herself less than anyone. One American reviewer of her poems likened her to the nightingale singing with its breast against a thorn.
Margaret Lane, Daily Telegraph, The Queen of the Wisecrack 8 *Apr* 1971

8 It is difficult to say anything about Dorothy Parker that has not been said, as it is about the Venus of Milo. Helen could make a scholar famous with a kiss; she could make a fool immortal with a jibe.
W. Somerset Maugham

9 Mrs Parker may be amused but it is plain that she is really horrified.
William Plomer

10 It was said of her that in her first book of poems, *Enough Rope* published in 1926, she established herself as 'master of the cynical-sentimental genre with the whip-lash ending.'
The Times, Obituary 9 *Jun* 1967

11 She is not Emily Brontë or Jane Austen, but she has been at some pains to write well, and she has put into what she has written a voice, a state of mind, an era, a few moments of human experience that nobody else has conveyed.
Edmund Wilson

12 Her work is so potent a distillation of nectar and wormwood, of ambrosia and deadly nightshade, as might suggest to the rest of us that we write far too much.
Alexander Woollcott, WHILE ROME BURNS 1934

BORIS (LEONIDOVICH) PASTERNAK

Born 1890. World famous for his novel *Dr Zhivago*, published outside Russia 1958. Awarded, but compelled to refuse, Nobel Prize for Literature 1958. Died 1960.

1 What worries Authority is not that Pasternak has unpleasant things to say about Stalin and Lenin; they are not mentioned in *Dr Zhivago*; they might never have existed. The really worrying thing is that his attitude through and through is subversive of all political action, as all considerable Western art since the Renaissance has been, and must be, subversive, because it can only illuminate the human condition which it is the task (and the duty?) of Authority to falsify.
Edward Crankshaw, Observer 7 *Sep* 1958

2 At a time when much political pressure was put on Russian writers to make their work 'socially useful' Pasternak kept his independence and artistic integrity and served no end but his own high standards of art and craftsmanship. Life was not easy for him. He was continually attacked and disparaged and suffered almost everything but open persecution.
The Times, Obituary 1 *Jun* 1960

3 Pasternak's survival through the Stalin epoch, when independent-minded writers died like flies in winter, will always remain an unexplained paradox. His life was lonely. His best work was produced against a roar of opposition or (at best) a freezing silence; his death was tragic; and after his death the vindictiveness of the State was let loose on two wretched women whose crime was that they supported and loved him.
John Wain, Observer 12 *Nov* 1961

ANNA MATVEYEVNA PAVLOVA

Born c.1882. Russian ballet dancer. Established a world-wide reputation with her interpretation of Fokine's Dying Swan. Died 1931.

4 People waiting for her to leave the theatre never dreamed of daring to ask for her autograph, any more than they would ask royalty.
Sir Frederick Ashton. Quoted Margot Fonteyn, PAVLOVA IMPRESSIONS 1984

5 She had bad taste and chose dreadful music. She liked Hungarian composers and dainty tippety-tip dances. And her feet were ugly. Such large, lumpy shoes. And her dresses! It was terrible but the audiences loved it. They didn't know any better in those days.
George Balanchine. Quoted Cecil Beaton, DIARY 10 *Sep* 1965

6 Frederick Ashton told us that from today's point of view Pavlova was technically not a good dancer; that she had no strength, and that half a dozen of today's Covent Garden ballerinas could dance her off the stage. Nevertheless her showmanship was so remarkable that the audience were given the impression that they were seeing more than they were.
Cecil Beaton, DIARY 1960

7 For me, Pavlova was the epitome of all that was rare and mysterious. From the moment that evening when she appeared on the stage, with her big beak of a nose, the V-shaped smile, and the long spears of blue-painted eyes which gave her the head of a peacock, she was to me the personification of magic.
Ibid.

8 This evasive dragon-fly of a dancer reduced herself to a mere machine for bringing 'art' of a chocolate-box kind to the deprived masses.
Richard Buckle, Observer, Chocolate-box Goddess 13 *Mar* 1983

9 She never failed to affect me profoundly. Her art, although brilliant, had a quality pale and luminous, as delicate as a white rose petal. As she danced every move was the centre of gravity. The moment she made her entrance, no matter how gay or winsome she was, I wanted to weep.
Charles Chaplin, MY AUTOBIOGRAPHY 1964

10 The woman and artist I hold above all others in the history of the ballet.
Margot Fonteyn, PAVLOVA IMPRESSIONS 1984

11 Pavlova was jealous of Nijinsky. One evening when they appeared together the audience shouted his name louder than hers and she fainted behind the curtain in an uncontrollable fit of jealousy and resentment.
Romola Nijinsky, NIJINSKY 1934

12 It takes me at least six months to learn a new ballet. The comparison may seem a little gross, but an artist who is preparing a new role is rather like a pregnant woman. I become a much nicer person, and because I

am completely absorbed in my work life seems so much sweeter.
Pavlova. Quoted Margot Fonteyn, PAVLOVA IMPRESSIONS 1984

1 Bring me my costume for the Swan Dance.
Pavlova, reputed last words. Quoted Francis Birrell and F. L. Lucas, THE ART OF DYING

EVA (DUARTE) PERON

Born 1919 in Argentina. Second wife of President Juan Peron. Was a great support to him as she had a considerable political following in her own right. After she died in 1952 he gradually lost favour, and was exiled, although he returned later.

2 A Court hairdresser who travels with her keeps her hair long and blonde and changes her hair style almost every day, swinging between a peak of high curls and a bun on the neck.
Robert Clyde, Daily Mail 4 *Jul* 1947

3 She has made herself dictator of the theatre, radio and film professions and through revolutionary 'legislation' exercises a tyranny over the directors and others who once ignored her. As a dictator she was once able to make a picture in which she starred, but it was a failure and nothing has been heard of it since.
Ibid.

4 Wrapped in furs and sparkling with diamonds, she still addresses the workers of Buenos Aires as one of them: 'Nosotros los descamisados' — We the Shirtless. And in Argentina, if not in Europe, she gets away with it. To her own people, those from whom she sprang, she is a dream come true. Cinderella become Queen.
Observer, Profile 13 *Jul* 1947

5 I was very sad for many days when I discovered that in the world there were poor people and rich people; and the strange thing is that the existence of the poor did not cause me as much pain as the knowledge that at the same time there were people who were rich.
Eva Peron, MY LIFE'S CAUSE 1956

6 On July 10 (1947), a news agency message from Rome reported that an official spokesman at the Argentine Embassy there had said that Madame Peron had cancelled her visit to London 'because it was considered certain that she would not be received by the King and Queen'.
Robert Waithman, News Chronicle 28 *Jul* 1947

PRINCE PHILIP, DUKE OF EDINBURGH

Born 1921 in Greece, son of Prince George of Greece and Princess Alice. Consort of Queen Elizabeth II. Married 1947.

7 Philip of Edinburgh, although as always extremely handsome and pleasing, looked worn out. But he was the success of the ball, and was wildly gay with his policeman's hat and handcuffs. He leapt about and jumped into the air as he greeted everybody. His charm is colossal, like all Mountbattens, and he and Princess Elizabeth seemed supremely happy and often danced together.
Sir Henry Channon, DIARY 30 *May* 1945

8 Philip has but few qualifications to commend him to the British public.
Daily Worker 7 *Feb* 1947

9 If he would let his hair grow I could get him in with the Rolling Stones. He is the working girl's Adam Faith. He is as sophisticated as Noël Coward, as charming as Chevalier, and as versatile as the Governor of Pentonville Prison.
Bud Flanagan. Quoted in his Obituary, Daily Express 21 *Oct* 1980

10 In Australia, during a visit to some caves he was warned to beware of the drips. 'Oh those! I've run into plenty in my life,' he replied.
Sir Leslie Hollis, CAPTAIN GENERAL 1961

11 When Prince Charles, at prep school, came out with a word that once would not have been heard within Palace bounds, Philip laughed. 'He may have picked it up from one of the workmen,' he said 'but I am afraid he may equally have picked it up from me.'
Ibid.

PABLO (RUIZY) PICASSO

Born 1881. Spanish artist who was the dominant figure in progressive twentieth-century art. *Guernica*, 1936, first earned him popular appreciation. Died 1973.

12 When Picasso was painting the Demoiselles d'Avignon, Augustus John asked him what he was trying to do, as he could not

understand it. Picasso replied 'Je cherche la liberté'.
Cecil Beaton, DIARY *Jun* 1960

1 Gertrude Stein had just been reading some poetry by Pablo Picasso. 'I read his poems,' she told us happily, 'and then I seized him by the shoulders and shook him good and hard. "Pablo," I said, "Go home and paint."'
Bennett Cerf, TRY AND STOP ME 1947

2 Picasso took us to his Left Bank studio. We came upon the most deplorable, barnlike garret that even Chatterton would have been loath to die in. Hanging from a nail in one rafter was a stark electric bulb which enabled us to see a rickety old iron bed and a broken-down stove. Resting against the wall was a pile of old dusty canvasses. He picked up one — a Cézanne, and a most beautiful one. He picked up another and another. We must have looked at fifty masterpieces.
Charles Chaplin, MY AUTOBIOGRAPHY 1964

3 In 1906 Gertrude Stein posed eight times for Picasso's portrait of her, after which he wiped the face off, saying he couldn't 'see' her any more, and then finished the likeness in Spain, where he couldn't see her at all.
Edmund Fuller, ANECDOTES 1942

4 One night at the beginning of the World War, Picasso and Gertrude Stein were taking a walk when they saw a camouflaged truck for the first time. He was amazed by its resemblance to cubist art, and, in the tone of a man who has just been plagiarized, said 'Why, it is we who invented that!' Later, when a new field uniform for the French army was being discussed, he told Cocteau 'If they want to make an army invisible at a distance, all they have to do is dress the men as harlequins.'
Ibid.

5 His work presents an unhealthy apology for the aesthetics of capitalism, provoking the resentment of ordinary people.
V. Kemenov (Soviet critic)

6 A friend went to Picasso and said 'Can I have a word in your eye.'
Lord Mancroft, Speech to Auctioneers and Estate Agents, Dorchester Hotel 31 *Oct* 1957

7 Nothing unites the English like war. Nothing divides them like Picasso.
Hugh Mills, PRUDENCE AND THE PILL

MARY PICKFORD

Born 1893, in Canada, was one of the first, and certainly the greatest in world-wide acclaim, of silent film stars. Married Douglas Fairbanks Snr., and was co-founder of United Artists Films. Died 1978.

8 It took longer to make one of Mary's contracts than it did one of Mary's pictures.
Sam Goldwyn

9 Mary Pickford was known to an adoring public as America's Sweetheart and to the heads of the studio as the Bank of America's Sweetheart.
David Niven, BRING ON THE EMPTY HORSES 1975

10 Mary Pickford's marriage to Douglas Fairbanks had ended in divorce the year before I arrived in Hollywood. Mary was a wan and gallant hostess, relying more and more on the companionship of a serious, curly-haired young actor-singer whom she subsequently married — Buddy Rogers.
Ibid.

11 That prissy bitch.
Mabel Normand

12 I can't afford to work for only ten thousand dollars a week.
Mary Pickford to Adolph Zukor

LUIGI PIRANDELLO

Born 1867. Italian playwright, novelist and short-story writer. Achieved international fame with *Six Characters in Search of an Author*, 1921. Awarded Nobel Prize for Literature, 1934. Died 1936.

13 His themes became the relativity of truth, the tragicomic absurdity of existence, the uncertain boundaries between sanity and insanity, the unbridgeable chasm of incomprehension between individuals. His anarchist rebellion, sinister yet deeply compassionate, grasped the nature but never the roots of the inter-war crisis of values. Perhaps this imaginative failure partially explains Pirandello's adherence to Fascism.
Gaspare Giudice, PIRANDELLO 1975

14 In 1918, when he was fifty and working on *Six Characters in Search of an Author*, Luigi Pirandello found himself both a prisoner and an outcast in life. Like an obsessive presence, only his characters peopled his

solitude, splinters of a broken dream that had sprung back fully armed to threaten and cajole him. Shut in his study he conversed with them, waving his hands wildly, flashing his eyes and making the strangest faces in the world.
Ibid.

1 Pirandello's main theme is the power and prevalence of illusion; it is for him the dominant factor in life and its gradual dispelling is tragedy.
J. A. Hammerton, CONCISE UNIVERSAL BIOGRAPHY

2 Pirandello's real importance in modern drama derives from his ability to create middle-class characters of universal significance. His obscure philosophy, which informs all his plays, is at once questionable in itself and difficult to understand.
Ibid.

EZRA (LOOMIS) POUND

Born 1885. American poet and essayist who lived in Europe from 1907. Came under heavy criticism for his Fascist sympathies during World War II. Was arrested by the Americans and committed to an asylum for the insane, where he remained until 1958 when he was released through the efforts of Robert Frost. Died 1972.

3 Pound is at the heart of the literary history of our century. His place as a poet, though, is far from certain, and discussion of it has been bedevilled by the tragic second half of his life, which began with his broadcasts from Rome on behalf of the Axis during the war. Inevitably, whatever he himself may have thought, he appeared a traitor to his country.
Walter Allen, Daily Telegraph 28 *Mar* 1968

4 In 1945 Pound was arrested by the Americans and treated with what hindsight suggests was unwitting cruelty. Arraigned for treason in Washington, he stood mute and, after examination by psychiatrists, was declared unfit to plead. The psychiatrists who reported him insane said among other things; 'He has long been recognised as eccentric, querulous and egocentric.'
Ibid.

5 He was confined in St Elizabeth's Mental Hospital, Washington, until 1958. When he was released he remarked: 'How could one live in America, outside a mental home?'
Daily Telegraph, Obituary 3 *Nov* 1972

6 I confess I am seldom interested in what he is saying, but only in the way he says it.
T. S. Eliot, The Dial, Isolated superiority, Jan 1928

7 He made a deafening noise in preaching and propagandising, yet at the same time he was an ascetic and a contemplative and there were great silences in him; his poetic self-cultivation was a Loyolan spiritual exercise, a discipline he imposed on himself daily with no Romantic waiting on inspiration. The noisiness and the silent contemplation were equally essential, the two halves of a Messianic task.
P. N. Furbank, The Times 27 *Sep* 1969

8 Any poet born in this century or the last ten years of the preceding century who can honestly say that he has not been influenced by or learned greatly from the work of Ezra Pound deserves to be pitied rather than rebuked.
Ernest Hemingway. Quoted Carlos Baker, ERNEST HEMINGWAY: A LIFE STORY 1961

9 Ezra Pound was kinder and more Christian about people than I was. His own writing, when he would hit it right, was so perfect and he was so sincere in his mistakes and so enamoured of his errors, and so kind to people, that I always thought of him as some sort of saint. He was also irascible, but so perhaps have been many saints.
Ernest Hemingway, A MOVABLE FEAST 1961

10 The spectacle of Pound's degeneration is a terrible one, and no one ought to pretend that it is anything but what it is.
F. R. Leavis. Quoted Charles Norman, EZRA POUND 1969

11 I like, respect, and in a sense reverence Ezra Pound; I have found him a true, unspoilt and disinterested individual . . . there is almost nowhere in the past that he has not visited. He is a great time-trotter . . . But where the present is concerned it is a different matter. When he tries to be up to date it is an uncomfortable business. He has never loved anything living as he has loved the dead.
Wyndham Lewis, AN ANTHOLOGY OF HIS PROSE (*edited by E. W. F. Tomlin*) 1969

12 Ezra Pound was inclined to mumble into his red beard, a habit perhaps brought on by his defensiveness, the result, in turn, of attacks delivered on him during the years of his domicile in England. He was particularly a type the English do not understand or appreciate. As a consequence of his attitude

in the 1939 war, little good is heard of him today.
Osbert Sitwell, LAUGHTER IN THE NEXT ROOM 1949

1 His kindness was very great to many young authors and artists, but he seldom allowed it to be suspected by its recipients. I remember almost the last time I met Yeats, I mentioned that I had seen Pound in Italy and he remarked, 'anyone *must* like Ezra who has seen him feeding the stray cats in Rapallo'.
Ibid.

ENOCH POWELL

Born 1912. British Conservative politician. Minister of Health, 1960–3. His views on the curtailment of immigration and the repatriation of non-whites involved him in much controversy. Resigned from Cabinet 1968. Re-entered parliament as an Ulster Unionist, 1974.

2 There was nothing languid or easy-going about Enoch Powell. A former Fellow of Trinity, Cambridge, and Professor of Greek in Australia, he was probably the most intellectually formidable of the men who have passed through the Research Department. He took an interest in almost every subject, and on almost every subject he had strong and pungently expressed views. Only some of these were eccentric.
Lord Butler, THE ART OF THE POSSIBLE 1971

3 While he was answering questions at the Bull Ring in Birmingham during the 1954 election campaign he called on the electorate to vote Labour. One of the very few in the audience not mesmerised by him shouted 'Judas'. Powell turned and the expression on his face was of indescribable and immeasurable anguish. 'Judas,' he said 'was paid. I am making a sacrifice.' And so he was.
Patrick Cosgrave, The Times 14 *Jun* 1982

4 Much though I enjoy a good lunch with him I often feel I should go into training for it, lest any slip of grammar or sloppiness of thought should invite a withering attack. I recall one such when as we said farewell I asked him to remember me to his wife. He looked at me for some seconds and then: 'There is no need to remember you to Pam. She remembers you very well.'
Ibid.

5 There was no colour problem until Enoch Powell created one.
David Frost. Quoted in TV Times

6 Mr Powell's glittering eye, fervent speech and wealth of classical and statistical allusion hypnotised many for a time. Under hypnosis they were persuaded that because he sounded so logical he must be right. But a prophet who announces that the end of the world will take place next Wednesday at noon will find if the world safely passes the deadline that on Thursday even a claim on his part to have a dead cert for the 3.30 at Kempton Park will be treated with almost universal scepticism.
Bernard Levin, The Times 5 *Oct* 1984

7 He has pressed into service some of the best rhetoric and most extreme logic heard from a politician in modern times. Unafraid of irony, glorying in hyperbole, drawing on a deep reservoir of withering scorn, he has never hesitated to embarrass his colleagues in his anxiety to stimulate them.
Observer, Profile 24 *Apr* 1966

8 The trouble is that all through his career he has been a brilliant conversational terrorist.
Arnold Wesker. Quoted Patrick Cosgrave, The Times 14 *Jun* 1982

9 His voice was that of an old-style Imperialist whose dream had been destroyed and who for some years had been harrowed by the postwar devaluation of British citizenship.
David Wood, The Times

ELVIS PRESLEY

Born 1935. American entertainer, the leading exponent of rock-and-roll in the 1950s. Died 1977.

10 . . . the grossness, egomania and barbaric vulgarity that was, apparently, Elvis.
Martin Amis, reviewing Albert Goldman's ELVIS, *Observer* 6 *Dec* 1981

11 It may indeed be the case that Elvis was no more than a horrible, and horribly uncomplicated, embodiment of American Success, but *Elvis* leaves us none the wiser.
Ibid.

12 The master bedroom — black suede walls, crimson carpets and curtains, 81 square feet of bed with mortuary headboard and speckled armrests. On the bed lies Elvis himself, propped up like a big fat woman recovering from some operation on her reproductive organs.
Albert Goldman, ELVIS 1981

13 Elvis was a silly little country boy who just happened to sing like a nigger, the acne-

spotted, self-pity of his early songs making a strong appeal to the hysterically self-pitying mood of millions of teenagers.
Ibid.

1 Presley inherited most of the bizarrely worst (and the best) traits of pop superstar life-style. He had the usual large wardrobes and flashy car fleets. He wasted the usual large amount of time and money on orgies of destructiveness. He made more than the usual amount of third-rate movies.
Derek Jewell, Observer 30 *Jul* 1972

2 Early in his career he was asked which was his favourite among all the records he had made. He answered that it must be *Don't Be Cruel*. Why? 'Because it has sold the most copies.'
Dominic Kennedy, Radio Times 19 *Aug* 1971

3 It simply isn't easy to get more than a few clichéd comments out of the man. Conversing with 'the King' was not unlike talking to a pleasant but not particularly articulate farm labourer.
Ibid.

4 To Middle America rock seemed no more than a barrage of abuse hurled over gigantic loud speakers in a language they couldn't recognise or decipher . . . The music was packaged in an insolent sexuality; youth was libido and authority repression. Liberty was wearing blue suede shoes that year. No wonder Middle America was frightened; what his guitar was doing to their eardrums, his pelvis was doing to their daughters.
Charles Nicholl, Daily Telegraph 13 *Jul* 1972

5 It was Elvis who turned on a whole new generation of young people to a new form of music and a new life-style. He was in fact the complete original — flash and aggressive, Elvis Presley translated the mood of the young people in the 50s to his vibrant, wild, sensual music.
Jerry Rubin. Quoted Dominic Kennedy, Radio Times 19 *Aug* 1971

6 An aging, fat, sentimental, drug-addled Elvis tried to sock it one more time to the bejewelled blue rinses at Vegas — and failed.
Laurie Taylor, Observer 23 *Dec* 1981

J. B. (JOHN BOYNTON) PRIESTLEY

Born 1894. English novelist, playwright and essayist. First attracted popular attention with *The Good Companions*, 1929. Gained a wide public with his regular broadcasts during World War II. Died 1984.

7 I've read nearly everything he ever wrote, and not for one moment did I ever think I was wasting my time.
Anthony Burgess, Observer 19 *Aug* 1984

8 Some of us remember, during the war, the series of postscripts he gave on the BBC after the Sunday nine o'clock news. He spoke common sense in a comforting Yorkshire accent husky with pipe smoke, he spoke of decency, he told us why we were fighting the war.
Ibid.

9 There have always been critics ready to sneer at his being too wholesome.
Ibid.

10 He deliberately turned his back on the moral ambiguities of life and was content, as the eighteenth-century novelists were, with a simplicity, both ethical and psychological, which the ordinary reader could handle.
Ibid.

11 He was always more subtle than he wished to appear.
Ibid.

12 My first publisher, who was also and always his, spoke of him as 'the gasfire Dickens'.
Ibid.

13 Priestley was a kind of one-man public opinion poll. He understood the mood of the people very well, and he played a major part in preparing the way for the Labour Government of 1945.
Michael Foot, BBC Radio 4, A workmanlike man 8 *Sep* 1984

14 Priestley came to our table for some talk. From what he said he will be calling himself a great man any day now. I shan't care if he does. He is a robust-minded person, and if he believes in himself let him say so.
Reginald Pound, THEIR MOODS AND MINE 1937

15 The man whose voice, in *Postscript* after the Sunday evening news in 1940–1, did much to put heart into a nation that appeared to be in for the beating of its life.
Kenneth Young, Sunday Telegraph 19 *Aug* 1984

Why did Priestley, happily travelling round the world with his third wife, Jacquetta Hawkes the archaeologist, always look so grumpy? He explained that he was born so, that he had a 'treacherous' face. 'That face', he wrote in his final chapter of autobiography *Instead of the Trees* 'expresses far more than I really feel. I look furious when I am no more than mildly annoyed.'
Ibid.

R

GRIGORI (YEFIMOVICH) RASPUTIN

Born 1872. Russian monk, who had a corrupting influence in the country's affairs, mainly because of his power over the Tsarina, until a conspiracy among members of the court resulted in his assassination 1916.

1 They accuse Rasputin of kissing women etc. Read the Apostles; they kissed everybody as a form of greeting.
Tsarina Alexandra, letter to the Tsar

2 What a good example it is of the hopeless divorcement from reality not only of the Tsaritsa, but also of the Tsar that they became besotted by this filthy peasant who was constantly drunk and whose sexual voracity should have earned him a prize in any agricultural show.
Second Earl of Birkenhead, Daily Telegraph 11 *Nov* 1960

3 When Rasputin's body was dragged from the river and taken to a mortuary two women appeared and asked for the body. This was refused; but they were allowed to take away the sodden clothes. The two women were the Tsarina and her lady-in-waiting.
Owen Blake, Sunday Referee 5 *Mar* 1939

4 In 1904 he underwent what he called a conversion, and believing or pretending to believe that he was divinely inspired, began to travel the countryside, preaching an individual form of a doctrine then popular in Russia. From the axiom that repentance alone can ensure salvation, he drew the corollary that in order to repent it was first necessary to sin and, claiming to be a second Messiah, declared that he alone was able to pronounce absolution.
J. A. Hammerton, CONCISE UNIVERSAL BIOGRAPHY

5 He makes no secret of his debauched and scandalous life, yet at the Holy Synod itself has as many friends as foes, and many people believe he actually has a divine mission.
Raymond Poincaré, MEMOIRS 1928

6 It is one of the strangest comments on the Russian atmosphere of that time that people should have taken Rasputin so seriously.
Norman Stone, Observer, An ogre of sanctity 6 *Jun* 1982

7 Though Rasputin did not understand his gifts he did understand how far they could take him. He had a wonderful time. Through his well-to-do contacts he made a lot of money; he also made endless sexual conquests among both upper-class and lower-class women.
Ibid.

TERENCE (MERVYN) RATTIGAN

Born 1911. English playwright. His successes include *French Without Tears*, 1936, *The Winslow Boy*, 1946, and *Separate Tables*, 1954.

8 It was at Harrow that the French master, M. Laborde, who had told his form to write an original playlet, returned Rattigan's effort with the comment 'French execrable, but shows strong dramatic sense'. Eleven years later the pupil justified his master's confidence with peculiar propriety by writing *French Without Tears* which netted him £20,000. His dramatic sense was still as strong, his French still as execrable.
Paul Dehn

RUFUS DANIEL ISAACS, FIRST MARQUESS OF READING

Born 1860. British lawyer and politician. Elected Liberal MP for Reading 1904, Attorney-General 1910, Lord Chief Justice 1913, Ambassador to Washington 1918, Viceroy of India 1921, Foreign Secretary 1931. Died 1935.

9 When Reading was appointed Viceroy of India Sir Alfred Mond said 'It means the end of Lloyd George. Directly Reading's calming influence is withdrawn from him his power will decline.' If this was true Reading's appointment was one of the major disasters of British history. It led to the reign of the pygmies which began at the Carlton Club in October 1922, and lasted until May 1940.
Dingle Foot, Sunday Times 5 *Nov* 1967

Though Reading did not know where he was going, he knew he was going somewhere. He was on the make, from his first years on the Stock Exchange. Essentially he was an intermediary, a fixer. He brought men and Governments together and, like any stockbroker, took a commission for himself. His attempt at speculation on his own account came near to disaster.
H. Montgomery Hyde, LORD READING 1967

2 The element in Lord Reading of Dick Whittington, or Sindbad the Sailor, so largely stressed in contemporary accounts of his extraordinary career, had by now (in 1926) completely vanished, or at any rate was absent from his aura. Though he certainly brought with him a feeling of ambitions gratified and of marked worldly success, to me he resembled the phantom of a great man, but a spectre heavy in spite of his phantomhood and of his light weight physically. One seemed to see him, like an apparition at a seance, through curtains; an affable Caesar, ponderous, though thinly cast in bronze, laurel-wreathed, fine-featured, quick-witted (that could be deduced from his eyes) but slightly damaged by life and rendered complacent by the progress of years.
Osbert Sitwell, LAUGHTER IN THE NEXT ROOM 1949

3 I remember someone remarking to Lord Reading, 'Whatever we do, we must not allow you to take any action at present. We must keep you in reserve as our queen bee.' In reply to which sentiment I produced, in a passing silence, and with a voice as though echoing from a tomb, the question, 'Even if the hive is being burned down?'
Ibid.

4 Rufus Isaacs had a remarkable career. He went to India twice, the first time as a ship's boy, the second as Viceroy.
A. J. P. Taylor, Observer 15 *Oct* 1967

RONALD (WILSON) REAGAN

Born 1911. Well known as an American film actor before turning to politics. Governor of California 1967–75. Elected President of United States 1980, and for a second term, 1984.

5 President Reagan, TV-tested is the latest face in a long line of dumbbells.
Saul Bellow. Quoted Martin Amis, Observer 11 *Dec* 1983

6 In Hollywood he was not only the genial B-movie star, but also the union leader who bored his first wife, actress Jane Wyman, into divorce with his one-track political mind.
Robert Chesshyre, Observer 29 *Jan* 1984

7 Reagan himself wrote 20 years ago in his ghosted autobiography *Where's the Rest of Me?* 'An actor spends at least half his time in fantasy.' In his case the fantasy lingers on.
Ibid.

8 His conversational style is anecdotal and sometimes scatological. He will shock serious-minded visitors by devoting much of a meeting to story-telling, frequently missing the point of the discussion. Even well-known people frequently get the feeling that he doesn't know who they are.
Ibid.

9 Reagan is intellectually idle, uncaring of detail, at times naïve almost to the point of simple-mindedness, prejudiced and 30 years out of date in his world view, scary on nuclear war, indifferent to blacks and the poor, confusingly ready to agree to conflicting ideas.
Ibid.

10 He's a great TV personality and he has the marvellous gift of physical fitness. Absolutely nothing really bothers him. Whatever happens, he just smiles and waves at the press.
Billy Graham. Quoted John Mortimer, Sunday Times 19 *Jul* 1984

11 I have a strange feeling that he will wake up one day and ask, 'What movie am I in?'
Sheilah Graham, The Times 22 *Aug* 1981

12 Ronnie is a very soft touch, and I don't want anyone taking advantage of him.
Nancy Reagan, Observer, Sayings of the Week 25 *Nov* 1984

13 Ninety-seven members of the Ronald Reagan Battalion of El Salvador's army have just celebrated the American president's inauguration. They have deserted.
The Times, Diary 29 *Jan* 1985

14 He has, I think, a total sense of unreality. They just prop him up, get him from one sound stage to another. This is very dangerous.
Gore Vidal. Quoted Lorna Sage, Observer 16 *Sep* 1984

15 I am responsible for the presidency of

Ronald Reagan. Warwick the president-maker. In 1959 I was casting *The Best Man*, about a presidential candidate, and an agent offered me Ronald Reagan for the part, and I turned him down on the grounds that he was not credible. If I had said yes he would have run two years on Broadway, won all the prizes, and never gone into politics.
Ibid.

1 Daffy Duck and his mallard friends in LA.
Ibid.

2 Whenever Ronald Reagan entered a room, for 30 years I and everyone else would, like startled gazelles, pound across the room in the opposite direction, as he's one of the greatest bores that ever drew breath.
Ibid.

3 The words that come out of his mouth don't always start in his heart; his heart and his mouth don't work together.
An 87-year-old Washington great-great-grandmother. Quoted by Robert Chesshyre, Observer, Agency of America 26 *Jun* 1983
Ibid.

4 The captain of the ship, though amiable and well-meaning, was (a) ignorant of all but the barest rudiments of navigation in foreign waters and (b) asleep in his hammock a lot of the time.
David Watt, Observer, reviewing Alexander Haig's CAVEAT 13 *May* 1984

5 The President arrived at the White House with almost no qualifications for the conduct of American foreign policy except for some broad ideological presuppositions about the villainy of the Soviet Union.
Ibid.

6 Reagan is a phenomenon on his own. A desperate Democrat summed it up for me by saying, 'If only he could be king we should be all right. He would open dams and pat children and we wouldn't have to bother with his policies. As far as I am concerned he could be a constitutional monarch for life.".
David Watt, The Times 5 *Oct* 1984

7 What's really worrying about Reagan is that he always seems to be waiting for someone to say 'CUT' and has no idea how they've decided the script should end.
Katherine Whitehorn, Observer, Act your self 4 *Dec* 1982

SIR MICHAEL (SCUDAMORE) REDGRAVE

Born 1908. English actor in theatre and films, who played many notable Shakespearean roles at the Old Vic. Died 1985.

8 When he played Antony in *Antony and Cleopatra* at Stratford in the 1953 season a critic wrote 'From the first decisive entrance the look of him was so right, a careless, laughing and abandoned magnificence. Here is a man in a life's fever of love, consumed with the need to touch, agonised by jealousy and self-reproach; a man of heroic stature and ferocious pride, bold, generous, and great-hearted, a very world-sharer.'
Hal Burton, Radio Times 17 *Feb* 1966

9 Michael Redgave has often enjoyed success when creating weak characters, men who are failures; he endows pathetic people with an intensity of emotion which gives them a rare truth and validity, as in his memorable film performances; the schizophrenic ventriloquist in *Dead of Night*, and the seedy schoolmaster in Terence Rattigan's *The Browning Version*.
Ibid.

10 Playing King Lear, he began finely, conveying grief as well as rage at Cordelia's refusal to flatter him. Physically, already the whole of Lear was there, a sky-scraping oak ready to resist all the lightning in the world.
Kenneth Tynan 1953

JOHN (CHARLES WALSHAM) REITH FIRST BARON OF STONEHAVEN

Born 1889. The first Director-General of the British Broadcasting Corporation, pioneered and developed radio services and the world's first regular television service. Made his mark by insisting on rigid standards of programme content, and staff behaviour. Died 1971.

11 The three most frightening men with whom I have ever had dealings were Mussolini, Northcliffe and Reith. Sir John has not, I think, the same capacity for inspiring intense devotion as the other two. He still believes too much in the power of the scowl.
Vernon Bartlett, News Chronicle 15 *Jun* 1938

12 What are you to make of a man who, in his great Mussolinian study at Broadcasting House, has a framed certificate near his desk

to vouch for the fact that he never missed a single Sunday School during his boyhood?
Ibid.

1 He has a very good conceit of himself, and is none the worse for knowing his worth.
A. J. Cummings, News Chronicle 17 *Nov* 1949

2 Lord Reith is a very tall, dominating, heavy-browed figure. Even Mr Churchill found him overpowering and dubbed him 'Lord Wuthering Heights'.
Ibid.

3 Dante without the poetry, loving without the mystery, Mephistopheles without the fun.
Alan Dent. Quoted James Agate, EGO 4 5 *Apr* 1937

4 Meet him at your own risk. His grimness may alarm. His size will stupefy you. Six feet four inches of Aberdeen granite. Shoulders of terrific breadth. A square jaw. Deep-set eyes that smoulder with perpetual fire.
Passing Show 20 *Aug* 1932

5 I want to banish ignorance and misery and enrich the human race, not deprive it and propagandise it.
Reith to Stanley Baldwin

6 At the end of 1922 the British Broadcasting Company, financed by a group of manufacturers, was given an exclusive licence to send out wireless programmes. Its manager was a Scots engineer, John Reith. Calvinist upbringing, harsh and ruthless in character, Reith turned broadcasting into a mission. It was to bring into every home 'all that was best in every department of human knowledge, endeavour and achievement'. He used what he called 'the brute force of monopoly' to stamp Christian morality on the British people. He stamped it also on his employees. Producers, or even electricians, found themselves out of a job if touched by a breath of scandal. Announcers had to put on dinner jackets before addressing the microphone.
A. J. P. Taylor, ENGLISH HISTORY 1914–1945 1965

7 When he moved from the BBC into other spheres of administration his performances, though the gifts he brought to them were the same, were far less conspicuous. The reason is, perhaps, that his early successes were a result of a co-ordination of his many qualities and that his later tasks engaged as a rule only a few of them. His great gifts were never given the same scope again.
The Times, Obituary 17 *Jun* 1971

8 His judgement was such that he never aroused that slumbering force of British opinion which has only to stir to bring down governments and could when roused have swept him and his system away.
Ibid.

JOACHIM VON RIBBENTROP

Born 1893. German politician, Hitler's foreign minister 1938–45. Executed for war crimes 1946.

9 Ribbentrop was arrogant. He was reported to have given King Edward VIII the Hitler salute.
Geoffrey Bocca, Sunday Express 12 *Feb* 1956

10 'Aren't you a damned bad ambassador?' Nancy Astor asked him. When Ribbentrop asked why she replied, 'Because you have no sense of humour.' 'Oh, but I have,' he exclaimed. 'You should see me telling jokes to Hitler, and how we roar with laughter,' which is the kind of answer one might expect to get when one asks a silly question.
Ibid.

11 Ribbentrop looks like the captain of someone's yacht, square, breezy, and with a sea-going look. Actually he was once a wine-merchant. He is not quite without charm, but shakes hands in an over-hearty way, and his accent is Long Island without a trace of Teutonic flavour.
Sir Henry Channon, DIARY 29 *May* 1936

12 Von Ribbentrop has been captured. This champagne salesman who turned a 'diplomat' of the Nazi school — who knew so much about us that he said 'England will never fight' — was found asleep in bed, unclothed, in a hideout in a Hamburg boarding-house. Strapped to his body was a tin of poison. Three letters, one addressed to Mr 'Vincent' Churchill, one to Mr Eden and one to Field-Marshal Montgomery, were found in his room.
Evening Standard 15 *Jun* 1945

13 If Ribbentrop had taken Bismarck as his exemplar he would not have dinned so often into the Fuehrer's ears that Britain would not fight.
J. B. Frith, Daily Telegraph 7 *Mar* 1940

14 One of his besetting sins is vanity. He was at great pains to acquire his *von*. He was not born a *von*, and he has since done nothing in particular to claim it. He therefore got himself adopted by an aunt, or a great aunt whose husband had somehow got the magic symbol. A *von* by adoption! Bismarck would have set his Great Dane at him.
Ibid.

SIR RALPH (DAVID) RICHARDSON

Born 1902. English stage and film actor. Actor-director of Old Vic 1944–7. Died 1983.

1 'I don't ride motor-bikes for speed but for the swinging, pitching *rhythm* of the thing. Eighty-five m.p.h. will do me nicely. And you can't feel the breeze in a crash helmet so I never wear one. How do you think I got these?' He traces a pattern of faintly visible scars on his massive forehead. 'Motorbike accidents, all of them,' he says gleefully.
Elizabeth Cowley, Radio Times 20 *Apr* 1972

2 With his ripe face and his excitable voice, his amiable combination of eccentricity and down-to-earth common sense, he was ideally equipped to make an ordinary character seem extraordinary, or an extraordinary one seem ordinary.
The Times, Obituary 11 *Oct* 1983

3 There was the unique physical presence, at once rakish and stately, as of a pirate turned prelate.
Kenneth Tynan, SHOW PEOPLE 1978

4 There was the balsa-wood lightness of movement which enabled him to fall flat on his face three times in a single act — a rare feat for a septuagenarian.
Ibid.

5 I once described his voice as 'something between bland and grandiose; blandiose, perhaps'. Or as I wrote in another context, when he played Cyrano de Bergerac in 1946: 'His voice is most delicate; breathlight of texture . . . It is a yeasty, agile voice. Where Olivier would pounce upon a line and rip its heart out, Richardson skips and lilts and bounces along it, shaving off pathos in great flakes.'
Ibid.

6 What Sir Ralph does, without question, is to dignify every production he appears in. He once said 'I don't mind how small the part is, so long as it's interesting.'
Nicholas Wapshott, The Times 13 *Dec* 1982

7 He still keeps a 750 cc BMW motor-bike in the garage. 'The most important thing about motor-bikes,' he said, 'is to buy a big one. They are oh so much better — except when you come off and they fall on top of you.'
Ibid.

PAUL ROBESON

Born 1898. American Negro singer and actor. His left-wing political views forced him to live abroad for a number of years. Died 1976.

8 It is the quality of warmth and colour in his voice, even in melancholy, which gives it so intense an emotional appeal. His voice is like an organ. It is a voice which somehow vibrates with the very pulse of life.
Ethel Mannin, CONFESSIONS AND IMPRESSIONS 1930

9 He had been acting in amateur theatricals for years without ever considering it as a possible career, and then Eugene O'Neill saw him and wanted him for *The Emperor Jones*. In that play he was required to whistle — in the scene in which he lies resting in the forest — but, he told me, I couldn't whistle, so I sang. He had always liked singing, to please himself, but it was then that others discovered he had a voice.
Ibid.

10 When he comes into a room something happens, as positively as when a blind is pulled up and the sunlight pours in, or a fire is lighted in a cold room.
Ibid.

11 When he is not speaking there is a kind of brooding melancholy about him, rather like a shy child, but when he laughs it is as though a great fountain of spontaneous happiness is suddenly released in him — the eager spontaneous happiness of a child.
Ibid.

12 When Robeson sings some of the more melancholy spirituals his voice has all the rich sombreness of black velvet.
Ibid.

SIR GEORGE ROBEY

Born 1869. Stage name of Edward George Wade. English comedian and music-hall entertainer. Died 1954.

13 I had quite a talk with Robey. He is a very gloomy man, with very reactionary ideas on everything. He says he lives absolutely alone and prefers that, and is still very miserable. Decent fellow, I should say.
Arnold Bennett, LETTERS TO A NEPHEW 1936

14 His eyebrows are so famous that a letter from Australia addressed with a drawing of them and the one word 'England' reached Robey safely.
Hadden Knight, Sunday Referee 8 *Jan* 1939

1 When he played Sir John Falstaff in *Henry IV* they wanted his famous eyebrows subdued somewhat. 'I'm not plucking my eyebrows for Shakespeare or anybody else,' he said, and they had to quieten them down with greasepaint instead.
Ibid.

2 When he appeared on the BBC's *Saturday Night Music Hall* fifty listeners wrote in to complain that some of the things he said were 'suggestive'. 'Dear me. It's always my fate to be misunderstood,' said George. 'This does seem to be a world full of wicked thoughts.'
Ibid.

3 While playing at Swansea I rowed out with a realistic dummy as my companion. Then, in full view of the crowds on the beach, I seized the dummy and acted as if we were having a quarrel to the death. I could hear the cries from the shore. I lifted a scull and rammed it into the prostrate figure. The excitement became frantic. Boats began to put off. Standing erect I emitted a final blood-thirsty yell and emptied the six chambers of my revolver into my victim. It was a good stunt. When I stepped on to the stage that night I was received with loud cheers and cries of 'What have you done with the body, George?'
George Robey, LOOKING BACK ON LIFE 1933

JOHN D. (DAVISON) ROCKEFELLER Sr

Born 1839. American industrialist, financier and philanthropist. Laid the foundation of his fortune with Standard Oil. Died 1937.

4 He is the father of trusts, the world's foremost pioneer centraliser of business machinery and power, the vaulting apostle and exemplar of business efficiency, the demonstrator-in-chief of co-operation's superiority over competition — always for co-operators and frequently for consumers.
William R. Allen, ROCKEFELLER

5 His clothes concerned him little, if at all. One suit had a big patch on the coat, and a bright shine on the pants. 'What's wrong with this suit?' he asked crankily, when a friend urged him to discard it. 'Everything', said his friend. 'Your father would be ashamed of you. You know how neatly he used to dress.' 'But,' protested Rockefeller triumphantly, 'I'm wearing a suit of my father's right now.'
Bennett Cerf, TRY AND STOP ME 1947

6 To ensure peacefulness at night on his 3000 acre estate near New York — from which he had already removed a railway line and a road — he directed that his retinue of servants should retire beyond the gates at sundown. The 70 negro guards remaining had their shoes soled with an inch of rubber so that there would not be any crunching sound on the gravel paths.
Daily Telegraph, Obituary 24 *May* 1937

7 He found his chief pleasures in the companionship of his family and the acquaintances of the Baptist Church. The pleasures of intellectual conversation never meant anything to him. The small affairs, the trivial chatter of people who talked about their neighbours and their Sunday School completely satisfied his social and intellectual appetites.
John T. Flynn, GOD'S GOLD 1933

8 While his subtle, ruminative, daring mind solved large problems by an acid process of thought he presented to the world a front of silence which was like smooth steel.
Allen Nevins, A STUDY IN POWER: JOHN ROCKEFELLER

9 The story of his life is the story of oil. Scandal after scandal is associated with his name in the building up of the great Standard Oil Company. He coupled immense driving force, rigid economy and a robot-like efficiency with bribery and graft: established a widespread system of espionage: undercut his competitors with the aid of secret rebates on transport of oil by rail.
The (London) Star 24*May* 1937

10 While he was amassing his immense fortune, relentlessly and sometimes unscrupulously, he read family prayers every morning, was superintendent of a Baptist Sunday School and encouraged his daughter to become a missionary.
Ibid.

11 When he drove into the rough and spent a long time poking in the grass for the missing ball the caddie mentioned to him that other members, when they drove into the rough, only looked for the ball for a minute or two, and if they did not find it, dropped a new one on the fairway, and played on. 'Huh', said Rockefeller. 'They must have barrels of money.'
Sunday Referee 14 *Feb* 1937

12 John D. Rockefeller, ninety-eight next July, is being kept alive so that he may realise his

great ambition of living to be 100 years old. Except for one thing, his normal day is just the same as that of any retired business man with plenty of money. The exception is that John D. spends a part of each day lying in an oxygen tent. The doctors consider that this is doing more than anything to prolong his life.
Ibid.

AUGUSTE RODIN

Born 1840 in France. Sculptor whose work was much influenced by Michelangelo. Among his most famous pieces are *The Thinker* and *The Burghers of Calais*. Died 1917.

1 In 1906 Rodin made a portrait bust of George Bernard Shaw. Shaw was very excited by the way Rodin had brought life to the clay and wrote afterwards 'The hand of God is in his hand.'
Guy Brett, The Times 24 *Jan* 1970

2 This monstrous and excellent old pagan was indifferent to all the values which ordinary men have sanctified as necessary for their social life. But he was accepted. In his old age he was The Master. From the University of Oxford he received an honorary degree at the same time as General Booth of the Salvation Army.
Geoffrey Grigson, John o' London's Weekly 15 *Sep* 1939

3 Once, in taking me round his studio, he pointed out Shaw's head as that of an Englishman, but he had forgotten the name! This is not surprising for Rodin was indifferent to external reputations, and he was more ignorant than most intelligent men of politics, of literature or philosophical thought. He saw everything by the light of his artistic symbols.
Arthur Lynch, John o' London's Weekly 15 *Aug* 1931

4 Rodin neglected his ordinary life which stretched out behind him like a path overgrown with weeds in a deserted garden.
Rainer Maria Rilke

5 When a lady asked Rodin if I spoke French well he replied with his characteristic serious veracity. 'Mr Shaw does not speak French well; but he expresses himself with such violence that he imposes himself.'
Bernard Shaw, letter to Jacob Epstein

6 Rodin asked if it would be possible for me to come to Paris and sit for him . . . It was a curious experience, for the bust, which began at the end of fifteen minutes' work like a brilliant sketch by Sarah Bernhardt, went through the whole history of sculpture since the Middle Ages. When it reached the twelfth century it was such a jewel that I begged him to let me take it away; but he said he could 'carry it further'; and to my horror it became successively a Bernini, a Canova or Thorwalden, a Gibson or Foley before it became a Rodin.
G. B. Shaw. Quoted Hesketh Pearson, BERNARD SHAW 1942

7 He went to Nature for his form and to his own mind for expressive ideas. These were conceived as he watched his models moving from pose to pose, as he sketched with lightning rapidity, and out of a correlated group of such sketches and his memories of such poses the final ideas took shape.
Horace Shipp, Teacher's World 12 Aug 1931

WILL ROGERS

Born 1879. American actor, entertainer and columnist. Specialised in the character of a philosophical, rope-spinning cowboy. Killed in an air crash in the Arctic when flying with Wiley Post, pioneer aviator, 1935.

8 He didn't become a headliner until he started talking and that was by accident. He got his ropes tangled up one day and while he was straightening them out he explained his difficulties to the audience. His Oklahoma drawl made people laugh, and Will looked up angrily. Then he realised they were laughing with him. He kept on talking—and never stopped.
Bennett Cerf, SHAKE WELL BEFORE USING 1948

9 Legend has it that Will Rogers once walked up to the gate of Buckingham Palace and said to the guard, 'I am Will Rogers and I have come to see the King.' The guards drew themselves up haughtily and Rogers continued, 'You tell him that when the Prince of Wales was out my way he told me to look up his old man sometime, so here I am.' Rogers was admitted, had a long chat with the king, and stayed to lunch.
Edmund Fuller, ANECDOTES 1942

10 W. R. Hearst invited Will Rogers to San Simeon for a weekend. Hearst had assembled a considerable company and Rogers was the star guest whom Hearst did

not fail to show off to his best advantage. A few days later Hearst received from Rogers a bill for several thousand dollars for services as a professional entertainer. He called Rogers on the phone and protested, saying 'I didn't engage you as an entertainer. I invited you as a guest.' Rogers snapped 'When people invite me as a guest they invite Mrs Rogers, too. When they ask me to come alone, I go as a professional entertainer.'
Ibid.

1 To a man who proudly said 'My ancestors came over with the *Mayflower*,' Will Rogers replied 'My ancestors were waiting on the beach.'
Ibid.

2 Rogers was seriously suggested as a candidate for the Presidency. Representative Everett G. Howard declared on the floor of Congress 'Rogers is a statesman, experienced, courageous, safe and sound, and offers excellent material for the Presidency.' 'Haw' chuckled Rogers. 'Do you want a President who is funny on purpose?'
P. J. O'Brien, WILL ROGERS: AMBASSADOR OF GOODWILL 1936

3 Rogers and his friend Irvin S. Cobb were going to meet President Coolidge for the first time. Coolidge was famous for his solemnity and taciturnity. Cobb said to Rogers 'I bet you can't make him smile.' As the President shook hands with Rogers he said something through tight lips. Will leaned over as though to hear better, and said: 'Pardon me; I didn't get the name.' The President smiled.
Ibid.

FIELD MARSHAL ERWIN ROMMEL

Born 1891. German military leader, commanded a panzer division in France, 1940, and the Afrika Korps in the Western Desert 1941–3. Accused of implication in the plot to kill Hitler, and committed suicide 1944.

4 A superb soldier, brave, energetic, resourceful and lucky, but a bully, a *mauvais coucheur*, and, when things went wrong, a defeatist.
Michael Howard, Observer 13 *Nov* 1977

5 Rommel was built up as a key figure in the plot against Hitler at a time when this was regarded as an essential qualification for all good Germans. But Rommel neither knew of that conspiracy nor approved of it, and the accusations which led to his forced suicide were made by smaller fry who hoped, by invoking the prestige of the great Field Marshal, to obtain some sanction for their own activities.
Ibid.

6 Rommel has always been one of Britain's favourite generals of the Second World War. Apart from his incontestable merits as a commander, his talents proved a splendid alibi for the mediocre British performance in the Western Desert.
Ibid.

(ANNA) ELEANOR ROOSEVELT

Born 1884. Wife of F. D. Roosevelt. Worked for social reform. Wrote a newspaper column, *My Day*. Was United States delegate to United Nations 1945–53 and 1961. Died 1962.

7 A young private secretary was called on the phone one morning by a lady whose voice was unfamiliar. 'I saw your soldier husband in Germany,' said the stranger. 'Perhaps you will have a bite with me tomorrow so that I can tell you all about him?' They arranged to meet in a hotel lobby. When the secretary asked 'How will I know you?' the stranger told her, 'Just look for a tall, grey-haired lady.' That is how she came to have lunch next day with Mrs Franklin D. Roosevelt.
Bennett Cerf, SHAKE WELL BEFORE USING 1948

8 I was surprised to observe how discourteous cameras had been to her; they had shown merely a heavy face with a too large mouth; their inaccurate lenses had transformed her wide, friendly smile into a grin, and ignored the expression of her eyes, which was gentle and slyly humorous; they had also ignored her quality of distinction which, in its essence, was curiously Victorian; I could imagine her driving through the nineteenth-century English countryside to take tea with Mrs Gaskell.
Noël Coward, FUTURE INDEFINITE 1954

9 Mrs Roosevelt often entertained her personal guests in her two-room suite on the second floor. Her sitting room, a drab parlour with sofa and desk, adjoined a small dressing room where she slept in a narrow bed. As in her husband's suite, the walls were covered with framed photographs of official life. There were so many pictures that we had to draw a detailed plan of their

arrangement each time we cleaned or painted the walls.
J. B. West, UPSTAIRS AT THE WHITE HOUSE 1974

1 On Sunday nights Mrs Roosevelt's table was like a European salon. The President did attend, if he felt well, and listened to authors, artists, actresses, playwrights, sculptors, dancers, world travellers, old family friends — mixed in with Ambassadors, Supreme Court Justices, Cabinet Officers, and Presidential advisors. Eleanor Roosevelt, using a large silver chafing dish she'd brought from Hyde Park, scrambled eggs at the table. But the main course was conversation. We called the menu 'scrambled eggs with brains'.
Ibid.

2 Eleanor Roosevelt's life was filled with visitors from early morning until late at night. Her house was full of guests, some of whom stayed for months, and some she just picked up off the street. Sometimes she invited so many people, she forgot who they were.
Ibid.

3 The tall, imposing woman smiled, showing more teeth than I've ever seen, and extended a slim graceful hand. It was surprisingly soft in my grasp. She was wearing a dark skirt and a white ruffled blouse, and wisps of grey were beginning to stray from her hair, which was loosely pulled back in a knot. When she spoke, her voice was high-pitched and shrill, and she talked so fast I had trouble understanding her.
J. B. West, of his first meeting 1 *Mar* 1941, *ibid.*

FRANKLIN D. (DELANO) ROOSEVELT

Born 1882. Overcame the crippling handicap of polio to become governor of New York 1929–33. Elected president of the United States 1932, and launched his New Deal programme to counter the Depression. Was the first American president to be elected for a third term, and had been elected to serve a fourth term on his death in 1945.

•

4 In 1940 when the United States as well as ourselves were in dire peril, and he realised it, he gave us all the help he could. In his final term of office as President, for which he should never have stood, he wanted to give half Europe to Stalin and to bring the British Empire to an end. He succeeded in both. But historians may judge that neither was of great benefit to humanity.
Lord Boothby, RECOLLECTIONS OF A REBEL 1978

5 I once asked a leading member of the Democratic Party of the United States, who must be nameless, whether Franklin Roosevelt ever had any deep sense of purpose about anything. He hesitated and then said, 'Only one. To remain in office.'
Ibid.

6 The best newspaperman who has ever been President of the United States.
Heywood Broun. Quoted D. Boorstin, THE IMAGE

7 In Franklin Roosevelt there died the greatest American friend we have ever known and the greatest champion of freedom who has ever brought help and comfort from the New World to the Old.
Winston Churchill, TRIUMPH AND TRAGEDY

8 Not since Lincoln has there been such an awful manipulator of the good, the bad, and the bewildered in between.
Alistair Cooke, AMERICA

9 My view was of a man who saw the United States as would a kindly and attentive landlord, concerned in all aspects with the lives of his tenants and the estate in which they dwelt . . . When he had decided, that was the truth.
J. K. Galbraith, A LIFE IN OUR TIMES 1981

10 Sometimes Roosevelt made terrific appointments. He shopped for ambassadors, it seemed, like a housewife choosing among apples over the telephone.
John Gunther, ROOSEVELT IN RETROSPECT 1950

11 He would rather follow public opinion than lead it.
Harry Hopkins. Quoted G. Wolfskill and J. A. Hudson, ALL BUT THE PEOPLE: F. D. ROOSEVELT AND HIS CRITICS

12 He was nearly christened Isaac, but his father happened to admire Franklin Delano at the time.
Geoffrey Madan, NOTEBOOKS 1981

13 He was a bear in the mornings until he had his coffee and the first of his 40 daily cigarettes.
TV Times 20 *Oct* 1984

14 At formal receptions, the gardeners set up a wall of ferns at the south end of the Blue Room. A special seat, like a bicycle seat, was placed between the ferns. It protruded just enough for the President to sit on it and still look as if he was standing. His legs, shrunken

and useless, could not balance him. With his heavy, steel braces, he could only remain in an upright position with the assistance of someone or something.
J. B. West, UPSTAIRS AT THE WHITE HOUSE 1974

1 I soon learnt that the White House staff took extraordinary precautions to conceal Mr Roosevelt's inability to walk. Special ramps had been built all over the White House for the President's wheel chair. During State dinners, butlers seated the President first, then rolled the wheel chair out of sight. Only then were guests received in the dining room. For ceremonies in the East Room, the doormen would quietly close the double doors which were covered with red velvet curtains, after all the guests had assembled. Mr Roosevelt then rode to the doors in his wheel chair, someone lifted him from the chair, and we flung open the doors and curtains. The President, on the arm of an aide, swung his legs the two steps to the podium, on which he could lean while speaking. No photographs were permitted. His entrances were passed off as Presidential dramatics.
Ibid.

THEODORE ROOSEVELT

Born 1858. Succeeded to the presidency of the United States on the assassination of McKinley, 1901. Secured the independence of Panama, to allow the construction of the Canal. Re-elected as president 1904. Awarded Nobel Peace Prize 1906 for his mediation in the Russo-Japanese War. Died 1919.

2 He contained within him the best and worst of America, the whole spectrum from practical enlightenment and sound moral judgement to sentimentalism and braggadocio.
John M. Blum, THE REPUBLICAN ROOSEVELT

3 One always thinks of him as a glorified bouncer engaged eternally in clearing out bar-rooms — and not too proud to gouge when the inspiration came to him, or to bite in the clinches, or to oppose the relatively fragile brass knuckles of the code with chair-legs, bung-starters, cuspidors, demi-johns and ice picks.
H. L. Mencken, PREJUDICES (*Second Series*) 1921

4 Theodore, if there is one thing more than another for which I admire you, it is your original discovery of the ten commandments.
Thomas B. Reed. Quoted W. A. Robinson, LIFE OF THEODORE ROOSEVELT

5 Teddy was reform in a derby, the gayest, cockiest, most fashionable derby you ever saw.
William Allen White. Quoted Eric Goldman, RENDEZVOUS WITH DESTINY

ARCHIBALD PHILIP PRIMROSE, FIFTH EARL OF ROSEBERY

Born 1847. First chairman of the LCC, 1889. Foreign Secretary 1892 and Prime Minister 1894 after which he gradually withdrew from politics and devoted himself to the writing of biographies, notably Napoleon, 1904; Lord Randolph Churchill, 1906; Chatham, 1910, and to horseracing, winning the Derby three times. Died 1929.

6 He was not self-swayed, like Gladstone, but he was self-enfolded.
Margot Asquith, AUTOBIOGRAPHY 1920

7 He outlived his future by ten years and his past by more than twenty.
Winston Churchill, GREAT CONTEMPORARIES 1937

8 He is a one eyed fellow in blinkers.
D. Lloyd George. Quoted A. J. Sylvester, LIFE WITH LLOYD GEORGE

BERTRAND (ARTHUR WILLIAM) RUSSELL, THIRD EARL RUSSELL

Born 1872 in Wales. English philosopher, mathematician. Collaborated with A. N. Whitehead to produce *Principa Mathematica*, 1910–13.

9 The dictionary definition of philosophical gives its meaning as 'calm and temperate'. That is rubbish. I don't believe there is such a thing as a calm philosopher. Bertrand Russell, in my opinion the greatest, certainly isn't.
A. J. Ayer, The Times 28 *Aug* 1968

10 In trying to recall his face I am able to see it only in profile — the sharp, narrow silhouette of an aggressive jester.
Arthur Koestler, STRANGER ON THE SQUARE 1984

11 The beauty of Bertrand Russell's beautiful mathematical mind is absolute, like the third movement of Beethoven's A Minor

Quartet, or the complete circle of a logical proposition as propounded and proved by Spinoza.
Ethel Mannin, CONFESSIONS AND IMPRESSIONS 1930

1 I remember a dark blue flannel suit ruled with thin white lines, which he felt authorised to wear on semi-formal occasions, because his tailor had told him it would almost do as a blue serge, and, as he justly remarked, if it would *almost* do for the tailor, it would *quite* do for anybody else.
Edward Marsh, A NUMBER OF PEOPLE 1939

2 Bertrand Russell is my grandmother's first cousin. I think he's adorable. It's so funny, he talks in exactly the same voice that she had.
Nancy Mitford, Sunday Times 28 *Aug* 1966

3 He asked me, in the voice of one whose life is mostly in his head, what were my seven children's ages. Hopeless, was his verdict; they were all ruined long ago — this is conformity with his theory that children should be taken out of the scope of home influences as soon as possible after birth.
Reginald Pound, THEIR MOODS AND MINE 1937

4 His life, for all its waywardness, had a certain anachronistic consistency, reminiscent of that of the aristocratic rebels of the early nineteenth century. His principles were curious but, such as they were, they governed his actions. In private life he showed none of the acerbity which marred his writings, but was a genial conversationalist and not devoid of human sympathy.
Russell, writing his own obituary for The Listener 1937

ERNEST RUTHERFORD, FIRST BARON RUTHERFORD

Born 1871 in New Zealand. British physicist, researcher in radioactivity. Awarded Nobel Prize for Chemistry 1901. Died 1937.

5 As for the atomic bomb, it was a good thing he did not live to see it. It was not what he was about at all.
John Campbell, The Times 23 *Feb* 1984

6 He was able to excuse himself from attending an anti-submarine committee with the words 'If, as I have reason to believe, I have disintegrated the nucleus of the atom this is of greater significance than the war.'
David Wilson, RUTHERFORD: SIMPLE GENIUS 1984

7 His style was breezily informal, and he would sit on a lab stool, scattering ash and enthusiasm in all directions and intoning audibly but tunelessly *Onward Christian Soldiers* whenever things went well.
Ibid.

S

VICTORIA (MAY) SACKVILLE-WEST

Born 1892. English novelist and poet. Of her novels, one of her earliest successes was *The Edwardians*, 1930, but by then she had already attracted attention with her long poem about the countryside, *The Land*, in 1926. Died 1962.

1 In later years Vita came to bear a strong resemblance to a crusty Anglo-Indian colonel.
Peter Alexander, ROY CAMPBELL 1982

2 The gentle Vita whose strong hands cupped the fragile moth and nursed the injured nightingale.
Mitchell A. Leaska (editor, LETTERS OF VITA SACKVILLE-WEST TO VIRGINIA WOOLF 1984

3 The exalted woman who strode her own acres and lived in castles.
Ibid.

4 I love seeing you in London. It is like a country-bred puppy on a lead, seeking to escape up some side-street from the crowds on the pavement and the fierce traffic in the street. Your hand was trembling with panic when we crossed Piccadilly. How one loves the odd corners of the people whom one loves.
Harold Nicolson, letter to Vita Sackville-West 15 *Aug* 1956

5 I know I was cruel to other children because I remember stuffing their nostrils with putty, and beating a little boy with stinging nettles.
V. Sackville-West. Quoted Nigel Nicolson, PORTRAIT OF A MARRIAGE

6 At home (where even the butler wrote novels) she fed stags out of buckets, planted bulbs (and sold books) by the thousand, showered Virginia Woolf with gifts of towering pies, butter mountains, laundry baskets full of figs. 'I have no coal,' she wrote majestically in 1926, 'but am felling an oak to show my rustic independence of the coal strike.'
Hilary Spurling, Observer, Virginia creeper 11 *Nov* 1984

7 Vita on holiday abroad could be trusted to hire a castle by the week as naturally as most people took rooms in a boarding house.
Ibid.

ANWAR EL SADAT

Born 1918. Egyptian politician. Succeeded Nasser as President 1970. Negotiated Egypt–Israeli Peace Treaty at Camp David through the mediation of President Carter. Assassinated in Cairo 1981.

8 I told President Carter about one of my meetings in which Sadat clapped his hands and had a huge globe brought into the living room, on which with a pointer he gave me a lecture on what US global policy ought to be. His prescriptions would have made Theodore Roosevelt sound like a pacifist!
Zbigniew Brzezinski, POWER AND PRINCIPLE: MEMOIRS OF THE NATIONAL SECURITY ADVISER 1977–1981 1983

9 President Carter deeply cared for that expansive, impetuous, bold Egyptian, who embodied qualities so different from those of the highly-controlled, precise Georgian with the computer-like mind. We would laugh together at Sadat's inaccuracies and sweeping assertions, and yet at the same time we marvelled at his courage and the grandiose scope of his historical vision.
Ibid.

10 By going to Jerusalem Sadat achieved a world-wide constituency as a super-star but lost the constituency which was naturally his as President of Egypt — the Arab World.
Mohammed Heikal, AUTUMN OF FURY 1983

11 Sadat was more than the sum of his parts. By one of the miracles of creation the peasant's son, the originally under-estimated politician, had the wisdom and courage of the statesman, and occasionally the might of the prophet.
Henry Kissinger, The Times, Anwar Sadat the prophet we took for granted 12 *Oct* 1981

12 There have so far been two dominant and conflicting interpretations of Sadat. In one version he was a world statesman and super-patriot ('the greatest since Bismarck', said Kissinger). In the other he was a superstar of international showbiz.
Robert Stephens, Observer 8 *May* 1984

HERBERT (LOUIS) SAMUEL, FIRST VISCOUNT SAMUEL

Born 1870. British politician. Home Secretary, 1916 and 1931–2. High Commissioner for Palestine 1920–2, Leader of the Liberal Party in the Commons, 1931–5, and in the Lords 1941–5. Died 1963.

1 I once asked Lloyd George what he really thought of Herbert Samuel. He looked up, with a twinkle in his eye, and said: 'Well, I made him the first proconsul in Jerusalem since Pontius Pilate.'
Lord Boothby, RECOLLECTIONS OF A REBEL 1978

2 When they circumcised him they threw away the wrong bit.
D. Lloyd George. Quoted John Gloag, The Listener 7 *Sep* 1978

3 Among the minor reforms with which he was associated was the introduction of Summer Time during the last war and the phrase 'Summer Time' was his invention.
Robert Lynd, News Chronicle 7 *Aug* 1945

4 The belief in reason, the devotion to duty, the granite honesty of the man have been sources of political weakness as well as strength. They have led him to underestimate the power of evil in human affairs. As late as the autumn of 1937 he thought Hitler, although dangerous 'not a man who would do what he knew to be a crime as Napoleon would have'.
Richard Moore, News Chronicle 13 *Sep* 1957

5 His tragedy is that he has been on the side of the angels, but the angels have been only intermittently victorious.
Ibid.

6 When the dramatic Cabinet crisis came in 1916, by which Lloyd George ousted Asquith, Samuel was offered the War Office. He refused it. 'I greatly disliked the way the change had come about, and to take office in Ll.G's Government would have been to acquiesce in it.' This remarkable and rare attitude ended his ten years in office.
Observer, Profile 20 *Nov* 1949

EUGEN SANDOW

Born 1867 in Germany. Wrestler, gymnast, champion weight lifter, physical culture expert. Died 1925.

7 Paderewski, meeting Sandow, said 'I do your exercises.' Sandow smiled. 'Does being a pianist require such strength?' Paderewski struck a chord on the piano. 'You are the strongest man in the world, play that chord.' Sandow played the chord. 'Now go on playing it over and over again.' For three minutes the studio reverberated. Then the iron fingers rebelled. The ruddy face paled with effort. 'I can play no more.' 'Ah,' said Paderewski 'I can play that chord for thirty minutes before I fail.'
Bruce Clavering, Sunday Referee 9 *Aug* 1936

8 Eugen Sandow once tried to entice Bernard Shaw as a pupil and develop him physically. Shaw said 'You misunderstand my case. I have seen you supporting on your magnificent chest twenty men, two grand pianos and a couple of elephants; and I have no doubt you could train me to do the same. But my object as to pianos and elephants and crowds is to keep them off my chest, not to heap them on to it.' Sandow gave him up as hopeless and presently died prematurely, thus confirming Shaw's mistrust of exercises and his resolution not to burden himself with superfluous muscle.
Hesketh Pearson, BERNARD SHAW 1942

JOHN SINGER SARGENT

Born 1856, in Florence, of American nationality. Fashionable portrait painter. Lived and worked in London after 1884. Died 1925.

9 The ladies Sargent paints, according to Meynell, generally bore him so much that he is obliged to retire every now and then behind a screen and refresh himself by putting out his tongue at them.
Wifred Scawen Blunt, DIARY 14 *May* 1907

10 On the rare occasions he was called upon for a speech he would stand struggling with his nervousness, unable to utter. On one occasion, blurting out 'It's a damned shame' he subsided into his seat amid a tempest of applause.
Evan Charteris, JOHN SARGENT 1927

11 Sargent is interesting round and about his own subject, though he talks slower and with more difficulty in finding his words than anyone I ever met. When he can't finish a sentence he waves his fingers before his face as a sort of signal for the conversation to go on without him.
Ibid.

1 King George V admired Sargent neither as a painter nor as a man, and would not let Asquith give him the O.M.
Roy Jenkins, ASQUITH 1964

2 Sargent used frequently to halt his painting to rest his sitters by playing to them. Dr Playfair's maid once commented of his practice: 'Isn't it nice that Mr Sargent feels like painting when he tires of playing the piano.'
David MacKibbin, SARGENT'S BOSTON

3 Roger Fry said of Sargent's portrait of Ian Hamilton 'I cannot see the man for the likeness.'
Geoffrey Madan, NOTEBOOKS 1981

4 Imagine my excitement when I was invited to meet the great man at a house where he was dining, and was going to do a drawing. I had pictured him so often! Slim, dark, slightly sinister-looking, clean shaven, exquisitely dressed. When I was confronted with a bearded giant, uncouth and inarticulate, I felt that I had been cheated. But that was only because I didn't know him. I doubt if anyone really knew him; he had such difficulty expressing himself, except in paint; but I eventually got over my shock, and lost some of my terror of this big, shy man.
Ernest Thesiger, PRACTICALLY TRUE 1927

SIR (HAROLD) MALCOLM SARGENT

Born 1895. English conductor. 1951–7 conducted the BBC Symphony Orchestra. Gained wide popularity from his conducting of Promenade Concerts. Died 1967.

5 'What do you have to know to play the cymbals?' somebody asked Sir Malcolm Sargent. 'Nothing', was the reply. 'Just when.'
Leslie Ayre THE WIT OF MUSIC

6 So long as Sargent is living I shall not worry about the interpretation of my works.
Sir Edward Elgar

7 Malcolm Sargent was conducting a Royal Choral Society rehearsal of 'The Messiah'. He was displeased with the women's section's rendering of 'For Unto Us a Child is Born'. Calling for attention he begged 'Just a little more reverence, please and not so much astonishment.'
Edmund Fuller, ANECDOTES 1942

8 In Madrid, after one rehearsal and as he came in for the next,they gave him the full exuberant fanfare normally reserved for the most popular matador. It is magnificently typical of Sir Malcolm that he knew the correct riposte; he threw his hat across the arena.
Observer, Profile 30 *July* 1950

9 He bought his first piano score of *The Messiah* for a penny, and he knew it backwards by the time he was thirteen.
C. B. Rees, Radio Times 20 *Aug* 1937

10 His ceaseless activity never led Sargent to abandon the provinces in their considerable need. 'Somebody,' he said, 'has to be a general practitioner of music.'
Charles Reid, MALCOLM SARGENT

11 My 'Flash Harry' nickname came after I'd been doing a Brains Trust. The announcer said we were now going over to Manchester for a concert by me. It sounded as if I'd gone there straight away — in a flash. Then Sir Thomas Beecham, when he heard I was conducting in the Far East said it was just a 'Flash in Japan'.
Sir Malcolm Sargent, Sunday Times 25 *Apr* 1965

12 Like Peter Pan, Sir Malcolm Sargent has been the same age for ever. He was probably born elegant, his eyes set in a solid twinkle, with a carnation in his buttonhole and an inexhaustible supply of effervescence.
Sunday Times 25 *Aug* 1965

WILLIAM SAROYAN

Born 1908. American author, novelist and playwright. First attracted attention with *The Daring Young Man on the Flying Trapeze*, a collection of short stories, 1934. Died 1981.

13 The last time I saw him Army discipline had not weighed too heavily upon his ebullient spirit. Our phone operator announced, 'A man who says he is the world's greatest author is here to see you.' 'Send Private Saroyan in,' I answered.
Bennett Cerf, TRY AND STOP ME 1947

14 'Poetic shouts' was one description of his short prose pieces, and the shouts were exuberantly and unashamedly in favour of mortal human life. His subjects were the lives of ordinary American people, often

American immigrants, frequently poor, the beauty they had not known; and himself.
The Times, Obituary 19 *May* 1981

JEAN-PAUL SARTRE

Born 1905. French philosopher, playwright, novelist. A leading exponent of Existentialism. Awarded Nobel Prize for Literature, 1964.

1 In Paris, Jean-Paul Sartre sent out invitations to the swanky première of his dual bill, *The Tombless Dead* and *The Respectful Prostitute*, forgot to hold one for himself, and was refused admission.
Bennett Cerf, SHAKE WELL BEFORE USING 1948

2 Sartre says: 'Disgust and delight — they come to the same thing.' The vileness of the human flesh obsesses Sartre, as it has so often obsessed the Puritan evangelists before him.
Maurice Cranston, John o' London's Weekly 14 *Oct* 1949

3 His adult life resembled his childhood in the sense that he lorded it over admiring women.
James Fenton, The Times 22 *Nov* 1984

4 He is a philosopher remarkable for the force, one might almost say the animal vigour, of his thought; a novelist of great fecundity and a sumptuous flow of words, mixed a little too carefully with vulgar expressions and low-class slang; a playwright able to sustain themes apparently void of dramatic interest; and a political journalist with a word to say on all contemporary problems.
Observer, Profile 7 *Mar* 1947

5 The ineptitude of M. Sartre's political performance has tempted some British critics to dismiss him as a phoney, particularly as he rarely hesitates to adapt the facts to fit the cause for which he currently cares.
Observer, Profile 4 *Dec* 1960

6 His favourite café the Flore in St Germain des Prés (he later had to flee from the crowds) became a meeting place of the Left wing intellectual *élite* — and for any people who wanted to be thought to belong to it. Busloads of tourists in Paris are still shown the Flore as the place from which the great man used to pontificate.
Ibid.

SIEGFRIED (LORRAINE) SASSOON

Born 1886. English novelist and poet, best known for *Memoirs of a Fox-Hunting Man*, 1928; *Memoirs of an Infantry Officer*, 1930. Died 1967.

7 Like many other fighting soldiers he conceived a loathing for the civilians at home which verged on mania, particularly those who indulged in patriotic cant.
Second Earl of Birkenhead, Daily Telegraph 8 *Sep* 1966

8 Sassoon's intolerable state of mind built up to his formal anti-war Protest of 1917 — 'I am making this statement as an act of wilful defiance of military authority . . .' which was read out in the House of Commons and led the Army in its wisdom to second him to a shellshock hospital at Craiglockhart, Edinburgh (the following year he returned to the Somme and was wounded in the head: his second wound).
Richard Holmes, The Times 5 *May* 1982

9 Siegfried Sassoon was a war poet. Years passed and he suddenly disclosed to the public that he was not so young as they thought him, and that he had a past full of aunts, mahogany, old silver, village cricket, and fox-hunting, of which nobody had ever guessed.
Sir John Squire, John o'London's Weekly 7 *Oct* 1938

10 While he needed to participate in life to write about it, by nature he only wished to witness or reflect upon it; he himself would refer to this as his Enoch Arden complex.
The Times, Obituary 4 *Sep* 1967

DOROTHY L. (LEIGH) SAYERS

Born 1893. English author of detective novels featuring Lord Peter Wimsey. Also wrote a religious play for radio, *The Man Born to Be King*, 1941. Died 1957.

11 *Anyone* would have seemed feeble against the terrific vitality, bullying and bounce of that dreadful woman, Dorothy L. Sayers.
J. R. Ackerley. Quoted Hilary Spurling, Observer 23 *Sep* 1984

12 An enormously definite person.
John Gielgud. Quoted on BBC Radio 4 20 *Jan* 1982

13 On Tuesday 17 December 1957 she returned home from London where she had been doing her Christmas shopping. All she wanted was to have a bath and go to bed but first the cats must be seen to. She threw her

bag and fur coat into the room that led off from the hall and walked towards the kitchen. At the foot of the stair, Death, about whom she had written so much, caught up with her and she sank to the floor in a heap—untidy to the last.
Janet Hitchman, SUCH A STRANGE LADY 1975

1 Dorothy L. Sayers was 64 when she died, but looked years older. She had burnt herself out like a box of fireworks into which a spark had been dropped.
Ibid.

2 I had an amusing correspondence with Miss Dorothy Sayers, in the first chapter of whose *Nine Tailors*, a Baronet had been murdered, leaving an only daughter, but also a younger brother (a most unpleasant character) who remained plain 'Mr' throughout the book. I felt it my duty to ask Miss Sayers why Edward had not succeeded to the baronetcy. She answered that as a matter of fact there had been an intermediate brother, who had emigrated to Fiji and died leaving a son by a native wife; but that as this circumstance had no bearing on the story, she hadn't thought it worth mentioning. 'Anyhow', she added in vindictive postscript, 'nothing shall induce me to let Edward be a Baronet.'
Edward Marsh, A NUMBER OF PEOPLE 1939

3 We conversed until 2.15 a.m. I liked the old dear but found her heavy going.
Charles Williams. Quoted Humphrey Carpenter, THE INKLINGS

ARTUR SCHNABEL

Born 1874 in Austria. Pianist. Internationally famous particularly for his interpretation of Beethoven's piano sonatas. Died 1951.

4 Schnabel, refusing to play encores, explained 'Applause is a receipt, not a bill.'
Irving Kolodin, THE MUSICAL LIFE 1958

5 A spinster used to visit the Schnabel home in Bielitz, Austrian Silesia, to give piano lessons to his older sister. At five, Artur, without instruction, was playing his sister's weekly task piece by ear — and without wrong notes.
Observer, Profile 13 *Jun* 1946

6 In the Spring of 1933 his broadcasts were quietly suppressed, and he was dropped from a Brahms festival prospectus. He and his family took one of the next two trains out of Berlin. Fürtwangler begged him to come back. 'If every German musician who has lost his job through race or creed is reinstated I will return — not otherwise,' said Schnabel.
Ibid.

7 The notes I handle no better than many pianists. But the pauses between the notes — ah, there is where the art resides.
Artur Schnabel, Chicago Daily News 11 *Jun* 1958

8 Have I a secret about playing the piano? It is a very simple one. I sit down on the piano stool and I make myself comfortable — and I always make sure the lid over the keyboard is open before I start to play.
Artur Schnabel. Quoted Nat Shapiro, ENCYCLOPEDIA OF QUOTATIONS ABOUT MUSIC 1978

9 During the rehearsal of the Beethoven concerto Schnabel said to the conductor 'You are there, and I am here. But where is Beethoven?'
Nat Shapiro, AN ENCYLOPEDIA OF QUOTATIONS ABOUT MUSIC 1978

ALBERT SCHWEITZER

Born 1875 in Alsace. Physician, missionary, theologian, organist. In 1913 went to the Gabon to work in a medical mission at Lambaréné. Wrote a biography of Bach and edited his organ music. Awarded Nobel Peace Prize, 1952. Died 1965.

10 Mrs Clara Urquhart, one of his closest associates over a period of 15 years, when asked why so many women, many of them rich, had gone to work at Lambaréné over the years, said 'They are mostly women who would have been nuns if they had been religious. They go to dedicate themselves. Schweitzer is a very alive and attractive person.'
John Ardagh, Observer 19 *Apr* 1964

11 The most favourably inclined of Dr Schweitzer's visitors admit that his hospital is the most backward in the world. Incontestably Schweitzer is a great man — one of the greatest of this or any time and his heart is great and good. But also he can be cranky on occasion, dictatorial, prejudiced and somewhat vain. And why not?
John Gunther, INSIDE AFRICA 1955

1 From the beginning of his career he was something of a heretic in his interpretation of Christianity. What he lacked in orthodoxy he made up for in his passionate belief in the ethics of Jesus. It might be said of him that he was driven to become a medical missionary by a creed that would have shocked and startled most missionaries.
Robert Lynd, News Chronicle 16 *Mar* 1933

2 It is in his attitude to Africans that Schweitzer has remained a characteristically nineteenth-century figure. Stern but paternal, he refers to them as 'my savages'. He has learned to speak no African language. Africans never sit down in his study, and he has no sympathy for the African plea for equality of status. 'The African is my brother', he says, 'but he is my younger brother by several centuries.'
Observer, Profile 23 *Oct* 1955

3 Since 1913 Africa has changed, but Schweitzer has continued unchanged. Some visitors to Lambaréné have been surprised by the ramshackle hospital, with its plank beds, primitive equipment and with the patients' relatives, dogs, hens, chickens and goats mingling with the sick . . . Schweitzer prefers to keep his forest hospital primitive, and takes a pride in using the building methods of the ancient Egyptians.
Ibid.

4 The handsome and rugged sage, with his immense white moustache and unruly hair, isolated in Equatorial Africa, dividing his time beween healing leprous Africans, playing Bach on the organ and writing the philosophy of civilisation, is a symbol of the idealism of the last century.
Ibid.

5 Dr Schweitzer has come home to the Alsatian village of Gunsbach from his jungle hospital in Africa and has promised to play the organ. I travelled with him on the last stage of his train journey across France. He had not had time to practise, so he practised in the train by tapping out rhythms with his feet as if he were dancing. A peasant and his children in the same compartment watched fascinated as Dr Schweitzer stamped out the bass notes of a Bach Fugue on his imaginary pedal board.
Roland Pullen, Sunday Express 30 *Aug* 1959

ROBERT FALCON SCOTT

Born 1862. English polar explorer. Reached the South Pole in January 1912, thirty-five days after Amundsen, but, with four companions, died on the return journey.

6 There is little doubt that his explorations were directed towards a single competitive end. In his own words: 'I submit that efforts to reach a spot on the globe which has hitherto been untrodden by human feet and unseen by human eye is itself laudable.'
Second Earl of Birkenhead, Daily Telegraph 14 *Mar* 1974

7 Scott applied to Lloyd George for assistance in the financing of his last and fatal Polar expedition. Lloyd George referred him to a certain wealthy man of some prominence in the political scene. 'How did you get on?' asked Lloyd George when he saw the explorer again. 'He gave me a thousand pounds' replied Scott, 'but he has undertaken to raise 20 thousand pounds if I can persuade you to come with me, and a million if I manage to leave you there.'
Edmund Fuller, ANECDOTES 1942

8 There was a memorial service at St Paul's Cathedral for one of the most inefficient Polar expeditions, and one of the worst of Polar explorers.
Roland Huntford, SCOTT AND AMUNDSEN 1979

9 It is natural to make easy romance out of a story of a race to the Pole. But in fact there was no race. Scott's expedition was an expedition to make scientific observations and a journey to the Pole was but one of its incidents . . . Scott and his party carried on their work, discoverers and explorers in that sense to the end. When their strength was already failing they went on collecting specimens of rocks and fossils, and pulled them with them until they died. This was the cause to which they gave their lives, not empty notoriety.
Lord Kennet, Daily Telegraph 18 *Jan* 1937

10 Scott was not a great explorer. He made too many mistakes and paid the penalty.
Sir Martin Lindsay, Observer 6 *Nov* 1977

11 Scott's failure has moved the generations far more deeply than Amundsen's win.
James Morris, The Times 7 *Aug* 1972

12 Scott was a natural leader if ever there was one. Frequently he prefaced his remarks to me with 'my dear fellow' — a conventional expression, I know, but I never failed to get a thrill of pride from his use of it.
Herbert G. Ponting, THE GREAT WHITE SOUTH

DAVID O. (OLIVER) SELZNICK

Born 1902. American film producer responsible for *Gone With the Wind*, 1939. Died 1965.

1 David O. Selznick was overfond of writing memos. A member of his staff did something wrong, was fearful of the worst, and thought he might as well get it over with. So he sent Selznick a note beginning, 'In reply to your memo of tomorrow . . .'
Leslie Halliwell, THE FILMGOER'S BOOK OF QUOTES 1978

2 For all his arrogance and exasperating self-indulgence, he was a man of intelligence and considerable charm — a typical Hollywood combination of oafishness and sophistication.
John Houseman, RUNTHROUGH

3 Selznick gave the impression that he stormed through life demanding to see the manager — and when the manager appeared Selznick would hand him a twenty-page memo announcing his instant banishment to Elba.
Lloyd Shearer. Quoted Rudy Behlmer, MEMO FROM DAVID O. SELZNICK

ROBERT W. (WILLIAM) SERVICE

Born 1874 in England. Canadian poet who wrote popular verse about the Yukon gold rush. His best known collection, *Songs of a Sourdough*, 1907. His best-known ballad, *The Shooting of Dan McGrew*. Died 1958.

4 Everything suddenly came together in his mind and out poured a host of knockabout characters who belong somewhere between boy's comic fantasies and Hollywood Westerns.
Eric Davidson, The Times 1 *Sep* 1976

5 Dreamer and fumbler, I was the stuff of which failures are made.
Robert W. Service, PLOUGHMAN OF THE MOON 1946

6 I always found ordinary men by far the more interesting, and would rather win the approval of a barman than a professor.
Ibid.

7 It was said that *Dan McGrew* was intended originally for recitation at a Yukon church social, but it was never given because some of the language was thought to be on the strong side for such an occasion. Service, who had scratched out the ballad on the back of old envelopes, let them gather dust until a bonus from his bank enabled him to publish in Toronto. By 1940 two million copies had been sold.
The Times, Obituary 13 *Sep* 1958

GEORGE BERNARD SHAW

Born 1856 in Dublin, moved to London in 1876, entered journalism as a music critic and after writing a number of unsuccessful novels, found his true metier when encouraged by William Archer to try his hand at writing plays. Died 1950.

8 Shaw's plays are the price we pay for Shaw's prefaces.
James Agate, EGO 10 *Mar* 1932

9 As a teacher, as a propagandist, Mr Shaw is no good at all, even in his own generation. But as a personality he is immortal.
Max Beerbohm, AROUND THEATRES

10 Shaw's judgements are often scatterbrained, but at least he has brains to scatter.
Max Beerbohm. Quoted S. N. Behrens, CONVERSATION WITH MAX 1960

11 Shaw came in just as lunch was served. Naturally self-conscious and egotistic; but he evidently made a decent effort against this. Talked most of the time during lunch; had a marked accent and a habit of rubbing his hands constantly while talking.
Arnold Bennett, DIARIES 1896–1910

12 This astonishing Mr Shaw has been greater than anything even he has ever written.
John Mason Brown

13 A budding young anthologist sought to include a Shaw piece in a new collection. 'I hope you understand', he wrote to Shaw, 'that I cannot afford to pay your usual fee as I am a very young man.' Shaw replied 'I'll wait for you to grow up.'
Bennett Cerf, SHAKE WELL BEFORE USING 1948

14 Sam Goldwyn was supposed to be imploring Shaw for permission to film *Pygmalion*. 'I don't care if the picture loses money,' he declared. 'It is the contribution to art I am thinking of.' 'That's the difference between us,' Shaw assured him. 'You think of nothing but art, but I think of nothing but money.'
Bennett Cerf, TRY AND STOP ME 1947

15 G.B.S. looked aged and feeble and was dressed in very dark tweeds and a black overcoat. His white whiskers and pink face

looked like an enamelled portrait, and had that pink lifeless quality of the very old.
Sir Henry Channon, DIARY 26 *Feb* 1944

1 Bernard Shaw is dead, that old fraud with his mania for publicity and money. I do not think his works will live, though he tried to be a modern Voltaire, and up to a point succeeded.
Ibid. 2 *Nov* 1950

2 I have never read a reply by Bernard Shaw that did not leave me in better, and not worse temper or frame of mind; which did not seem to come out of the inexhaustible fountains of fair-mindedness and intellectual geniality. I have learned to have a warmer admiration and affection out of all that argument than most people get out of agreement.
G. K. Chesterton, AUTOBIOGRAPHY 1936

3 Mr Shaw is (I suspect) the only man on earth who has never written any poetry.
G. K. Chesterton, ORTHODOXY 1908

4 Shaw relished every opportunity to have himself painted, sketched, photographed or carved, because each likeness provided him with a new extension of himself.
Peter Conrad, Observer, Multitude of Shaws, 7 *Oct* 1979

5 The finest playwright and most fatuous politician of his time.
Colin R. Coote, Daily Telegraph 5 *Oct* 1972

6 I recall how Nancy Astor forced a recalcitrant Bernard Shaw into signing a first edition which I was auctioning on behalf of disabled soldiers. Thank Heaven, it fetched very little, and I gave it to a taxi driver in New York just to hurt Shaw's ego.
Ibid.

7 Shaw was never an original thinker, but always daringly anticipated what intelligent people were on the point of saying.
Robert Graves and Alan Hodge, THE LONG WEEKEND 1940

8 Whenever Bernard Shaw was wanted urgently for a rehearsal it was almost certain he would be found at a grimy little cinema. If he had a weakness it was for Jackie Coogan.
Cedric Hardwicke, LET'S PRETEND 1932

9 He identified genius with immunity from the cravings and turpitudes which make us human. Hence his regime of sexual continence which so confused and dismayed the women he persisted in loving, and hence too his abstinent diet of grated vegetables.
Michael Holroyd, THE GENIUS OF SHAW 1979

10 George Bernard Shaw — flibbertygibbet pope of chaos; portent and epitome of this generation's moral and spiritual disorder.
Henry Arthur James, MY DEAR WELLS

11 He said he was a finer fellow than Shakespeare. I merely prefer myself to Mr Shaw.
Percy Wyndham Lewis, BLASTING AND BOMBARDIERING 1937

12 That noisiest of old cocks.
Percy Wyndham Lewis

13 When *An Englishwoman's Love-Letters*, subsequently acknowledged by Laurence Housman, was published anonymously, there was a great to-do, and one of the newspapers sent reply-paid telegrams to all the well-known writers, 'Are you author Love Letters Englishwoman?' It was rumoured that G.B.S. replied 'Am author love-letters many Englishwomen, which do you mean?'
Edward Marsh, A NUMBER OF PEOPLE 1939

14 I was told of Shaw's introduction to an eminent authoress, who found him so agreeable that she wrote next day asking him to come and see her. 'Nothing,' he replied 'shall induce me to imperil the memory of our one perfect meeting.'
Ibid.

15 Shaw got everything wrong — Shakespeare, Caesar, the Soviet Union, Mussolini, St Paul. He had a sparkling intelligence but a low understanding; this enabled him to be very funny, but when he was serious he was absurd.
Malcolm Muggeridge, CHRONICLES OF WASTED TIME 1972

16 I do not think Shaw will be a great literary figure in 2000 AD. He is an amazingly brilliant contemporary, but not in the Hardy class.
Harold Nicolson, DIARY 11 *Dec* 1950

17 The foaming denouncers of the bourgeoisie, and the more-water-in-your-beer reformers of whom Shaw is the prototype.
George Orwell, THE ROAD TO WIGAN PIER 1937

18 Shaw is the most fraudulent, inept writer of Victorian melodramas ever to gull a timid critic or fool a dull public.
John Osborne

19 He never had much patience with the intricacy of stage 'business'. He once told me

he would rather write the whole dialogue of *Hamlet* than manage the entrance and the exit of the ghost.
Blanche Patch, THIRTY YEARS WITH G.B.S. 1951

1 In the churchyard at Ayot St Lawrence there is a tomb bearing the inscription 'Jane Eversley. Born 1815. Died 1895. Her time was short.' Shaw felt that a place where the inhabitants who died at eighty were considered short-lived had the right climate for him.
Hesketh Pearson, BERNARD SHAW 1942

2 His influence over the more serious young men and women following the war of 1914–18 was far greater than exercised by Wells, Chesterton, Belloc, Galsworthy and Bennett or any other writer. The qualities in him that specially appealed to youth were his irreverence for tradition and office, his indifference to vested interests and inflated reputations, his contempt for current morality, his championship of unpopular causes and persecuted people, his vitality and humour, and above all his inability to take solemn people seriously. There was always something of the rebellious schoolboy about him.
Ibid.

3 Shaw was a cast-iron theorist. He said that a fact could hit you in the face, but could not mean anything to you until it was fitted into a plan of thought. One of his reproaches to the universities was that they were full of learned fools with omnivorous memories who could remember any quantity of facts and could make no more use of their collection than of used postage stamps.
Ibid.

4 Clergymen always flocked to hear him address the Fabian Society. Once he was lecturing on *Flogging as Punishment* and as usual questions were invited when he sat down. The last question was from a parson; 'In the army many men guilty of misdemeanours ask to be flogged. What has the lecturer to say to that?' Shaw had this to say; 'The subject of my lecture was *Flogging as a Punishment*, not *Flogging as a Luxury*.'
Ibid.

5 Shaw had a particular objection to his first Christian name. 'Jawj' he once said 'is so horribly ugly and difficult that all attempts to call me by it are foredoomed to failure.' He warned an acquaintance that 'nothing exasperates me more than to be Georged in print'.
Ibid.

6 Shaw confessed, 'I wrote *Androcles and the Lion* partly to show Barrie how a play for children should be handled.' Doubtless the children would have thoroughly enjoyed it, but unfortunately the grown-ups, never having given Christianity a thought, considered the play blasphemous and instead of foisting it on their offspring, forbade them to see it.
Ibid.

7 Even when conversing he could not keep still: jumping up and down, crossing and uncrossing his legs, shoving his hands in his pockets and pulling them out, sitting straight up or lying right back in his chair, bending forward, stretching backward, never remaining in one position for two minutes together.
Ibid.

8 He had a horror of earthly burial, but when he went behind the scenes (at his mother's cremation) and saw the coffin pushed into what seemed a chamber radiant with sunshine, and bursting into twirling ribbons of soaring garnet-coloured flame, he was transported by the wonderful aesthetic effect, and became more ardent than ever in his advocacy of cremation, which he carried to the length of declaring that earth burial should be made a criminal offence.
Ibid.

9 The absence of fine shades and atmosphere explains why repertory companies in a hurry so often choose a Shaw play. You have only to learn the lines, slam them across, and the piece comes to life.
J. B. Priestley, THOUGHTS IN THE WILDERNESS

10 It is more important to remember that he began to flourish in the nineties than to remember he was born in Ireland.
Edward Shanks, LIFE OF G. B. SHAW 1924

11 The more I learn about other men's methods the more I perceive that nobody except myself ever dreams of taking the trouble to attain really exhaustive literary expression. In fact I am quite the most extraordinary man in London; and you are quite welcome to give that fact on my authority.
G. B. Shaw, letter to Ernest Rhys

12 My last book has turned the tables on the people who will not admit that I am serious; they used to laugh when I was serious, but now the fashion has changed, they take off

their hats when I joke, which is still more trying.
G. B. Shaw of CAESAR AND CLEOPATRA, *in a letter to Forbes Robertson* 21 *Dec* 1903

1 I am a pig-headed, arrogant, obstinate, domineering man of genius, deaf to reason, and invincibly determined to have my own way about my own books.
G. B. Shaw. Quoted Hesketh Pearson, BERNARD SHAW 1942

2 If people didn't laugh at me they couldn't endure me. As an ordinary human being I am frankly impossible; even as a 'Variety' turn I am only just bearable. My mental and moral superiority are insufferable. No chink can be observed by the naked eye in my armour. Such a preposterous personification of repulsive virtues is intolerable. So my fellow-citizens stuff their fingers in their ears and drown my words in senseless cackle.
Ibid.

3 My part as the Dauphin in *St Joan* appealed to me enormously, but I was very nervous lest my reading of it should not be what Shaw wanted. So I was alarmed when after the first rehearsal he came up to me in a most solemn manner and with that fascinating brogue of his said: 'There is one thing I wnt you to do about this part.' Humbly I said I would try to do anything he wished, upon which he continued, 'I want you to go home to bed and stay there until the first night. You already know as much about the part as I do.'
Ernest Thesiger, PRACTICALLY TRUE 1927

4 Shaw never allows any lines of his plays to be cut, and of course nothing may be interpolated; but he made an exception in my case, and I may claim to have written one line in *St Joan*. I said it by accident, and when he was revising the proofs he telegraphed to me to ask the exact words I had put in, as he wished to include them in the authorised version of the play — and there they stand.
Ibid.

5 In youth he had the face of an undernourished curate; in maturity a head which Rodin sculpted as '*Une vraie tête de Christ*'.
Irving Wardle, THE GENIUS OF SHAW (*edited by Michael Holroyd*) 1979

6 He is an idiot child screaming in a hospital.
H. G. Wells, Daily Chronicle 1914

7 Considering his perennial flow of eloquence and how wonderfully and prolifically he wrote, he seems to have had extraordinarily little to say.
Rebecca West. Quoted Jill Craigie, The Times 6 *Dec* 1982

8 I agree about Shaw — he is haunted by the mystery he flouts. He is an atheist who trembles in the haunted corridor.
W. B. Yeats in a letter to George Russell (A.E.) 1 *Jul* 1921

JEAN (JULIUS CHRISTIAN) SIBELIUS

Born 1865 in Finland. Composer. Most of his music, notably his tone-poem *Finlandia*, was inspired by the landscape and legends of Finland. Died 1957.

9 What you get in Sibelius, for the greater part of the time, is an extreme reticence and a slow delivery; and that of course is extremely popular in England, it is our tradition. We get it, possibly, from the Government.
Sir Thomas Beecham. Quoted Lord Boothby, MY YESTERDAY, YOUR TOMORROW 1962

10 At supper Sibelius said to Edwin Evans, a critic himself 'Never pay any attention to what the critics say. A statue has never been set up in honour of a critic.'
Harriet Cohen, Daily Telegraph 23 *Sep* 1957

11 In 1930 there were rumours that he had started on his Eighth Symphony. I was staying in Finland in the late summer of 1931 and asked Sibelius 'What about the Eighth Symphony? I don't believe it exists.' His eyes twinkled. He took a cigarette packet, opened it up and drew two sets of five lines. On them he wrote a large chord, and said 'That is the opening chord of my Eighth Symphony. Who knows? Perhaps I possess the only existing manuscript?'
Ibid.

WALTER (RICHARD) SICKERT

Born 1860 in Munich. British painter and etcher, influenced by French ideas which he introduced into British art. Musical scenes were a favourite subject. Died 1942.

12 Clementine Churchill told us about her friendship with Walter Sickert whom she knew first when she was a gangling, fifteen-year-old school-girl at Dieppe. She said he

was a most wonderful-looking man, living in lodgings that were owned by a Madame Villain, who had several children running round with a marked resemblance to him. But of course as a schoolgirl she had no idea that the rather possessive housekeeper was anything more than that.
Cecil Beaton, DIARY 1962

1 He was, I think, the most selfish human being I have ever come across.
Clementine Churchill. Quoted Cecil Beaton, DIARY 1962

2 When Virginia Woolf, unleashing her fancy, applauded Sickert's portraits as more revealing than any biography, and other pictures by him as realistic stories comparable with Balzac's, he was delighted: 'I have always been a literary painter, thank goodness, like all decent painters.' What the devil can he have meant?
Raymond Mortimer, Sunday Times 13 *Jun* 1976

3 He usually preferred to paint ill-lit subjects with a richly sombre palette. Enid Bagnold remembers his love for dust, especially on mirrors, and for the folds of a dirty sheet in shadow, the model's naked body on the bed, her flesh green-shadowed, reverberating softly in a splendour of unpolished light.
Denys Sutton, WALTER SICKERT 1976

4 He married three times. His first wife, who brought him some money to spend, was a daughter of Cobden. One of Sickert's favourite openings was 'I was standing under the statue of my first father-in-law, in Camden Town.'
George Malcolm Thomson, Evening Standard 2 *Jul* 1947

5 In later years a series of photographs supplied all the material he needed for a portrait. One snapshot enlarged on to the canvas saved an immense amount of wearisome drawing. Many were shocked by his labour-saving device. They should not have been.
Ibid.

6 When Neville Chamberlain was given an honorary degree by the University of Reading, an arresting figure (receiving a Doctorate of Letters) sat with him on the platform. He wore a hairy tweed suit, check socks and black bedroom slippers. It was Walter Sickert in one of his less startling disguises.
Ibid.

JOHN ALLENBROOK SIMON, VISCOUNT SIMON

Born 1873. British politician. Foreign Secretary 1931–5. Home Secretary 1935–7. His advocacy of disarmament and the appeasement of Hitler caused him to fall into disfavour. Died 1954.

7 Simon; reptilian good-fellowship. A head like a hive.
Cyril Asquith. Quoted Geoffrey Madan, NOTEBOOKS 1981

8 He is at his worst in the mood described by one jealous rival as going about slapping people on the back and calling them by the wrong Christian names.
A. J. Cummings, Daily News and Westminster Gazette

9 This stone, with no unpardonable pride,/ Proves by its record what the world denied:/ Simon could do a natural thing—he died.
John Sparrow, epitaph. Quoted Harold Nicolson, DIARY 11 *Jan* 1954

10 A case against a man he was defending rested entirely on the memory of an ironmonger. The day before the ironmonger was called as a witness Simon went into the shop and bought a piece of wire. Next day he questioned the witness. 'You remember all your customers?' 'Certainly.' 'You remember those who came into your shop yesterday?' 'Every one.' 'Is anybody in court who came into your shop yesterday?' 'Nobody.' Simon produced the piece of wire and his client won the day.
Sunday Referee

DAME EDITH SITWELL

Born 1887. English essayist and poet. Sister of Sir Osbert and Sir Sacheverell. Wrote *Façade* in 1922, which was set to music by William Walton. Died 1964.

11 Edith arrived, a tall graceful scarecrow with the white hands of a medieval saint.
Cecil Beaton, DIARY 7 *Dec* 1926

12 Gradually, I found her formidable aspect less striking than her sympathetic girlishness. In spite of her cadaverous appearance, her complexion is as fresh as a convolvulus, and she has a disarming girlish manner of not being able to contain her laughter.
Ibid.

13 A young faun-like creature, looking surprisingly Victorian in her crudely-cut Pre-Raphaelite dress, with her matador's jet hat,

and necklace, her long medieval fingers covered with enormous rings. When the hat was discarded she became a Brontë heroine, and her pale silken hair fell in rat's tails about her face, while the big teapot-handle bun made the nape of her neck appear even more impossibly slender.
Ibid.

1 The last time I was honoured by having the Queen Mother to lunch Edith Sitwell was the pièce de résistance. A huge ambulance drove up to the house and a pair of stalwart men moved to bring the poet out into the daylight. A pair of long medieval shoes appeared, then a muffled figure and finally a golden melon of a hat. Edith was wheeled into place and given two strong martinis.
Ibid. 1968

2 She looks like a high altar on the move.
Elizabeth Bowen

3 She is genuinely bogus.
Christopher Hassall

4 Edith, whose mother had convinced her that she was physically grotesque and whose father ignored her because, as first-born, she was not a boy, decided to be a poet pretty early; but she was nearly thirty before she had her first poems published in (yes) the *Daily Mirror* and felt able to leave the family's vast and ghost-ridden house to live on next to nothing in Bayswater.
J. W. Lambert, Sunday Times 19 *Nov* 1978

5 She, hardly less extravagant than her mother, got into worse financial difficulties the more money she earned, and in her turn looked to the bottle.
Ibid.

6 The paradox of her life was that the public recognition of her later years left her unhappier than before, in spite of a passion for platform appearances and a delight even in Hollywood.
Anthony Powell, Daily Telegraph 23 *Nov* 1978

7 Edith has built up her personality in many fortuitous ways — her strange appearance, her lovely hands, her Dantesque headdress, and all the Sitwellian legend. But I cannot feel that she is a great poet. A great personality, yes: a true eccentric: but not a major poet.
Vita Sackville-West, letter to Harold Nicolson 23 *Mar* 1960

8 Vulgarians whom I will not allow to intrude upon my private life are in the habit of saying and writing that I am an 'eccentric'. I am eccentric only inasmuch as I do not suffer fools gladly and I am adamant in refusing to allow ignoramuses to teach me the spiritual and technical side of the art which I have practised for nearly half a century.
Edith Sitwell, TAKEN CARE OF: AN AUTOBIOGRAPHY 1965

9 Edith made a great mistake by not going in for lawn tennis.
Sir George Sitwell (her father). Quoted Osbert Sitwell, LAUGHTER IN THE NEXT ROOM 1949

10 Edith's poems make *me* look ridiculous.
Ibid.

11 I remember an old lady writing a very angry letter to the *Spectator*, after she had read some of my sister's early poems. 'I have long been familiar,' she insisted, 'with the best poetry, Shelley and Wordsworth were on my father's shelf from our earliest infancy — though somehow Keats did not find his way on to it until later. I am thus qualified to give my opinion — and what do Miss Sitwell's poems consist of but *words, words, words*!' I may ask of what else could they consist, dead larks, or fragments of a stage elephant?
Osbert Sitwell, LAUGHTER IN THE NEXT ROOM 1949

12 The total effect of her poetry, like that of her personality, lent themselves to criticism, and sometimes even to ridicule, but about both there was a fine aristocratic indifference to common standards that tended to make the criticism and ridicule seem boorish.
The Times, Obituary 10 *Dec* 1964

13 Her verses always danced rather than walked, her voice was incantatory rather than conversational. The texture of her poems was both enriched and sometimes made a little monotonous by a fondness for certain recurrent symbols, lions, deserts, skeletons, the sun, and for certain favourite colours, green and gold.
Ibid.

14 Edith is wholly ignorant. She said the poor streets of Scarborough were terrible but that she did not think that the fishermen took drugs very much. She also said that port was made with methylated spirit; she knew this for a fact because her charwoman had told her.
Evelyn Waugh, DIARY 22 *Aug* 1930

SIR OSBERT SITWELL

Born 1892. English author and poet. Brother of Dame Edith and Sir Sacheverell. Wrote a series of autobiographical family memoirs beginning with *Left Hand, Right Hand*, 1944. Died 1969.

1 Osbert Sitwell was an excellent journalist and also an accomplished courtier, somehow never quite finding a place as either.
John Pearson, FAÇADES 1978

2 We had migrated to 2 Carlyle Square from Swan Walk. Most of the possessions we took with us consisted of pictures, glass and books. As Arnold Bennett noted in his diary (Dined at Osbert Sitwell's. A house with much better bric-a-brac than furniture. In fact there was scarcely any what I call furniture. 15 June 1919). As so often in my life I had just the bare luxuries of life, and not the necessities.
Osbert Sitwell, LAUGHTER IN THE NEXT ROOM 1949

SIR SACHEVERELL SITWELL

Born 1897. English author and poet, brother of Dame Edith and Sir Osbert. Wrote travel books, and books on the history of art.

3 The opener of British eyes to the baroque and the rococo, aesthete of aesthetes, and pioneer of new forms of sensibility, Sir Sacheverell has delighted and entertained countless others, while dancing for his own delight.
Philip Howard, The Times 15 *Nov* 1972

4 Sacheverell's writing has similarities with Swinburne's in its aversion to the ordinary, love of the exotic and exquisite and its excess of adjectival sensation over thought. Interviewing him is like interviewing a kingfisher or a humming bird.
Ibid.

JAN CHRISTIAAN SMUTS

Born 1870. South African soldier and politician; after commanding Boer forces 1901–2, joined with Botha to co-operate with Britain in setting up the Union of South Africa, 1910. Prime Minister 1919–24, 1939–48. Was a member of British war councils in both World Wars. Died 1950.

5 He was a white supremacist. He regarded apartheid as hypocritical and impracticable but he never envisaged anything more than minority representation for Coloureds and Africans.
Robert Blake, Sunday Times 11 *Feb* 1968

6 As Britain's old enemy and new friend Smuts invented the word 'Commonwealth' to encourage a continuing relationship between the white dominions, yet his own country was the first to be forced out of that association.
Douglas Brown, Daily Telegraph 11 *Feb* 1968

7 The saint who fed the birds at Bondelswaart and fattened up the vultures at Bullhoek.
Roy Campbell

8 Smuts ended his life defeated and deserted. He complained to a friend 'My old comrades have turned against me.' The friend replied 'How can they turn against you? They are all dead.'
W. K. Hancock, SMUTS VOL. 2 THE FIELDS OF FORCE 1968

9 The cry for reprisals against German air attacks was common to all demagogues. The experts, such as they were, opposed this demand. This did not suit public opinion, Smuts stepped into the breach, his first assignment as a member of the war cabinet. His report, completed in October 1917, was an epoch-making document. There stem from it all the great achievements of our contemporary civilisation; the indiscriminate bombing of cities in the second World War, the nuclear bombs dropped on Hiroshima and Nagasaki; and the present preparations for destroying mankind.
A. J. P. Taylor, ENGLISH HISTORY 1914–1945 1965

10 Was Smuts a citizen of Vanity Fair or the Kingdom of Heaven? Straining charity very far one might say he had a foot in both camps. At any rate he was a master at making commonplaces look like wisdom.
A. J. P. Taylor, Observer 12 *Jun* 1966

DAME ETHEL (MARY) SMYTH

Born 1859. English composer, author and militant suffragette. Among her most important compositions are *The Wreckers, The Boatswain's Mate* and the *Mass in D.* Died 1944.

11 I arrived in the main courtyard of Holloway prison to find the noble company of martyrs (suffragettes) marching round it and singing

lustily their war-chant, 'The March of Women', while the composer, beaming approbation from an overlooking upper window, beat time in almost Bacchic fury with a toothbrush.
Sir Thomas Beecham

1 Without question the most remarkable of her sex that I have been privileged to know.
Ibid.

2 Two ideals long divided her enthusiasm between them — music and the women's cause. She fought gallantly on behalf of both. So when, in 1923, she was created a Dame of the British Empire, nobody was quite sure whether the distinction was political or artistic, though most people were probably right in thinking it was simply uncommon merit in all that she undertook that had gained her this well-deserved recognition.
Everyman 7 *Mar* 1929

3 Ethel Smyth looks like an unmade bed.
Siegfried Sassoon, DIARIES 1920–22

4 She would be like Richard Wagner, if only she looked a bit more feminine.
Osbert Sitwell. Quoted Elizabeth Lutyens, A GOLDFISH BOWL

5 Because I have conducted my own operas and love sheep-dogs; because I generally dress in tweeds, and sometimes, at winter afternoon concerts have even conducted in them; because I was a militant suffragette; because I have written books, spoken speeches, broadcast, and don't always make sure my hat is on straight, for these and other equally pertinent reasons, in a certain sense I am well known.
Dame Ethel Smyth, AS TIME WENT ON 1936

6 Benson, when Archbishop of Canterbury, once complained that in my Mass 'God was not *implored*, but was *commanded* to have mercy'. It was explained that what was intended was an expression of intense terror. 'Indeed?' said the Archbishop. 'I can only repeat that to me it sounded like orders issued in an extremely peremptory manner.'
Ibid.

C. P. (CHARLES PERCY) SNOW, BARON SNOW OF LEICESTER

Born 1905. English author of a long series of novels, beginning with *Strangers and Brothers*, on the theme of the ethics of power.

7 As a novelist he doesn't exist; he doesn't begin to exist. He can't be said to know what a novel is. I heard (can I have dreamt it?) that his novels are composed for him by an electronic brain called Charlie.
F. R. Leavis, lecture in Cambridge 28 *Feb* 1962

8 He had a brief and ridiculous career as the back legs of a pantomime horse at the Ministry of Technology (the front legs were played by Frank Cousins, and two more weirdly over-parted Ministers can never have held office).
Bernard Levin, Observer 24 *Oct* 1982

9 He has made everyone aware that the scientist is still an outsider who has yet to be properly integrated into a humanist society.
Observer, Profile 9 *Apr* 1961

10 Genial and portly, a shrewd and smiling Buddha looking (deliberately, one feels) much older than his fifty-six years, he entertains guests at a literary party in his flat in Cromwell Road.
Ibid.

11 He likes to play the part of a benevolent literary dictator, dispensing praise and blame to a little court of admirers, in rather the same way as Addison must have done at Button's Coffee House.
Ibid.

12 In his novels Snow often talks of 'the corridors of power'. His own career runs like a thick-piled Wilton carpet through all the corridors.
Robert Pitman, Sunday Express 18 *Mar* 1962

PHILIP SNOWDEN, FIRST VISCOUNT, SNOWDEN OF ICKORNSHAW

Born 1864. British politician. One of the dominating figures in the Labour Party from 1911 to 1931. Chancellor of the Exchequer 1924, 1929–31. Joined National Government, 1931. Appointed Lord Privy Seal and created a viscount. Died 1937.

13 He was not a revolutionary in the ordinary use of the word. He wanted to revolutionise the social and economic life of the nation, but not through a physical upheaval.
A. J. Cummings, News Chronicle 17 *May* 1937

14 If Philip Snowden, enthusiastic young

Exciseman, had not fallen off his bicycle while riding at Falmouth, Snowden the statesman might never have been known. For twelve months he could move only in a wheel chair and during that time he soaked himself in Socialist literature. He emerged from his convalescence, crippled for life, a fiery convert to the new gospel that was being spread.
The People 16 *May* 1937

1 He possessed, when in the mood, the most vitriolic tongue of any Member of Parliament, but his humanity and integrity were unquestionable. Unfortunately, however, he belonged to the Gladstonian period of free trade, balance of payments, and paying your way even if it meant reducing benefits associated with social welfare.
Manny Shinwell, LEAD WITH THE LEFT 1981

2 He stood for the traditional virtues of hard work, thrift, frugality, foresight. In economic terms this meant an absolute adherence to the gold standard, free trade, economy and deflation — exactly the opposite of what was needed in a situation of depression and mass unemployment.
Robert Skidelskey, Sunday Times, 1000 Makers of the Twentieth Century

3 For your private information I may say that my ideal Cabinet would be one in which I held all the offices.
Snowden, in a letter to Reginald Pound. Quoted, THEIR MOODS AND MINE 1937

4 He always had a reputation for bitterness and sarcasm, and in a broadcast speech he denounced the 1931 election programme of the Socialist Party as 'the most fantastic and impracticable programme ever put before the electors'. 'It is Bolshevism run mad', was his final condemnation.
Sunday Dispatch 16 *May* 1937

5 It is hard not to see Snowden as an almost classic example of the lovable and unworldly idealist who, at the touch of reality, turned rancid; a tragic and deeply moving example.
Colin Welch, Daily Telegraph 10 *Nov* 1966

6 He stands on the steps of No 10 Downing Steet, a cripple yet firm as a rock with his two rubber-tipped walking sticks. Under his crag-like nose his thin lips are stretched in a smile, full of spry courage, shrewdness, malice and sarcastic humour.
Ibid.

MURIEL (SARAH) SPARK

Born 1918 in Scotland. Novelist who first attracted popular attention with *The Ballad of Peckham Rye*, 1960, and *The Prime of Miss Jean Brodie*, 1961.

7 She is the best sweet-and-sour writer we have.
Francis Hope, Observer 28 *Apr* 1963

8 Her prose is like a bird, darting from place to place, palpitating with nervous energy; but a bird with a bright beady eye and a sharp beak as well.
Ibid.

9 A small, bird-like Scot, she has something of the sparrow in her movement and expression; something, sometimes, of the hawk.
Nicholas Shakespeare, The Times, Suffering and the vital Spark 21 *Nov* 1983

10 I wait until I have a kind of caterpillar curled up in my mind. I write the title, my name, and Chapter One. Then I start: I like to have the title, which I repeat through the book like a refrain. The rest I make up as I go along.
Muriel Spark. Quoted Nicholas Shakespeare, The Times, Suffering and the vital Spark 21 *Nov* 1983

SIR STANLEY SPENCER

Born 1891. English artist. His work included Resurrection pictures, and many paintings inspired by the village of Cookham. Died 1959.

11 He was awkward about washing, fascinated by bad smells and the uninhibited habits and excrement of dogs. He was a clothes fetishist and eventually a transvestist.
Louise Collis, A PRIVATE VIEW OF STANLEY SPENCER 1972

12 He carries a pocket Bible with him and his speech is salted with Biblical phraseology. 'Seek, and the technicalities shall be added unto you', he says.
Picture Post 2 *Oct* 1943

13 Alfred Munnings obtained photographic copies of Spencer's anatomical studies which he supposed pornographic and flourished them before a police inspector and the Dean of Westminster for prosecuting evidence which naturally never followed.
Reginald Pound, THE ENGLISHMAN; A BIOGRAPHY OF SIR ALFRED MUNNINGS 1962

14 'The Resurrection', painted in Cookham

churchyard and described as an allegory of the saving of the black and white races, is in all probability the most important picture painted by any English artist during the present century.
The Times, 28 *Feb* 1927

1 His deformation and distortions do not appear to be arbitrary or theoretical, but rather as if things bulged when he looked at them.
The Times, Obituary 16 *Dec* 1959

2 In his expression of religious ideas through homely symbols he reminds one very much of Bunyan.
Ibid.

3 He was living in a tiny single room at Hampstead, desperately poor, when I first met him in 1918. He arrived for lunch one day wearing a grubby pyjama top under his coat and exclaimed 'I know I'm dirty, but I don't smell, do I?'
H. D. Ziman, Daily Telegraph 18 *May* 1962

4 He continued to write frequently to his first wife Hilda after their divorce, and indeed after her death. While she was alive he would visit her and read out long passages.
Ibid.

JOSEPH STALIN

Born 1879, in Russia. Original name Joseph Vissarionovich Dzhugashvili. Soviet political leader. General Secretary of the Communist Party 1922. After Lenin's death shared the leadership until he consolidated his power by engineering a series of purges to dispose of rivals. Assumed full leadership on the invasion of Russia, 1941. Died 1953.

5 Stalin's laugh could be heard above all the other noises at the Kremlin banquet.
Vernon Bartlett, News Chronicle 21 *Jan* 1949

6 If Hitler invaded Hell I would make at least a favourable reference to the Devil in the House of Commons.
Winston Churchill, on accepting Stalin as an ally. Quoted Michael Foot, ANEURIN BEVAN VOL. I

7 Stalin with his wary, slit eyes, staring like some Mongolian shepherd, at a distant prospect, brooding on loot and murder, and vast metal statues of himself, erected in distant places.
Malcolm Muggeridge, TREAD SOFTLY FOR YOU TREAD ON MY JOKES 1966

8 An important part of Stalin's political skill lay in his barefaced ability to take credit for the successes of his colleagues, and discredit them with his own crimes.
Michael Ratcliffe, The Times 2 *May* 1974

9 Unlike the other dictators, Stalin has an irrepressible sense of humour. He is not a Russian; he is a handsome Georgian with the attractive dark eyes of his race. There is an odd mixture of the Pope and the field-marshal in him; you might guess him to be the illegitimate soldier-son of a cardinal. I should call his manners perfect if only he had been able to conceal the fact that we amused him so much.
G. B. Shaw, after visiting Moscow in 1931

10 It is joyful news that Hitler is now under the thumb of Stalin whose interest in peace is overwhelming.
G. B. Shaw, letter to The Times on the signing of the Nazi-Soviet Treaty 28 *Aug* 1939

11 One of the many paradoxes in forming his career was that the more powerful he became the less secure he felt. Of all the terrible public dramas of his career only the Second World War was demonstrably real. The rest is phantasmagoria.
Adam M. Ulam, STALIN: THE MAN AND HIS ERA 1974

GERTRUDE STEIN

Born 1874, in America, settled in Paris 1903. Poet, novelist and critic. Aroused wide literary controversy by attempting to create a style of writing characterised by the use of words for their associations and sounds rather than their literal meaning. Died 1946.

12 Nobody would have mistaken Gertrude Stein and Alice B. Toklas for devotees of Bergdorf–Goodman. They were not interested in ensembles. Both of them were champion dawdlers. At the last moment they would dress themselves in whatever happened to be handy and sally forth. In those days there was an employment agency for domestics located directly below the Random House offices. Gertrude arrived for lunch one day a full hour late, and announced cheerfully 'That fool elevator boy of yours dumped us on the employment agency. He thought we were cooks.'
Bennet Cerf, TRY AND STOP ME 1947

13 The morning that Gertrude Stein arrived in Hollywood she demanded that Dashiell Hammett, Charlie Chaplin and Dorothy

Parker be produced for a dinner party that evening. They not only came, but boasted about it afterwards.
Ibid.

1 Gertrude Stein's novel *Mrs Reynolds* was smuggled out of France during the German occupation by a friend who brought it to New York via Sweden and Great Britain. The lady had one unpleasant moment in England when an alert customs officer mistook it for a secret document written in an ingenious and entirely undecipherable code. Finally he conceded grudgingly that it was a novel all right, but added that it was the first one he had seen that seemed to read the same from back to front as from front to back.
Ibid.

2 Gertrude's latest book, *Ida*, was supposed to be about the Duchess of Windsor, and I sent a copy to Government House in Nassau. 'It was nice of you to send me *Ida*', wrote the Duchess, 'but I must confess I didn't understand a word of it.'
Ibid.

3 When Gertrude Stein visited New York in 1933 she dared to dispute a statement of the great Alexander Woollcott. 'I will forgive you this once,' he said grandly. 'You have not been here long enough to know that *nobody* disputes me.' 'Woollcott,' said Miss Stein with a hearty laugh, 'you are a colossal fool.' The host, who happened to be myself, was delighted.
Ibid.

4 One of the few people who refused to be overawed by Miss Stein's astonishing flow of rhetoric was Mortimer Adler, the author of *How to Read a Book*. He and Gertrude got into a terrific argument. Miss Toklas trembled on the outskirts of the battlefield and was heard to remark 'Dear me! Gertrude is saying some things tonight that she won't understand herself for six months.'
Ibid.

5 Moss Hart once asked her if she had written any other plays besides *Four Saints in Three Acts*. 'Of course I have,' answered Gertrude. 'Seventy-seven, to be exact.'
Ibid.

6 Miss Stein was seated on a chair in the centre of the drawing room, dressed in brown, wearing a lace collar, her hands in her lap. For some reason she looked like Van Gogh's portrait of Madam Rouiln, only instead of red hair with a bun on top Gertrude had short-cropped brown hair. The guests stood around at a respectful distance.
Charles Chaplin, MY AUTOBIOGRAPHY 1964

7 At lunch my hostess placed me next to Gertrude and in some way we got on to the subject of art. I believe it started by me admiring the view from the dining-room window. But Gertrude showed little enthusiasm. 'Nature,' she said, 'is commonplace. Imitation is more interesting.' She enlarged on this thesis stating that imitation marble looked more beautiful than the real thing and that a Turner sunset was lovelier than any real sky. Although these pronouncements were rather derivative I politely agreed with her.
Ibid.

8 Gertrude Stein was very big but not tall, and was heavily built like a peasant woman. She had beautiful eyes and a strong German-Jewish face, and she reminded me of a northern Italian peasant woman with her mobile face and her lovely, thick, alive, immigrant hair which she wore put up in the same way as she had probably worn it at college.
Ernest Hemingway, A MOVEABLE FEAST 1961

9 I was unimpressed by American authors like Ernest Hemingway and Scott Fitzgerald, their attitude being 'Look, Mom, I'm an author'. I respected Gertrude as the most manly of the lot.
Anita Loos, A GIRL LIKE I 1967

10 Always in her pose, as she sat, there was something monumental, as if she was sitting to a painter who was making a record for posterity; the body turned to stone from flesh, but more powerful, in no way dead, and her massive philosopher's head had the eagle lines of a Red Indian warrior.
Osbert Sitwell, LAUGHTER IN THE NEXT ROOM 1949

11 I accompanied Miss Alice Toklas and Miss Stein to Oxford to hear that gifted writer deliver her celebrated lecture under the auspices of my friend Harold Acton. I remember a certain commotion arising, and some accompanying laughter, when towards the middle of her discourse she remarked 'Everything is the same, and everything is different!' Most undergraduates had come to the hall to amuse themselves after the lecture at the expense of a writer widely and angrily derided, her work dismissed as the

'stutterings of a lunatic'. But in the presence of this obviously distinguished woman, the wiser of them recognised that there was nothing much to be done in this line. At the end two young gentlemen, not so easily discouraged, shot up to heckle her from positions widely apart in the audience, but they asked an identical question. 'Miss Stein, if everything is the same, how can everything be different?' In a most genial comforting manner, Miss Stein replied, 'Well, look at you two dear boys!'
Ibid.

JOHN (ERNEST) STEINBECK

Born 1902 in America, novelist, short story writer and author of screen plays. Gained recognition with *Of Mice and Men*, 1937 and *The Grapes of Wrath*, 1939. Awarded Nobel Prize for Literature, 1962. Died 1968.

1 Early in his career he was interested in trying to imitate the structure and movement of specific musical compositions, as well as more generally trying to imitate certain musical forms.
Jackson J. Benson, THE TRUE ADVENTURE OF JOHN STEINBECK, WRITER 1984

2 Sending dispatches from Vietnam, he had to struggle between detestation of the war and loyalty to his President. He was a man of simple honour and it shows in his books.
Anthony Burgess, Observer 22 *Apr* 1984

3 John Steinbeck carried bricks for the new Madison Square Garden building. Then he took a winter job as watchman for an estate seven thousand feet high in the Sierras. There he finished his first novel, *The Cup of Gold* just about the time a giant pine cracked through the roof of the house. 'The living room was wrecked,' admits Steinbeck, 'but my manuscript was undamaged.'
Bennett Cerf, SHAKE WELL BEFORE USING 1948

4 He was radical and great hearted without being doctrinaire and revolutionary.
The Times, Obituary 22 *Dec* 1968

ADLAI (EWING) STEVENSON

Born 1900. American Democratic politician. Governor of Illinois, 1949–53. Unsuccessfully opposed Eisenhower for the Presidency, 1952, 1956. Ambassador to the UN 1961–5. Died 1965.

5 He was out of phase with his time. He remained a gentleman in the face of a declining political market for civility.
Henry S. Ashmore, AS WE KNEW ADLAI (*edited by Edward P. Doyle*)

6 In this job, he's got the nerve of a burglar.
John F. Kennedy, of Stevenson as US Ambassador to the UN. Quoted Time magazine 24 *Feb* 1961

7 He is not like what I imagined him. A heavy man, with slim body, but heavy appearance, reddish face, alert eyes, a rather prancing manner — in fact a deception.
Harold Nicolson, DIARY 29 *Jul* 1953

8 To a large extent he was unlucky in his time. Anyone condemned to run twice for the presidency against Mr Eisenhower in the atmosphere of 1952 and 1956 was almost bound to suffer the crippling disadvantage of being 'the man who lost twice'.
The Times, Obituary 15 *Jul* 1965

LEOPOLD (ANTON STANISLAW) STOKOWSKI

Born 1882 in England. American conductor of the Philadelphia Orchestra 1913–36. Orchestrated Bach's organ music. Died 1977.

9 At a rehearsal in Philadelphia Leopold Stokowski seized an offending musician by the coat collar and exclaimed, 'My man, you don't know your brass from your oboe.'
Bennett Cerf, SHAKE WELL BEFORE USING 1948

10 It is such an elusive thing, how conductors affect orchestras. Somebody like Stokowski, whom one might be tempted to write off as a silly old fool, staggered on to the rostrum at a venerable age, hardly able to lift a hand. Yet people are riveted by the sight of him, and scared stiff too. He drops a languid hand in a camp gesture, and a tough and cynical brass section lets go with a blazing fortissimo. 'Not together', he snaps, and the next time it damn well will be together because that's the way it has to be.
Anthony Pay. Quoted Robin Ray, WORDS ON MUSIC 1984

MARIE STOPES

Born 1880. English birth control pioneer. Author of *Married Love*, 1918 and *Wise Parenthood*. Opened Britain's first birth control clinic in Islington, 1921. Died 1958.

11 When Marie Stopes's mother, Charlotte,

said with mock distress to her daughter one day, 'Oh what should I do if I had a dozen children?' Marie burst out with unexpected ferocity, 'You would drown all the others and keep me.'
Keith Briant, MARIE STOPES

1 A fascinating combination of scientist and would-be poet, of mystic and crank, of propagandist and neurotic, Marie Stopes splendidly embraced the challenge of society and set up her first birth-control clinic in London in 1921, but she completely failed to write a poem of any consequence.
Ibid.

2 She was such a woman as men privately delight in and publicly dread; feminine indeed but neither nervous nor hysterical, and not at all given to cant or chatter.
Edward Candy, Sunday Times 25 *Jun* 1967

3 Halifax was most amusing about his interview yesterday with Dr Marie Stopes, who came to the Foreign Office, and said that she had had affairs with over 100 Germans and then with at least 100 Americans so that she knew men better than most women. She was prepared, she told Lord Halifax, to accept Cabinet Office and would he pass on her request to the Prime Minister?
Sir Henry Channon, DIARY 17 *Apr* 1940

4 Her frontal attacks on old taboos, her quasi-prophetic tone, her flowery fervour, aroused strong opposition from those who disagreed with her for religious reasons or felt that she had overstepped the bounds of good taste.
Daily Telegraph, Obituary 3 *Oct* 1958

5 How she must have laughed, and how we join in her laughter forty years later, at the following communication from a baronet and MP. 'Will you be so kind as to cancel on your mailing list the copy of Birth Control News. It is not the kind of document I care to have in a mixed household.'
Ruth Hall, DEAR DR STOPES: SEX IN THE 1920s 1978

6 The opposition can always fall back on taboo. The subject is (in their eyes) obscene; no lady would dream of alluding to it in mixed society; reproduction is a shocking subject and there's an end to it. Huxley had to leave reproduction out of his text book, and you are as helpless as Huxley.
George Bernard Shaw, letter to Marie Stopes 1924

7 Dr Marie Stopes made contraceptive devices respectable in a somewhat gushing book, *Married Love*. For this she deserves to be remembered among the great benefactors of the age.
A. J. P. Taylor, ENGLISH HISTORY 1914–1945 1965

(GILES) LYTTON STRACHEY

Born 1880. Biographer, known chiefly for his *Eminent Victorians*, 1918, *Queen Victoria*, 1921, *Elizabeth and Essex*, 1928. Died 1932.

8 He seemed almost indecently lacking in ordinariness.
Gerald Brennan, SOUTH FROM GRANADA

9 *Eminent Victorians* is the work of a great anarch, a revolutionary textbook on bourgeois society written in the language through which the bourgeois ear could be lulled and beguiled, the Mandarin style, and the bourgeois responded with fascination to the music, like seals to the Eriskay love-lilt.
Cyril Connolly, ENEMIES OF PROMISE 1938

10 Lytton Strachey chose to appear before a military tribunal as a conscientious objector. To the chairman's stock question, which had previously never failed to embarrass a claimant, 'Tell me, Mr Strachey, what would you do if you saw a German soldier trying to violate your sister?' He replied with an air of noble virtue, 'I would try to get beween them.'
Robert Graves, GOODBYE TO ALL THAT 1929

11 He told us of the extraordinary impression that was caused by an air cushion which he inflated during the proceedings as a protest against the hardness of the benches.
Ibid.

12 Asked by the chairman of the tribunal, at his examination as a conscientious objector, 'I understand, Mr Strachey, that you have a conscientious objection to all war?' he replied, in his curious falsetto voice, 'Oh no, not at all, only to *this* war.'
Ibid.

13 I remember the tall, flagging figure of my friend Lytton Strachey, with his rather narrow, singular beard, long, inquisitive nose, and air of someone pleasantly awakening from a trance, jigging about with an amiable debility.
Osbert Sitwell, LAUGHTER IN THE NEXT ROOM 1949

14 When he was in Rome, Princess San Faustino entertained him to luncheon and treated him and her other guests to a long

explanation of a scheme she had recently thought of to aid the unemployed. It was all dependent on growing the soya bean. Factories and synthetic chocolates and motor-cars and building material and bath salts all were to be made of this magic substance. She worked the whole idea up to an enthusiastic but boring climax, when she turned to the guest of honour and appealed to him. 'Mr Strachey, what do you think of my scheme?' He replied in his highest, most discouraging key, 'I'm afraid I don't *like beans*.'
Ibid.

1 A man now of about forty, he had achieved no renown (though he had possessed a high reputation for wit, learning and personality among his own friends at Cambridge) nor had he sought any until the publication of *Eminent Victorians* raised him to the zenith of fame and popularity with a generation no longer tolerant of either the pretensions or the achievements of the Victorian great.
Ibid.

2 His individual combination of kindness, selfishness, cleverness, shyness and sociability made him peculiarly unlike anyone else. As I watched him, I remember comparing him in my mind to a benevolent but rather irritable pelican.
Ibid.

IGOR (FEDEROVICH) STRAVINSKY

Born 1882 in Russia. Composer who worked with, and wrote ballets for Diaghilev, e.g. *The Firebird, Rites of Spring,* and *Petrouchka*. Left Russia in 1914 and eventually settled in the United States. Died 1971.

3 You may not agree with Stravinsky, but you must admit that everything he touches is out of the ordinary. Stravinsky composes nothing indifferent or second rate. His work is a search for new possibilities, but it is difficult to listen to.
Ernest Ansermet

4 When part of *The Firebird* was adapted as a popular tune he claimed that the version was 'devoid of merit' and lowered his prestige. He demanded 250,000 dollars damages, but the suit was unsuccessful. The *New York Times* headed the result 'Igor Mortis!'
Gerald Brooke, The Lady 14 *Jun* 1962

5 Stravinsky tells the story of an exchange between Gershwin and himself. 'How much will you charge to come over and give me lessons in orchestration?' said Gershwin. 'How much do you make in a year?' asked Stravinsky. 'A hundred thousand dollars a year,' said Gershwin. There was a moment's silence and then Stravinsky said, 'How about you giving *me* lessons?'
Bennett Cerf, TRY AND STOP ME 1947

6 A small man who cast a giant shadow.
Alex Coleman, TV Times 3 *Apr* 1982

7 I received intense pleasure from watching him conducting and extracting the maximum effort from each instrument of the orchestra (he looked like an ant inspecting his troop of aphis).
Cyril Connolly, Sunday Times 5 *Nov* 1972

8 In all the photographs I've seen of him Stravinsky looks to me like a man who was potty-trained too early, and that music proves it so far as I'm concerned.
Russell Hoban, THE MOUSE AND HIS CHILD

9 His music is the music of a tightrope-walker; edgy, dangerous.
Nicholas Nobokov, ITV documentary 7 *Apr* 1982

10 He can take liberties that I could not allow myself because he is less of a musical craftsman.
Maurice Ravel

11 Ever since *Sacré du Printemps* was first performed people have made the mistake of trying to understand it. There is nothing to understand, but much to be moved by.
Sacheverell Sitwell, Radio Times 23 *Jan* 1931

12 I knew a Russian peasant who could make his horse micturate by whistling softly. That same whistling sound I have heard in several pieces of electronic music, and it makes me suffer the same desire as the horse. But some electronic sounds have the effect of colonic irrigation also; on me at least.
Igor Stravinsky, DIALOGUE AND A DIARY 1968

(JOHAN) AUGUST STRINDBERG

Born 1849 in Sweden. Author of short stories, novels and plays. Died 1912.

13 He was a great writer without being a guiding spirit.
Georg Brandes

14 After all the polysyllables of psycho-analysis have been poured over his head, we may say in the common slang that he had a tile missing, and then add, as G. K. Chesteron

once superbly added concerning a daft genius, that missing tiles may let in a lot of light.
Ivor Brown, Observer 23 *Jan* 1949

1 His plays, which reflect his horror of the growing independence of women, are counter-thrusts at the feminism of Ibsen.
John o' London's Weekly 2 *Aug* 1930

2 He became obsessed with the idea that a former friend, with whose wife he had been intimate, wished to murder him. For a time he became a raving madman, suffering from delusions of persecution, and hallucinations, seeing warnings of danger in every occurrence, and flying from place to place to escape them.
Ibid.

3 Strindberg's imagination was so hyperactive that he could attend a funeral of a young poet as a pall-bearer and two days later persuade himself that he had been present at the young man's death, describing it in detail. On learning that the San Francisco earthquake of 1906 had been preceded by sightings of a mysterious and hitherto unknown bird, he immediately saw one in Stockholm and waited — not entirely in gloom, one supposes — for his beloved and reviled city to be dragged beneath the waves.
Michael Ratcliffe, Observer 28 *Oct* 1984

4 He is a master of obfuscation, concealing shyness in aggression and a natural conviviality in stormy Napoleonic poses for the public eye.
Ibid.

5 He loved gardening, food, travel, playing Beethoven, cards, drink.
Ibid.

6 After some further conversation consisting mainly of embarrassed silences and a pale smile or two by A.S. and floods of energetic eloquence by G.B.S., A.S. took out his watch and said in German 'At two o'clock I am going to be sick.' The visitor accepted this delicate intimation and withdrew.
G. B. Shaw, letter to William Archer

7 Not a single one of Strindberg's plays is a period piece, neither subject, nor situation nor language is dated. He wrote of all time for all times.
Elizabeth Sprigge, THE STRANGE LIFE OF AUGUST STRINDBERG 1949

8 All his life Strindberg had been feared and often hated by his countrymen. In his rage and misery at the plight of mankind, he was savage in his attack on institutions and on individuals, but gradually people realised that it was always the oppressor that he attacked, and never the oppressed.
Ibid.

9 On our wedding morn he brusquely started from a dream, and not at once remembering that he now legitimately enjoyed the company of a young woman, attempted to throttle the interloper. Something familiar in my protesting voice brought him back to consciousness. He soothingly reassured me that the attack had nothing to do with me, but was intended as a mere matter of habit, for his first wife.
Freda Strindberg, MARRIAGE WITH A GENIUS

10 From his early days he was a desperately unhappy man, who could write in his autobiography 'To search for God and to find the Devil! That is what has happened to me.'
J. C. Trewin, Radio Times 1 *Nov* 1946

11 When I was asked by Strindberg to undertake the thorny task of producing his plays I requested that I might read them. 'No you will not!' was the irritable answer, and to my reasonable remonstrance that as the prospective producer of them I ought to know something about them his astonishing retort was: 'I never permit anybody to read what I write.'
Gustav Uddgren, STRINDBERG THE MAN 1936

12 When I was found in possession of a copy of Strindberg's *Married* my uncle was so horrified that he dropped the book and refused to pick it up except with a pair of tongs. I was treated as a criminal by my relatives, and they did not wish to be seen publicly together with me.
Ibid.

GRAHAM (VIVIAN) SUTHERLAND

Born 1903. English painter. Produced controversial portraits of Somerset Maugham and Winston Churchill (reputed to have been destroyed by Lady Churchill). Designed tapestry for Coventry Cathedral. Died 1980.

12 He is working on the drawings for a portrait of Willie (Somerset Maugham); and those I've seen are brilliant. Graham does not spare any horses, and he has made Willie as sour as a quince — yet Willie seems delighted.
Cecil Beaton, DIARY 1949

J. M. SYNGE

1 It's an outrage — but it's a masterpiece.
Lord Beaverbrook, on first seeing Graham Sutherland's portrait of himself

2 This portrait is a remarkable example of modern art. It certainly combines force with candour.
Winston Churchill on Graham Sutherland's portrait of himself

3 Sir Winston Churchill hated the picture [Sutherland's portrait] because he had his own image of himself — strong, fearless, the familiar bulldog figure — and he was very displeased to see himself portrayed as the tired old warrior.
Lord Clark, Sunday Times 15 *Jan* 1978

4 Sutherland remained true to his own stated aim. 'I want neither to flatter nor denigrate', although he was well aware that '"to portray" has become synonymous with "to betray"'.
Richard Cork, Sunday Times 15 *Jan* 1978

5 He has never tried to create the kind of 3-D picture you can imagine yourself walking about in, which is why nobody ever appears in them. 'I am the figure in my landscapes' he says when asked about their emptiness.
Observer, Profile 22 *Apr* 1962

6 His first portrait was of Maugham, and he has always been at his best with portraiture when dealing with sacred monsters.
Marina Vaizey, Sunday Times 15 *Jan* 1978

J. M. (JOHN MILLINGTON) SYNGE

Born 1871 in Ireland. Dramatist who wrote plays of Irish peasant life, notably *Riders to the Sea*, 1904 and *The Playboy of the Western World*, 1907. Died 1909.

7 Synge was a faker of peasant speech. It is high time that all the tosh that was formerly spouted by Synge, and still is by sentimentalists late for the fair, was stopped.
St John Ervine

8 He painted a grimace on the fair face of Ireland, it was said; he shows priests being tossed in blankets and women betraying their husbands. 'I restored sex' he replied, 'and people were so surprised they saw the sex only.'
David H. Greene and Edward M. Stephens, J. M. SYNGE 1959

9 Synge was the rushing up of the buried fire, an explosion of all that had been denied or refused, a furious impartiality, an indifferent turbulent sorrow. His work, like that of Burns, was to say all that people did not want to have said.
W. B. Yeats, AUTOBIOGRAPHIES 1955

10 He felt that modern poetry — and he was more poet than *prosateur* — had become like 'pressed flowers, odourless, one-dimensional', and that 'before verse can become human again it must learn to be brutal'.
Kenneth Young, Daily Telegraph 5 *Jun* 1959

T

SIR RABINDRANATH TAGORE

Born 1861 in India. Author, educator and poet. Awarded Nobel Prize for Literature, 1913. Died 1941.

1 His life was dominated by one ideal — that all the peoples of the earth should live in harmony, each having its place in the sun, each contributing to the welfare of the whole.
Daily Sketch 8 *Aug* 1941

2 We met someone who had never heard of Tagore — a French consul in a Mediterranean port. When told that we were on our way to India to visit Tagore he replied: 'Tagore! Tagore, Calcutta, Benares, Mysore, all those lovely cities! Well my friends, enjoy yourselves at Tagore!'
Gaetan Fouquet, John o' London's Weekly 8 *Feb* 1936

3 Meeting him confirmed my opinion of him being a nice old English lady.
Thomas Mann, DIARIES 1918–39 1983

4 Who is this patriarch with the Luminous eyes? Is he a wanderer from some legendary land? What is he doing in the Noise-and-Speed age? He is the Man from the East. The Human Poem. The Seeker for the Perfect Life. The Philosopher. The Mystic. Sir Rabindranath Tagore, of Santiniketan, Bengal, India.
Passing Show 10 *Dec* 1932

5 As he thinks, so he lives and writes. He pours out poems. He lives continually in the spiritual exaltation of a poem. Therefore he is famous in the world. Therefore he is revered in his village. The simple folk come to his cottage eager for a word of hope and wisdom. They do not disturb him. He can meditate in their presence.
Ibid.

ELIZABETH TAYLOR

Born 1932 in London. Taken to America as a child. Trained as a film actress, and when only thirteen years old achieved fame for her performance in *National Velvet*. Won Academy awards for her performances in *Butterfield 8*, 1960 and *Who's Afraid of Virginia Woolf?*, 1966.

6 They say that when Elizabeth Taylor took her sixth husband and the justice of the peace wanted details of her previous marriages she said, 'What is this, a memory test?'
Leslie Halliwell, THE FILMGOER'S BOOK OF QUOTES 1978

7 Taylor's empire is world-wide. 'She would have made a perfect maharanee,' said an Indian, 'beautiful, plump, jewel-studded and very hairy.'
Brenda Maddox, WHO'S AFRAID OF ELIZABETH TAYLOR? 1977

8 Taylor is pop royalty. Lucille Ball curtsied when the Burtons appeared on *I Love Lucy* and called Taylor 'Your Highness' and 'Your Majesty'.
Ibid.

9 Academics rush to recite the names of her husbands like bright kids rattling off their multiplication tables.
Ibid.

10 Miss Taylor lists about, her hands fluttering idly like a wind-up doll in need of a new mainspring.
New York Times, of her performance in Private Lives 9 *May* 1983

11 She is short, with a large head and an anvil-shaped torso which, when clothed, seems to have been stuffed into a quality holdall.
Deborah Norton, Observer 27 *Nov* 1977

12 (Her life is) a serial that countless women under hair-dryers have been reading avidly for 30 years, in which the heroine is a beautiful, hard-working rich film star with four children, six husbands, and a bad back.
Ibid.

13 Just how garish her commonplace accent, squeakily shrill voice, and the childish petulance with which she delivers her lines are, my pen is neither scratchy nor leaky enough to convey.
John Simon of her in Taming of the Shrew

14 I don't pretend to be an ordinary housewife.
Elizabeth Taylor in an interview

NORMAN TEBBIT

Born 1931. British politician. Secretary of the Department of Trade and Industry, 1983.

1 A semi-house-trained polecat.
Michael Foot

2 He is a rough sod, but very able. He would put his knee in your stomach just to attract your attention with a smile on his face but he is the sort of fellow you could do a deal with. He would drive a hard bargain, but you know he would deliver.
Len Murray, The Times 2 *Sep* 1984

3 The American adage 'don't get mad, get even' doesn't apply to Norman. He gets mad *and* even.
Observer, Profile 7 *Oct* 1984

4 It is unnerving to see someone with that collection of prejudices be so brilliant as well.
Ibid.

5 He has an untrained mind yet he can read a brief prepared by some mandarin with a double-first and tear it to shreds.
Ibid.

SHIRLEY TEMPLE

Born 1928 in California. The most popular child film star of all time. Appeared in her first film at the age of four. Retired after making *Rebecca of Sunnybrook Farm* in 1938. In adult life took an active part in public affairs and was appointed American delegate to United Nations, 1969.

6 Honey, when Santa Claus bundled you up and dropped you down Creation's Chimney, he gave the world one of the very nicest, and dearest and most delectable Christmas presents that ever was.
Irvin Cobb, speech on making Shirley Temple a special Academy Award 1935

7 Shirley Temple's mother used to bring the necessary cinematic tears to the child-star's eye by telling her that her pet dog had had an accident. After the successful shot Mummy used to explain that the accident was not serious and the pet would recover.
Sheilah Graham, MY HOLLYWOOD 1984

8 The greatest reason for the phenomenal success of this six-year-old child is that she is Everybody's Child. She is the 'dream' child of every mother and father, the 'dream' sister of every boy and girl, the 'dream' child of every unmarried person. She is the lovable creature everybody wants to have in the house.
Lore Leni, Passing Show 19 *Oct* 1935

9 She has joined the film immortals by adding her footprints to those perpetuated in the cement of Graumann's Chinese Theatre — Hollywood's Hall of Fame, where all the great stars have made their mark. And she is only six years old.
Ibid.

10 She is reputed to have more fan mail than anyone else in Hollywood. Dolls, dresses, puzzles, books, furniture are named after her. When she wears a frock in a film hundreds of thousands of mothers everywhere want to dress their children in similar frocks.
Ibid.

11 During this depression, when the spirit of the people is lower than at any other time, it is a splendid thing that for just fifteen cents an American can go to a movie and look at the smiling face of a baby and forget his troubles.
President F. D. Roosevelt in 1935

MOTHER TERESA OF CALCUTTA

Born 1910 in Yugoslavia of Albanian parents. Original name Agnes Gouxha Bojaxhiv. From the Loreto Convent in Calcutta founded, in 1948, her Missionary Sisters of Charity. Awarded the Nobel Peace Prize, 1979.

12 She is among the last of the great missionary superstars.
Arun Chacko, The Times 14 *Aug* 1983

13 Her organisation can hardly be called democratic. Under the order's vow of obedience no member can venture out without the Sister Superior's approval, receive private mail, entertain private guests, watch films, read books other than related work, or call each other by a pet name lest that reduce affection for Jesus. Failure to abide by these regulations can lead to expulsion.
Ibid.

14 Mother Teresa is neither particularly educated nor intelligent, and some of her statements make one wince. But her faith, single-mindedness, grit and stamina have moved mountains.
Ibid.

1 An interviewer recently asked Mother Teresa if she would have taken Galileo's side or the Church's in that momentous medieval astronomical controversy had she been around at the time. The possible claimant for eventual canonisation smiled and without batting an eyelid said: *The Church*.
Ibid.

2 Without her faith Mother Teresa would be remarkable only for her ordinariness, and she rejoices in this fact for it is evidence of the power for which she and many others with her are but channels.
Kathryn Spink, FOR THE BROTHERHOOD OF MAN UNDER THE FATHERHOOD OF GOD 1981

3 One interviewer in particular must remember with some embarrassment questioning Mother Teresa on television as to how she came to be doing such remarkable work. 'Jesus' was the simple and uncompromising reply. The interviewer who had evidently been expecting a considerably more prolonged and involved reply, was left floundering among his notes for the next question.
Ibid.

DAME ELLEN (ALICE) TERRY

Born 1847. English actress, notably in Shakespearean roles, frequently partnered Henry Irving. Died 1928.

4 She was terribly mischievous; in 1902 when she was playing in *The Merry Wives*, she put a pin in the padding Herbert Tree was wearing as Falstaff. He got through just one scene before his whole stomach collapsed.
John Gielgud, AN ACTOR AND HIS TIME 1979

5 I saw her once on the Palace Pier at Brighton, playing the Trial Scene from *The Merchant of Venice*. She had to be wheeled down the long pier in a bath chair to reach the theatre; but when she came striding on in the trial scene you would never have thought she was an invalid and an old lady, except that she had white hair under her scarlet cap. She achieved the most perfect phrasing when speaking Shakespeare, a kind of frankness, which made it seem as if she had been taught the passage in the next room by Shakespeare himself. I heard her do the 'Mercy' speech many times at charity matinées, and she never failed to thrill her audience, although she often hesitated from forgetfulness.
Ibid.

6 Ellen had three marriages, several love affairs and two illegitimate children, and although she and Irving were honoured guests in my grandparents' house there was never that intense devotion between the sisters that biographers would like to suggest.
Ibid.

7 When I saw Ellen Terry as the Nurse in Doris Keane's *Romeo and Juliet* in 1919 she could hardly remember a word, and Basil Sydney and Leon Quartermaine, who were playing Romeo and Mercutio respectively, whispered every line in her ear, and then she said the line herself and it sounded as if she had just thought of it. One would have thought it would have made her nervous, but she still had confidence in her charisma and in the audience, and managed to enchant them just the same.
Ibid.

8 She had a somewhat irregular private life. She did occasionally come to our house, but my mother thought her restless and fidgetty and preferred the acting of her sister Marion. I fell madly in love with Ellen the first time I ever saw her on the stage. I decided the restlessness was part of her glory, because what I remember most about her is her movement, although she was then in her seventies, deaf, rather blind and very vague. But when she came on you really believed that she was walking on the flagstones of Venice or the fields of Windsor. She moved with an extraordinary spontaneity and grace, holding her skirts gathered in two hands or bunched over one arm, and crossed the stage with an unforgettable impression of swiftness.
Ibid.

9 Ellen Terry was all personality; the warmth and ripeness of summer was with her; she suffused every stage she trod with her peach-golden glow.
Pamela Hansford Johnson, John o' London's Weekly 13 *May* 1949

10 Gielgud remembers Ellen Terry as an old lady, swathed in shawls and crowned with a huge black hat, unable to recollect lines or which was which among her vast crowd of nephews and nieces. She beckoned the young John to her and said, 'Which are you, and do you read your Shakespeare?'
John Mortimer, IN CHARACTER 1983

11 She was always delightfully sweet to me, though I often wondered whether she really knew who I was. One day, just before

Christmas, I saw her driving down the King's Road in a hansom. I happened to be carrying a large bunch of lilies which I had just bought, so I hailed the hansom and made it pull up, and thrusting the flowers over the apron of the cab, I said 'Here, Miss Terry, these are for you, with a happy Christmas.' 'Oh how kind! Thank you, thank you! Who are you?' 'Never mind who I am,' I answered, trying to get away. 'No. no. I know your face quite well. Tell me your name,' she insisted. So at last I said, 'My name is Ernest Thesiger.' 'Oh no it *isn't*' she said.
Ernest Thesiger, PRACTICALLY TRUE 1927

1 I met her first at a private view of her son Gordon Craig's pictures, and overhearing a remark I made to my companion on the occasion she rushed impulsively up to me and said: 'Oh, you like that picture? Tell me your name and I will write to my son and tell him.' 'Where is he now?' I asked. 'Oh, he is in Belgium or Berlin or Birmingham or Bermuda — some place beginning with a B; but I will write to him at once.'
Ibid.

MARGARET (HILDA) THATCHER

Born 1925, née Roberts. English politician. Succeeded Edward Heath as leader of the Conservative Party. First British woman Prime Minister 1979. Re-elected 1983.

2 Mrs Thatcher may be a woman, but she isn't a sister.
Anonymous feminist. Quoted Observer 7 Oct 1979

3 She slipped into her place as demurely tight-lipped as ever and glossy with her best suburban grooming; fresh-flowered summer frock and every wave of her hair in place. How *does* she keep her hair so unchangeably immaculate.
Barbara Castle, THE CASTLE DIARIES 1974–76 1980

4 Politicians are either warriors or healers. Margaret Thatcher is a healer.
Patrick Cosgrave, BIOGRAPHY OF MARGARET THATCHER

5 When she is attacking the opposition she makes it sound as if she is criticising the next door neighbour's curtains.
Ken Dodd, BBC 1 TV, Parkinson Show 15 Mar 1980

6 She sounded like the book of Revelations read out over a railway station public address system by a headmistress of a certain age wearing calico knickers.
Clive James, of the 1979 election result, THE CRYSTAL BUCKET 1981

7 She is a very ordinary woman, occupying a position where ordinary virtues are not enough.
Paul Johnson, Observer 20 Nov 1983

8 She is of such charming brutality.
Helmut Kohl, Chancellor of West Germany. Quoted The Times, Diary 23 Sep 1983

9 Conservative leaders have always been able to recognise a vested interest when they saw one. But she does not seem keen on institutions whether it be the TUC, the CBI, Whitehall or even the City.
Len Murray, The Times 2 Sep 1984

10 If Mrs Thatcher started to believe what the papers said about her there is no knowing what she might get up to. Why, only last week she was described in this column as 'mean, moody and magnificent'. The mind begins to boggle alarmingly.
John O'Sullivan, Daily Telegraph 25 May 1979

11 Plunder Woman.
Harry Urwin, Trade Union Congress, Brighton 6 Sep 1980

12 Mrs Thatcher plays, I suspect, to an unseen gallery of headmistresses, economists and the Madame Tussaud version of Winston Churchill.
Katherine Whitehorn, Observer, Act your self 4 Dec 1983

DYLAN (MORLAIS) THOMAS

Born 1914 in Wales. Poet, whose most popular work, *Under Milk Wood*, was written for radio, and produced posthumously, 1954. Died 1953.

13 Most of Dylan Thomas is a blend of answerless riddle, outworn poeticism, and careful linguistic folly.
Kingsley Amis. Quoted Observer, Profile 14 Jan 1962

14 Dylan Thomas grew up with an intense desire to be a poet. As he showed by a youthful plagiarism, his desire to be a poet was probably greater than his desire to write poetry.
Anon., New Yorker 21 Nov 1977

15 He came round to my Horizon office once and talked about the Belsen films he had seen — an emaciated figure in the last agony

of starvation trying to pluck a handful of grass. 'I am that man', he said 'that's me' — meaning that he was human and so nothing of man's degradation should be foreign to him.
Cyril Connolly

1 When he disappeared, it was a relief; when he reappeared, it was a pleasure.
Geoffrey Grigson, RECOLLECTIONS

2 The first time I saw Dylan Thomas I felt as if Rubens had suddenly taken it into his head to paint a youthful Silenus.
Edith Sitwell, TAKEN CARE OF: AN AUTOBIOGRAPHY 1965

3 In full face he looked as William Blake must have looked as a young man. He had full eyes — like those of Blake — giving at first the impression of being unseeing, but seeing all, looking over immeasurable distances.
Ibid.

4 I have never known anyone more capable of endearing himself to others. And this was not only the result of his great warmth, charm and touching funniness. I have never known anyone with a more holy and childlike innocence of mind.
Ibid.

5 He came to luncheon with me and as he arrived he said 'I am sorry to smell so awful, Edith. It's Margate.' I said 'Yes, of course my dear boy, it's Margate.'
Ibid.

JAMES (HENRY) THOMAS

Born 1874. British socialist politician. General Secretary of the National Union of Railwaymen 1918–24. Elected MP for Derby 1910. Cabinet minister 1924 and 1930. Was largely responsible for persuading trade unions to give financial and political support to the Labour Party. Died 1949.

6 I was rung up by Mr J. H. Thomas, and had him here immediately after dinner. He was in a very *émotioné* condition and told me that every hour of his day was a new experience of hell. He made one or two quite chimerical suggestions, which I convinced him were absurd. He is in a tragic position — responsible for, and actively directing a strike in which he does not believe, though he maintains that on the merits his men have a very good case.
H. H. Asquith, at the time of the 1915 coal strike

7 He sent my father [Stanley Baldwin] a photograph of himself in full morning rig, top hat, buttonhole, everything, and inscribed it, 'From one toff to another'. My father evidently likes it. I see he has it on his desk.
Oliver Baldwin. Quoted Reginald Pound, THEIR MOODS AND MINE 1937

8 At 3.30 he entered the Chamber, sad and aged, but sunburnt still. Very soon took place one of the most poignant scenes the House has ever witnessed. He read a statement which was simple and rather heartrending. He accepted the findings of the tribunal, but declared that he had never consciously betrayed a budget or any other secret. He was leaving the ''ouse' after twenty-seven years in its midst. He had now only his wife who still trusted and loved him. He hoped no other member would ever be in a situation as cruel, as terrible as the one he today found himself in. Then he sat down for only a second and there was a loud murmur of pity and suppressed admiration through the House. Mr Baldwin sat with his head in his hands. Churchill wiped away his tears. Thomas rose again and slowly made his way out, not forgetting to turn and bow, for the last time, to the Speaker.
Sir Henry Channon, DIARY 11 *Jun* 1936

9 One day [in about 1920] Aneurin Bevan went to Golders Green to hear Jimmy Thomas, the railwaymen's leader, explain to a great meeting why the union had capitulated in a clash with the Government. Afterwards he heard Thomas remark to an aide, 'When the buggers are giving you trouble, give 'em a mass meeting. It gets it out of their system.'
Michael Foot, LIFE OF ANEURIN BEVAN 1962

10 He had several comicalities of which one couldn't be quite sure whether they were intentional or not. His 'aitches' of course, are celebrated, and I think he must have misplaced them with conscious art. John Buchan told me of a reporter who asked him after a meeting what Mr Thomas could possibly have meant by the 'Haddock Committee', as the subject of his speech hadn't been even remotely connected with fish or any kind; and John was able to tell him that what had been in question was an *ad hoc* committee.
Edward Marsh, A NUMBER OF PEOPLE 1939

11 His speaking was quite unlike anyone else's. hardly a sentence worked out, and an accurate report would have been

unintelligible, but his delivery left no doubt of his meaning. His usual technique in an after-dinner speech was to begin by seizing on something that had fallen from a previous speaker, turn it to ridicule, and proceed to a series of outrageous insults which set everyone, including the victim, in a roar; and then without any transition, to rise from this mood and say quite simply and seriously, often with moving eloquence, what he really felt and meant about the subject in hand.
Ibid.

DAME (AGNES) SYBIL THORNDIKE

Born 1882. English actress, played leading roles in Shakespeare and Shaw. Died 1976.

1 *Saint Joan*, of course, was written for her, and it was her acting masterpiece, though she must have got sick and tired of hearing people say so. Her performance was unrivalled. Her tearing up of the recantation in the trial was a moment of really great acting that I shall never forget. She was as convincing in the slangy colloquial passages as in the great poetic speeches, blending the different sides of the character with unerring judgement, and never for a moment allowing sentimentality or sanctimoniousness to intrude on the simple directness of her approach.
John Gielgud, AN ACTOR AND HIS TIME 1979

2 Her good works were manifold, her influences for good shone from her like a beacon, but she hated to be praised or to be thought sweet or saintly. 'I hate pathos,' she said once. 'It's soft and weak. But tragedy has fight.'
Ibid.

3 In those days (1922) Sybil had sandy hair arranged in coils round her ears, like radio receivers, and wore long, straight dresses in bright colours with strings of beads round her neck. She exuded vitality, enthusiasm, generosity, and we were all spellbound as we listened to her.
Ibid.

4 How fitting it was that her very last public appearance should have been at the Old Vic on its farewell night. At the end of the performance she was wheeled down the aisle in her chair, to smile and wave for the last time to the people sitting in the theatre she had loved so well. Lively, passionate, argumentative, always travelling, acting, learning a new language or a new poem, a magnificent wife and mother, she was surely one of the rarest women of our time. 'Oh Lewis,' she cried once, 'if only we could be the first actors to play on the moon.'
Ibid.

5 Her beauty grew, fittingly, in her old age, and her noble head, veiled in the white silk scarf she always wore, singled her out in any gathering, whether at theatres or parties, or in church. During these last years it was sad to see her the victim of continual pain. But magnificently she rose above it. 'My piffling arthritis' she would say.
Ibid.

JAMES (GROVER) THURBER

Born 1894 in America. Humorous writer whose work was for many years a feature of *The New Yorker*. His *Secret Life of Walter Mitty* was the basis of a film providing Danny Kaye with one of his most famous roles. Died 1961.

6 When Harold Ross once complained, 'Thurber's women don't have any sex appeal,' Marc Connelly reminded him, 'They do for Thurber's men.'
Bennett Cerf, TRY AND STOP ME 1947

7 Harold Ross, editor of the *New Yorker*, once tried to stop private telephone calls in his office and went so far as to install a public coin booth in the reception room. The next morning we found the booth torn loose from its roots, on its back in his own private office. Stretched out inside, a calla lily in his hand and a wreath on his head, was James Thurber.
Ibid.

8 Thurber was signed by Mr Goldwyn to do a screen treatment of *The Catbird Seat* as well as *Walter Mitty*, but when he turned in a script Mr Goldwyn told him to revise it. Mr Thurber told Mr Goldwyn to go climb a tree. What's more he returned every penny of the 28,000 dollars he had received in advance and even made his agent throw in his ten per cent commission.
Bennett Cerf, MIX WELL BEFORE USING 1948

9 The ending of the screen version of *The Secret Life of Walter Mitty* was re-written ten times and still left Sam Goldwyn nursing considerable doubts. 'I'm going to call Thurber himself and see what he thinks of it,' decided Mr G. Thurber was located in the *New Yorker* office and listened patiently while Goldwyn, in Hollywood, described the ending in vivid detail. 'Look, Mr

Goldwyn,' said Thurber finally, 'I don't know anything about motion pictures. I don't know what you've done with the rest of my story and I don't particularly care. I sold you the story and that's that. How can I say whether or not your new ending is right?' Mr Goldwyn thought this over for a few moments and then cried approvingly, 'Thank you my boy. Why can't I get criticism like that in my own studio?'
Ibid.

1 His America was one of dark veneers and clumpy handles on the sideboard. Of close-patterned carpets. Of enormous steam radios whose valves seemed to steam and bubble, like kettles. Of squashy armchairs, with white linen covers on the arm-rests.
Radio Times 6 *Nov* 1969

2 When Thurber and E. B. White collaborated on *Is Sex Necessary?* their publisher stared in discomfiture at the illustrations and said 'I gather this is the kind of drawing you want in the book?' 'These *are* the drawings that go in the book,' answered White.
The Times, Obituary 3 *Nov* 1961

3 A favourite trick of his in his early newspaper days was to draw small dogs on telephone pads, page after page of them. A reporter answering the phone would snatch at the phone-pad, tear off the dog picture seeking a clean page — then find dog picture after dog picture.
World's Press News 15 *Jul* 1937

4 One of his funniest drawings shows the second Mrs Harris being introduced by her husband to a guest explaining 'That's my first wife up there.' 'Up there' is the top of a bookcase on which a woman crouches on hands and knees. Ross (editor of *New Yorker*) wrote to Thurber saying, 'I can't quite get this. Is the woman on top of the bookcase dead or stuffed?' Thurber replied, 'I don't know.'
Ibid.

JOSIP BROZ TITO

Born 1892 in Yugoslavia. Led partisan resistance against the Germans in World War II. Became premier in 1945 and president in 1953. Opposed Russian influence and preserved the country's status as an independent Communist republic. Died 1980.

5 He was 49 when he showed that the conspirator was at heart a warrior leader who could combine personal courage and total ruthlessness with revered paternalism and within three years achieve such dignity and authority that he could meet Churchill as an equal and start to question Stalin's orders.
Phyllis Auty, TITO: A BIOGRAPHY 1970

6 By making himself a world figure with claims to international influence greatly in excess of his country's real resources he gave his people, still simmering with mutual hates and suspicions, an identity and new national pride.
Ibid.

7 He is still the man who translated that dreariest of books, 'The Short History of the Communist Party' as an official Comintern assignment — and spent the money on a diamond ring, which he still wears.
Ibid.

8 In 1938 Moscow made Tito General Secretary of the Jugo-Slav Communist Party. He commented later, 'I had no ambition to take over the leadership of the party, but I wanted the leadership to be strong, firm and revolutionary. I had never thought of becoming the head, but I did want the head to be a man who could work.' As a reluctant leader he has lasted well.
Ibid.

9 Tito was a poor speaker. His education was inadequate and his knowledge superficial. He read little, could not spell, and his Serbo-Croatian was faulty. In early life he was dismissed from one job after another.
Milovan Djilas, TITO: THE STORY FROM INSIDE 1981

10 Not one of the great ideas of Yugoslav Communism was his. I conceived the idea of self-government in 1950.
Ibid.

11 Despite all the talk of Marxism and Communism Tito emerges as a Balkan leader of the traditional type, the only self-made monarch of the post-war world who, at a time when other, older monarchies were bending over backwards to assume 'democratic' manners, clearly takes immense pleasure in all the trappings of personal power.
David Floyd, Daily Telegraph 7 *May* 1970

12 As for his attitude to Moscow — in the darkest days of the war, alone and hard pressed, he could signal to Stalin, the man no

one ever answered back, 'If you cannot help us, at least do not hamper us.'
Fitzroy Maclean, DISPUTED BARRICADE 1957

1 One thing struck me immediately: Tito's readiness to discuss any question on its merits and, if necessary, take a decision there and then. He seemed perfectly sure of himself. To find such independence in a Communist was for me a novel experience.
Fitzroy Maclean, Sunday Express 25 *Jul* 1948

2 His firm insistence that a communist cannot be asked to place loyalty to Russia higher than to his own country marked the turning point in the post-war history of communism.
The Times, Obituary 5 *May* 1980

3 He lived ostentatiously — his diamond ring, his exaggerated uniforms, his love of flashy cars and speedboats, his island of Brioni — were as much part of his character as his political shrewdness and his courage.
Ibid.

4 So indoctrinated was Tito with what he believed to be Communist obedience that he failed to realise until 1948 that his creation of an independent Yugoslav State, however Socialist, was the last thing to please Stalin.
Elizabeth Wiskemann, Times Literary Supplement 16 *May* 1970

J. R. R. (JOHN RONALD REUEL) TOLKIEN

Born 1892 in the Orange Free State. At the age of four, on the death of his father, returned with his mother to Birmingham. In 1925 was elected Professor of Anglo-Saxon at Oxford. Created the fictional *Hobbit*, 1937 and followed this with his *Lord of the Rings* trilogy 1954–5. Died 1973.

5 Tolkien's area of scholarship was confined to Anglo-Saxon and early Middle English, as well as related Germanic languages. Moreover he approached it primarily through philology.
Humphrey Carpenter, THE INKLINGS 1978

6 Though Tolkien lived in the twentieth century he can scarcely be called a modern writer. His roots were buried deep in early literature, and the major names in twentieth-century writing meant little or nothing to him. He read very little modern fiction, and took no serious notice of it.
Ibid.

7 Tolkien managed to get the discussion round to the proposed English Prelim. I had a talk with him afterwards. He is a smooth, pale, fluent little chap — can't read Spenser because of the forms — thinks all literature is written for the amusement of *men* between thirty and forty — we ought to vote ourselves out of existence if we were honest — still the sound changes and the gobbets are great fun for the dons. His pet abomination is the idea of 'liberal studies'. Technical hobbies are more in his line. No harm in him; only needs a smack or so.
C. S. Lewis, DIARY *May* 1926

8 All who love that kind of children's book that can be read and re-read by adults should take note that a new star has appeared in this constellation. To the trained eye some of the characters will seem almost mythopoeic.
C. S. Lewis, The Times, reviewing The Hobbit 7 *Oct* 1937

9 No common receipt for children's stories will give you creatures so rooted in their own soil and history as those of Professor Tolkien — who obviously knows much more about them than he needs for his tale.
C. S. Lewis, Times Literary Supplement 2 *Oct* 1937

ARTURO TOSCANINI

Born 1867. Italian conductor. Became musical director of La Scala, Milan, 1898 and principal conductor of the Metropolitan Opera, New York, 1908. Died 1957.

10 One day after rehearsals Toscanini said to Bill Primrose, his principal viola player, 'Primrose you will come to dinner with me tonight. My wife is away and we shall be alone.' Primrose nearly fainted. To think that he was going to have an evening alone with the maestro! He goes to Toscanini's house. They're alone, with the butler in attendance. Toscanini gobbles up his spaghetti, swallows his chianti without a word, and then rushes into the television room. He turns to the station that features wrestling, and watches with a non-stop verbal accompaniment: 'Hit him in ze stomm-ahk. Get 'im by ze leg. Jump on 'im.' Poor Primrose. Music was never discussed.
Neville Cardus, CONVERSATIONS WITH CARDUS

11 Toscanini had a painful experience one evening with a soloist who began his cadenza bravely enough but soon got into difficulty. Obviously flustered, he wandered farther

and farther off key. The maestro and the entire orchestra held their breaths. Just before their cue to resume playing, the soloist managed to recover the original key. Toscanini bowed and said 'Welcome home.'
Bennett Cerf, TRY AND STOP ME 1947

1 During a rehearsal a second violinist grazed the string next to the one he intended to play. The sound of the slip was almost inaudible. Few people would have noticed it. But Toscanini stopped the orchestra, pointed his baton at the culprit and said sharply 'One string will be quite enough if you please.'
Edmund Fuller, ANECDOTES 1942

2 Arturo Toscanini had an astounding and infallible memory. Early in his career, when he was a cellist, he formed an acquaintance with the violinists Romanini and Erico Polo, and with the composer Bolzoni who wrote an Adagio which the group performed on a special occasion. More than a year later the two violinists and Toscanini again met, but Bolzoni was absent. 'What a pity,' exclaimed someone, 'that Bolzoni has the score. If he had left us a copy we might have had that quartet we liked so much.' Toscanini said, 'Give me a pencil and paper.' Whereupon he proceeded to write down all four parts of the Adagio from memory.
Ibid.

3 He had a legendary gift of memory. Once he had read a score he knew it by heart. A bassoon player once told him, as the opera was about to begin, that his E flat key was broken, but that a new bassoon was coming for the second act. 'There is no E flat in the bassoon part in the first act' Toscanini reassured him.
Lionel Hale, News Chronicle 26 *Feb* 1936

4 Caruso, at the height of his fame, wished to absent himself from one of the rehearsals at the Metropolitan. Toscanini, who was conducting, thought otherwise. Caruso appeared, three minutes late. Toscanini ordered him to be early next time; and next time Caruso was early.
Ibid.

5 One of the players among the second violins at a rehearsal of Beethoven's Ninth Symphony at Turin played a false note. 'I would kill a man for that,' cried Toscanini, and beat the man over the head with his baton. He was summoned for assault; in court he pleaded 'sublime frenzy'; his fellow Italians acquitted him.
Ibid.

6 He suffered a beating-up from black-shirted thugs at Bologna rather than play the tawdry Fascist anthem at an inappropriate moment.
Spike Hughes, Daily Herald 4 *Jun* 1935

7 Toscanini has always insisted on practically unlimited rehearsal time. After 30 rehearsals of Beethoven's Mass in D with the orchestra and choir of La Scala he put away his baton and said quietly 'Ladies and gentlemen — next year.' And that was in 1927, the centenary of Beethoven's death, when all Italy had waited for this performance.
Observer, Profile 30 *Jun* 1946

8 A volcano that smiles as well as sleeps, it is difficult to convey a picture of *that*. I have seen the volcano in eruption. It is unforgettable. A wrong note, a slurred phrase, a misplaced accent, one fatal second of inattention, and the lava spurts and streams and spreads in short-lived fury, white, pure, but unsmoking. In half a minute the volcano sleeps. In two minutes it smiles 'Bene, bene'.
C. B. Rees, Radio Times 21 *Jun* 1946

ARNOLD TOYNBEE

Born 1889. English historian, nephew of Arnold Toynbee, social reformer, who founded Toynbee Hall. Author of *A Study of History*, which examines the reasons for the rise and fall of civilisations. Died 1975.

9 Toynbee envisages a Christian society which assimilates all that Confucius, Buddha, Socrates, Mahomet and the seers yet unborn have to teach. He is one of the few great thinkers of our time who is fundamentally an optimist.
Lorney Bolton, News Chronicle 13 *May* 1948

10 One journalist asked him what purpose had impelled him to devote thirty-five years of his life to this single great work (*A Study of History*). Toynbee rose politely in his seat and replied with the one word 'Curiosity'.
Harold Nicolson, DIARY 12 *Oct* 1954

11 He began by thinking that religion existed for the sake of civilisation but has become convinced that civilisation exists for the sake of religion. This view has made him the butt of both Marxists and 'realists', the two most popular schools of academic historian.
Observer, Profile 14 *Dec* 1947

12 Future philosophers of history will judge Dr

Toynbee's vast work as a deeply felt personal vision of the historical process, a vision which expressed the despair of the liberal who has seen the liberal dream turn to ashes, as well as the hope of a liberal who has turned again to God.
Times Literary Supplement 22 *Oct* 1954

1 Perhaps we have been unfair to Dr Toynbee's work in treating it as a study of history. We should have thought of it as the record of one soul's pilgrimage — a kind of *Umana Commedia*.
Ibid.

2 His vast learning, his unflagging industry, the graces of his literary style, his moderation and urbanity, all these must command our admiration and respect . . . He has taken Spengler's thesis that there is a regular pattern of growth and decay in the history of civilisations and rejecting Spengler's organic analogy, recast his pattern in moral terms.
Ibid.

SPENCER TRACY

Born 1900. American film star. Winner of two Academy awards. Some of his most successful roles were in partnership with Katherine Hepburn. Died 1967.

3 Spence is the best we have, because you don't see the mechanism working.
Humphrey Bogart

4 The guy's good. There's nobody in the business who can touch him, and you're a fool to try. And the bastard knows it, so don't fall for that humble stuff.
Clark Gable

5 Tracy's formula is — get there on time, know the jokes, say them the best way you can, take the money and get home by six o'clock.
Clark Gable. Quoted David Niven, BRING ON THE EMPTY HORSES 1975

6 He's like an old oak tree or the summer, or the wind. He belongs to the era when men were men.
Katherine Hepburn

7 I think that Spencer always thought that acting was a rather silly way for a man to make a living.
Ibid.

8 Spencer Tracy gave me a jarring insight into his great personal problem. 'What's this?' he asked, pointing to the dessert. 'It looks like trifle,' I said. He sniffed at a spoonful like a bird-dog. 'There's something in it. What is it?' 'A touch of rum, I think,' I said. He pushed his plate away. 'That's all I need', he said. 'One mouthful of that and I'd be gone for a week. I'm not kidding. I have to fight it all the time. I'm a real alcoholic and that little bit would start me off.'
David Niven, BRING ON THE EMPTY HORSES 1975

SIR HERBERT BEERBOHM TREE

Born 1853. English actor-manager, who had a major influence on the theatre and on the leading actors of his day. Managed Her Majesty's Theatre, London, from 1897 until his death in 1917.

9 Returning an appallingly bad play submitted by some amateur, he wrote 'My dear sir, I have only just now found time to read your play. My dear sir!'
Cecil Beaton, DIARY 13 *Jul* 1944

10 At a rehearsal Tree, directing, said 'Now, ladies — a little more virginity.'
Ibid.

11 When asked why he had turned down *Peter Pan* — one of those nightmare miscalculations that make West End managers run mad — he said 'God knows — and I have promised to tell no one else.'
Madeleine Bingham, THE GREAT LOVER: THE LIFE AND ART OF HERBERT BEERBOHM TREE 1979

12 Long runs made him so fidgety that he would hand round boiled lobster or a dead rabbit to stir things up on the stage. Once when playing Mephistopheles to Henry Ainley's Faust, he had Faust's cup screwed to the table so that Aînley was forced to lap up his wine like a dog.
Ibid.

13 He founded RADA. 'A cross beween a whitebait and a rabbit' was his infuriating advice to a young actor pondering how to interpret his part.
Ibid.

14 What people still remember best about Tree is his love of spectacular staging — playing Shakespeare on horseback, or in an oak wood with real rabbits, or an English country garden faithfully copied from photos in *Country Life*.
Ibid.

1 Funny without being vulgar.
W. S. Gilbert, of Tree's Hamlet

2 He did not know the ABC of his profession. He only knew the XYZ.
Hesketh Pearson, BERNARD SHAW 1942

3 Tree did not know what a stage manager was, just as he did not know what an author was. He had not even made up his mind too definitely what an actor was.
G. B. Shaw. Quoted Hesketh Pearson, BERNARD SHAW 1942

LEON TROTSKY

Born 1879 in Russia. Original name Lev Davidovich Bronstein. Russian revolutionary, organiser of the Red Army during the Civil War 1918–20. After Lenin's death in 1924 opposed Stalin and was exiled to Mexico, where he organised the Fourth Communist International; dedicated to world revolution until assassinated in 1940.

4 Exile before 1917 was Trotsky's way of preparing for history; exile after 1929 left him playing at history. Finally there was nothing but what amounted to a suspended sentence of death.
Max Beloff, Daily Telegraph 25 *Oct* 1963

5 In the early days of the revolution Trotsky used to come to the theatre. From box or circle he would wave his fists and shout contemptuously at the audience: 'The blood of the people is running in the gutters, and you, you thickheads and vulgarians, you lower yourselves to listen to the stupidities that a pack of rotten actors spit at you.'
Feodor Chaliapin, MAN AND MASK: FORTY YEARS IN THE LIFE OF A SINGER 1932

6 In the first Russian revolution of 1917 banishment to Siberia was abolished, with the abolition of Tsardom; but later the Bolsheviks revived it and now Trotsky himself, successor to the power of the Tsar, goes out to exile, to a lonely village on the Chinese border.
Children's Newspaper 4 *Feb* 1928

7 Isadora Duncan stopped at a peasant's cottage to have tea. To her great surprise she found that the peasants were Trotsky's father and mother, living on black bread and tea in the poorest conditions. Amazed, she said 'I cannot believe your great son would allow you to live and suffer like this'. 'Our son is the cause of it,' they said. 'He believes in this Communism with his whole heart and soul, and his parents are no more to him than any other comrades. There must be plenty for all or suffering for all — the common lot.'
Mary Desti, ISADORA DUNCAN'S END 1929

8 There are many who would sigh with relief if he supplanted Joseph Stalin. Such a happening might rapidly change the course of history.
Juan Ricci, Daily Sketch 20 *Jan* 1940

9 He writes for the American Press, adds chapter after chapter to his great history. Winston Churchill said Trotsky was the best paid writer in the English language.
Ibid.

10 Lenin supplied the guide-lines of policy; Trotsky improvised brilliantly to meet each changing situation.
Paul Winterton, News Chronicle 27 *Mar* 1940

11 He was completely ruthless. In the task of destroying those whom he regarded as the enemies of the people he showed no more mercy than Robespierre or Marat. He not merely used terrorism as a weapon — long after the Revolution he wrote a book defending its use.
Ibid.

12 That his end should have been a violent one is not remarkable. The remarkable thing is that he lived so long.
Ibid.

HARRY S. TRUMAN

Born 1884. American politician. Became president in 1945 on the death of F. D. Roosevelt. Re-elected in 1948. Authorised the dropping of atomic bombs on Japan. Died 1972.

13 The captain with the mighty heart.
Dean Acheson, PRESENT AT THE CREATION 1970

14 Truman seemed to stand for nothing more than honesty in war contracting, which was like standing for virtue in Hollywood, or adequate rainfall in the Middle East.
George E. Allen, PRESIDENTS WHO HAVE KNOWN ME

15 Truman fiddles while Byrnes roams.
Geoffrey Madan, NOTEBOOK 1946

16 Truman is short, square, simple, and looks one straight in the face.
Harold Nicolson, DIARIES 8 *Aug* 1945

1 What took his countrymen and the world by surprise was his remarkable capacity to grow in office, and in directions that were not to be foreseen in his background and experience.
The Times, Obituary 27 *Dec* 1972

2 He started writing to Bess, his childhood sweetheart, in the early 1900s and continued until well after he retired as President. He wrote to her every day they were apart which was often — Bess hated Washington life — and the letters give fascinating glimpses of a man who worried about money, his health (he hated going to the dentist), cars, and not getting enough sleep.
TV Times 20 *Oct* 1984

3 The President's salty language was a bone of contention. He was known to slip a 'hell' or 'damn' into his public utterances, causing quite a furore, unlike most Presidents, who only cursed privately. Mrs Truman was forever saying, 'You shouldn't have said that'. A story that made the rounds had a famous woman Democrat rushing to the White House to plead with Mrs Truman to have Harry clean up his language. It seemed he'd called someone's statements 'a bunch of horse manure'. Unruffled, Bessie Truman is said to have smilingly replied, 'You don't know how many years it took to tone it down to that.'
J. B. West, UPSTAIRS AT THE WHITE HOUSE 1974

U

PETER (ALEXANDER) USTINOV

Born 1921 in London of Russian parents. English actor, author, playwright and script-writer. Wrote his first successful play, with encouragement from James Agate, when he was 19. While serving in the Army during the war acted in, and, in collaboration with Eric Ambler, wrote the script for *The Way Ahead*. Won Academy awards for his performance in *Topkapi* and *Spartacus*.

1 His large pale face is set with intelligent eyes. When he ambles about the room I am reminded of a performing hippo walking on its hind legs. But as a conversationalist he is as mercurial as any Harlequin.
Lesley Blanch, Leader 8 *Dec* 1945

2 He had lunch with Harold Macmillan to discuss his book on Russia. This enabled him to perfect, from original sources, his Macmillian imitation. The clue, he said, was to talk as though you had a cathedral in your mouth.
Maureen Cleave, Observer magazine

3 Being of extravagantly mixed descent, keenly curious about human affairs and very clever, he knows no limits of language, geography or intellect. He suits every requirement, fits every bill. He can narrate 'Peter and the Wolf' in Danish, prepare a German television programme about national anthems, and produce Massenet's 'Don Quichotte' in French.
Ibid.

4 The performer was a giant black man. He danced a kind of ceremonial ritual . . . His body had been dusted with asbestos powder and at the climax of the dance he set fire to himself. Flames seemed to leap up from every portion of his lanky body until the loincloth was a cinder and what remained of it dropped to the floor. On the evening Noël [Coward] witnessed this doubtful divertissement the fiery dancer came so near his table he shrank back in feigned alarm.

'Is there no *limit*,' he cried 'to the talents of Peter Ustinov?'
William Marchant, THE PRIVILEGE OF HIS COMPANY 1980

MAURICE UTRILLO

Born 1883 in France. Artist known particularly for his Parisian street scenes. Died 1955.

5 Maurice began life with his unmarried mother and his unmarried grandmother in a Paris garret. His mother took up art. The Glaxo age had not arrived. When his mother was busy and her baby boy bawled, grandmother soothed him with strong red wine. By the time he was 10 he had a thirst like a rowing blue's and a liver like a sponge.
Stephen and Ethel Longstreet, MAN OF MONTMARTRE 1959

6 Often friends would lock him in a room. When he screamed for drink they promised him a bottle of wine for each completed picture. On to the canvas he spread white coolness while his head burned and throbbed.
Robert Pitman, Sunday Express 22 *Mar* 1959

7 The cruel sport of Montmarte was Utrillo-baiting; teasing the idiot who ran about exposing himself ('I paint with it') and who collapsed in the gutter each dawn. He eventually worked from postcards — which scandalised many critics — because he was not to be trusted on the streets.
Wendy Roche, Observer 11 *Dec* 1983

8 After an alcoholic breakdown at 18 his mother, Suzanne Valadon, taught him to paint in an effort to save his sanity. His reputation and wealth soon grew. But still he drank — fuel alcohol, eau-de-cologne, anything — and his pathetic life was a succession of internments in asylums and prison with Valadon in distraught pursuit.
Ibid.

V

RUDOLPH VALENTINO

Born 1895 in Italy. Real name Rodolpho d'Antonguolla. Actor, went to Hollywood and gained a world-wide reputation as the first great screen lover, in the era of silent films. Played romantic roles in early classics including *The Four Horsemen of the Apocalypse*, 1921, *The Sheik*, 1921 and *Blood and Sand*, 1922. Died suddenly, 1926.

1 I watched him on the screen and I couldn't see any technique at all.
Gary Cooper, WELL, IT WAS THIS WAY 1958

2 Valentino silently acted out the fantasies of women all over the world. Valentino and his world were a dream. A whole generation of females wanted to ride off into a sandy paradise with him. At thirteen I had been such a female.
Bette Davis, THE LONELY LIFE 1963

3 He had the acting talents of the average wardrobe.
Clyde Jeavons and Jeremy Pascall, A PICTORIAL HISTORY OF SEX IN THE MOVIES

RALPH VAUGHAN WILLIAMS

Born 1872. English composer. Wrote nine symphonies, including *London Symphony*, and many other orchestral works. Died 1958.

4 With all his big and shaggy grandeur, there was also a little of the sprite in him. I remember well the adorable remark he made to his wife Ursula when they acquired the house in Hanover Terrace, and he was in his early eighties. She said 'I'm afraid we can only get a twenty-year lease', to which he replied 'Never mind, my dear, we can renew it.'
John Barbirolli, Sunday Times 15 *Nov* 1964

5 He had an insatiable curiosity about any possibility of utilising instruments not currently in use, one might say, in the classic armoury. I remember, for instance, when he was criticised for using the vibraphone in his Eighth Symphony; he said to me, with that marvellous twinkle in his eye: 'Why not, John? It makes a lovely noise.'
Ibid.

6 The first performance of his song cycle, 'On Wenlock Edge' was given at our Cambridge music club, over the fish shop in Petty Cury. He came to hear it and in my mind's eye I can still see his tweed-clad figure sitting modestly in front with the splendid head that so interested Epstein.
Sir Arthur Bliss. Quoted Henry Raynor, Daily Telegraph 29 *Jul* 1961

7 At one of the Leith festivals he was taking the chorus through a final rehearsal of the St Matthew Passion. His wrath increased with every bar until at length he shut his score with a bang. Wiping his brow he shouted, 'You will never be able to sing Bach! Never!' . . . There was a chilling silence. Then he opened his score again, barked out, 'Bar forty-two!' and continued the rehearsal. The chorus sang with a new voice. At the end he said quietly, 'Why couldn't you sing like that at first?'
Basil Maine, Morning Post 8 *Aug* 1930

8 I don't know whether I like it, but it is what I meant.
R. Vaughan Williams of his Fourth Symphony. Quoted Sir Adrian Boult on BBC 1 *Aug* 1965

9 Although a declared agnostic, he was able all his life to set to music words in the accepted terms of Christian revelation as if they meant as much to him as they must have meant to George Herbert or John Bunyan.
Ursula Vaughan Williams, R.V.W. A BIOGRAPHY OF RALPH VAUGHAN WILLIAMS 1964

(RICHARD HORATIO) EDGAR WALLACE

Born 1875. English author and playwright. Wrote mainly crime thrillers, and became famous for his prolific output, and the speed at which he wrote. He was working on the film script of *King Kong* when he died suddenly in 1932.

1 Telephone message from Edgar Wallace. 'That you, Pound old cock? About your '*Who I Am*' series. I wish I could join in. Sorry I can't. You see, I'm a bastard.'
Reginald Pound, THEIR MOODS AND MINE 1937

2 Went to see Edgar Wallace at Wyndham's Theatre where he was rehearsing his new play *Smoky Cell*. He had his hat on and his cigarette holder was more freakishly long than usual. The last time I saw him he gave me his advice on how to run a family. 'Don't let 'em get too much in your foreground, old cock. Keep 'em where they belong, at home. Your work comes first. I've always had a regular understanding about that with my lot.' So when he rose from his place in the stalls this time he said: 'Well old cock, have you taken my advice to your bosom? You'll be a damn fool if you don't.'
Ibid.

SIR WILLIAM (TURNER) WALTON

Born 1902. English composer. First came to attention with *Façade*, a musical setting of poems by Edith Sitwell. Wrote symphonies, oratorios, and film scores. Died 1983.

3 It is his exceptional musical energy, its passionate exuberance, what Laurence Olivier called its 'gutsiness' that so puzzles those who meet the man who composes it. When he talks he stays behind a curtain of self-deprecation, peering out as if he viewed all that goes on with amused tolerance. He does not talk about music. He talks about gardening.
Caroline Moorehead, The Times 29 *Mar* 1982

4 One day when my brother Sacheverell came to visit me he mentioned, I remember, the sole redeeming point of Oxford for him; that he had met in a — as it seemed to him — leaden city, the only English musical genius it had been his lot to encounter, a boy of sixteen called W. T. Walton.
Osbert Sitwell, LAUGHTER IN THE NEXT ROOM 1949

5 Dr Strong, Dean of Christ Church for many years, had been so greatly impressed by the evident musical talent of this young boy from Oldham, who was in the Cathedral Choir School, that he obtained a modification in his favour of the rule governing the qualifying age, so that Walton should be able to enter Christ Church as an undergraduate at an early age. Walton was said, no doubt erroneously, to be in consequence the youngest member of the University since the reign of Henry VIII.
Ibid.

6 William Walton was staying with us (in Amalfi). He spent most of the time by himself in a room containing a typical South Italian piano — similar to those upon which, as you pass beneath in the street of a southern Catholic city, you hear young girls practising, high up, from iron-barred convent windows. Here he would sit composing and copying out at a large table facing a window on the cloister the whiteness of which in the sun filled the smoky air with a redoubled and spectral light. He would hardly move except to go to the window-ledge from time to time, where he would cut a Toscana cigar in two with a safety-razor blade he kept for the purpose. He smoked these half-cigars almost always as he wrote.
Ibid.

7 His mother told me that he could sing bits from the *Messiah* before he could talk.
Ibid.

8 In all probability it was his long training in the Cathedral Choir which developed his natural talent for choral music, such as for *Belshazzar's Feast*, and for the setting of words, as so brilliantly evinced in *Façade*.
Ibid.

9 Walton wrote *Belshazzar's Feast* in that barn out there. He made such a frightful din on

the piano we had to banish him from the house.
Sacheverell Sitwell. Quoted Alan Hamilton, The Times, Profile 16 *Nov* 1982

ANDY WARHOL

Born 1930. American artist and film director. Controversial exponent of pop art, innovator of new techniques and experimenter in exploiting familiar objects, such as tins of soup.

1 The most famous living artist in America is Andy Warhol, unfortunately.
John Heilpern, Observer 16 *Dec* 1979

2 Andy doesn't actually seem to do anything. Furthermore, he is such a mild-mannered man, as meek as a priest, that it doesn't seem right that he should.
Ibid.

3 Warhol's art belongs less to the history of painting than the history of publicity.
Hilton Kramer, art critic. Quoted John Heilpern, Observer 16 *Dec* 1979

4 About 1959 his paintings of rows of repeated Campbell's soup cans, dollar bills, trading stamps, typewriters, telephones, Marilyn Monroe, and Dick Tracy heralded the start of a new movement called Pop Art, which, as Warhol exemplified it, was impersonal, was frequently reproduced in quantity like industrial goods, was often executed by studio assistants, and was significant in legitimising commercial products as subject matter.
Charles Van Doren, editor of WEBSTER'S AMERICAN BIOGRAPHIES 1974

EVELYN (ARTHUR ST JOHN) WAUGH

Born 1903. English author who excelled in black humour and satire. Author of *Decline and Fall*, 1928, and *Brideshead Revisited*, 1945. Died 1966.

5 On my first day at St Cyprian's, a day school in Hampstead the bullies descended on me, led by a boy who wore green tweed knickerbockers. He stood on his toes and slowly thrust his face with a diabolical stare, closer and closer to mine until the eyes converged into one enormous Cyclops nightmare. The tortures that followed were devilish in their invention, conducted under expert leadership. The boy had a name that became better known later. It was Evelyn Waugh.
Cecil Beaton, DIARIES 1922–1939

6 I flattered Evelyn by taking him around the precincts and photographing him in every conceivable posture. Then, to show how versatile I was, I bade him sit still while I made a crayon sketch of him. I knew that Evelyn, sitting back, pot-belly proffered, was peering with incredibly bright popping eyes and vivisectionist's knowledge, awaiting like a tiger the opportunity to tear me to shreds. But I was never off guard. When he saw the result of the sitting he exclaimed 'Oh that's cheating! Anyone can do a passable drawing with a red pencil.'
Cecil Beaton, DIARY 1949

7 Evelyn Waugh's recent visit to Hollywood was unique in many respects. His expenses were paid in full as a pure gamble by MGM, who wanted to film his *Brideshead Revisited*, but felt that basic changes in the story were essential. Waugh listened stolidly to their pleas, flatly refused to allow the changes, and the whole project went up in smoke. A critic called him 'the most self-assured and unmoveable Briton who ever visited California'.
Bennett Cerf, SHAKE WELL BEFORE USING 1948

8 *Decline and Fall* is the book of which one critic said 'It has the desperate jauntiness of an orchestra fiddling away for dear life on a sinking ship.' Connoisseurs remember it lovingly for one priceless sentence that might be called the epitome of British humour: 'Meet my daughter', said the bishop, with some disgust.
Bennett Cerf, TRY AND STOP ME 1947

9 Evelyn Waugh, alias Mr Wu. I never know — is he good, trying to be wicked? Or just wicked, trying to be nice? He looks like a ventriloquist's doll, with his shiny nose; I feel his ideals are measured by publisher's royalties. He told me today that anyone could write a novel, given six weeks, pen, paper and no telephone or wife.
Sir Henry Channon, DIARY 16 *Dec* 1934

10 I am reading an advance copy of Evelyn Waugh's new novel, *Brideshead Revisited*. It is obvious that the mis-en-scène is Madresfield and the hero Hugh Lygon. In fact all the Beauchamp family figure in it.
Ibid. 25 *Apr* 1945

11 I expect you know my friend, Evelyn Waugh, who, like you, your Holiness, is a Roman Catholic.
Randolph Churchill Jnr in audience with the Pope

1 A writer's old age can be very strange. Sometimes it is like his books; Evelyn Waugh, who made such fun of Apthorpe's 'thunderbox', died in the WC.
Graham Greene, The Times, letter 25 *Jan* 1982

ARCHIBALD PERCIVAL WAVELL, FIRST EARL WAVELL

Born 1883. British soldier. Commander-in-Chief, Middle East, 1939–41. Defeated the Italians in North Africa. Viceroy of India 1943–7. Died 1950.

2 When Wavell rightly decided to evacuate Somaliland, and carried out a brilliant retreat, Churchill complained that his casualties had been too light. Wavell sent him a telegram which said, 'Butchery is not the mark of a good tactician', and that was the end of him.
Lord Boothby, RECOLLECTIONS OF A REBEL 1978

3 A very cosy evening, with the beam of history on that house (The Embassy, Cairo) and I alone with Wavell for an hour and a half. He seemed surprised when I told him how famous he was at home, and that a grateful Nation would no doubt present him with a second Blenheim. 'I hope not' he laughed and when I said he was a second Nelson (a foolish remark) he retorted 'Why? Because I have only one eye?'
Sir Henry Channon, DIARY 4 *Jan* 1941

4 He is like his photographs, grey, gracious and smiling, but is alleged to be more silent than Coolidge. He has a queer expression due to having only one eye and sometimes does not focus accurately.
Ibid.

5 He has a grandeur of character and genius which is transcendent. It is his detachment and long sudden silences which disturb and worry people.
Sir Henry Channon, DIARY 2 *Aug* 1943

6 For all his erudition he is childish and ignorant in some ways.
Ibid.

7 His one eye had an uncanny way of seeing through one's weaknesses. He remained in some ways a simple soldier, and would talk of 'billets', but his humour overflowed, though it was of the acrostic kind. He could do the *Times* crossword in 20 minutes.
Ibid. 26 *May* 1950

8 I do not understand his intellect. It may be my own fault, but I always feel in the presence of the chairman of a golf club.
Winston Churchill. Quoted Lord Butler, THE ART OF THE POSSIBLE 1971

BEATRICE WEBB

Born 1859 née Potter. Wife of Sidney Webb, with whom she collaborated in writing books on politics and economics. Died 1943.

9 It was said that only one person knew as much about everything as Sidney Webb — and that was Mrs Sidney Webb.
John Mather, Daily Express 14 *Oct* 1947

10 When a man said to Beatrice Webb, 'Much of this talk about feminism is nonsense; any woman would rather be beautiful than clever,' she replied, 'Quite true. But that is because so many men are stupid and so few are blind.'
Ibid.

11 Cold, commanding, too often right to be pleasant.
Hesketh Pearson, BERNARD SHAW 1942

12 Wispy, untidy, drab, with a stain on her skirt and a key on her watch-chain.
Virginia Woolf, DIARY 1925–30

SIDNEY (JAMES) WEBB, BARON PASSFIELD

Born 1859. English economist. With his wife Beatrice was instrumental in the creation of the Fabian Society. Died 1947.

13 Socialism will die of sheer boredom. Sidney Webb and people of that kind forget they have to deal with human beings.
Dean Inge. Quoted John Mather, Daily Express 14 *Oct* 1947

14 It was Sidney Webb who gave the British Labour Movement its most lasting slogan — which anybody is entitled to think has been dropped recently — 'the inevitability of gradualness'.
Ibid.

15 Lenin is said to have learned his English by reading the works of Sidney Webb.
News Chronicle 1 *May* 1943

16 His head down, talking rapidly with a slight lisp, imparting volumes of information.
Hesketh Pearson, BERNARD SHAW 1942

1 He was apt to be bored by women, especially by sentimental or temperamental women and by professional beauties; they don't interest him and he resents their claims to admiration and attention.
Beatrice Webb, OUR PARTNERSHIP

2 With his big head, bulgy eyes, bushy moustache and close-cut beard (which gained him the name of 'Nannie' in the House of Commons), small but rotund body, tapering legs and diminutive hands and feet, he lends himself to the cubist treatment of the ridiculous.
Ibid.

(CICELY) VERONICA WEDGWOOD

Born 1910. English historian. Her work includes popular studies of the 17th century, among them *Oliver Cromwell*, 1939; *The King's Peace*, 1955; *The King's War*, 1959.

3 She has gone on her way without a qualm, writing readable history for mass consumption without once asking, let alone answering, any question which modern scholarship would think relevant.
John Kenyon, HISTORY MEN

4 She has championed 'How' history as against 'Why' history, pleading on behalf of 'Romantic impetus' in historical enquiry, flowing story-telling, readability, pace and colour.
Marina Warner, The Times, Return of the history woman 4 *Jul* 1984

(GEORGE) ORSON WELLES

Born 1915. American actor, writer, director, producer for the stage, cinema and radio. In 1934 caused widespread panic in America with the realism of his radio play *The War of the Worlds*, which convinced many listeners that Earth had been invaded by Martians. Of his films, *Citizen Kane*, 1941 and *The Third Man*, 1949 are probably the most enduring. Died 1985.

5 'Cartoonist, Actor, Poet — and Only Ten.' So ran a headline in a Wisconsin paper thirty-five years ago. It referred to a phenomenal child who could 'talk like a cultured adult' at the age of two, made his stage debut at three, was a practised painter and magician at eight, and at ten created a small-town *furore* with a production of *Androcles and the Lion* in which he played both the Lion and Androcles. This was young Orson.
Lindsay Anderson, Radio Times 11 *Mar* 1960

6 Mrs Campbell was in good form castigating Orson Welles's production of *Julius Caesar*. 'They have no reverence, these boys. They speak the lines as if they have written them themselves. Mr Welles's Brutus is like an obstetrician who very seriously visits a lady in order to placate her nerves.'
Cecil Beaton, DIARY 1938

7 An active loafer, a wise madman.
Jean Cocteau. Quoted Leslie Halliwell, THE FILMGOER'S BOOK OF QUOTES 1978

8 Orson Welles once lectured in a small Middle-Western town before a sparse audience. He began with a brief sketch of his career: 'I'm a director of plays, a producer of plays. I'm an actor of the stage and motion pictures. I'm a writer and producer of motion pictures. I write, direct and act on the radio. I'm a magician and painter. I've published books. I play the violin and the piano'. At this point he paused and surveyed his audience, saying 'It's a pity there's so many of me and so few of you.'
Edmund Fuller, ANECDOTES 1942

9 He could not, either by temperament or ability, make the films Hollywood wanted. The years following *The Magnificent Ambersons* saw an amassment of unfinished projects and haphazard wanderings over Europe, with flashes of acting genius in between. Paul Holt called him 'the oldest *enfant terrible* in the world'.
Leslie Halliwell, THE FILMGOER'S BOOK OF QUOTES 1978

10 By the sixties he was encased in make-up and his own fat, like a huge operatic version of W. C. Fields.
Pauline Kael. Quoted Leslie Halliwell, THE FILMGOER'S BOOK OF QUOTES 1978

11 The sad thing is that he has consistently put his very real talents to the task of glorifying his imaginary genius.
John Simon. Quoted ibid.

12 He is 51 and one of the few famous people who don't look like anybody else. Most well-pictured people are disappointing in the flesh. They're either smaller, spottier, uglier, older, fatter. Mr Welles plays Orson Welles like it was Cinerama.
Sunday Times 26 *Feb* 1967

H. G. (HERBERT GEORGE) WELLS

Born 1866. English writer who first attracted attention with highly imaginative and original science-fiction short stories, then went on to novels of social commentary, and works popularising science and history. Died 1946.

1 Some of Wells's early books did really help me to think, although I have no use for his materialism. As a social 'reformer' his real aim is to bring more love and sympathy into the world and there I am with him. On the question of means, I differ. He seems to believe that it can be done by science. I do not. There would be very little flick in the ideal Socialist State as planned by him. His Utopias are always peopled with a swarm of budding Wells's who think as he does himself.
J. D. Beresford, letter to Reginald Pound. Quoted THEIR MOODS AND MINE 1937

2 H. G. Wells spoke in Boston one evening and later attended a reception at the home of the mayor. When he left he took the mayor's hat by mistake, and didn't discover his error until he reached Buffalo. He toyed with the idea of returning the hat, but after admiring himself in the mirror decided to send the following note: 'Dear Mr Mayor, I'm afraid I've got your hat. I like it so much that I propose to keep it. I shall long remember you, your madeira, and your fine, hospitable city. I take off your hat to you sir. Sincerely, H. G. Wells.'
Bennett Cerf, SHAKE WELL BEFORE USING 1948

3 I like Wells, he is so warm, such a passionate declaimer or reasoner or whatever you like. But ugh — he hurts me. He always seems to be looking at life as a cold and hungry little boy in the street stares at a shop where there is hot pork.
D. H. Lawrence, letter to A. D. McLeod Apr 1913

4 The despair of H. G. Wells who saw, at the very end of his life, the ruin of everything in which he had so ardently believed, was the despair of the 'progressive' mind, dumbfounded by the failure of man's attempt to prove that he is self-sufficient.
J. B. Morton, John o' London's Weekly 30 *Mar* 1951

5 I doubt whether in the whole course of our history, any one individual has explored as many avenues, turned over so many stones, ventured along so many *culs-de-sac*. Science, history, politics, all were within his compass; it was Mr Polly at the top of his bent — Polly Agonistes.
Malcolm Muggeridge, Observer 11 *Sep* 1966

6 A by-product of Wells's Fabian experience was the discovery that progressive girls made spirited bed-fellows, and had the advantage, by contrast with his previous somewhat squalid encounters in this field, of being respectfully disposed, hygienic and free of charge.
Ibid.

7 At a Nevinson party I set eyes on H. G. Wells, tittering with a languid girl who afterwards said, 'Oh dear, I thought he was Edgar Wallace.'
Reginald Pound, THEIR MOODS AND MINE 1937

MAE WEST

Born 1892. American stage and film actress who became famous for playing comedy roles exploiting sexual innuendo. Died 1980.

8 In a non-permissive age, she made remarkable inroads against the taboos of her day, and did so without even lowering her neckline. Indeed her most effective moment may have been in a scene in which she drove a funfair crowd wild with a dance that did nothing but tease. As she disappears into the tent, she wraps up years of experience, enjoyment and disapproval of the sex war into one word: 'Suckers!'
Leslie Halliwell, THE FILMGOER'S BOOK OF QUOTES 1978

9 She stole everything but the cameras.
George Raft

10 By making sex a shared joke, she defused the subject of much of its offensive power — though clearly not enough for many people in the 1920s and 1930s, when she was constantly the target of outraged moralists even while she fortunately remained the darling of the public.
The Times, Obituary 24 *Nov* 1980

11 She had become the world's shorthand for the idea of sex, a living embodiment of the dangerous truth that sex could be profitable and sex could be fun.
Ibid.

REBECCA WEST

Born 1892 in Ireland. Pen-name of Dame Cecily Isabel Fairfield, literary critic and author of biographies and psychological novels. Died 1983.

1 In New York for a visit, Rebecca West was confronted by a well-known boulevardier and his young friend. Although they are several inches apart in height these two Beau Brummels affect identical suits, shirts, cravats and haircuts. 'My God,' commented Miss West, 'they look like a nest of tables.'
Bennett Cerf, SHAKE WELL BEFORE USING 1948

2 This magnificent creature with the wonderful forehead, the wide-set, deep-seeing eyes, the surprisingly, enchantingly high-pitched voice, discourses slowly and with exquisite precision upon the follies, vanities, obliquities, nobilities and beauties of mankind.
Edward Crankshaw, Observer, Obituary 20 *Mar* 1983

3 Miss West sent H. G. Wells an ultimatum. He must choose. Either he could leave Jane and marry her, go on living with her, with a guarantee of £3000 a year; or say goodbye. She knew that the last was the only possible choice.
Norman and Jeanne Mackenzie, THE TIME TRAVELLER: THE LIFE OF H. G. WELLS 1973

4 In appearance she is small and provocative, a lovely naughty child, with her flashing gipsy eyes and her shining black hair. There is always a sort of mockery in her eyes and about her mouth. In spite of my positive reactions to people I have never been able to make up my mind what sort of person she really is. Admiring her in so many ways, her looks, her wit, her intellect, her vivacity, I wish I knew her really well — but she is not easy to know, and she appears to dislike more people than she likes.
Ethel Mannin, CONFESSIONS AND IMPRESSIONS 1930

5 Dame Rebecca West, 84 this Christmas, was in coruscating form lunching at the Ritz last week. Summing up another great lady of her vintage (who had better remain anonymous) she observed: 'She looks at you as if you're a washing machine which has broken down.'
Sunday Times 21 *Nov* 1976

6 She regarded me as a piece of fiction — like one of her novels — that she could edit and improve.
Anthony West (her son), HERITAGE 1984

EDITH (NEWBOLD) WHARTON

Born 1862, née Jones. American author of novels depicting New York society. Died 1937.

7 Like her friend Henry James she was an American who spent a lot of her time in Europe, and, like him, she was interested in the patterns of behaviour or schemes of moral judgment which are sometimes set up as concealments or expressions of powerful emotion.
Anne Barnes, The Times 9 *Jul* 1983

8 Edith Wharton, author of *Ethan Frome*, was what some people would call a first-rate snob. She explained that 'only eight people in New York were worth dining with' and therefore had only eight chairs in her dining room. She was taken aback, however, when she learned that Mrs William Waldorf Astor had referred to her as 'that Bohemian'.
Bennett Cerf, TRY AND STOP ME 1947

9 She represented the twentieth-century viewpoint that art could be combined with the mobility which wealth confers, with going everywhere and seeing everything, with knowing everyone, collecting furniture and owning beautiful houses.
Cyril Connolly, Observer 28 *Aug* 1966

10 The Angel of Devastation.
Henry James

11 She pushes her people out over the rapids like so many Blondins. The reader watches their every sway; and is never allowed to forget the long drop down.
Michael Ratcliffe

REX WHISTLER

Born 1905. English painter, book illustrator, stage designer. Among his mural designs, the best known are at the Tate Gallery. Died 1944.

12 Rex, so romantic with his luminous face, Roman nose, and large crown to his head, exudes warm-heartedness and sympathy, but he is a strangely remote person. I doubt if many people even impinge on his inner feelings.
Cecil Beaton, DIARY *Aug* 1928

13 Rex Whistler has arrived to stay for a few days. Elegant, vague, gentle and strange, like an exquisite goat, he is a delightful satyr and full of charm. His newly-grown moustache lends him a French air. He is in

the Welsh Guards, and is in charge of a tank. Anyone more unsuitable, I cannot imagine.
Sir Henry Channon, DIARY 2 *Mar* 1942

ELLEN WILKINSON

Born 1892. English Labour politician. Elected member of parliament for Middlesbrough, 1924, and Jarrow, 1931. Minister for Education, 1931. Died 1947.

1 Ellen Wilkinson had a funny, rather amusing impertinence in her voice and movements. I always felt that I should want to shout 'carrots' after her. Not because of the colour of her hair, it's something of her mentality that comes through. She always reminded me of another old saying: 'Ginger for pluck'. She had that quality developed very fully.
Naomi Jacob, ME — A CHRONICLE ABOUT OTHER PEOPLE 1933

2 Churchill picked her to look after the people in the bomb shelters. During the worst nights of the blitz she was to be found in the middle of it, cheering the people in the shelters, moving about all over the place, from the church crypts to the pubs, where I have seen her sink a pint with the fire-fighters during a break in the blitz.
Ian Mackay, News Chronicle 7 *Feb* 1947

3 She was always in trouble, breaking her skull in a car crash one year, and her leg in an air crash the next, and hardly ever free from some ailment or other during her latter years. But all the while she was living intensely and leaving her impression on the life of her time.
Ibid.

4 Shrewd: a thin determined mouth, keen eyes, and a gorgeous whirl of red hair through which she occasionally runs a tiny hand with a gesture irresistibly reminiscent of — Tallulah Bankhead.
Ethel Mannin, CONFESSIONS AND IMPRESSIONS 1930

5 Perhaps it is because she is so tiny one gets the impression of concentrated energy stored up in her like an electrically charged battery. It is almost as if one can see the flame of life burning in her. With her tiny, eager face and that mass of waving shining hair. She is rather lovely and she looks ridiculously young.
Ibid.

6 I had dinner with Ellen Wilkinson at the House of Commons. She is one of the six women in England, apart from the professional writing classes, whose names jump into the mind when we editorial people want a woman to adorn our columns on some not wholly frivolous topic.
Reginald Pound, THEIR MOODS AND MINE 1937

CHARLES (WALTER STANSBY) WILLIAMS

Born 1886. Joined the Oxford University Press in 1908. A novelist, poet, playwright and critic, he wrote in a highly original style of religious fantasy and symbolism. Died 1945.

7 In the presence of this man I felt myself transformed into a person who was incapable of doing anything base or unloving.
W. H. Auden. Quoted Alice Mary Hadfield, CHARLES WILLIAMS: AN EXPLORATION OF HIS LIFE AND WORK 1984

8 He was a saint of a man. It was nothing he particularly did or said, and we never discussed religion. One just felt ten times a better person in his presence.
W. H. Auden. Quoted Roy Perrott, Observer 28 *Jun* 1970

9 He seemed to me to approximate, more nearly than any man I have ever known, to the saint.
T. S. Eliot, The Listener 19 *Dec* 1945

10 I have just read what I think is a really great book, *The Place of the Lion* by Charles Williams. It is based on the Platonic theory of the other world in which the archetypes of all earthly qualities exist; and in the novel these archetypes are sucking our world back. The lion of strength appears in the world and the strength starts going out of houses and things into him. The archetypal butterfly (enormous) appears and all the butterflies in the world fly back into him. But every man contains and ought to be able to rule these forces; and there is one man in the book who does. It is not only a most exciting fantasy, but a deeply religious and (unobtrusively) a profoundly learned book.
C. S. Lewis, letter to Arthur Greeves 26 *Feb* 1936

11 He is of humble origin (there are still traces of Cockney in his voice), ugly as a chimpanzee, but so radiant (he emanates more love than any man I have ever known) that as soon as he begins talking he is transfigured and looks like an angel. He

sweeps some people quite off their feet and has many disciples. Women find him so attractive that if he were a bad man he could do what he liked, either as a Don Juan or as a charlatan.
Ibid.

SHIRLEY WILLIAMS

Born 1930, née Shirley Catlin, daughter of Vera Brittain, author of *Testament of Youth*. English politician. Entered parliament as Labour member for Hitchin 1964. Held various posts before resigning from the party to become one of the founders of the Social Democratic Party, 1981.

1 You'll never get on in politics dear, with *that* hair.
Lady Astor to Shirley Williams. Quoted John Cole, Observer, The acceptable face of socialism 30 *Nov* 1980

2 We were waiting for Shirley — late as usual. She blew in at last in the same crumpled white frock that she had been wearing all day, her hair uncombed.
Barbara Castle, THE CASTLE DIARIES 1974–76 1980

3 Her nature cast her as the happy warrior of British politics.
John Cole, Observer 30 *Nov* 1980

4 She is famously, perpetually late, so late that slightly exasperated civil servants in ministries where she has worked talk of 'Greenwich' time and 'Shirley' time.
The Times 22 *Nov* 1976

5 Shirley Williams has such an advantage over Margaret Thatcher because she's a member of the upper-middle class and can achieve that distraught kitchen-sink-revolutionary look that one cannot get unless one's been to a really good school.
Dame Rebecca West, on her 83rd birthday in an interview with Jilly Cooper

TENNESSEE (THOMAS LANIER) WILLIAMS

Born 1911. American playwright. His best-known works are *The Glass Menagerie*, 1945, *A Streetcar Named Desire*, 1947, *Cat on a Hot Tin Roof*, 1955 and *Night of the Iguana*, 1961. Died 1983.

6 Tennessee is 34, a terrific Rodinesque character of force and vitality and a great writer of poetic prose. After luncheon he retired to his room and began another play. This evening, in the House, when I told Beverley Baxter about my weekend guest, he said it was like entertaining Shakespeare.
Sir Henry Channon, DIARY 27 *Jun* 1945

7 You have to go steadily back in time to find his landmarks. *The Night of the Iguana* was his last successful play, in 1961. For nearly forty years his career went downhill, for the last 25 pretty steeply. And yet his reputation never really faded.
Robert Cushman, Observer 27 *Feb* 1983

8 Williams was a fully-paid-up paranoid. Kenneth Tynan has left an affectionate portrait of Williams preparing to meet Ernest Hemingway. ('They tell me that Mr Hemingway usually kicks people like me in the crotch.')
Ibid.

9 Williams had always had talents for melodrama and farce; some of his later work became unconsciously farcical as the melodrama jumped out of control.
Ibid.

10 His first success was the autobiographical *The Glass Menagerie*. The young heroine's cherished glass animals were part of Williams's and his sister's own past. They stand for the bright, vulnerable creatures who go through all his plays, subjected to increasingly harsh pressures.
Ibid.

11 His appearance and personality are, perhaps, wilfully enigmatic. He would be at home amid the debris of a Mexican fiesta — a small, round brown pottery image with half-closed eyes and a sleepy smile, entangled with paper flowers and grinning marzipan skulls.
Observer, Profile 26 *Jan* 1958

12 He has a great mistrust of comfort, both physical and spiritual. 'Don't look forward to the day you stop suffering,' he once said. 'Because when it comes you'll *know* you're dead.'
Ibid.

13 He finds it easier to communicate with strangers than friends. He can talk across the footlights but not across the table.
Ibid.

HENRY WILLIAMSON

Born 1895. English author. His novel *Tarka the Otter* won the Hawthornden Prize in 1927. His later years, from 1950 onwards, were occupied with a highly ambitious fifteen-volume sequence called *A Chronicle of Ancient Sunlight*, following the course of life of his hero Phillip Maddison. Died 1977.

1 Mr Williamson almost turned himself into an otter before he knew enough of Tarka to write about him. And he is so sensitive to the beauty of the English language and so unsatisfied with his work that Tarka was endlessly revised, being practically rewritten seventeen times.
Children's Newspaper 7 *Jul* 1928

2 He was bitter about his brief contact with the newspaper life. He had a few weeks at Carmelite House, as a reporter. 'It was ghastly. They tried to kill me at the roots. I escaped with just enough of my branches to keep me going.' He was given the job of finding someone to sign an article on 'Will side-whiskers return?' In his distress he turned to Dr Macnamara at the Ministry of Labour, whom he had met once. The Minister nodded towards some figures, running into millions, on a chart covering one side of the room 'Do you see those? They show the number of men out of work, many of them in despair, men who until a little time ago were breaking the Hindenburg line and are now breaking their hearts. And you, who were one of them, come to me with the question, Will side-whiskers return?' Henry said, very humbly, 'I understand. There'll be one more on that list next week, sir.' He took train for Devonshire, sick of everything. He found a cottage, not much more than a shed from his description of it, for £5 a year and with less than a quarter's rent in hand started to live his precarious writing life.
Reginald Pound, THEIR MOODS AND MINE 1937

3 His childhood, by his accounts of it, was a deep and lasting laceration of his being and perhaps all childhood is painful to him by association. He speaks of his children less with tenderness than with an objective appreciation, as if they are friendly little animals.
Ibid.

4 I'm beginning my series of war novels, like a chain of Dartmoor tors, soon. I can't rest. The fever will drive me to an early grave. Yet I hate writing. I hoped for some companionship in this life, but my sort fights alone.
Henry Williamson, letter to Reginald Pound

(JAMES) HAROLD WILSON, LORD WILSON OF RIEVELAUX

Born 1916. British politician. Elected leader of the Labour Party in succession to Gaitskell 1963. Prime Minister 1964–70 and 1974–6.

5 He may deliberate for ages on a matter of principle, but once he has made up his mind there is nothing on earth which will induce him to reveal his decision.
Anon., Punch 10 *Jan* 1973

6 If ever Harold Wilson went to school without his boots it was because he was too big for them.
Ivor Bulmer-Thomas, speech at Conservative Conference 1949

7 I think he has been taking comfort in his brandy again.
Barbara Castle, DIARY 1974–76 1984

8 Somebody once said in a very biting leading article that Harold Wilson can't nominate peers because the only person he knows intimately is his driver.
Richard Crossman, DIARIES 20 *Dec* 1968

9 I was standing in the gents and who should come in but Harold Wilson. He had come up [to Oxford] for the degree-giving to see his son Robin, the one who is a mathematical genius. Harold was looking 10 years younger, his hair rather untidy, all that pontifical statesmanship off him, nice and fresh just as I knew him before, and I thought 'How different he is when he is not the PM, but just the father of that boy.'
Richard Crossman, DIARIES 1 *Nov* 1969

10 He is such an impersonal person. You can't feel that you could ever be really close friends with him, or in fact that he would ever have close friends.
Hugh Gaitskell, DIARY 1945–1956 1983

11 Of the Queen's relationship with Wilson a member of the outer Royal circle remarked: 'Funny, really; the Royals will often get on famously with a bit of a rum cove. Attraction of opposites, I suppose.'
Alan Hamilton

12 He is not fit to lead the Labour Party because he thinks the split over disarmament is not an important issue.
Denis Healey. Quoted Caroline Moorehead, The Times 17 *Mar* 1975

1 He had given, for a time, a tremendously effective impression, which turned out on closer inspection to be only activity.
Bernard Levin, THE PENDULUM YEARS 1976

2 'I can't forgive Harold Wilson,' said Enoch Powell, 'for spoiling my opinion of the Emperor Diocletian.' It seems that the emperor had withdrawn into private life at the height of his power, an action Mr Powell greatly admired until Harold Wilson followed suit.
John Mortimer, IN CHARACTER 1983

3 He always looks as though he were on the verge of being found out.
Dame Rebecca West, in an interview by Frederick Raphael, Radio Times 28 *Oct* 1978

(THOMAS) WOODROW WILSON

Born 1856. President of the United States 1913–21. It was largely his initiative, and his Fourteen Points plan, that led to the setting up of the League of Nations, but the United States refused to join it, and he died a disappointed man in 1924.

4 There is a famous Washington story that Mrs Wilson had declared 'When Woodrow proposed to me I was so surprised that I nearly fell out of bed.'
Sir Henry Channon, DIARY 1 *Jul* 1943

5 The action of the United States in the First World War depended upon the workings of this man's mind and spirit to the exclusion of almost every other factor.
Winston Churchill, WORLD CRISIS 1929

6 The spacious philanthropy which he exhaled upon Europe stopped quite sharply at the coasts of his own country.
Ibid.

7 He was like a nonconformist minister, perhaps a Presbyterian. His thought and his temperament were essentially theological, not intellectual.
J. M. Keynes, ECONOMIC CONSEQUENCES OF THE PEACE 1919

8 All the time he spoke he stood looking straight in front of him, with his hands behind his back. He looked terribly tired. I gathered afterwards that he scarcely had time to sleep, that often he would be up all night trying to unravel the hopeless tangle of lies and evasions which was almost daily served up to him.
Beverley Nichols, TWENTY-FIVE 1926

9 He made a mistake in coming to Europe with a poor staff, and a worse mistake in coming without his opponents, Elihu Root and Taft for example. Instead he left them in American to conspire against him, and they used the tragedy of Europe for their political ends.
General Smuts. Quoted Sarah Gertrude Millin, SMUTS 1938

WALLIS WARFIELD, DUCHESS OF WINDSOR

Born 1896 in America. Her association with Edward VIII led to his abdication in 1936. She married him in 1937.

10 Mrs Simpson: half governess, half *earwig*.
Cyril Asquith. Quoted Geoffrey Madan, NOTEBOOKS 1981

11 At Somerset Maugham's Christmas Day party in the South of France in 1936, just after Edward VIII's abdication, the ex-king's girl friend, Mrs Simpson, joined them in a game of bridge during which Maugham apologised to his partner because he only had two kings. 'What's the use of them?' cracked Mrs Simpson. 'They only abdicate.'
Lord Boothby, RECOLLECTIONS OF A REBEL 1978

12 Hark the Herald Angels sing/Mrs Simpson's pinched our king.
Children's street song 1936

13 Lunched with Emerald [Cunard] to meet Mrs Simpson. She is a nice, quiet, well-bred mouse of a woman with large startled eyes and a huge mole. I think she is surprised and rather conscience stricken by her present position and the limelight which consequently falls upon her.
Sir Henry Channon, DIARY 23 *Jan* 1935

14 We went to the Opera and were joined by the Prince of Wales and the Menage Simpson. I was interested to see what an extraordinary hold Mrs Simpson has over the Prince. In the interval she told him to hurry away as he would be late joining the Queen at the LCC Ball — and she made him take a cigar from out of his breast pocket. 'It doesn't look very pretty' she said. He went, but was back in half an hour.
Ibid. 31 *May* 1935

15 The King is Mrs Simpson's absolute slave, and will go nowhere where she is not invited, and she, clever woman, with her high-pitched voice, chic clothes, moles and sense of humour is behaving well. She encourages the king to meet people of importance and

to be polite; above all she makes him happy. The Empire ought to be grateful.
Ibid. 10 *May* 1936

1 Wallis, taking a taxi on her now famous journey to Scotland is reported to have said 'King's Cross'. 'I'm sorry lady' answered the driver.
Ibid. 11 *Nov* 1936

2 Wallis is a very vulgar woman in gesture, she sticks her beautifully scented face within two inches and just asks to be kissed, only of course you don't do it.
Lord Eccles, BY SAFE HAND: LETTERS OF DAVID AND SYBIL ECCLES 1939–42 1983

3 As a royal consort she had every conceivable disadvantage. She was an American — she was a commoner — and truly common at that, not even a millionaire's daughter, let alone an untitled member of an aristocratic family; she had a former husband living — whom she had divorced; and a present husband, Ernest Simpson.
A. J. P. Taylor, ENGLISH HISTORY 1944–1945 1965

ORDE (CHARLES) WINGATE

Born 1903. British soldier. Defeated the Italians in Ethiopia, 1941. Organised the Chindits in guerilla fighting against the Japanese in Burma, 1942. Killed in an air crash, 1944.

4 In spite of a puritan upbringing which left him with a mystical obsession with the Old Testament, Wingate had a disconcerting habit of receiving callers and conducting strategy discussions in the nude. Military colleagues grew accustomed to this in time, but Eliahu Elath, the future Israeli ambassador to the Court of St James, was somewhat flustered to find himself engaged in an intense discussion on Zionism with a completely naked man.
Catherine Caufield, THE EMPEROR OF AMERICA AND OTHER MAGNIFICENT ECCENTRICS 1981

5 He had a special uniform reserved for VIP occasions. It was covered with grease stains and expressed to perfection his disdain for considerations of rank.
Ibid.

6 Wingate maintained that every man should be his own doctor. One of his theories about health in the tropics was that eating half a dozen raw onions a day was the best way to stay fit. Sometimes he ate nothing but onions and grapes for days at a time.
Ibid.

7 Wingate pioneered the use of air mobility within the battlefield. He did not make the mistake, which the Americans made in Vietnam, of confusing air mobility with ground mobility by constantly moving troops around by air once they were committed.
Sir Robert Thompson, foreword to WINGATE IN PEACE AND WAR *(edited by Arthur Swinton)* 1972

SIR P. G. (PELHAM GRENVILLE) WODEHOUSE

Born 1881. English novelist and playwright. Created Jeeves, Bertie Wooster, and Blandings Castle. Collaborated with Guy Bolton in the production of Broadway musicals. Died 1975.

8 His fairy-tale England was sometimes mistaken for the real thing by innocent-minded foreigners, such as the enemy agent who, when dropped in the Fen country during the 1939–45 war, was instantly arrested because he was wearing a pair of Wodehouse-inspired spats.
W. A. Darlington, Daily Telegraph, Obituary 17 *Feb* 1975

9 With my strict socialist childhood Bertie Wooster and Jeeves had about them a flavour of forbidden fruit, like Sade or Casanova in the eyes of a Methodist.
Malcolm Muggeridge, TREAD SOFTLY FOR YOU TREAD ON MY JOKES 1966

10 His mind as an artist had been set in his teens and, superb craftsman though he was, he remained a teenager even in his eighties — and a late Victorian one at that. Boat race night of Mafeking year might be said to be roughly the point at which he came to a standstill.
The Times, Obituary 17 *Feb* 1975

11 The failure of academic literary criticism to take any account of Wodehouse's supreme mastery of the English language or the profound influence he has had on every worthwhile English novelist in the past 50 years demonstrates in better and conciser form than anything else how the Eng. Lit. industry is divorced from the subject it claims to study.
Auberon Waugh, New Statesman 21 *Feb* 1975

1 Shakespeare's characters are as memorable as Wodehouse's, but the latter's plots are much better. I have no difficulty in believing nearly everything in Wodehouse, but I am hard put to it to understand the extraordinary behaviour of Hamlet, *et al.*
Woodrow Wyatt, reviewing WODEHOUSE NUGGETS (*edited by Richard Usborne*), *The Times* 24 *Nov* 1983

2 There are almost as many quotations in Wodehouse as there are in Shakespeare.
Ibid.

SIR HENRY (JOSEPH) WOOD

Born 1869. English conductor. Began the Promenade Concerts in 1895, and conducted them until his death in 1944.

3 Henry Wood conceived his job not as bringing music to the best people, but as bringing the best music to the people.
James Agate, Daily Express 25 *Aug* 1944

4 Old Timber was a national hero, the Churchill of the concert halls, who had kept on conducting our war-wearied orchestras while bombs crashed all round him.
Reginald Pound, SIR HENRY WOOD 1969

5 In 1912 he conducted the British premiere of Schoenberg's Five Pieces for orchestra. 'Stick to it, gentlemen!' he called to the orchestra during rehearsals. 'Stick to it! This is nothing to what you'll have to play in 25 years' time.'
Ibid.

6 He dragged British orchestral music alive out of the abyss.
G. B. Shaw. Quoted Reginald Pound, SIR HENRY WOOD 1969

VIRGINIA (ADELAIDE) WOOLF

Born 1882, née Stephen. English novelist and essayist. A member of the Bloomsbury Group. Her novels attracted attention for their experiments in conveying inner experience. Among them are *Mrs Dalloway*, 1925; *To the Lighthouse*, 1927; *The Waves*, 1931. Died 1941.

7 She left 4,000 letters, 30 volumes of diary, and an inexhaustible supply of literary critics eager to write about her.
John Carey, Sunday Times 11 *Nov* 1984

8 Virginia Woolf is dead, a grey, highly-strung woman of dignity and charm, but she was unstable and often had periods of madness. She led the Bloomsbury movement, did much to make England so Left – yet she always remained a lady, and was never violent. She could not stand human contacts, and people fatigued her.
Sir Henry Channon, DIARY 5 *Apr* 1941

9 I do remember finding Virginia Woolf immensely beautiful and immensely frightening; and one of my *fears* — I don't think I was quite alone in this — was that she would speak to me one day (but she never did).
Hugo Dyson in conversation with Roger Green, BBC Radio Oxford, May 1971

10 I do not believe that she wrote one word of fiction which does not push out boundaries a little way; one book which does not break new ground and form part of the total experiment.
Susan Hill, Daily Telegraph 5 *May* 1974

11 There is nothing of her distinction, charm, and occasional affection and kindness in her diary. She seems neurotic, vain and envious. But it is fascinating none the less.
Harold Nicolson, DIARY 1 *Nov* 1953

12 She was always fussing as to whether the prestige of Bloomsbury was going up or down.
Anthony Powell, Daily Telegraph 22 *Jun* 1984

13 Virginia Woolf herself never got used to the fact that if you write books some people are bound to be rude about them.
Ibid.

14 Virginia Woolf, notably beautiful with a beauty of bone and form and line that belonged to the stars rather than the sun, manifested in her appearance, in spite of the modernity that was clearly there, a Victorian distinction.
Osbert Sitwell, LAUGHTER IN THE NEXT ROOM 1949

15 The novels of Virginia Woolf were greatly esteemed by a small intellectual group and their destruction of the tight narrative frame has influenced later writers. They are irrelevant for the historian.
A. J. P. Taylor, ENGLISH HISTORY 1914–1945 1965

16 Few people can be so tortured by writing as I am. Only Flaubert, I think.
Virginia Woolf, DIARY VOL. 5 1936–1941

ALEXANDER WOOLLCOTT

Born 1887. American author and broadcaster, who became famous on the air as the 'Town Crier'. Was the model for Kaufman and Hart's *The Man Who Came to Dinner*. Died 1943.

1 A Seidlitz Powder in Times Square.
Heywood Broun. Quoted Bennett Cerf, TRY AND STOP ME 1947

2 Woollcott's manners, atrocious to begin with, became progressively worse when he discovered how much people were willing to take from a great celebrity. *The Man Who Came to Dinner* crystallised and enhanced the Woollcott myth a hundredfold; it turned his insults into high comedy, and undoubtedly prevented him from being socked on the jaw at least twice a week.
Bennett Cerf, TRY AND STOP ME 1947

3 He settled down for an indefinite run as the country's most respected dramatic critic, most relentless and feared gossip, and infinitely most accomplished raconteur. All three qualities made a radio career inevitable, and as the 'Town Crier' Woollcott became famous, wealthy and more ruthless and domineering than ever. His social life was unbelievably complicated. He spent weeks at the White House, and told the Roosevelts whom to have to dine with him.
Ibid.

4 He bought an island in Vermont, charged his guests hotel rates, and banished them when they wouldn't play croquet, cribbage or hearts according to his own special rules.
Ibid.

5 Just a New Jersey Nero who mistook his pinafore for a toga.
Edna Ferber. Quoted Bennett Cerf, TRY AND STOP ME 1947

Y

W. B. (WILLIAM BUTLER) YEATS

Born 1865 in Ireland. Poet and dramatist. Helped found the Abbey Theatre. Awarded Nobel Prize for Literature, 1923. Died 1939.

1 Yeats was completely tone deaf and never exhibited any curiosity about music or about myself as a composer.
Arnold Bax, Illustrated 12 *May* 1945

2 When C. S. Lewis met Yeats at Oxford in 1921 he was 'half fascinated and half repelled, and finally the more repelled because of the fascination'.
Humphrey Carpenter, THE INKLINGS 1978

3 Willie Yeats stood for enchantment.
G. K. Chesterton, AUTOBIOGRAPHY

4 I left him in my room to himself and at lunch time he told me had done an excellent morning's work, having written four lines and destroyed them.
John Drinkwater, DISCOVERY

5 The Spanish doctor who treated Yeats in Majorca reported to his Irish colleague 'We have here an antique cardio-sclerotic of advanced years.' Gogarty tried to slur over the death sentence. 'Read it slowly and distinctly,' Yeats ordered. He inclined his head. He followed the cadence with his finger. As the sound died away he exclaimed, 'Do you know, I would rather be
6 called "Cardio-sclerotic" than Lord of Lower Egypt.'
T. R. Henn, THE LONELY TOWER 1965

7 Often there is a 'poltroonery' in Yeats' diction; he cements his lines 'silver-proud' and then pesters them with ramparts, towers, helmets, swords and 'fiery blood'. In offering this phallocentric vision, he imagines an Ireland which appears to be entirely surrounded by semen.
Tom Paulin, Observer 10 *Jun* 1984

8 He drew freely on savage ideas of blood, earth, race, myth. And so there falls across Yeats' imagination always that 'shadow of a gunman' which Sean O'Casey so subversively observed.
Ibid.

9 Yeats is not a man of this world; and when you hurl an enormous, smashing chunk of it at him, he dodges it, small blame to him.
G. B. Shaw, letter to Sean O'Casey. Quoted Eileen O'Casey SEAN 1971

10 His scorn for the modern English and their love of compromise was extreme. 'You know,' he said to me one evening, 'what the Englishman's idea of compromise is? He says, Some people say there is a God. Some people say there is no God. The truth probably lies somewhere between these two statements.'
Wilfred Whitten, John o' London's Weekly 24 *Jun* 1949

Z

SIR BASIL ZAHAROFF

Born 1849 in Turkey. Original name Basileisos Zacharias. Financier who made an immense fortune as a dealer in munitions, supplying both sides during World War I. After the war further enlarged his fortune by investing in the Casino at Monte Carlo. Died 1936.

1 He prospered on death by sowing lies and deceit, by fomenting rumours of war so that nation would bid against nation for the weapons he had to sell. He was the first man to 'cash in big' when Science turned its attention to making slaughter almost automatic.
Horatio Bottomley, John Bull 5 *Dec* 1936

2 A multi-millionaire, the world's Number One Merchant of Death. We shall not — heaven help us! — see his like again.
Ibid.

3 He anticipated the market and extended it by making sure that his customers knew each others' secrets. He sold the armament secrets of nations to their rivals — under a strict pledge of secrecy of course — and then made more millions out of the fear he created.
Ibid.

4 When the First World War broke out he had interests in the French armaments firm of Schneider-Creusot, shipyards in Turkey, shipyards in Russia, big interests in Vickers and partnerships with Krupps.
Paul Brickhill, Sunday Express 18 *Sep* 1949

5 He fomented wars. He unseated kings and posed as a prince himself. But when it was all boiled down he was essentially a super-salesman without a conscience.
Ibid.

6 Millions passed through his hands. Millions stuck to his fingers. He fought vicariously in every major and minor war for half a century. He dictated the government of a dozen countries for a quarter.
Ian Ward, A MERCHANT OF DEATH

7 Zaharoff's life may be an indictment of our political traditions but it is in no sense a personal condemnation. Millions of his contemporaries would have played the same game, had they thought of it and known how.
H. G. Wells

DARRYL F. (FRANCIS) ZANUCK

Born 1902. Film executive who began his career by writing scripts for silent movies for Warner Brothers in 1924, and by 1927 was an executive producer. Left Warners in 1933 to take part in the merger which resulted in the setting up of 20th Century-Fox.

8 Zanuck is Goldwyn without the accent.
Eddie Cantor. Quoted Edmund Fuller, ANECDOTES 1942

9 He couldn't stand stubbornness in anybody but himself.
Mel Gussow, LIFE OF DARRYL F. ZANUCK

10 Goodbye Mr Zanuck; it certainly has been a pleasure working at 16th Century Fox.
Jean Renoir

11 I was on the set with Jolson who was going to sing a song to his mother. Normally the scene would have been sub-titled, but I said, 'As we have a microphone here why not have Jolson turn to his mother and tell her he is going to sing her a song?' We shot it and the synchronisation was perfect. They were the first words spoken on the screen.
Darryl F. Zanuck. Quoted Peter Waymark, The Times 29 *Aug* 1970

FLORENZ ZIEGFELD

Born 1869. American theatrical producer. His Ziegfeld Follies, based on the Folies Bergère, established a new form of American theatrical revue. Died 1932.

12 Nothing irritated Ziegfeld so much as to call him 'the C. B. Cochran of America' and nothing annoys me more than to call me 'the Flo Ziegfeld of England'.
C. B. Cochran, Daily Telegraph 23 *Jul* 1932

1 Ziegfeld went everywhere to find girls for his Follies. They had to be blonde, between 18 and 25 years of age, 5 ft 6 ins in height, 8 st 6 lb in weight, and intelligent. He would examine the girls who applied to him for jobs with the thoroughness of a horse-dealer.
Daily Telegraph, Obituary 23 *Jul* 1932

2 He made a large fortune but he has died poor. Two or three years ago he borrowed a couple of thousand pounds from a friend he met on Fifth Avenue. Instead of applying the money to meeting a pressing emergency he spent £1500 on jewellery for his wife [Billie Burke], flowers for the leading ladies in his show, and making other gifts, which expressed his kindly, though erratic, disposition.
Ibid.

3 As far as Ziegfeld was concerned the only reason anyone came to see any of his revues was to see his girls. Men came to see their bodies and women to see their clothes, if any.
Norman Geddes, MIRACLE IN THE EVENING

4 He squandered money on his productions, his whims, his affectations. He wore imported lavender shirts, went in for 500-word conversations by long-distance telephone, sent to South Africa for baby elephants and often sent special messengers to Baltimore for terrapin.
Ward Morehouse, Theatre Arts *May* 1956

Index

Authors of quotations are referenced by page number followed by the number of the quotation on that page. (The subjects of their quotations are listed in the contents.)

A

Acheson, Dean, 53:14, 54:1, 275:13
Ackerley, J. R., 246:11
Ackroyd, Peter, 121:5, 121:6, 121:7
Adams, Sam Hopkins, 164:5
Adamson, Joe, 180:9
A. F., Radio Times, 37:11
Agate, James, 2:12, 3:1, 3:2, 68:10, 147:13, 221:3, 249:8, 290:3
Aherne, Brian, 104:2
Aitken, Conrad, 129:9
Alanbrooke, Viscount, 84:2
Alexander, Norah, 106:7, 106:8
Alexander, Peter, 243:1
Alexandra, Tsarina, 232:1
Ali, Muhammad, 7:5
Allen, Fred, 113:1, 113:2
Allen, George, 275:14
Allen, Trevor, 113:6, 113:7
Allen, Walter, 4:5, 22:7, 22:8, 22:9, 22:10, 175:1, 181:1, 228:3, 228:4
Allen, William R., 237:4
Amery, L. S., 14:11, 78:10
Amin, Idi, 7:13
Amis, Kingsley, 51:5, 268:13
Amis, Martin, 45:7, 45:8, 158:6, 215:1, 215:2, 229:10, 229:11
Amory, Mark, 152:1, 152:2
Amundsen, Roald, 8:11, 9:1
Anderson, Lindsay, 156:3, 282:5
Anne, Princess, 10:11, 10:12, 10:13, 10:14, 10:15
Anon, 41:6, 99:9, 102:6, 121:8, 177:6, 206:7, 234:3, 268:2, 268:14, 287:5
Anouilh, Jean, 11:4
Ansermet, Ernest, 262:3
Antongini, Tom, 102:10, 102:11, 102:12
Appleyard, Bryan, 11:5, 11:6, 185:2, 185:3
Archer, Lt Col C., 12:1, 12:2
Ardagh, John, 247:10
Arless, Leslie, 203:11
Armour, Richard, 110:9
Armstrong, H. G., 176:1
Arnold, Bruce, 222:1
Arraras, Don Joaquin, 141:1
Ashe, Geoffrey, 179:9
Ashmore, Henry S., 260:5
Ashton, Sir Frederick, 14:5, 225:4
Asquith, Cyril, 183:7, 186:1, 253:7, 288:10
Asquith, H. H., 14:12, 14:13, 30:3, 30:4, 269:6
Asquith, Margot, 55:2, 93:10, 93:11, 99:10, 186:2, 241:6
Asquith, Raymond, 55:3
Astor, Michael, 17:13, 17:14
Astor, Nancy, 17:15, 18:1, 18:2, 286:1
Athenaeum magazine, 124:11
Atherton, Gertrude, 44:14
Atticus, 207:4, 207:5
Attlee, Clement, 18:3, 18:4, 27:5, 52:6, 54:2, 65:8
Auden, John, 22:11
Auden, W. H., 143:1, 285:7, 285:8
Auty, Phyllis, 271:5, 271:6, 271:7, 271:8
Ayer, A. J., 241:9
Ayre, Leslie, 40:5, 245:5
Aza, Bert, 131:7, 131:8

B

Bacall, Lauren, 58:2
Bacon, Admiral Sir Reginald H., 133:1, 133:2
Baden-Powell, Agnes, 202:6
Baden-Powell, Lady Olave, 25:2
Baines, Jocelyn, 91:8
Baird Television Ltd, 25.8
Balanchine, George, 225:5
Baldwin, Margaret, 27:6
Baldwin, Oliver, 27:7, 269:7
Baldwin, Stanley, 14:14, 27:8, 27:9, 84:3, 99:11, 196:7, 196:8, 211:6
Balfour, A. J., 15:1, 159:5
Balogh, Lord, 114:1
Banks-Smith, Nancy, 202:9
Barbirolli, Sir John, 32:12, 183:4, 278:4, 278:5
Barker, Danny, 13:4
Barker, Dudley, 81:7
Barkley, William, 61:8
Barnard, Robert, 83:3, 83:4
Barnes, Anne, 284:7
Barnes, Julian, 213:1
Barnes, Susan, 59:6, 78:11, 161:3, 161:4, 161:5, 161:6
Barrie, J. M., 159:6
Barrymore, John, 37:1, 37:2
Bartlett, Vernon, 20:8, 20:9, 20:10, 20:11, 82:11, 104:12, 114:2, 154:3, 154:4, 154:10, 170:7, 170:8, 170:9, 199:10, 213:11, 213:12, 214:1, 214:2, 234:11, 234:12, 258:5
Baruch, Bernard, 87:5, 87:6
Battiscombe, Georgina, 6:1, 6:2, 6:3, 6:4, 6:5, 6:6, 6:7, 6:8, 6:9 116:3
Bax, Sir Arnold, 38:5, 292:1
Baxter, John, 128:1
Beaton, Cecil, 64:2, 68:11, 69:1, 72:5, 72:6, 72:7, 72:8, 81:3, 81:4, 89:4, 89:5, 89:6, 89:7, 91:2, 93:5, 93:6, 93:12, 93:13, 93:14, 94:1, 95:4, 108:9, 108:10, 108:11, 123:6, 123:7, 126:1, 126:2, 126:3, 148:1, 148.2, 165.8, 167:9, 179.1, 210.2, 220:1, 220:2, 220:3, 220:4, 225:6, 225:7, 226:12, 252:12, 253:11, 253:12, 253:12, 253:13, 254:1, 263:13, 274:9, 274:10, 280:5, 280:6, 282:6, 284:12
Beaverbrook, Lord, 46:7, 196:9, 264:1
Beecham, Sir Thomas, 40:6, 74:10, 76:12, 105:6, 105:7, 252:9, 255:11, 256:1
Beerbohm, Max, 113:8, 249:9, 249:10

Beevers, John, 18:5, 18:6, 18:7, 18:8, 18:9, 202:10
Begin, Menachem, 42:7
Behan, Beatrice, 43:1
Behan, Kathleen, 43:2
Behrman, S. N. 192:8
Bell, Alan, 51:6, 203:6
Bell, Colin, 101:1, 101:2
Bell, Gertrude, 84:4
Bell, Michael, 119:15
Bellow, Saul, 233:5
Beloff, Max, 275:4
Benet, Stephen Vincent, 9:8
Bennett, Alan, 152:3
Bennet, Arnold, 46:8, 120:1, 236:13, 249:11
Bennet, Arthur, 81:8
Benson, A. C., 15:2, 63:8, 173:5, 173:6, 173:7
Benson, E. F., 143:2
Benson, Jackson J., 260:1
Berenson, Bernard, 48:13, 121:9
Beresford, J. D., 283:1
Bergonzi, Bernard, 81:9, 121:10
Bernays, Robert, 15:3, 55:4, 169:3, 169:4
Bernhardt, Sarah, 50:4
Betjeman, John, 51:7, 193:1, 193:2
Bevan, Aneurin, 84:5, 84:6, 84:7, 84:8, 161:7
Beveridge, William, 53:6
Bevin, Ernest, 188:1, 188:2
Bickford, Charles, 106:9
Bingham, Madeleine, 274:11, 274:12, 274:13, 274:14
Binyon, Michael, 145:8
Birkenhead, Earl of, 38:8, 78:12
Birkenhead, Second Earl of, 41:11, 41:12, 55.5, 55:6, 91:9, 104:13, 128:10, 129:1, 129:2, 129:3, 166:11, 166:12, 215:7, 232:2, 246:7, 248:6
Birrell, Augustine, 162:6
Bishop, Sir Frederick, 114:3
Bishop, George W., 3:3
Blake, Lord, 212:3, 212:4
Blake, Owen, 171:11, 171:12, 171:13, 171:14, 232:3
Blake, Robert, 39:1, 39:2, 114:4, 114:5, 114:6, 114:7, 114:8, 114:9, 255:5
Blanch, Lesley, 277:1
Bland, Alexander, 107:14, 107:15, 107:16, 108:1
Blériot, Louis, 56:4
Bliss, Sir Arthur, 120:2, 278:6
Blum, John M., 241:2
Blume, Mary, 167:10
Blunden, Edmund, 57:1
Blunt, Dr Alfred, 116:13
Blunt, William Scawen, 244:9
Blythe, Ronald, 149:11
Bocca, Geoffrey, 18:10, 18:11, 88:6, 88:7, 235:9. 235:10
Bogart, Humphrey, 274:3
Bold, Alan, 71:4, 71:5
Bolitho, Hector, 148:14
Bolt, Robert, 191:10
Bolton, Lorney, 273:9
Bonham Carter, Mark, 15:4, 16:9, 16:10, 16:11
Bonham Carter, Lady Violet, 15:5, 85:5, 162:7, 186:3, 189:4, 197:2
Boothby, Lord, 27:10, 27:11, 27:12, 27:13, 40:7. 40:8. 40:9. 59:7, 59:8, 74:9, 78:13, 78:14, 78:15, 78:16, 84:9, 84:10, 84:11, 84:12, 84:13, 85:1, 85:2, 85:3, 95:5, 97:8, 104:14, 114:10, 120:3, 150:4, 154:11, 163:4, 166:13, 170:10, 170:11, 171:15, 183:5, 190:4, 190:5, 190:6, 196:10, 196:11, 196:11, 196:12, 197:1, 208:13, 240:4, 240:5, 244:1, 281:2, 288:11
Bottomley, Horatio, 59:14, 293:1, 293:2, 293:3
Boult, Sir Adrian, 60:10
Bowen, Elizabeth, 201:9, 201:10, 254:2
Bowles, Paul, 22:12
Boyd-Carpenter, John, 166:6
Bradburg, David, 89:8
Bradbury, Malcolm, 8:3, 8:4, 8:5, 8:6, 45:9
Bradley, Ian, 68:1, 68:2, 68:3, 68:4
Bradley, General Omar, 5:5
Bramstead, Ernest K., 154:5
Brandes, George, 262:13
Brennan, Gerald, 261:8
Brent, Douglas, 153:6, 153:7
Bresler, Fenton, 178:7
Breslin, J., 217:6
Brett, Guy, 238:1
Briant, Keith, 260:11, 261:1
Brickhall, Paul, 293:4, 293:5
Brian, Alan, 43:3, 88:8
Brittain, Vera, 163:11
Brook, Donald, 187:8, 187:9
Brook-Shepherd, Gordon, 168:4
Brooke, Gerald, 262:4
Brooke, Rupert, 134:11
Brooks, Cleanth, 129:10
Brophy, John, 102:13, 102:14
Broun, Heywood, 37:3, 240:6, 291:1
Brousson, Jean Jacques, 140:10, 140:11
Brown, Douglas, 255:6
Brown, Ivor, 12:3, 111:1, 173:8, 219:2, 262:14
Brown, John Mason, 9:9, 249:12
Brownlow, Kevin, 106:10, 152:10
Bruccoli, Matthew J., 133:9
Bryan, J. III, 116:14
Brzezinski, Zbigniew, 74:4, 243:8, 243:9
Buchan, John, 30:5
Buchman, Frank, 171:1
Buckle, Richard, 216:5, 225:8
Bullock, Alan, 171:2
Bulmer-Thomas, Ivor, 287:6
Burgess, Anthony, 4:6, 91:10, 120:4, 133:10, 133:11, 133:12, 133:13, 181:2, 181:3, 230:7, 230:8, 230:9, 230:10, 230:11, 230:12, 260:2
Burgoyne, Elizabeth, 44:4, 44:5, 44:6, 133:3
Burke, Thomas, 109:13, 109:14
Burton, Hal, 234:8, 234:9
Butler, Lord, 27:14, 54:3, 54:4, 79:1, 79:2, 85:4, 114:11, 147:9, 229:2
Byron, Arthur, 51:8

C

Cadogan, Sir Alexander, 110:10
Calder, Ritchie, 117:13, 117:14
Callaghan, James, 68:5, 68:6, 68:7, 138:1
Camber, Melinda, 177:1
Campbell, James, 26:7
Campbell, John, 79:3, 242:5
Campbell, Mrs Patrick, 111:2, 152:11
Campbell, Roy, 255:7
Campbell-Bannerman, H., 30:6
Candy, Edward, 261:2
Cantor, Eddie, 293:8

Capote, Truman, 72:9
Cardus, Neville, 40:10, 40:11, 41:1, 272:10
Carey, John, 93:4, 94:2, 94:3, 290:7
Carlton, David, 114:12
Carnegie, Andrew, 73:2
Carpenter, Humphrey, 193:3, 193:4, 193:5, 193:6, 272:5, 272:6, 292:2
Carson, Edward Henry, 73:9
Carter, Jimmy, 98:10
Carver, Field Marshal Lord, 208:14, 209:1
Castle, Barbara, 68:8, 75:4, 75:5, 75:6, 81:5, 123:8, 178:3, 268:3, 286:2, 287:7
Castlerosse, Lord, 39:3, 39:4, 39:5, 189:5
Caufield, Catherine, 34:4, 34:5, 289:4, 289:5, 289:6
Cecil, Lord David, 16:12, 16:13, 41:13, 193:7
Cecil, Lord Robert, 159:7
Cendrars, Blaise, 124:3
Cerf, Bennett, 12:6, 31:12, 31:13, 37:4, 37:5, 46:9, 50:1, 69:2, 69:3, 81:10, 81:11, 81:12, 87:7, 90:11, 90:12, 92:7, 101:3, 101:4, 101:5, 110:1, 113:3, 116:15, 117:15, 130:10, 132:4, 133:14, 134:1, 134:2, 150:5, 150:6, 150:7, 150:8, 165:9, 165:10, 165:11, 192:9, 192:10, 192:11, 195:3, 204:5, 204:6, 224:4, 227:1, 237:5, 238:8, 239:7, 245:13, 246:1, 249:13, 249:14, 258:12, 258:13, 259:1, 259:2, 259:3, 259:4, 259:5, 260:3, 260:9, 262:5, 270:6, 270:7, 270:8, 270:9, 272:11, 280:7, 280:8, 283:2, 284:1, 284:8, 291:2, 291:3, 291:4
Chacko, Arun, 266:12, 266:13, 266:14, 267:1
Chaliapin, Feodor, 191:11, 275:5
Chamberlain, Neville, 79:4
Chandler, Raymond, 80:6, 80:7, 80:8
Channon, Sir Henry, 16:14, 17:1, 17:2, 19:1, 19:2, 21:1, 25:7, 28:1, 28:2, 28:3, 28:4, 45:1, 52:7, 53:7, 53:8, 54:5, 61:9, 61:10, 67:5, 67:6, 67:7, 67:8, 77:9, 77:10, 79:5, 79:6, 83:5, 85:6, 85:7, 87:2, 93:7, 93:8, 94:5, 94:6, 94:7, 97:9, 98:1, 98:2, 101:6, 104:15, 107:8, 114:13, 115:1, 115:2, 115:3, 115:4, 115:5, 117:1, 117:2, 117:3, 117:4, 123:9, 145:11, 148:15, 148:16, 149:12, 149:13, 151:8, 153:8, 160:8, 163:5, 163:6, 163:7, 171:3, 171:4, 172:1, 175:2, 179:2, 179:3, 185:4 186:4, 190:7, 199:11, 200:4, 200:11, 202:11, 203:1, 204:7, 204:8, 209:6, 209:7, 209:8, 211:7, 219:3, 219:6, 226:7, 235:11, 249:15, 250:1, 261:3, 269:8, 280:9, 280:10, 281:3, 281:4, 281:5, 281:6, 281:7, 284:13, 286:6, 288:4, 288:13, 288:14, 288:15, 289:1. 290:8
Chaplin, Charles, 80:9, 197:11, 203:7, 211:8, 211:9, 216:6, 216:7, 216:8, 223:8, 223:9, 225:9, 227:2, 259:6, 259:7
Chapman, Ernest, 56:7, 56:8
Chapple, Frank, 45:11, 184:9
Chare, Harriet, 217:2, 217:3, 217:4
Charteris, Evan, 244:10, 244:11
Charteris, General J., 142:7
Chasen, David, 58:3
Chesshyre, Robert, 233:6, 233:7, 233:8, 233:9
Chester, Sir Norman, 53:9, 53:10, 53:11, 53:12
Chesterton, G. K., 250:2, 250:3, 292:3
Children's Newspaper, 13:9, 13:10, 25:10, 77:1, 87:8, 162:8, 195:9, 275:6, 287:1
Children's street song, 288:12
Christie, Agatha, 83:6
Church, Richard, 57.2, 103:1
Churchill, Clementine, 85:8, 253:1
Churchill, Randolph Jnr, 280:11
Churchill, Sarah, 61:11
Churchill, Winston, 5:6, 17:3, 21:2, 28:5, 30:7, 52:8, 64:3, 79:7, 79:8, 85:9, 85:10, 98:3, 98:4, 123:10, 137:5, 137:6, 142:8, 142:9, 146:1, 167:15, 168:5, 169:5, 169:6, 171:5, 171:6, 186:5, 191:12, 197:3, 207:12, 240:7, 241:7, 258:6, 264:2, 281:8, 288:5, 288:6
Ciano, Count, 154:12
Clairmont, Leonard, 155:1
Clark, Sir Kenneth, 115:12, 264:3
Clark, Ronald W., 143:3, 143:4
Clark-Kennedy, A. E., 76:6, 76:7, 76:8
Clarke, Tom, 218:9
Clavering, Bruce, 78:1, 78:2, 78:3, 78:4, 78:5, 223:10, 244:7
Clemenceau, Georges, 137:7
Cleave, Maureen, 277:2, 277:3
Clyde, Robert, 226:2, 226:3
Cobb, Irvin, 266:6
Cochran, C. B., 293:12
Cockburn, Claud, 183:8
Cocteau, Jean, 216:9, 282:7
Cohen, Harriet, 252:10, 252:11
Cole, Herbert, 189:1
Cole, John, 286:3
Colebrook, L., 135:2
Coleman, Alex, 262:6
Collier, James Lincoln, 13:5
Collier, Hon John, 125:1
Collins, Dorothy, 81:13, 81:14
Collins, Larry, 212:5
Collins, Norman, 111:11, 112:1, 112:2, 200:5
Collis, Louise, 257:11
Colson, Percy, 205:12
Colvin, Ian, 73:10, 73:11
Compton, Dr Arthur, 118:1
Condon, Leo, 34:13, 34:14
Connolly, Cyril. 12:7, 38:9, 48:14, 48:15, 89:9, 89:10, 99:1, 136:1, 139:13, 146:7, 166:14, 195:4, 195:5, 206:8, 206:9, 261:9, 262:7, 268:15, 284:9
Connor, Sir William, 85:11
Conrad, Joseph, 91:11
Conrad, Mrs Joseph, 91:12
Conrad, Peter, 250:4
Cooke, Alistair, 117:5, 240:8
Cooper, Diana, 171:7
Cooper, Duff, 15:6, 15:7, 15:8, 79:9, 79:10, 85:12, 186:6, 186:7, 197:4, 214:3
Cooper, Gary, 94:11, 278:1
Cooper, Leo, 199:1
Coote, Colin R., 28:6, 28:7, 28:8, 28:9, 28:10. 28:11, 117:6, 250:5, 250:6
Cork, Richard, 264:4
Corker, David, 45:10
Cosgrave, Patrick, 67:9, 229:3, 229:4, 268:4

Cottle, Basil, 158:7
Cotton, Ian, 222:6
Coward Noel, 19:3, 95:6, 108:12, 136:2, 212:6, 239:8
Cowley, Elizabeth, 236:1
Cowley, Malcolm, 195:2
Cox, Geoffrey, 1:1
Cox, Jack, 24:7, 24:8, 24:9, 24:10, 24:11, 25:1
Cox, James B., 172:2
THE CRACK-UP, *Introduction to Penguin edition*, 134:7
Craig, Mary, 179:11
Crankshaw, Edward, 10:9, 77:2, 77:3, 92:1, 225:1, 284:2
Cranston, Maurice, 246:2
Crawford, Joan, 145:1
Crawford, Lord, 183:9
Crosby, Bing, 98:11
Crossman, Richard, 52:9, 52:10, 52:11, 52:12, 52:13, 178:4, 287:8, 287:9
Crowley, Aleister, 182:8, 182:9
Crozier, Brian, 141:2
Cudlipp, Hugh, 9:6, 28:12, 39:6, 39:7, 79:11, 85:13, 85:14
Cukor, George, 96:5, 191:7
Cummings, A. J. 78:6, 78:7, 78:8, 218:10, 235:1, 235:2, 253:8, 256:13
Curran, James, 45:12
Curtis, Tony, 208:3
Curzon, Lord, 28:13, 186:8
Cushman, Robert, 66:2, 286:7, 286:8, 286:9, 286:10
Cute, David, 160:9, 160:10, 160:11

D

Daily Express, 46:1, 60:1, 60:2, 60:3, 60:4, 169:7, 169:8, 216:10
Daily Mirror, 138:2, 138:3, 161:11
Daily Sketch, 69:4, 265:1
Daily Star, 42:8
Daily Telegraph, 25:9, 92:8, 92:9, 106:11, 146:2, 156:4, 160:1, 180:3, 191:2, 191:8, 202:7, 215:4, 223:1, 228:5, 237:6, 261:4, 294:1, 294:2
Daily Worker, 226:8
Dali, Salvador, 101:7, 101:8, 101:9, 101:10
Daniel, John 72:10
Dark, Sidney, 222:2, 222:3
Darlington, W. A., 35:1, 35:2, 35:3, 35:4, 35:5, 35:6, 35:7, 126:4, 126:5, 289:8
Davenport, John, 195:6
Davidson, Eric, 249:4
Davidson, Jo, 147:10
Davie, Michael, 161:1, 161:2, 164:6, 164:7, 164:8, 164:9, 177:7
Davies, W. H., 64:4
Davis, Bette, 104:3, 104:4, 104:5, 104:6, 104:7, 278:2
Davis, Kenneth C., 195:10
Day, Philip, 4:7
De Beauvoir, Simone, 33:9
Dehn, Paul, 232:8
Dell, Edward, T., 193:8
Delmer, Sefton, 94:8, 129:4, 129:5
De Mille, William, 106:12
Denning, Vere, 128:2
Dent, Alan, 37:10, 235:3
Desti, Mary, 112:3, 275:7
De Valois, Ninette, 108:2
Devlin, Tim, 51:9
Diaghilev, Serge, 108:3
Diamant, Dora, 182:1
Dick, Kay, 4:8, 4:9
Digilio, Don, 7:6
Dilkes, David, 99:12, 99:13
Dinnage, Rosemary, 143:5, 143:6
Djilas, Milovan, 271:9, 271:10
Dodd, Ken, 268:5
Dodd, William, 155:2
Dondero, George, A., 101:11
Dos Passos, John, 110:2
Douglas, James, 95:7
Douglas-Home, Sir Alec, 2:2, 104:17, 105:1, 184:1
Downie, R. Angus, 141:6, 141:7, 141:8
Drennan, Robert, E., 130:11
Drinkwater, John, 292:4
Duder, Lewis, 192:5
Dugdale, Blanche, E., 30:8, 30:9
Du Maurier, Daphne, 111:3, 111:4, 111:5
Du Maurier, Sir Gerald, 95:8
Dumesnil, M., 112:4
Duncan, Irma, 112:5
Duncan, Isadora, 113:9
Duncan, Ronald, 63:11
Dundee, Angelo, 7:7
Dunn, Peter, 75:7, 75:8, 75:9
Dunne, P., 141:3
Duse, Eleanora, 113:10
Dyson, Hugo, 290:9

E

E. B., T. P.'s Weekly, 195:8
Eccles, Lord, 289:2
Eckman, Fern Marja, 27:1
Eden, Sir Anthony, 79:12
Edinger, George, 216:11
Edwards, Helen, 103:10, 103:11
Edwards, Oliver, 110:3
Einstein, Albert, 118:2, 118:3
Eisenhower, Dwight D., 5:7, 110:11, 209:2
Eisenhower, Mamie, 118:14
Elgar, Sir Edward, 120:5, 120:6, 245:6
Eliot, Sir John, 137:8, 160:2
Eliot, T.S., 228:6, 285:9
Eliot, Walter, 19:4
Elizabeth, Queen, the Queen Mother, 74:5
Ellis, Alice Thomas, 143:11
Ellis, Keith, 115:13
Ellman, Richard, 181:4
Elwin, Malcolm, 92:2
Empson, William, 121:11, 121:12
Enright, D.J., 62:9, 62:10, 182:2
Epstein, Jacob, 125:2
Ervine, St John, 264:7
Esher, Lord, 15:9
Evening Standard, 235:12
Everyman, 256:2
Ewart, Gavin, 203:8, 203:9

F

Fadiman, Clifton, 129:11
Fairlie, James, 35:8
Faulkner, John, 129:12
Fay, Stephen, 43:4
Fenton, Eric, 105:8, 105:9, 105:10, 105:11, 105:12
Fenton, James, 40:1, 40:2, 66:3, 69:5, 246:3
Ferber, Edna, 130:12, 130:13, 291:5
Ferris, Paul, 66:4, 66:5
Feuchtwanger, Lion, 137:9
Field, Michael, 209:9
Fisher, H. A. L., 99:14
Fisher, John, 74:11, 75:1, 75:2
Fisher, Admiral Lord, 162:9, 178:1
Fishlock, Trevor, 147:4
Fitzgerald, C. P., 202:4

Fitzgerald, F. Scott, 9:11, 134:3, 156:5
Fitzroy, Sir Almeric, 197:5
Flanagan, Bud, 226:9
Fleming, Alexander, 135:3
Flossenburg, camp doctor at, 58:13
Floyd, David, 184:2, 271:11
Flynn, Errol, 136:12
Flynn, John T., 237:7
Foch, Marshal, 87:9, 137:10
Foot, Dingle, 232:9
Foot, Michael, 21:3, 52:14, 53:1, 147:5, 230:13, 266:1, 269:9
Fonteyn, Margot, 220:5, 220:6, 225:10
Ford, Henry, 116:1, 139:1
Forster, E. M., 91:3, 92:3, 224:1
Forsyth, Frederick, 196:4
Foster, T., 9:2
Fouquet, Gaetan, 265:2
Fraenkel, Heinrich, 154:7, 154:8, 168:9
Frank, Hans, 171:8
Fraser, Antonia, 34:6, 34:7
Freed, Arthur, 205:3
Freedland, Michael, 180:10
Freeman, D. S., 1:2
Freud, Sigmund, 143:7
Frith, J. B., 30:10, 55:7, 235:13, 235:14
Frost, David, 229:5
Frost, Robert, 143:13, 143:14
Fulford, Roger, 6:10, 116:4, 116:5, 116:6
Fuller, Edmund, 35:9, 35:10, 37:6, 80:10, 92:10, 92:11, 92:12, 103:2, 107:9, 116:2, 137:11, 137:12, 150:9, 150:10, 155:3, 157:10, 163:12, 185:5, 227:3, 227:4, 238:9, 238:10, 239:1, 245:7, 248:7, 273:1, 273:2, 282:8
Fuller, John, 189:8
Furbank, P. N., 139:14, 228:7
Fyfe, Hamilton, 35:11, 35:12, 35:13, 56:5

G

Gable, Clark, 274:4, 274:5
Gaitskell, Hugh, 287:10
Galbraith, J. K., 240:9
Galsworthy, John, 189:9
Garbo, Greta, 148:3
Gardner, Ava, 145:2
Gaudier-Brzeska, Henri, 124:12
Gavin, J. L., 55:8
Geddes, Diana, 33:10, 33:11
Geddes, Norman, 294:3
Gelb, Arthur and Barbara, 221:8, 221:9
Gelhorn, Martha, 166:15
George V, King, 6:11
Geyelin, Philip L., 180:4
Gielgud, John, 17:4, 35:14, 37:7, 66:6, 69:6, 69:7, 69:8, 69:9, 69:10, 95:9, 111:6, 111:7, 111:8, 126:6, 126:7, 126:8, 126:9, 153:4, 221:4, 221:5, 223:2, 223:3, 246:12, 267:4, 267:5, 267:6, 267:7, 267:8, 270:1, 270:2, 270:3, 270:4, 270:5
Gilbert, W. S., 275:1
Gilette, George Francis, 118:4
Gill, Brendan, 31:14, 31:15, 31:16, 32:1, 32:2, 32:3, 32:4, 111:9
Gish, Lillian, 148:4, 148:5, 153:1
Giudice, Gaspare, 227:13, 227:14
Glanville, Brian, 66:12
Glyn, Elinor, 153:9, 153:10, 153:11, 153:12
Gogarty, Oliver St John, 55:10
Gold, Herb, 182:10
Golding, Louis, 125:3
Goldman, Albert, 229:12, 229:13
Goldwyn, Sam, 227:8
Goodwin, General Sir Richard, 7:14
Gorer, Geoffrey, 141:9
Gosse, Edmund, 134:12, 162:10
Gradidge, Roderick, 198:1
Graham, Billy, 106:13, 217:7, 217:8, 233:10
Graham, Sheila, 96:6, 134:4, 233:11, 266:7
Graham, Stephen, 157:3
Granville, Lord, 116:7
Graves, Richard Perceval, 173:9
Graves, Robert, 23:1, 79:13, 250:7, 261:10, 261:11, 261:12
Gray, Simon, 8:7, 8:8, 8:9
Green, A. Wigfall, 130:9
Green, Benny, 13:6
Green, Cyril Harry, 131:9, 131:10
Green, David, 61:12
Green, Geoffrey, 67:1
Green, H. F. D., 151:1, 151:2
Green, O. M., 82:12
Greene, David H., 264:8
Greene, Graham, 17:10, 106:14, 107:1, 124:8, 148:6, 165:4, 187:5, 281:1
Greenspun, Hank, 174:8
Grenfell, Joyce, 19:5, 19:6, 126:10
Grey of Fallodon, Viscount, 159:8
Grey, Lita, 80:11
Griffin, Gerald, 103:3
Grigson, Geoffrey, 164:1, 238:2, 269:1
Grimond, Jo, 162:11
Gris, Henri, 87:3
Gross, John, 45:2, 65:9, 65:10
Grosvenor, Pete, 151:3
Guardian, The, 138:13
Guinness, Jonathan and Catherine, 207:6
Gunther, John, 240:10, 247:11
Gussow, Mel, 293:9

H

Haffner, Sebastian, 2:1
Haig, Earl, 160:3
Haldane, J. B. S., 118:5, 118:6, 161:12
Haldane, Lord, 160:4
Hale, Lionel, 273:3, 273:4, 273:5
Haley, William, 19:7
Halifax, Lord, 79:14, 154:6, 155:4
Hall, John, 168:1
Hall, Malcolm Macalister, 33:12, 33:13, 33:14, 33:15
Hall, Ruth, 261:5
Halliwell, Leslie, 10:3, 10:4, 32:5, 37:8, 37:9, 107:2, 109:2, 132:5, 132:6, 156:6, 169:10, 169:11, 170:1, 188:6, 205:4, 205:5, 249:1, 265:6, 282:9, 283:8
Hamilton, Alan, 123:11, 123:12, 123:13, 123:14, 221:6, 221:7, 287:11
Hamilton, Ian, 43:7, 43:8
Hamilton, Mary Agnes, 58:10, 58:11
Hammerton, J. A., 228:1, 228:2, 232:4
Hammond, Percy, 32:6
Hancock, W. K., 255:8
Handley, Vernon, 60:11
Hardie, Keir, 148:17

Hardwicke, Cedric, 250:8
Hardy, Barbara, 140:1
Hardy, Robert, 66:7
Harriman, Margaret, Case, 32:7
Harris, Kenneth, 21:4, 21:5, 21:6, 21:7
Harrison, Rosina, 19:8, 19:9
Hart, James D., 10:1
Hart, Moss, 10:5
Harvey, Anthony, 167:11
Hassall, Christopher, 64:5, 254:3
Hastings, Ronald, 206:1
Hatch, Robert, 80:12
Hathaway, Henry, 208:4
Hawkes, Howard, 58:4
Hayman, Ronald, 62:11
Heald, Tim, 59:9
Healey, Denis, 174:3, 180:12, 287:12
Hecht, Ben, 10:2
Heenan, Cardinal John, 179:10
Heikal, Mohammed, 243:10
Heilpern, John, 280:1, 280:2
Hemingway, Ernest, 108:13, 130:1, 194:3, 194:4, 228:8, 228:9, 259:8
Hemingway, Leicester, 167:1
Henderson, Sir Nevile, 155:5
Henderson, Nicholas, 54:6, 54:7, 54:8, 67:10, 67:11
Hendrick, Burton J., 73:3
Henn, T. R., 292:5
Hepburn, Katherine, 167:12, 274:6, 274:7
Heren, Louis, 172:8
Heseltine, Philip, 105:13, 106:1
Hess, Stephen, 217:10, 217:11
Hewins, Ralph, 151:4
Hewitt-Myring, Philip, 172:3
Heyworth, Peter, 186:13, 187:1
Hickey, William, 135:4, 135:5, 135:6
Higham, Charles, 187:6, 188:7
Hill, Ralph, 120:7
Hill, Susan, 290:10
Hillary, Sir Edmund, 168:8
Hillcourt, William, 25:2
Hillier, Bevis, 46:10, 200:6
Hillmore, Peter, 46:2
Hillson, Norman, 28:14, 28:15, 28:16, 189:6
Hilton, Isabel, 76:1, 76:2
Hilton, Michael, 65:2
Hiro, Dilip, 184:5
Hitchcock, Alfred, 170:2, 188:8
Hitchcock, Patricia, 170:3
Hitchman, Janet, 246:13, 247:1
Hoban, Russell, 262:8
Hoghe, Alan, 79:13, 250:7
Hodgkin, E. C., 195:11
Hodgson, Geoffrey, 74:7
Hodson, Harold, 206:5, 206:6
Hodson, J. L., 11:11
Hoggart, Richard,23:2
Hohenloe, Prince Franz Joseph, 165:12, 166:1
Hollis, Christopher, 82:1
Hollis, Sir Leslie, 226:10, 226:11
Holloway, David, 57:3, 130:2, 130:3, 131:1, 212:7
Holroyd, Michael, 250:9
Holmes, Richard, 89:11, 89:12, 89:13, 89:14, 89:15, 104:16, 134:5, 143:8, 246:8
Home, Lord, *see* Douglas-Home, Sir Alec
Hoopes, Townsend, 110:12
Hoover, J. Edgar, 184:6
Hopcroft, Arthur, 204:3
Hope, Bob, 74:6, 74:7
Hope, Francis, 257:7, 257:8
Hopkins, Harry, 240:11
Hopkins, Robert, 167:13
Horgan, Paul, 34:8
Hoskins, Percy, 172:9
Houseman, John, 249:2
House of Commons, 19:10
Housman, A. E., 173:10
Housman, Laurence, 173:11, 173:12
Howard, Anthony, 1:3, 1:4, 1:5, 1:6, 183:1
Howard, Michael, 119:1, 119:2, 160:5, 160:6, 239:4, 239:5, 239:6
Howard, Percy, 38:10, 38:11
Howard, Peter, 21:8, 21:9
Howard, Philip, 92:13, 255:3, 255:4
Howarth, David, 176:2, 176:3, 176:4, 176:5, 176:6
Howe, Elspeth, 174:4
Howe, James Wong, 58:5
Hughes, Spike, 273:6
Huntford, Roland, 248:8
Huxley, Aldous, 121:13, 190:8
Huxley, Laura, 175:3
Hyde, H. Montgomery, 28:17, 233:1
Hytier, Jean, 151:9

I

Inge, Dean, 281:13, 281:14
Ingrams, Richard, 82:2
Ionesco, Eugene, 177:2
Isherwood, Christopher, 23:3, 140:2, 201:11
Ismay, Lord, 22:1
Israel, Lee, 32:8

J

Jacob, Naomi, 58:12, 97:1, 97:2, 97:3, 215:11, 285:1
Jacobs, Eric, 138:4
James, Capt, 85:15
James, Clive, 117:17, 161:8, 208:5, 268:6
James, D. Clayton, 199:1
James, Henry, 64:6, 92:4, 284:10
James, Henry Arthur, 250:10
James, Robert Rhodes, 85:16
Jarrell, Randall, 143:15
Jean, Marcel, 101:12
Jeavons, Clyde, 165:5, 278:3
Jeffs, Rae, 43:5, 43:6
Jenkins, Peter, 46:3
Jenkins, Roy, 17:5, 30:11, 30:12, 30:13, 54:9, 54:10, 75:10, 163:8, 163:9, 163:10, 183:10, 245:1
Jenkinson, Philip, 132:7, 132:8, 132:9
Jennings, Paul, 33:1, 61:1, 61:2
Jewell, Derek, 98:12, 124:4, 230:1
John, Romilly, 179:4, 179:5
John o'London's Weekly, 44:7, 44:8, 103:4, 112:6, 158:2, 263:1, 263:2
Johnson, Lyndon, 172:10
Johnson, Pamela Hansford, 50:5, 267:9
Johnson, Paul, 57:5, 57:6, 57:7, 75:11, 75:12, 268:7
Johnston, Alva, 156:7, 156:8, 156:9, 156:10, 156:11, 156:12, 157:1, 157:2
Joll, James, 155:6, 155:7, 155:8
Jones, Thomas, 65:11, 85:17
Joyce, James, 181:5

K

Kael, Pauline, 107:3, 282:10
Kafka, Franz, 182:3
Kalisch, Alfred, 106:2
Kane, Walter, 174:9
Kavanagh, Julie, 14:6, 14:7
Keats, John, 224:5, 224:6
Keegan, John, 105:2
Kelly, Gene, 17:11
Kemenov, V., 227:5
Kemp, Peter, 141:4
Kempton, Murray, 119:3
Kendall, Captain H. K., 97:4, 97:5, 97:6, 97:7
Kennedy, Dominic, 230:2, 230:3
Kennedy, John Fitzgerald, 217:9, 260:6
Kennedy, Ludovic, 59:10
Kennedy, Michael, 120:8
Kenner, Hugh, 121:14
Kennet, Lord, 248:9
Kenyon, John, 282:3
Kenyon, Nicholas, 61:3
Keynes, John Maynard, 87:10, 183:11 288:7
Kihm, Jean-Jacques, 90:1
King, Cecil Harmsworth, 166:2
Kinross, Lord, 20:12, 20:13
Kissinger, Henry, 147:6, 185:9, 185:10, 202:5, 243:11
Kitchener, Lord, 15:10, 117:8
Knight, Hadden, 236:14, 237:1, 237:2
Knipe, Michael, 174:10
Knox, Ronald, 82:3, 187:3
Koestler, Arthur, 222:7, 241:10
Kohl, Helmut, 268:8
Kolodin, Irving, 247:4
Konody, P. G., 222:2, 222:3
Korda, Alexander, 188:9
Koss, Stephen, 15:11
Kramer, Hilton, 280:3
Kramer, Stanley, 58:6
Krebs, Albin, 212:8
Kretzmer, Herbert, 7:8, 148:7

L

Lacey, Robert, 123:15, 148:18, 203:2
Laing, Margaret, 166:7
Lake, Geoffrey, 180:11
Lamb, Felicia, 224:2
Lambert, Constant, 181:6
Lambert, J. W., 221:10, 254:4, 254:5
Lancaster, Osbert, 86:1
Lancken-Wackenitz, Baron van der, 76:9
Lane, Margaret, 162:1, 224:7
Lange, Eitel, 155:9, 155:10, 155:11
Lapierre, Dominique, 212:5
Larkin, Philip, 13:7, 51:10, 51:11, 62:3
Larson, Arthur, 119:4
Laski, Harold, 155:12
Laski, Marghanita, 118:7
Lasky, Jesse Jnr, 107:4, 107:5
Laver, James, 3:4, 3:5
Law, A. Bonar, 15:12, 214:4
Lawrence, D. H., 4:10, 189:10, 283:3
Laws, Frederick, 121:15
Leader, The, 130:2, 139:3
Leaska, Mitchell A., 243:2, 243:3
Leasor, James, 168:6
Leavis, F. R., 228:10, 256:7
Lee, Jennie, 53:2, 146:3, 146:4
Lee, Laurie, 191:3, 191:4
Lees-Milne, James, 95:10
Legge, Robin H., 222:4
Legum, Colin, 22:2, 22:3, 42:9, 42:10
Lejeune, C. A., 128:3
Leni, Lore, 266:8, 266:9, 266:10
Lennon, Cynthia, 192:6, 192:7
Lennon, Peter, 170:4, 170:5, 170:6
Levin, Bernard, 151:5, 184:10, 200:12, 213:2, 229:6, 256:8, 288:1
Levy, Paul, 49:1
Lewis, C. S., 51:12, 189:11, 272:7, 272:8, 272:9, 285:10, 285:11
Lewis, David L., 184:7
Lewis, Percy Wyndham, 23:4, 121:16, 228:11, 250:11, 250:12
Lewis, Russell, 151:6
Liddell, Hart, B. H. 5:8, 142:10
Life magazine, 11:1, 148:8
Lindsay, Sir Martin, 248:10
Lippman, Walter, 92:14
Livingston, Arthur, 103:5, 103:6
Lloyd, Selwyn, 5:9
Lloyd George, David, 29:1, 55:9, 79:7, 99:15, 241:8, 244:2
Lockhart, R. H. Bruce, 155:13
London Mercury, 124:10
Long, Gavin, 199:2, 199:3
Longford, Elizabeth, 7:1, 7:2, 150:1
Longford, Lord, 59:1, 59:2
Longstreet, Stephen and Ethel, 277:5
Longworth, Alice Roosevelt, 92:15, 164:10
Loos, Anita, 96:7, 145:3, 145:4, 174:11, 197:8, 259:9
Lord, Graham, 59:ll, 171:9
Luce, Clare Boothe, 148:9
Lundquist, James, 195:7
Lustgarten, Edgar, 59:12
Lutz, Hermann, 159:9
Lynch, Arthur, 238:3
Lynd, Robert, 35:15, 77:4, 130:4, 130:5, 130:6, 178:8, 244:3, 248:1
Lynd, Sylvia, 167:2
Lyon, C. A., 25:3, 25:4, 25:5, 25:6
Lysaght, Charles Edward, 62:1
Lyttelton, G. W., 110:13, 189:12

M

McAdoo, Senator William, 164:11
Macaulay, Rose, 140:3, 143:9
MacCarthy, Desmond, 34:9, 95:11
MacCarthy, Mrs Desmond, 199:6
McCooey, Meriel, 205:8, 205:9
McCrystal, Cal, 172:11, 173:1
McDonald, Ian, 173:2, 173:3, 173:4
McDonald, Iverach, 157:4
McEwan, Lady Bridget, 94:9
McFee, William, 131:3
McIlvenney, Hugh, 7:9
MacInnes, Colin, 43:9
MacKay, Ian, 50:2, 285:2, 285:3
MacKenzie, Norman and Jeanne, 284:3
MacKibbin, David, 245:2
Maclean, Fitzroy, 271:12, 272:1
Macleod, Ian, 67:12
Macmillan, Harold, 5:10, 200:13, 221:1

Madan, Geoffrey, 29:2, 46:11, 48:9, 48:10, 86:2, 86:3, 116:8, 149:1, 173:13, 214:5, 217:15, 240:12, 245:3, 275:15
Maddox, Brenda, 265:7, 265:8, 265:9
Mailer, Norman, 7:10, 7:11
Maine, Basil, 38:6, 38:7, 120:9, 278:7
Malcolm, Sir Ian, 87:11
Malcolm X, 184:8
Mallory, Leslie, 137:1, 137:3
Manchester Guardian, The, 98:5
Mancroft, Lord, 227:6
Mann, Anthony, 2:3, 2:4, 2:5
Mann, Thomas, 265:3
Mannin, Ethel, 95:12, 95:13, 95:14, 95:15, 125:4, 125:5, 125:6, 125:7, 125:8, 125:9, 125:10, 164:2, 164:3, 188:3, 188:10, 204:9, 205:1, 216:1, 236:8, 236:9, 236:10, 236:11, 236:12, 241:11, 284:4, 285:4, 285:5
Mansfield, Katherine, 190:1, 201:12
Manvell, Roger, 154:7, 154:8, 168:9
Marchant, William, 277:4
Marder, Arthur J., 133:4
Margach, James, 200:14
Margrave, Seton, 128:4
Marjoribanks, Edward, 73:12, 73:13, 74:1
Marrot, H. V., 146:8, 146:9
Marsh, Edward, 15:13, 34:10, 34:11, 36:1, 55:11, 64:7, 64:8, 77:5, 86:4, 86:5, 86:6, 141:10, 178:2, 190:9, 190:10, 209:10, 219:4, 219:5, 242:1, 247:2, 250:13, 250:14, 269:10, 269:11
Marsh, Richard, 65:3, 65:4, 65:5
Marshall, Beatrice, 157:5
Martin, Sir Alec, 213:6
Martin, Kingsley, 54:11
Marx, Harpo, 192:12
Mary, Queen, 150:2
Masefield, John, 203:10
Mason, James, 203:12
Massie, Allan, 65:12
Mather, John, 281:9, 281:10
Matthews, T. S., 131:2, 165:6
Maugham, W. Somerset, 46:12, 46:13, 46:14, 113:11, 205:1, 224:8
Maurois, André, 135:7, 135:8, 135:9
Maxton, James, 192:1
May, Derwent, 182:4
Mazo, Earl, 217:10, 217:11
Medvedev, Roy, 207:13
Mencken, H. L., 124:9, 164:12, 241:3
Merrill, Gary, 104:8
Merton, Arthur S., 129:6
Meyer, Karl E., 164:13, 164:14, 164:15, 164:16
MI5 report, 88:9
Middleton, Edgar, 39:8, 39:9
Miller, Arthur, 107:6
Miller, Russell, 8:1
Mills, Hugh, 227:7
Milne, A. A., 206:13, 207:1
Milner, Lord, 186:9
Mitchell, Alexander, 8:1
Mitchison, Naomi, 9:4
Mitford, Jessica, 207:7
Mitford, Nancy, 207:8, 242:2
Monroe, Elizabeth, 30:14, 30:15
Moore, Gerald, 31:1, 56:9
Moore, Henry, 210:3
Moore, Martin, 44:9, 215:5, 215:6
Moore, Richard, 244:4, 244:5
Moorehead, Alan, 22:4
Moorehead, Caroline, 279:3
Morehouse, Ward, 294:4
Morgan, J. H., 74:2
Morgan, Janet, 83:7, 83:8, 83:9, 83:10
Morgan, Michele, 58:7
Morley, Christopher, 92:5
Morley, Sheridan, 95:16, 96:1
Morning Post, 25:11, 55:12, 71:8, 71:9, 98:6, 111:10, 172:4, 206:2
Morrell, Sydney, 77:6
Morris, James (later Jan), 5:12, 5:13, 201:5, 201:6, 248:11
Morris, Jan, *see* Morris, James
Morris, Lloyd, 109:3, 109:4
Morris, Rupert, 66:8, 66:9, 203:13
Mortimer, Edward, 42:11
Mortimer, John, 23:5, 46:4, 138:5, 152:5, 152:6, 152:7, 152:8, 152:9, 158:8, 184:11, 196:5, 196:6, 267:10, 288:2
Mortimer, Raymond, 7:3, 17:6, 23:6, 49:2, 64:9, 64:10, 140:4, 140:5, 140:6, 140:7, 199:7, 199:8, 199:9, 253:2
Morton, J. B., 283:4
Morton, Philip, 73:4, 73:5, 73:6, 73:7
Moseley, Leonard, 99:16, 195:12
Moseley, Roy, 187:6, 188:7
Mosley, Nicholas, 211:10
Mosley, Oswald, 59:13
Mottram, Eric, 9:10
Mountbatten, Lord, 5:11, 212:9, 212:10
Muggeridge, Malcolm, 41:14, 43:10, 43:11, 46:15, 86:7, 88:10, 100:1, 100:2, 105:3, 105:4, 115:6, 115:7, 115:8, 136:3, 136:4, 136:5, 146:10, 149:2, 151:7, 158:9, 167:3, 167:4, 167:5, 167:6, 186:10, 250:15, 258:7, 283:5, 283:6, 289:9
Muir, Frank, 112:7
Mumford, George, 56:6, 56:7
Munich radio station, 168:7
Murphy, Charles, J., 116:14
Murphy, Patrick, 223:4, 223:5, 223:6
Murray, Len, 68:9, 266:2, 268:9

N

Naida, Arojini, 147:11
Naipaul, V. S., 215:3
Nairne, Campbell, 131:4, 207:2
Namier, Lewis B., 190:11
Nardelli, P., 103:5, 103:6
Naughton, John, 210:5, 210:6, 210:7
Naylor, Ina R., 129:7
Neave, Airey, 156:1
Nevins, Allen, 237:8
Nevinson, C. R. W., 204:1
New Masses, 86:8
New York Herald Tribune, 94:12
New York Times, 94:13, 134:6, 265:10
News Chronicle, 50:3, 103:7, 103:8, 103:9, 162:2, 210:4, 281:15
Newspaper headline, 208:6
News Review, 151:10
Newton, E., 194:5
Nicholl, Charles, 230:4
Nichols, Beverley, 288:8
Nichols, Peter, 179:12
Nicoll, W. H., 29:3

Nicolson, Benedict, 49:3, 49:4, 49:5, 49:6
Nicolson, Harold, 1:7, 1:8, 1:9, 15:14, 15:15, 16:1, 20:1, 29:4, 29:5, 29:6, 29:7, 29:8, 42:1, 42:2, 42:3, 42:4, 44:10, 44:11, 44:12, 49:7, 49:8, 54:12, 57:8, 57:9, 80:13, 86:9, 86:10, 100:3, 115:9, 135:10, 145:9, 149:3, 149:4, 149:5, 149:6, 151:11, 156:2, 159:10, 162:12, 178:9, 184:3, 195:13, 201:1, 203:3, 209:3, 210:9, 212:11, 243:4, 250:16, 260:7, 273:10, 275:16, 290:11
Nicolson, Nigel, 5:14, 21:10
Nijinsky, Romola, 216:12, 217:1, 225:11
Nin, Anaïs, 206:10, 217:5
Niven, David, 128:5, 128:6, 128:7, 137:2, 145:5, 148:10, 148:11, 157:11, 184:4, 191:9, 209:4, 227:9, 227:10, 274:8
Nixon, Richard M., 119:5
Nobokov, Nicholas, 262:9
Norfolk, Duke of, 158:10
Normand, Mabel, 227:11
Norton, Deborah, 265:11, 265:12
Nott, Kathleen, 164:4
Noyes, Alfred, 176:7, 176:8

O

Oakes, Philip, 157:12, 168:2, 168:3, 191:5
O'Brien, Conor Cruise, 107:10, 107:11, 107:12
O'Brien, P. J., 239:2, 239:3
Observer, 1:10, 2:6, 2:7, 2:8, 2:9, 2:10, 8:10, 21:11, 27:2, 27:3, 29:9, 29:10, 29:11, 29:12, 33:2, 33:3, 33:4, 34:1, 34:2, 34:3, 39:9, 40:3, 40:4, 41:2, 41:3, 41:4, 51:13, 51:14, 54:13, 54:14, 61:4, 61:5, 61:6, 62:4, 62:5, 63:12, 63:13, 65:6, 65:7, 67:2, 75:13, 75:14, 76:3, 76:4, 76:5, 98:7, 98:8, 102:1, 102:2, 102:3, 102:4, 102:5, 132:1, 138:6, 138:7, 138:8, 147:7, 158:3, 158:11, 158:12, 159:1, 166:8, 166:9, 174:5, 174:6, 175:4, 175:5, 175:6, 180:5, 180:13, 182:6, 182:7, 184:12, 187:7, 199:4, 200:7, 200:8, 205:10, 207:14, 207:15, 213:3, 213:4, 226:4, 229:7, 244:6, 245:8, 246:4, 246:5, 246:6, 247:5, 247:6, 248:2, 248:3, 248:4, 256:9, 256:10, 256:11, 264:5, 266:3, 266:4, 266:5, 273:7, 273:11, 286:11 286:12, 286:13
O'Connor, T. P., 100:4, 100:5, 100:6, 208:12
O'Leary, Con, 112:8, 112:9
Olivier, Laurence, 208:7
Origo, Iris, 49:9
Orpen, Sir William, 209:11
Orwell, George, 23:7, 146:11, 185:6, 194:6, 250:17
Osborne, John, 96:2, 217:12, 250:18
O'Sullivan, John, 268:10

P

Page, Philip 106:3
Paget, Reginald, 161:9
Palestine Police description, 42:12
Palmer, Herbert, 103:12
Palmer, Raymond, 174:12, 174:13
Parker, Dorothy, 93:1, 154:1, 207:3
Parkes, Colonel Walter, 135:11, 135:12
Parkinson, Michael, 67:3, 98:13, 98:14, 98:15
Pascall, Jeremy, 165:5, 278:3
Pasley, Fred D., 72:1, 72:2
Passing Show, 36:2, 36:3, 36:4, 169:9, 218:2, 218:3, 235:4, 265:4, 265:5
Patch, Blanche, 250:19
Patten, Christopher, 67:13
Paulin, Tom, 292:7, 292:8
Pavlova, 225:12, 226:1
Pay, Anthony, 260:10
Payne, Robert, 150:11
Pearson, Hesketh, 36:5, 70:1, 70:2, 70:3, 70:4, 116:9, 244:8, 251:1, 251:2, 251:3, 251:4, 251:5, 251:6, 251:7, 251:8, 275:2, 281:11, 281:16
Pearson, John, 136:6, 136:7, 255:1
Pearson, Lester, 1:12
Penrose, B., 165:1
People, The, 256:14
Perles, Alfred, 206:11
Peron, Eva, 226:5
Perrott, Roy, 23:8, 122:1, 122:2, 122:3, 122:4, 122:5, 140:8, 140:9
Pertwee, Michael, 32:9
Peterborough, Daily Telegraph, 189:7
Phayre, Ignatius, 172:5
Pickford, Mary, 80:14, 128:8, 227:12
Pictorial Weekly, 218:4
Picture Post, 257:12
Pile, Stephen, 48:11, 48:12
Piper, Myfanwy, 48:11, 48:12
Pitman, Robert, 54:15, 64:11, 146:12, 158:4, 256:12, 277:6
Pliatsky, Leo, 109:7
Plomer, William, 224:9
Plummer, Christopher, 10:6
Poincaré, Raymond, 232:5
Ponting, Herbert G., 248:12
Porter, Henry, 191:6
Pound, Ezra, 206:12
Pound, Reginald, 3:6, 3:7, 3:8, 12:8, 17:7, 17:8, 29:13, 36:6, 39:11, 47:1, 47:2, 47:3, 53:3, 60:5, 60:6, 65:13, 65:14, 66:1, 77:7, 96:3, 98:9, 124:5, 141:11, 142:1, 142:2, 142:3, 154:2, 162:3, 162:4, 176:9, 185:7, 188:11, 196:2, 198:2, 210:1, 211:2, 211:3, 211:4, 211:5, 213:7, 216:2, 216:3, 216:4, 230:14, 242:3, 257:13, 279:1, 279:2, 283:7, 285:6, 287:2, 287:3, 290:4, 290:5
Powell, Anthony, 12:9, 12:10, 57:10, 57:11, 57:12, 134:8, 140:12, 142:4, 142:5, 142:6, 181:7, 190:2, 194:7, 194:8, 194:9, 213:5, 222:8, 222:9, 254:6, 290:12, 290:13
Powell, Enoch, 67:14, 138:9
Powell, Mrs Richard, 120:10, 120:11
Powers, Stefanie, 98:16
Preminger, Otto, 208:8
Priestley, J. B. 23:9, 49:10, 110:4, 132:2, 134:9, 146:13, 151:12, 157:6, 251:9
Pryce-Jones, Allan, 41:5
Pryce-Jones, David, 91:4
Pudney, John, 196:3
Pullen, Roland, 248:5

Q

Quennell, Peter, 194:10
Quigley, Isobel, 248:12
Quinton, Anthony, 159:2

R

Raban, Jonathan, 44:13
Race, Steve, 118:8
Radio Times, 73:8, 106:4, 162:5, 271:1
Radziwell, Princess Catherine, 215:8, 215:9
Raft, George, 283:9
Raine, Mary, 204:4
Rambert, Marie, 108:4, 108:5
Ramsaye, Terry, 128:9
Ramsey, Guy, 139:4
Ratcliffe, Michael, 88:1, 115:10, 258:8, 263:3, 263:4, 263:5, 284:11
Ratcliffe, S. K., 139:5, 139:6
Ravel, Maurice, 262:10
Raven, Simon, 38:12, 82:4
Ray, Robin, 41:7, 41:8, 187:2
Raymond, Ernest, 59:3
Raymond, John, 117:9, 149:7, 187:4
Raynor, Henry, 56:10
Read, Sir Herbert, 4:11, 122:6
Reagan, Nancy, 233:12
Reed, Thomas, B., 241:4
Rees, C. B., 33:5, 41:9, 41:10, 61:7, 245:9, 273:8
Rees, Jenny, 108:6
Rees, Nigel, 76:10, 76:11, 88:11, 124:1, 132:12, 186:11, 201:7, 203:4
Rees-Mogg, William, 53:4, 146:5
Reid, Charles, 33:6, 33:7, 245:10
Reid, Helen, 149:8
Reith, John, 235:5
Rennell, Lord, 57:13
Renoir, Jean, 293:10
Reuther, Walter, 110:14
Rhodes, Cecil, 185:8
R.H., Radio Times, 32:13
Ricci, Juan, 275:8, 275:9
Richardson, Joanna, 50:6
Richardson, Maurice, 99:2, 99:3, 99:4, 99:5
Ricks, Christopher, 144:1, 144:2
Riddell, Peter, 174:7
Riddell, Lord, 31:2, 31:3, 88:2, 88:3, 133:5, 133:6, 133:7, 133:8, 163:1, 222:5
Rilke, Rainer, Maria, 238:4
Robertson, E. Arnot, 104:9
Robey, George, 237:3
Robinson, David, 153:2, 153:3, 153:4
Robinson, Liam, 43:12
Roche, Wendy, 277:7, 277:8
Rodgers, W. T., 146:6
Roosevelt, Franklin D., 266:11
Rose, A. L., 20:2
Rosie, George, 102:7, 102:8, 102:9
Ross, Isabel, 93:2
Rosten, Leo., 118:19
Royal Society, 13:11
Rubin, Jerry, 230:5
Rubin, J. Robert, 148:13
Rueff, Suze, 50:7, 50:8, 50:9
Ruhrmund, Frank, 213:8, 213:9, 213:10
Russell, Bertrand, 64:12, 92:6, 118:10, 183:12, 190:3, 192:2, 192:3, 201:13, 242:4

S

Sackville-West, Victoria, 243:5, 254:7
St George, Noel, 81:6
Samedi Soir, 87:4
Sampson, Anthony, 109:8, 109:9
Samstag, Tony, 8:2
Samuel, Charles, 145:6
Sandburg, Carl, 94:14
Sanders, David, 166:3, 166:4
Sargent, Sir Malcolm, 245:11
Sarris, André, 80:15
Sassoon, Siegfried, 256:3
Scharlieb, Mary, 9:5
Schikel, Richard, 158:1
Schlesinger, Arthur Jnr, 183:2
Schmidt, Helmut, 10:10
Schnabel, Artur, 247:7, 247:8
Schulberg, B. P., 205:7
Scott, Michael Maxwell, 118:11
Seroff, Victor, 112:10, 112:11
Service, Robert W., 249:5, 249:6
Sewell, Brian, 24:1, 24:2, 24:3, 24:4, 24:5, 24:6
Shakespeare, Nicholas, 257:9
Shanks, Edward, 47:4, 110:5, 110:6, 110:7, 251:10
Shapiro, Nat, 247:9
Shaw, George Bernard, 12:4, 12:5, 36:7, 36:8, 36:9, 36:10, 36:11, 50:10, 70:5, 82:5, 82:6, 112:12, 113:12, 120:12, 125:11, 125:12, 146:14, 199:12, 221:2, 238:5, 238:6, 251:11, 251:12, 252:1, 252:2, 258:9, 258:10, 261:6, 263:6, 275:3, 290:6, 292:9
Shawcross, William, 63:6, 63:7
Shaw-Taylor, Desmond, 64:1
Shearer, Lloyd, 249:3
Sherfield, Lord, 1:13
Shinwell, Manny, 257:1
Shipman, David, 108:14
Shipp, Horace, 238:7
Shulman, Milton, 122:7
Sibelius, Jean, 33:8
Sigal, Clancy, 27:4
Sillitoe, Alan, 47:5
Silver, Eric, 42:13
Simon, John, 265:13, 282:11
Sinclair, Andrew, 72:3, 72:4, 210:8
Sinden, Donald, 3:9, 3:10, 3:11, 4:1, 145:7, 208:9
Sitwell, Edith, 175:7, 208:10, 254:8, 269:2, 269:3, 269:4, 269:5
Sitwell, Sir George, 254:9, 254:10
Sitwell, Osbert, 47:6, 70:6, 70:7, 70:8, 71:6, 71:7, 86:11, 121:1, 121:2, 122:8, 122:9, 122:10, 158:5, 194:11, 228:12, 229:1, 233:2, 233:3, 254:11, 255:2, 256:4, 259:10, 259:11, 261:13, 261:14, 262:1, 262:2, 279:4, 279:5, 279:6, 279:7, 279:8, 290:14
Sitwell, Sacheverell, 261:11, 279:9
Skidelsky, Robert, 211:11, 257:2
Slater, Mr Justice, 60:7
Smith, Anthony, 26:1, 26:2
Smith, Lady Eleanor, 55:13, 56:1, 56:2
Smith, Godfrey, 136:8, 136:9, 136:10, 136:11
Smith, Harvey, 11:2
Smith, Merriman, 119:6
Smoot, Senator Reed, 181:8
Smuts, General, 288:9
Smyth, Bob, 94:15
Smyth, Dame Ethel, 256:5, 256:6
Snowden, Viscount, 200:1, 257:3
Sokolova, Lydia, 108:7, 108:8
Solon, S. L., 139:7, 139:8, 139:9
Sommer, Dudley, 163:2
Spark, Muriel, 257:10

Sparrow, John, 253:9
Speight, Johnny, 79:15
Spender, J. A., 31:4
Spender, Stephen, 91:5, 91:6, 91:7, 122:11, 122:12
Spink, Kathryn, 267:2, 267:3
Spriggs, Elizabeth, 90:1, 263:7, 263:8
Spring, Howard, 132:3
Spurling, Hilary, 44:1, 44:2, 83:11, 83:12, 83:13, 83:14, 83:15, 113:13, 113:14, 243:6, 243:7
Squire, J. C., 134:13, 246:9
Stapley, William, 26:3, 26:4
Star, The (London), 237:9, 237:10
Steegmuller, Francis, 90:2, 90:3
Stein, Gertrude, 194:12
Stephens, Edward, M., 264:8
Stephens, Jan, 20:3
Stephens, Robert, 243:12
Stevas, Norman St John, 179:13, 180:1, 180:2
Stevens, G. W. 86:12
Stevenson, Adlai, 119:7, 119:8, 217:13
Stevenson, Frances, 16:2, 16:3
Stockwood, Mervyn, 46:5, 53:5, 209:5, 210:10, 212:1, 212:2
Stone, I. F., 110:15, 183:3
Stone, Norman, 232:6, 232:7
Stonesifer, Richard, 104:1
Storr, Anthony, 143:10
Strachey, Lytton, 16:4, 16:5, 16:6, 197:6, 201:8
Strachey, Ray, 224:3
Stratford, Esme Wingfield, 49:11, 49:12
Stravinsky, Igor, 90:4, 262:12
Stresemann, Gustav, 78:9
Strindberg, Freda, 263:9
Strong, L. A. G., 47:7, 47:8
Stuart, Francis, 107:13
Studio report, 17:12, 104:10
Sullivan, J. W. N., 118:12
Sun, 166;10
Sunday Dispatch, 257:4
Sunday Referee, 179:6, 237:11, 237:12, 253:10
Sunday Times, 179:7, 245:12, 282:12, 284:5
Sutherland, Douglas, 116:10
Sutton, Denys, 253:3
Swaffer, Hannen, 20:4, 32:10, 47:9, 81:1, 188:12, 218:11, 218:12
Swinnerton, Frank, 4:12, 4:13, 4:14, 5:1, 5:2, 57:4, 63:9, 175:8, 175:9, 175:10, 202:1, 202:2
Sydney journalist, A, 62:8
Symons, Julian, 60:8, 84:1

T

Tailor and Cutter, 86:13
Taylor, A. J. P., 9:7, 12:11, 16:7, 16:8, 21:12, 23:10, 29:14, 30:1, 30:2, 31:5, 31:6, 31:7, 31:8, 31:9, 62:2, 74:3, 79:16, 80:1, 80:2, 86:14, 86:15, 87:1, 93:9, 100:7, 100:8, 106:5, 115:11, 117:10, 117:11, 142:11, 142:12, 142:13, 142:14, 149:9, 149:10, 150:3, 160:7, 161:10, 175:11, 183:13, 186:12, 188:4, 188:5, 197:7, 200:2, 218:5, 218:6, 218:7, 218:8, 233:4, 235:6, 255:9, 255:10, 261:7, 289:3, 290:15
Taylor, Elizabeth, 265:14
Taylor, H. A., 56:3
Taylor, John Russell, 96:8, 96:9
Taylor, Laurie, 230:6
Taylor, Michael, M., 132:10
Taylor, Robert Lewis, 132:11, 171:10
Taylor-Martin, Patrick, 52:3, 52:4, 52:5
Teichmann, Howard, 90:13, 90:14, 131:5, 131:6, 192:13
Tellegen, Lou, 75:3
Tempel, Gudrun, 59:4
Templer, Field Marshal, 5:15
Thesiger, Ernest. 7:4, 36:12, 42:5, 47:10, 47:11, 48:1, 50:11, 50:12, 60:9, 70:9, 71:1, 71:2, 71:3, 121:3, 146:15, 147:1, 157:8, 157:9, 179:88, 195:1, 203:5, 245:4, 252:3, 252:4, 267:11, 268:1
Thomas, Dana Lee, 51:1
Thomas, Edward, 64:13
Thomas, Henry, 51:1
Thomas, J. P., 26:5, 26:6
Thomas, Sir Miles, 219:7
Thompson, Edward, 147:12
Thompson, Lawrence, 144:3
Thompson, Sir Robert, 289:7
Thomson, George Malcolm, 253:4, 253:5, 253:6
Thomson, Professor J. Arthur, 14:1, 14:2, 14:3, 14:4
Thorpe, Jeremy, 138:10
Time magazine, 10:7
Times, The, 4:2, 4:3, 4:4, 5:3, 5:4, 7:12, 11:12, 11:13, 13:8, 14:8, 14:9, 14:10, 20:5, 20:6, 20:7, 21:13, 22:5, 22:6, 34:12, 37:12, 37:13, 38:1, 44:3, 48:6, 53:13, 55:1, 66:10, 72:11, 72:12, 72:13, 89:1, 89:2, 89:3, 94:16, 99:6, 99:7, 106:6, 109:5, 117:12, 122:13, 123:1, 123:2, 124:6, 124:7, 127:1, 127:2, 129:8, 130:7, 147:8, 172:6, 172:7, 180:6, 187:10, 187:11, 197:9, 197:10, 200:9, 200:10, 205:11, 207:9, 207:10, 219:8, 224:10, 225:2, 233:13, 235:7, 235:8, 236:2, 245:14, 246:10, 249:7, 254:12, 254:13, 257:14, 258:1, 258:2, 260:4, 260:8, 271:2, 272:2, 272:3, 276:1, 283:10, 283:11, 286:4, 289:10
Times Literary Supplement, 82:7, 82:8, 82:9, 273:12, 274:1, 274:2
Tole, Frank, 11:7, 11:8, 11:9, 11:10
Tolkein, J. R. R., 193:9, 193:10, 193:11
Tolstoy, Leo, 157:7
Towner, Wesley, 183:6
Toynbee, Arnold J., 118:13
Toynbee, Philip, 12:12, 13:1, 13:2, 59:5, 90:5, 101:13, 130:8, 167:7, 182:5
T.P.'s Weekly, 140:13
Tracy, Honor, 138:11
Tracy, Morris de Haven, 196:1
Trevelyan, G. M., 159:11
Trevor, Claire, 58:8
Trevor-Roper, Hugh, 141:5
Trewin, J. C., 32:11, 263:10
Trickett, Rachel, 194:1
Truman, Harry, S., 119:9, 199:5
Turner, Pat., 204:2
Turner, W. J., 77:8
TV Times, 74:8, 119:10, 138:14, 180:7, 185:11, 240:13, 276:2
Tylden-Wright, David, 140:14
Tynan, Kenneth, 63:1, 63:2, 63:3, 63:4, 63:5, 66:11, 96:4, 99:8, 127:3, 234:10, 236:3, 236:4, 236:5

U

Uddgren, Gustav, 263:11, 263:12
Ulam, Adam, M., 258:11
Urwin, Harry, 268:11
USSR, official government announcement, 145:10
Utley, T. E., 21:14

V

Vaizey, Marina, 264:6
Van Doren, Charles, 48:7, 109:6, 113:4, 113:5, 165:7, 280:4
Van Every, Dale, 196:1
Vansittart, Lord, 168:10, 169:1, 192:2
Vaughan Williams, Ralph, 278:9
Vaughan Williams, Ursula, 278:9
Veblen, Thorstein, 116:11
Vidal, Gore, 73:1, 233:14, 233:15, 234:1, 234:2
Vidor, King, 95:1, 95:2, 107:7, 153:5
Van Hard, Julie, 51:2
Von Sternberg, Josef, 188:13
Vreeland, Diana, 105:5

W

Wain, John, 90:6, 90:7, 167:8, 225:3
Waitman, Robert, 226:6
Walden, George, 208:1, 208:2
Walker, Christopher, 42:14
Walker, Ronald, 9:3
Walpole, Hugh, 48:2
Walters, Douglas, 202:8
Walton, Harold, 2:11
Wapshott, Nicholas, 236:6, 236:7
Ward, Ian, 293:6
Wardle, Irving, 252:5
Warner, J. L., 137:4
Warner, Marina, 282:4
Waterhouse, Keith, 159:3
Watkins, Alan, 138:12, 178:5, 178:6
Watson, David Robin, 88
Watt, David, 234:4, 234:5,234:6
Waugh, Auberon, 289:11
Waugh, Evelyn, 207:11, 254:14
Webb, Beatrice, 200:3, 282:1, 282:2
Webb, James, W., 130:9
Wechsberg, Joseph, 206:3, 206:4
Week, The, 80:3
Weightman, John, 90:9, 90:10, 151:13, 151:14, 177:3, 177:4, 177:5
Welch, Colin, 211:1, 257:5, 257:6
Wellings, E. M., 62:6, 62:7
Wells, H. G., 163:3, 252:6, 293:7
Wesker, Arnold, 229:8
West, Anthony, 284:6
West, J. B., 119:11, 119:12, 119:13, 124:2, 239:9, 240:1, 240:2, 240:3, 240:14, 241:1, 276:3
West, Rebecca, 48:3, 143:12, 159:4, 252:7, 286:5, 288:3
Western Morning News, 11:3
Westrup, Sir Jack, 121:4
Wharton, Edith, 90:8
Whipple, T. K., 110:8
Whitaker, Frank, 90:15
White, William Allen, 93:3, 165:2, 241:5
Whitehorn, Katherine, 234:7, 268:12
Whitten, Wiilfred, 63:10, 292:10
Wild, Roland, 96:10, 96:11, 96:12, 96:13, 96:14,, 203:14
Wilder, Billy, 81:2, 208:11
Wilhelm II, Kaiser, 116:12, 215:10
Williams, Charles, 82:10, 123:3, 194:2, 247:3
Williams, David, 147:3
Williams, Francis, 21:15
Williams, Stephen, 135:1
Williams, Tennessee, 167:14
Williams, Sir William Emrys, 219:9
Williamson, Henry, 287:4
Wilson, A. N., 45:3, 45:4, 45:5, 45:6
Wilson, Angus, 13:3, 36:13, 147:2,202:3
Wilson, Cecil, 10:8
Wilson, David, 242:6, 242:7
Wilson, Desmond, 48:8
Wilson, Edmund, 123:4, 134:10, 224:11
Wilson, Harold, 67:4, 80:4, 21:2, 201:3
Wilson, Woodrow, 165:3
Winn, Godfrey, 80:5
Winterton, Paul, 275:10, 275:11, 275:12
Wiskemann, Elizabeth, 272:4
Withers, Percy, 173:14, 174:1, 174:2
Wolfe, Humbert, 48:4
Wood, David, 229:9
Woodward, Bob, 217:14
Woolf, Virginia, 48:5, 123:5, 181:9, 281:12, 290:16
Woollcott, Alexander, 58:9, 91:1, 224:12
Wordsworth, Christopher, 64:14
World's Press News, 42:6, 166:5, 271:3, 271:4
Worsthorne, Peregrine, 38:2, 38:3, 38:4
Wortham., H. E., 223:7
Wrench, Sir Evelyn, 191:1, 219:1
Wyatt, Woodrow, 75:15, 82:13, 82:14, 83:1, 83:2, 180:8, 185:1, 290:1, 290:2

Y

Yates, Ivan, 46:6
Yeats, W. B., 252:8, 264:9
Yeo, Leonard, 192:4
Yonnel, Jean, 51:3, 51:4
Young, G. M., 17:9
Young, Hugo, 109:10, 109:11, 109:12, 201:4
Young, Kenneth, 31:10, 31:11, 230:15, 231:1, 264:10

Z

Zanuck, Darryl F., 293:11
Zanuck, Richard, 95:3
Zebel, Sydney, 88:5
Ziegler, Philip, 94:10, 212:12
Ziman, H. D., 58:1, 65:1, 119:14, 139:10, 139:11, 139:12, 154:9, 189:2, 189:3, 258:3, 258:4
Zinman, David, 104:11

LUCY

Animal Ark™

Guinea-Pig in the Garage

Illustrated by Shelagh McNicholas

A division of Hachette Children's Books

Special thanks to Linda Kempton.
Thanks also to C. J. Hall, B.Vet.Med., M.R.C.V.S., for reviewing the veterinary information contained in this book.

First published in Great Britain in 1997
by Hodder Children's Books

This edition published in 2007

For more information on Animal Ark, please contact
www.animalark.co.uk

3

A Catalogue record for this book is available from the British Library

ISBN-13: 978 0 340 94442 4

Typeset in Baskerville by Avon DataSet Ltd,
Bidford-on-Avon, Warwickshire

Printed and bound in Great Britain by
Clays Ltd, St Ives plc

The paper and board used in this paperback by Hodder Children's Books are natural recyclable products made from wood grown in sustainable forests. The manufacturing processes conform to the environmental regulations of the country of origin.

Hodder Children's Books
a division of Hachette Children's Books
338 Euston Road, London NW1 3BH
An Hachette UK company
www.hachette.co.uk